INTRODUCTION TO ORBITAL MECHANICS

INTRODUCTION TO ORBITAL MECHANICS

FRANZ T. GEYLING, 1926 –
H. ROBERT WESTERMAN
Bell Telephone Laboratories
Whippany, New Jersey

ADDISON-WESLEY PUBLISHING COMPANY
Reading, Massachusetts · Menlo Park, California · London · Don Mills, Ontario

This book is in the
ADDISON-WESLEY AEROSPACE SERIES

Consulting Editor: DANIEL BERSHADER

 Printed in the United States of America. Published simultaneously in Canada. Library of Congress Catalog Card No. 77-109512.

To Helga and Paula
for their unfailing faith,
continuous encouragement, and
long-lasting patience

PREFACE

Longer ago than we care to recall, the idea of writing this book was conceived. Indeed, its genesis goes back to the time of the first satellite launches when specialists in applied physics, analytical dynamics, structures, fluid mechanics, and mathematics recognized challenging problems beyond the initial "space age" publicity. Originally, this book was based on the thought of sharing, with colleagues who, like ourselves, are without academic training in dynamical astronomy, the application and extension of celestial mechanics techniques. Today, the dearth of treatises on that subject has disappeared. Still, none of the available works seems to aim explicitly toward the objective we set for ourselves, namely, not only to derive and display the pertinent relations, but also to put them into the perspective of the present. Since celestial mechanics is a speciality with one of the longest histories in science, few modern claims to originality can be made in this field. The emphasis in this work is rather on evaluating the pertinent mathematical tradition in the light of current applications.

Attaining this end has not been undertaken lightly. Nearly a decade has passed since the first outline of the book was written; concepts and evaluations have changed and matured, not only because of our own efforts but with the aid of analysis and applications by numerous colleagues. Many aspects of the subject were studied—more than can be included here—and many considerations weighed before we decided on the presentation given in this text.

The driving forces behind this process of reappraisal have their origins in two events of fundamental significance to dynamical astronomy, especially perturbation theory: the appearance of the high-speed automatic computer and the availability of "man-made" orbits. So deeply do these two developments affect the subject that to apply the classical name of Celestial Mechanics is not appropriate—hence, the title and the spirit of this book.

As to the computer, its ability to relieve the theorist of straightforward calculation and analysis has yet to be fully developed. Its use in preparation of ephemerides appears obvious, but its effect, as we shall endeavor to show, is more subtle than the casual spectator might imagine. The same is true of the application of rocketry, which has been both rewarding and frustrating to the orbit mechanician. For the first time he can do more than passively observe the orbits nature provides, but, on the other hand, he can no longer limit his analysis to nearly circular and co-planar orbits or to forces yielding non-Keplerian effects of a strictly gravitational nature. Thus, the methodology developed over the last three centuries is not completely applicable to present problems; yet, to appreciate the full impact of the computer and space program, this earlier methodology must be understood first.

The central task of dynamical astronomy has always been to obtain the solution of the equations of motion of the heavenly bodies. Since this cannot be done in closed form, approximational methods are used. Two fundamentally different alternatives are available: numerical integration or analytic representation by series. The former is not discussed directly in this volume; suffice it to say that in certain cases it can be made reasonably accurate, but it never gives much physical or mathematical understanding of the problem. On the other hand, the analytic approach often yields considerable insight but, to achieve accuracy, a great deal of algebraic labor is involved.

The analytic methodology almost invariably employs Keplerian motion, i.e., an elliptic orbit, as a first approximation to the motion of a celestial body around a central mass; improvements are then sought by various perturbation schemes. In calculating successive positions of a body along its Keplerian reference trajectory, we find that the choice of independent variable is of great importance. The geometry of conic sections and hence the position of a body in such an orbit expressed in terms of angular coordinates measured from the focus or the center of the figure are simple, but the relations between these angular variables and the time are transcendental; this rules out closed expressions for the position as a function of time. Nevertheless, astronomers of the past, with the major aim of preparing ephemerides having uniform time increments, chose time as the independent variable. Thus, first the aforementioned angles, known in astronomical parlance as the true and eccentric anomalies, were developed by time series. Then the gravitational perturbing forces, superposed on the Keplerian model, were expanded in terms of the angular anomalies. This became necessary since the closed trigonometric expressions associated with mutual attractions in an n-body system make the required quadratures rather intractable otherwise. Working the two kinds of series expansions into each other, one could arrive at expressions of the so-called "disturbing functions" in terms of time, to be used for numerous analyses of the solar system. Because of the labor involved, this part of the work became a focal point of attention for the classicists. They brought many ingenious devices to bear on its reduction, particularly capitalizing on the specific characteristics of the gravitational force itself and on the orbit geometries provided by nature.

We can now see more specifically where modern conditions have wrought a change. The literal expansions of classical disturbing functions are inapplicable to many of the perturbing forces encountered with artificial celestial bodies and to their orbit geometries as well. Moreover, the transcendental relations between the angular variables and time are no more awkward to handle by automatic computers than the "direct" relations sought by classical astronomers. Hence, both the choice between alternative formulations of the perturbing force and the resulting perturbation methods, as well as the choice of independent variable have become open questions once more. These are the basic issues we discuss in this text.

We have tried to make this book useful to those engineers and scientists who, for various reasons, have more than a passing interest in orbital mechanics. The material should be accessible to anyone with a senior or first-year graduate-school background in physics or engineering who desires to understand the astronomical terminology and the working details of various perturbation techniques. Thus, the mathematical developments are straightforward (albeit laborious) and formal in nature. Since many problems of "space age" astronomy occur in several alternative forms, and since many of the techniques are somewhat involved, numerous illustrative examples are provided. In the spirit of "evaluation," we have inserted occasional comparisons between different formulations. Considering the multiplicity of publications in this field, even readers with some specialist background may find these comments helpful, if only to stimulate independent thought on such comparisons. In addition, an effort has been made to interpret the main features of several perturbation theories in terms of fundamental principles of mechanics. This revives the physical insight which has often been lost in classical accounts under the burden of routine astronomical calculations.

The thought that this work might serve as a textbook has occurred to the authors, and consideration has been given to practice problems. As the reader must be aware by now, extensive labor is connected with nontrivial examples of perturbation analysis; indeed, typical ones would serve as term projects rather than homework assignments. For this reason, the idea of exercises for the student has been abandoned. As a partial substitute, some detailed developments which parallel earlier demonstrations have been omitted. The reader should be able to single these out for his own practice.* By the same token, a few tutorial sections are included to assist the reader who is still developing his background in dynamics.

The book contains a set of methods selected and evaluated by the authors during several years on the basis of their own aerospace experience. This selection differs from the traditional scope of celestial mechanics texts by omissions to be discussed presently. First, however, a brief sketch of each chapter may be helpful.

Chapters 1 and 2 cover the integrals of particle motion, formulas for Keplerian orbits, definitions of elements, and series expansions for various limiting cases. This is standard material; on the other hand, its omission would have resulted in a serious lack of completeness.

* We also refer to the careful selection of basic exercises in J. M. A. Danby, *Fundamentals of Celestial Mechanics,* Macmillan, New York, 1962.

Chapter 3 gives an introduction to astronomical reference frames and ephemerides, their adjustment for various effects, and a discussion of astronomical chronometry. While this material contains no analytic challenge it summarizes the basic facts required by anyone involved in computing orbits, and is included because the rationale behind astronomical terminology is not always self-evident.

In Chapter 4 we examine the algebraic relations pertinent to orbit determination from various sorts of measurements, such as sight angles, ranges, and range rates. The governing (deterministic) equations are derived, and their relation to the classical formulations of Laplace, Lambert, and Gauss is considered. Statistical data processing and application of numerical methods are not treated; however, the concept of orbit determination is extended to include first-order "sensitivities" needed for orbit selection and trajectory design.

Chapter 5 begins with a discussion of various physical disturbances encountered by space vehicles and illustrates their fundamental effects in terms of elementary particle dynamics. The basic perturbation approach to solving dynamic equations is presented and specific formulations are discussed. These include the Encke method and several formulations in spherical coordinates, some of them from recent years.

The classical method of variation of parameters is treated in Chapter 6. Its derivation is given in terms of a disturbing function as well as a disturbing force, i.e., by way of Lagrange brackets and infinitesimal impulses. The discussion treats orbits with low eccentricity and inclination as a special case; the choice of independent variable and the merits of rectification are examined; first-order results are given for a variety of physical effects.

The groundwork for canonic perturbation methods is developed in Chapter 7, where Lagrange's and Hamilton's equations are derived by a direct method, as well as by variational arguments. The use of Hill-type equations is illustrated in deriving first-order coordinate perturbations for motion in the neighborhood of an unperturbed orbit.

In Chapter 8 we approach the theory of canonic transformations by variational arguments. Separability of the Hamilton-Jacobi equation is illustrated for the Kepler problem and for oblateness perturbations in spheroidal coordinates. Thereafter, iterative approaches to the nonseparable Hamilton-Jacobi equation are considered, leading to perturbations in the generating function according to the von Zeipel procedure.

Finally, in Chapter 9, we give an introduction to Hansen's method. Since this technique uses a combination of orbit elements and position coordinates as dependent variables, it occupies a somewhat special position among perturbation methods. Its manipulations are discussed in some detail and are illustrated with partially explicit results for oblateness perturbations.

Several topics are patently missing from this outline. Each would require at least a chapter for proper coverage, but a cursory treatment would be only a useless gesture toward a broader scope. One such area is the use of canonic methods in deriving perturbations of the coordinates, where some interesting results are on record. Another is the set of asymptotic methods which have been used so effectively in recent years for orbit-stability studies. Next, there is the summarizing of results from systematic and detailed numerical and analytic comparisons of the better-known perturbation methods. Beyond the province of satellite motion lie the multibody problems, including modern efforts in topological dynamics. Here one may confidently point to several recent and definitive publications.* Another subject of importance is the representation of powered flight and of atmospheric reentry; these naturally lead into the area of trajectory optimization, which is well documented elsewhere. Similarly, the statistical treatment of orbit determination is receiving ample attention in the current literature, although the varied, practical experiences with real-time trajectory computations still await comprehensive documentation. In addition to these topics in particle dynamics, the subject of attitude stabilization is due for definitive documentation.

Let this array of subjects outside the scope of this book put its contents into proper perspective. Several of these areas are being explored by the authors' colleagues, whose interaction with our writing effort has proved valuable in many ways. It is hoped that their own work may be published and that they find this book a useful foundation.

Whippany, New Jersey F.T.G.
November 1970 H.R.W.

* For example, V. Szebehely, *Theory of Orbits; The Restricted Problem of Three Bodies*, Academic Press, New York, 1967.

CONTENTS

Chapter 4 The Determination of Orbits

Chapter 5 Fundamentals of Perturbation Theory

Chapter 6 Perturbation in the Elements

Chapter 7 Lagrange's and Hamilton's Equations. Application to Moving Coordinates

Chapter 8 The Method of Canonical Transformations

Chapter one

THE CENTRAL FORCE PROBLEM

1. INTRODUCTION

This chapter provides an introduction to the Newtonian particle dynamics of n bodies with gravitational fields. After establishing the equations of motion and their well-known integrals we specialize the problem to that of two bodies. This can be solved analytically and, since it so frequently approximates the real state of affairs in orbital mechanics, it is the conceptual basis for most mathematical formulations of interest. We examine several approaches to this problem and derive the relations between constants of the motion and the initial position and velocity of one body with respect to the other.

2. THE MANY-BODY PROBLEM: FORMULATION

Classically, one of the most interesting and long-standing problems of celestial mechanics is that of the individual motion of several bodies, each under the influence of the others' gravitational fields. No complete analytic solution, except for certain special cases, has been found, even under the simplest assumptions. Nevertheless, sufficient progress has been made so that the results, though incomplete, are sufficiently illuminating to be of importance.

According to potential theory, any spherical body of finite radius having a mass density which is a function only of distance from its center presents a gravitational field, at points beyond its own radius, which is the same as if all its mass were concentrated at that center. If, then, we consider in this analysis only such bodies, we may treat them as mathematical points at positions occupied by the centers of the bodies. This allows for considerable simplification in the statement of the problem. In addition, such a formulation corresponds closely to the actual situation in the solar system, since the sun, planets, and natural satellites are all very nearly spherical. The question of an individual body's spin is not accounted for and will not be treated since it generally does not affect its gross motions.

Let us consider n bodies, the ith of these (in a rectangular coordinate frame with arbitrary origin) being at coordinates x_i, y_i, z_i and possessing mass m_i. The potential in which this body finds itself is given by

$$V_i = -\sum_{j=1}^{n}{}' \frac{Gm_i m_j}{r_{ij}}, \tag{1.2.1}$$

where G is the universal gravitation constant, r_{ij} is the distance to the jth mass point, and the prime on the summation sign indicates that the term $i = j$ is to be excluded. The quantity r_{ij} is given by

$$r_{ij} = [(x_i - x_j)^2 + (y_i - y_j)^2 + (z_i - z_j)^2]^{1/2}. \tag{1.2.2}$$

Assuming that no other forces are acting, we find that the equations of motion are

$$m_i \ddot{x}_i = -\sum_j{}' \frac{Gm_i m_j (x_i - x_j)}{r_{ij}^3}, \tag{1.2.3}$$

$$m_i \ddot{y}_i = -\sum_j{}' \frac{Gm_i m_j (y_i - y_j)}{r_{ij}^3}, \tag{1.2.4}$$

$$m_i \ddot{z}_i = -\sum_j{}' \frac{Gm_i m_j (z_i - z_j)}{r_{ij}^3}. \tag{1.2.5}$$

Since there are n bodies, there exist $3n$ equations of the form (1.2.3) through (1.2.5) for which, as mentioned earlier, no complete solution in closed form exists. However, certain general properties of the n-body motion can be stated and are of interest. These partial solutions of the problem are known as the *integrals of motion.*

3. THE MANY-BODY PROBLEM: INTEGRALS

Ten independent integrals of the equations of motion can be found and it can be shown that any others obtained can be expressed in terms of these. Let

$$\bar{x} = \frac{\Sigma_i m_i x_i}{\Sigma_i m_i}, \tag{1.3.1}$$

$$\bar{y} = \frac{\Sigma_i m_i y_i}{\Sigma_i m_i}, \tag{1.3.2}$$

$$\bar{z} = \frac{\Sigma_i m_i z_i}{\Sigma_i m_i}. \tag{1.3.3}$$

Then $(\bar{x}, \bar{y}, \bar{z})$ are the coordinates of the centroid or center of mass of the total system. Now if we sum (1.2.4) over all i, we get

$$\sum_i m_i \ddot{x}_i = -\sum_i \sum_j{}' \frac{Gm_i m_j}{r_{ij}^3}(x_i - x_j). \tag{1.3.4}$$

The right-hand side of (1.3.4) can be shown to be zero, since for each i, j combination we get terms involving $[(x_i - x_j) + (x_j - x_i)]$; hence, since $\sum m_i$ = constant, we have

$$\ddot{\bar{x}} = 0, \tag{1.3.5}$$

and, similarly,

$$\ddot{\bar{y}} = 0, \tag{1.3.6}$$

$$\ddot{\bar{z}} = 0. \tag{1.3.7}$$

These lead immediately to six integrals:

$$\dot{\bar{x}} = a_1; \qquad \dot{\bar{y}} = a_2; \qquad \dot{\bar{z}} = a_3; \tag{1.3.8}$$

and

$$\bar{x} = a_1 t + b_1; \qquad \bar{y} = a_2 t + b_2; \qquad \bar{z} = a_3 t + b_3. \tag{1.3.9}$$

These equations establish the fact that the center of mass of the system travels with uniform linear motion.

If we multiply (1.2.4) by $(-y_i)$ and (1.2.5) by (x_i), add, and sum over all i, we obtain

$$\sum_i m_i(x_i\ddot{y}_i - y_i\ddot{x}_i) = -\sum_i \sum_j{}' \frac{Gm_i m_j}{r_{ij}^3}(x_j y_i - x_i y_j). \tag{1.3.10}$$

We note that the left-hand side of (1.3.10) is equal to

$$\sum m_i \frac{d}{dt}(x_i\dot{y}_i - y_i\dot{x}_i)$$

and that the right-hand side, like that of (1.3.4), vanishes because of its antisymmetric properties; integrating the result, we obtain

$$\sum_i m_i(x_i\dot{y}_i - y_i\dot{x}_i) = c_1, \tag{1.3.11}$$

and, similarly,

$$\sum_i m_i(y_i\dot{z}_i - z_i\dot{y}_i) = c_2, \tag{1.3.12}$$

$$\sum_i m_i(z_i\dot{x}_i - x_i\dot{z}_i) = c_3. \tag{1.3.13}$$

These three integrals express the constancy of total angular momentum of the system.

The final integral is obtained most simply by noting that (1.2.4) through (1.2.6) can be written

$$m_i\ddot{x}_i = -\frac{\partial V_i}{\partial x_i}; \qquad m_i\ddot{y}_i = -\frac{\partial V_i}{\partial y_i}; \qquad m_i\ddot{z}_i = -\frac{\partial V_i}{\partial z_i}. \tag{1.3.14}$$

If we multiply the first of these by $\dot{x}_i$, the second by $\dot{y}_i$, the third by $\dot{z}_i$, add the results, and sum over i, then

$$\sum_i (m_i\dot{x}_i\ddot{x}_i + m_i\dot{y}_i\ddot{y}_i + m_i\dot{z}_i\ddot{z}_i) = -\sum_i \left(\frac{\partial V_i}{\partial x_i}\frac{dx_i}{dt} + \frac{\partial V_i}{\partial y_i}\frac{dy_i}{dt} + \frac{\partial V_i}{\partial z_i}\frac{dz_i}{dt}\right). \tag{1.3.15}$$

But the left-hand side can be written as

$$\sum_i \frac{m_i}{2}\frac{d}{dt}(\dot{x}_i^2 + \dot{y}_i^2 + \dot{z}_i^2),$$

and the right-hand side, since V_i is not an explicit function of time, is simply dV/dt. Hence

$$\sum_i \frac{m_i}{2}(\dot{x}_i^2 + \dot{y}_i^2 + \dot{z}_i^2) + V = \text{constant} = \mathscr{E}, \tag{1.3.16}$$

expressing the conservation of energy for the n-particle system.

4. THE TWO-BODY PROBLEM: VECTORIAL REPRESENTATION

Except for certain qualitative aspects and for cases with rather specialized initial conditions, the only additional progress which has been made toward the complete solution of Eqs. (1.2.4) through (1.2.6) is for the case $n = 2$. This case is of considerable interest, however, since, as hinted earlier, in many situations either the distances to other bodies are so great or the masses of the other bodies are so small that the two-body problem is a useful approximation to the real state of affairs.

We now examine this case in more detail. In so doing we employ vector notation, which illustrates a compact treatment that is possible not only for the two-body problem but also for certain aspects of many-body problems [1, 2, 3].*

For the two-body problem we may write (1.2.4) as

$$\ddot{x}_1 = -\frac{Gm_2(x_1 - x_2)}{r_{12}^3} \quad \text{and} \quad \ddot{x}_2 = -\frac{Gm_1(x_2 - x_1)}{r_{12}^3}.$$

Since for the relative motion, $x = x_1 - x_2$, we have

$$\ddot{x} = \frac{G}{r_{12}^3}[m_2(x_2 - x_1) + m_1(x_2 - x_1)] = -\frac{\mu x}{r^3}, \tag{1.4.1}$$

where $\mu = G(m_1 + m_2)$ and we have dropped the subscripts from r_{12}. The three equations of motion, corresponding to (1.4.1), are given in vector notation by

$$\ddot{\mathbf{r}} = -\mu\mathbf{r}/r^3, \tag{1.4.2}$$

with the bold letters indicating vector quantities. Forming the vector product with $\mathbf{r}$ on both sides, we have

$$\mathbf{r} \times \ddot{\mathbf{r}} = 0; \tag{1.4.3}$$

*Numbers in brackets are keyed to the list of references at the end of each chapter.

by integration this becomes

$$\mathbf{r} \times \dot{\mathbf{r}} = \mathbf{h}. \tag{1.4.4}$$

The invariant vector **h** represents the angular momentum, and the plane of motion is defined by

$$\mathbf{r} \cdot \mathbf{h} = 0. \tag{1.4.5}$$

Since **h** is equivalent to three constants of integration, three more must be determined. From (1.4.2), we get

$$\mathbf{h} \times \ddot{\mathbf{r}} = -\frac{\mu}{r^3}\mathbf{h} \times \mathbf{r} = -\frac{\mu}{r^3}(\mathbf{r} \times \dot{\mathbf{r}}) \times \mathbf{r}.$$

Following the expansion rule for triple vector products, this becomes

$$\frac{\mu}{r^3}[(\mathbf{r}\cdot\dot{\mathbf{r}})\mathbf{r} - (\mathbf{r}\cdot\mathbf{r})\dot{\mathbf{r}}] = \frac{\mu}{r^3}[(r\dot{r})\mathbf{r} - r^2\dot{\mathbf{r}}] = -\mu\frac{d}{dt}\left(\frac{\mathbf{r}}{r}\right) = -\mu\dot{\hat{\mathbf{r}}}, \tag{1.4.6}$$

where $\hat{\mathbf{r}}$ is the unit vector in the direction of **r**. Since

$$\mathbf{h} \times \ddot{\mathbf{r}} = -\mu\dot{\hat{\mathbf{r}}},$$

we have the first integral

$$\mathbf{h} \times \dot{\mathbf{r}} = -\mu\hat{\mathbf{r}} - \mathbf{P}, \tag{1.4.7}$$

where **P** lies in the plane of motion and would appear to furnish the desired three additional constants of integration. However, the scalar product of **h** and (1.4.7) yields

$$\mathbf{h} \cdot \mathbf{P} = 0, \tag{1.4.8}$$

indicating that the six constants we have found so far are not linearly independent. The additional constant required can be found from a geometric interpretation of (1.4.4) and (1.4.5): since $\mathbf{r} = r\hat{\mathbf{r}}$, we have

$$\dot{\mathbf{r}} = \dot{r}\hat{\mathbf{r}} + r\dot{\hat{\mathbf{r}}}. \tag{1.4.9}$$

But $\dot{\hat{\mathbf{r}}}$ is merely the change of orientation of **r** within the plane given by (1.4.5). Thus, let

$$|\dot{\hat{\mathbf{r}}}| = \dot{f},$$

where f is an angle to be defined later. Then (1.4.4) yields, in view of (1.4.9),

$$h = r^2\dot{f}. \tag{1.4.10}$$

Consequently, $dt = (r^2/h)df$ or

$$t = \frac{1}{h}\int_0^f f^2 df + \tau, \tag{1.4.11}$$

where τ is the sixth constant of integration. Its meaning and that of f become clear when we develop the explicit equation of the conic orbit from the vector representation (1.4.7). Forming the scalar product of that equation with **r**, we have

$$\mathbf{r}\cdot(\mathbf{h}\times\dot{\mathbf{r}}) = -\mu r - \mathbf{P}\cdot\mathbf{r} = -\mathbf{h}\cdot(\mathbf{r}\times\dot{\mathbf{r}}), \tag{1.4.12}$$

where the last equality follows from the transposition rules for triple scalar products. In view of (1.4.4) this becomes

$$\frac{h^2/\mu}{r} = 1 + \frac{\mathbf{P}\cdot\hat{\mathbf{r}}}{\mu}. \tag{1.4.13}$$

Since **P** is a fixed vector in the orbit plane, the dot product in (1.4.13) gives an indication of the (time-dependent) orientation of r. If we denote the angle between it and **P** as f, we have

$$r = \frac{h^2/\mu}{1+(\mathbf{P}/\mu)\cos f}. \tag{1.4.14}$$

From this it is obvious that **P** points to the position on the trajectory where the orbiting body has its closest approach to the center of attraction and τ in (1.4.11) marks the time of passage of the body through that point. Equation (1.4.14) is the general equation of a conic section.

More will be said about this subject in Chapter 2. The purpose of this section was to indicate how the vector treatment of particle dynamics brings out the essential features of the motion in very compact form. This accounts for its popularity in the discussion of n-body problems, where, in the absence of explicit solutions, much of the theory concerns conditions for collision, escape to infinity, and stability in general (for example, [2]).

5. THE TWO-BODY PROBLEM: POLAR COORDINATES

Let us now consider the two-body problem in terms of polar coordinates, which turn out to be convenient for numerous applications.

We take the position of the center of mass of the two bodies as the origin of our coordinate system so that $\bar{x} = \bar{y} = \bar{z} = 0$, and further set the frame of reference in motion with the same velocity as that of the centroid; then, relative to this system, $\dot{\bar{x}} = \dot{\bar{y}} = \dot{\bar{z}} = 0$ or, in other words, we shall be investigating the relative motion of the two bodies. From (1.3.1) we find

$$x_2 = -\frac{m_1}{m_2}x_1, \tag{1.5.1}$$

with similar equations for y and z. Equation (1.2.4) then becomes

$$\ddot{x}_1 = -Gm_2^3 x_1/(m_1+m_2)^2 r_1^3, \tag{1.5.2}$$

where r_1 is the distance from the centroid to the first body. Also

$$\ddot{y}_1 = -Gm_2^3 y_1/(m_1+m_2)^2 r_1^3, \tag{1.5.3}$$

$$\ddot{z}_1 = -Gm_2^3 z_1/(m_1+m_2)^2 r_1^3. \tag{1.5.4}$$

Likewise Eqs. (1.3.11) through (1.3.13) yield

$$x_1\dot{y}_1 - y_1\dot{x}_1 = c_1; \qquad y_1\dot{z}_1 - z_1\dot{y}_1 = c_2; \qquad z_1\dot{x}_1 - x_1\dot{z}_1 = c_3. \tag{1.5.5}$$

Now let us choose the orientation of the axes so that initially both z_1 and $\dot{z}_1$ are zero. Equation (1.5.4) yields $\ddot{z}_1 = 0$; and since $\dot{z}_1$ is already zero, both z_1 and $\dot{z}_1$ will remain so. Thus, the motion is in a plane, $c_2 = c_3 = 0$, and we need consider only the x, y equations.

Converting to polar coordinates, we let

$$x_1 = r_1 \cos\theta_1; \qquad y_1 = r_1 \sin\theta_1. \tag{1.5.6}$$

Equations (1.5.6) applied to the first of (1.5.5) give

$$r_1^2\dot{\theta}_1 = c_1, \tag{1.5.7}$$

and applied to (1.5.2) and (1.5.3) yield

$$\begin{aligned} \ddot{r}_1\cos\theta_1 - 2\dot{r}_1\dot{\theta}_1\sin\theta_1 - r_1\dot{\theta}_1^2\cos\theta_1 - r_1\ddot{\theta}_1\sin\theta_1 &= -\frac{Gm_2^3}{(m_1+m_2)^2}\frac{\cos\theta_1}{r_1^2}, \\ \ddot{r}_1\sin\theta_1 + 2\dot{r}_1\dot{\theta}_1\cos\theta_1 - r_1\dot{\theta}_1^2\sin\theta_1 + r_1\ddot{\theta}_1\cos\theta_1 &= -\frac{Gm_2^3}{(m_1+m_2)^2}\frac{\sin\theta_1}{r_1}. \end{aligned} \tag{1.5.8}$$

If we multiply the first of these by $\cos\theta_1$ and the second by $\sin\theta_1$ and add, we get

$$\ddot{r}_1 = -\frac{Gm_2^3}{(m_1+m_2)^2}\frac{1}{r_1^2} + r_1\dot{\theta}_1^2, \tag{1.5.9}$$

or, using (1.5.7), we have

$$\ddot{r}_1 = -\frac{Gm_2^3}{(m_1+m_2)^2}\frac{1}{r_1^2} + \frac{c_1^2}{r_1^3}. \tag{1.5.10}$$

But (1.5.7) also gives

$$\frac{d}{dt} = \frac{c_1}{r_1^2}\frac{d}{d\theta_1}, \tag{1.5.11}$$

and applying this to (1.5.10) yields

$$\frac{d^2r_1}{d\theta_1^2} - \frac{2}{r_1}\left(\frac{dr_1}{d\theta_1}\right)^2 = -\frac{Gm_2^3}{(m_1+m_2)^2c_1^2}r_1^2 + r_1. \tag{1.5.12}$$

With the help of the well-known substitution $r_1 = 1/u_1$ this equation yields the solution

$$r_1 = \frac{(m_1+m_2)^2}{Gm_2^3} \frac{1}{1+c_4 \cos(\theta_1-\omega)}, \tag{1.5.13}$$

where c_4 and ω are constants of integration. Now (1.5.13) is the equation of a conic section, representing a circle if $c_4 = 0$; an ellipse if $0 < c_4 < 1$; a parabola if $c_4 = 1$; and a hyperbola if $c_4 > 1$. We shall see something of the physical significance of c_1 and c_4 in Section 6.

Equation (1.5.13) gives the behavior of the body m_1 with respect to the center of mass of the system composed of m_1 and m_2. The curve followed by m_2 is obtained by application of Eq. (1.5.1) and its y-counterpart to Eqs. (1.5.6). This leads to

$$x_2 = -\frac{m_1}{m_2} r_1 \cos\theta_1; \qquad y_2 = -\frac{m_1}{m_2} r_1 \sin\theta_1; \tag{1.5.14}$$

that is, as expected, the position of m_2 is always diametrically across the centroid from that of m_1. The behavior of m_2 with respect to m_1 is obtained by noting that

$$r_{12} = \sqrt{(x_1-x_2)^2+(y_1-y_2)^2}, \tag{1.5.15}$$

or, using (1.5.6) and (1.5.14),

$$r_{12} = \frac{m_1+m_2}{m_2} r_1. \tag{1.5.16}$$

This is a very important result: it states that not only does each body individually move around the center of mass in a conic, but the motion of either with respect to the other is again a conic of the same type and shape with only the dimensions altered. Further, in most problems encountered in missile and satellite work, the mass of one object is very much less than the mass of the other. In this case, if we take $m_1 \ll m_2$, we find $r_{12} \simeq r_1$ so that even the dimensions of the conic followed by the first body are very close to those derived for the conic taken with respect to the center of mass. For example, for a missile with a weight of 10^5 kg orbiting the earth, the mass factor in (1.5.16) becomes $(1 \times 10^5 + 6 \times 10^{24})/6 \times 10^{24} = 1 + 1.7 \times 10^{-20}$, which is as close an approximation to unity as one may see in a long time. In addition, (1.5.14) shows that, for this example, the displacements of x_2 and y_2 from the centroid are about a factor of 10^{-20} less than those for x_1 and y_1; thus, even when r_1 has a value of 10^{17} km, the displacement of x_2 and y_2 is barely more than 1 meter! It is most convenient to be able to establish the position of one body with respect to the other, rather than to the center of mass.* These remarks apply equally well to the situation prevailing between the sun and planets, which

*Similarly, for $m_1 \ll m_2$, the constant $Gm_2^3/(m_1+m_2)^2$ of Eqs. (1.5.8) through (1.5.10), etc., becomes essentially Gm_2; for the earth, $Gm_2 \equiv \mu = 3.98602 \cdot 10^{14}$ m^3/sec^2. A list of useful astrophysical quantities is given at the end of this volume.

corroborates Kepler's observation that planetary orbits can be represented by essentially two-body motion. Hence conic sections are often referred to as Keplerian orbits.

6. THE TWO-BODY PROBLEM: PHYSICAL MEANING OF THE CONSTANTS OF INTEGRATION

Consider a polar coordinate system centered at the body M with the position of the second body, m ($m \ll M$), given by (r, θ). Since $r = r_{12}$ of the preceding section, we note—in view of the statement following (1.5.16)—that equations corresponding to (1.5.7) and (1.5.9) become

$$\ddot{r} - r\dot{\theta}^2 = -\mu/r^2, \tag{1.6.1}$$

$$\frac{d}{dt}(r^2\dot{\theta}) = 0, \tag{1.6.2}$$

where $\mu = GM$.

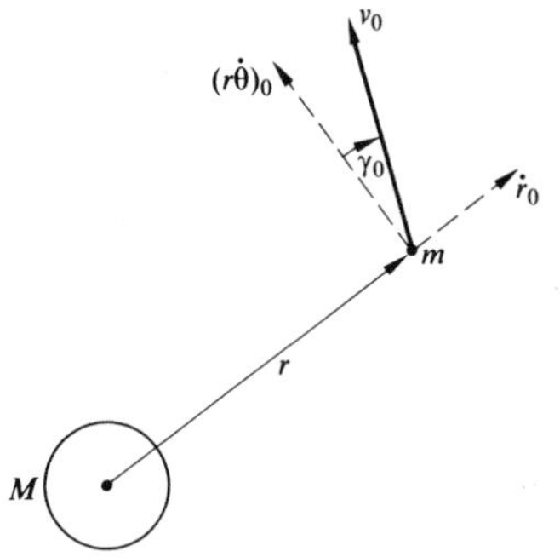

Figure 1.1

Suppose that the position and velocity of m are known at some time, say $t = 0$. Let us choose the line from the center of M to the position of m at $t = 0$ to be the reference axis ($\theta = 0$) and measure $\dot{\theta}$ in the direction of motion of m. Then at $t = 0$ (see Fig. 1.1),

$$\dot{r}_0 = v_0 \sin \gamma_0, \tag{1.6.3}$$

$$(r\dot{\theta})_0 = v_0 \cos \gamma_0, \tag{1.6.4}$$

where γ_0 is the complement of the angle between the velocity vector and the radius vector. Equation (1.6.2) yields

$$r^2\dot{\theta} = \text{constant} = r_0 v_0 \cos \gamma_0, \tag{1.6.5}$$

and we may also write

$$\frac{d}{dt} = \dot{\theta}\frac{d}{d\theta} = \frac{r_0 v_0 \cos \gamma_0}{r^2}\frac{d}{d\theta}.$$

Then, as was done in Section 5, we transform (1.6.1) to an equation whose independent variable is θ and whose dependent variable $u = 1/r$, yielding the ultimate solution

$$r = \frac{r_0^2 v_0^2 \cos^2 \gamma_0}{\mu} \frac{1}{1+\bar{c} \cos (\theta - \bar{\theta})}, \tag{1.6.6}$$

where the constants of integration $\bar{c}$ and $\bar{\theta}$ correspond to c_4 and ω in (1.5.13). We shall use the latter notation henceforth. The time derivative of (1.6.6) is

$$\dot{r} = \frac{r_0^2 v_0^2 \cos^2 \gamma_0}{\mu} \frac{c_4 \sin (\theta - \omega)\dot{\theta}}{[1+c_4 \cos (\theta - \omega)]^2},$$

or, using (1.6.5), we have

$$\dot{r} = \frac{\mu c_4 \sin (\theta - \omega)}{r_0 v_0 \cos \gamma_0}. \tag{1.6.7}$$

Evaluation of (1.6.6) at $t = 0$ gives

$$\frac{1}{1+c_4 \cos (\theta_0 - \omega)} = \frac{\mu}{r_0 v_0^2 \cos^2 \gamma_0}, \tag{1.6.8}$$

which can be rearranged to

$$c_4 \cos (\theta_0 - \omega) = \frac{r_0 v_0^2 \cos^2 \gamma_0}{\mu} - 1. \tag{1.6.9}$$

Likewise, from (1.6.7) and (1.6.3) we obtain

$$c_4 \sin (\theta_0 - \omega) = \frac{r_0 v_0^2 \sin \gamma_0 \cos \gamma_0}{\mu}, \tag{1.6.10}$$

so that, by squaring and adding, we find

$$c_4^2 = \frac{\mu^2 - 2\mu r_0 v_0^2 \cos^2 \gamma_0 + r_0^2 v_0^4 \cos^2 \gamma_0}{\mu^2}, \tag{1.6.11}$$

which serves to define one of the integration constants in terms of initial conditions.

Now ω is obviously just a reference angle entering into the argument of (1.6.6). To examine its geometric meaning, we consider the special initial condition $\theta_0 = \omega$ in (1.6.9) and (1.6.10). Barring the exceptional orbits resulting from $r_0 = 0$, $v_0 = 0$, or $\cos \gamma_0 = 0$ (radial motion only), we see that this implies $\sin \gamma_0 = 0$, which means that ω marks the points on the orbit where the velocity vector is perpendicular to the radius vector (see Fig. 1.1). Equation (1.6.6) also shows that r reaches its minimum value at $\theta = \omega$ and its maximum at $\theta = \omega + \pi$.

REFERENCES

1. J. M. A. Danby, *Fundamentals of Celestial Mechanics*, Macmillan, New York, 1962, p. 120.
2. H. Pollard, *Mathematical Introduction to Celestial Mechanics*, Prentice-Hall, Englewood Cliffs, N.J., 1966.
3. G. F. Khilmi, *Qualitative Methods in the Many-Body Problem*, translated from the Russian, Gordon and Breach, New York, 1961.

Chapter two

THE CONIC SECTIONS

1. INTRODUCTION

In the preceding chapter we established that the motion of one spherical mass around another can be described by a conic section. In this chapter, we discuss the characteristics of the conic sections and examine their relations to observed position and velocity in further detail. We discuss Kepler's laws, describe the eccentric anomaly, derive Kepler's equation, and give the other time relations for conic-section orbits. We also introduce the parameters that locate a conic trajectory in a three-dimensional reference frame and discuss various special cases for which some of the orbit parameters have to be redefined. Thus, time equations are derived for orbits of low and high eccentricity and methods are discussed for series developments of the anomalies and the radial distance in terms of time. This subject is important for many formal manipulations in celestial mechanics and furnishes the basis for accuracy estimates required in the numerical evaluation of conic-section orbits.

2. THE ELLIPTIC ORBIT

The polar equation of an ellipse with the origin at one focus (Fig. 2.1) is

$$r = \frac{a(1-e^2)}{1+e\cos f}, \tag{2.2.1}$$

where the angle f is measured from the line joining the occupied focus and the curve's closest point of approach to that focus. The semi-major axis is normally denoted by a and the eccentricity by e. If the semi-minor axis is b, the eccentricity is defined by

$$e^2 = (a^2-b^2)/a^2. \tag{2.2.2}$$

The angle f, which takes the place of $\theta-\bar{\theta}$ in Eq. (1.6.6), is called the *true anomaly.* The point of closest approach to the origin ($f = 0$) is designated by the prefix "peri-," the suffix denoting the body at the focus. The point farthest away is given the prefix "apo-" (the letter "o" sometimes being dropped for euphony). Thus, for the sun, we have perihelion and aphelion; for the earth, perigee and apogee; for the moon, periselene and aposelene; for an unspecified central body, pericenter and apocenter.

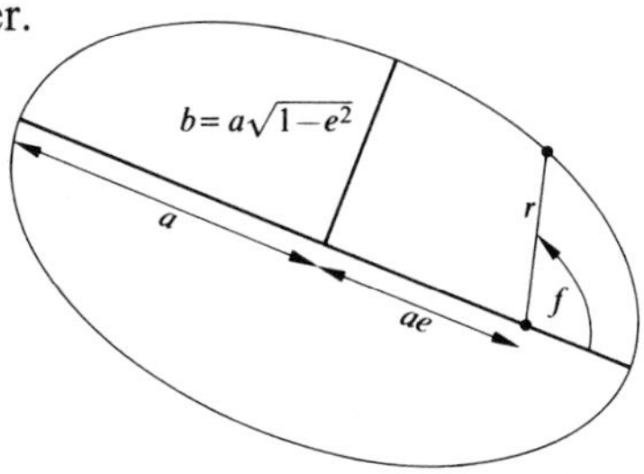

Figure 2.1

Comparison of (2.2.2) with (1.6.6) and (1.6.11) leads to

$$e^2 = \frac{\mu^2 - 2\mu r_0 v_0^2 \cos^2 \gamma_0 + r_0^2 v_0^4 \cos^2 \gamma_0}{\mu^2}$$

$$= 1 + \frac{(r_0 v_0^2 - 2\mu) r_0 v_0^2 \cos^2 \gamma_0}{\mu^2}, \qquad (2.2.3)$$

and

$$a = \mu r_0/(2\mu - r_0 v_0^2). \qquad (2.2.4)$$

For an elliptic orbit, where $e < 1$, we require that

$$v_0^2/2 - \mu/r_0 = \mathscr{E} < 0, \qquad (2.2.5)$$

where $\mathscr{E}$ is the energy per unit mass of the moving body. The minimum possible eccentricity, $e = 0$, is obtained with a circular orbit. According to (2.2.3) this requires that $v_0^2 = \mu/r_0$ and $\gamma_0 = 0$.

Since the energy of the moving body is conserved, we may generalize (2.2.5) to

$$\frac{1}{2}v^2 - \frac{\mu}{r} = \mathscr{E}. \qquad (2.2.6)$$

Then substitution into (2.2.4) yields

$$a = -\mu/2\mathscr{E} = \mu r/(2\mu - r v^2). \qquad (2.2.7)$$

The angular momentum per unit mass of the body in orbit (see 1.4.10 and 1.5.7) is given by

$$h = r_0 v_0 \cos \gamma_0. \qquad (2.2.8)$$

Using (2.2.3) and (2.2.4), we see that

$$a(1 - e^2) = h^2/\mu = r^4 \dot{f}^2/\mu, \qquad (2.2.9)$$

where the latter equality holds for any point of the orbit, since angular momentum is conserved. Finally, from (2.2.3), we obtain

$$e^2 = 1+2\mathscr{E}h^2/\mu^2. \tag{2.2.10}$$

These physical interpretations of the constants in (2.2.1) will be useful later on.

When θ of (1.6.6) is zero, $f = -\bar{\theta}$. By convention, f is always taken to be positive and is measured in the direction of motion of the orbiting body. If we denote the value of r at $f = 0$ (closest approach) by q and that at $f = \pi$ by Q, then

$$q = a(1-e); \qquad Q = a(1+e). \tag{2.2.11}$$

Further

$$(q+Q)/2 = a. \tag{2.2.12}$$

For this reason the semi-major axis is sometimes called the *mean distance*.

Equation (2.2.1) yields

$$\dot{r} = \frac{a(1-e^2)}{(1+e\cos f)^2} e\dot{f} \sin f,$$

or

$$\dot{r} = \frac{r^2 \dot{f} e \sin f}{a(1-e^2)}. \tag{2.2.13}$$

Using (2.2.9), we have

$$\dot{r} = \sqrt{\mu/a(1-e^2)}\, e \sin f. \tag{2.2.14}$$

This can also be expressed as a function of r: from Eq. (2.2.1)

$$e \cos f = \frac{a(1-e^2)}{r} - 1, \tag{2.2.15}$$

and hence

$$e^2 \sin^2 f = e^2 - \left[\frac{a(1-e^2)}{r} - 1\right]^2; \tag{2.2.16}$$

then the radial velocity component is

$$\dot{r} = \left[\frac{\mu}{a(1-e^2)}\right]^{1/2} \left\{e^2 - \left[\frac{a(1-e^2)}{r} - 1\right]^2\right\}^{1/2}. \tag{2.2.17}$$

The tangential velocity component $r\dot{f}$ follows from (2.2.9), in a straightforward fashion, as a function of r or f. Finally, solving (2.2.7) for v^2, we have

$$v^2 = 2\mu/r - \mu/a. \tag{2.2.18}$$

The three elementary laws of celestial mechanics are referred to as *Kepler's laws*. They were deduced over three centuries ago from observations on the planets and proved to be effective approximations to the true motions. They continue to be not only of historical interest, but also useful guides in cases where the idealized conditions required for the two-body problem are nearly fulfilled. In fact, most of the more refined theories known to us now take the two-body model as a point of departure. We have already derived two of Kepler's laws, and the third follows from an extension of the second.

Kepler's first law states that the orbit of a planet around the sun is an ellipse with the sun situated at one focus. We have already seen that the ellipse is a permissible orbit. It need only be pointed out that the other two orbit shapes would soon cause the planets to vanish to infinity, in order to establish the first law. In actuality, the fact that there are nine planets revolving around the sun, rather than one, means that no orbit is a perfect ellipse. However, since the distances between planets are so great and their masses so small in comparison to that of the sun, the departures from pure ellipses are quite small.

Kepler's second law states that the areas swept out by the radius vector from the sun to a planet in equal time intervals are constant. Consider an area element, ΔA, formed by two radii vectors r and $r+\Delta r$ separated by the angle Δf. These form a triangle and, passing to the limit, yield $dA = \frac{1}{2}r^2 df$, or

$$dA/dt = \tfrac{1}{2}r^2\dot{f}, \tag{2.2.19}$$

which is obviously constant by conservation of angular momentum.

Kepler's third law states that the ratio of the cube of the semi-major axis and the square of the period for any planet is equal to that for any other. To prove this, we can either calculate the period as

$$\int_0^{2\pi} \frac{df}{\dot{f}},$$

where $\dot{f}$ is expressed in terms of f by (2.2.9) and (2.2.1), or we may use the following geometrical argument. The area of an ellipse is $\pi ab = \pi a^2\sqrt{1-e^2}$. If T is the anomalistic period (time required for one complete revolution in terms of f), then (2.2.19) yields

$$r^2\dot{f} = \frac{2\pi a^2\sqrt{1-e^2}}{T}. \tag{2.2.20}$$

Frequently, it is convenient to speak of the *mean angular motion*, i.e., the rate at which the true anomaly is "swept out" by the radius vector, *averaged over the whole orbit*. If we denote this quantity by n, then

$$n = 2\pi/T \tag{2.2.21}$$

and

$$r^2\dot{f} = na^2\sqrt{1-e^2}. \tag{2.2.22}$$

But comparison with (2.2.9) leads to

$$n^2a^3 = \mu, \tag{2.2.23}$$

or

$$T = 2\pi\sqrt{a^3/\mu} \tag{2.2.24}$$

and

$$a^3/T^2 = \mu/4\pi^2. \tag{2.2.25}$$

Since the right-hand side of (2.2.25) is a universal constant, it is obvious that

$$a_1^3/T_1^2 = a_2^3/T_2^3 = \cdots, \tag{2.2.26}$$

which is a statement of the third law. In fact, since the orbiting body must have a finite mass, we should write (2.2.25) as $a^3/T^2 = (\mu + Gm)/4\pi^2$, where m is that mass. However, as we have seen in Chapter 1, this effect is quite small and can usually be ignored. Moreover, we are again ignoring the effects of the planets upon each other in stating this law.

It is frequently convenient to express the equation of the ellipse in terms of an angle subtended at its geometric center. If we measure this angle from the same line as we do the true anomaly and construct it in a particular way, the statement of elliptic motion becomes very simple. Its construction is performed as follows (Fig. 2.2). Given an ellipse of semi-major axis a and eccentricity e, we draw a circle of radius a from the center of the ellipse. For a particular value f of the true anomaly, we then construct a perpendicular to the major axis through the corresponding point on the ellipse and extend it to the circle. The angle E, subtended at the geometric center and measured from the line to the pericenter, is known as the *eccentric anomaly*.

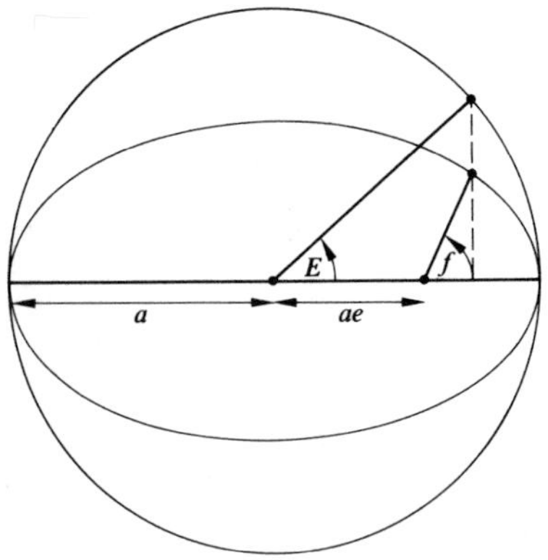

Figure 2.2

From Fig. 2.2 it can be seen that

$$a \cos E - ae = r \cos f. \tag{2.2.27}$$

It can also be seen from the figure that

$$r \sin f = a\sqrt{1-e^2} \sin E, \tag{2.2.28}$$

if we remember that the ellipse is derivable from the circle by an affine transformation reducing all the ordinate values by the same scale factor. The factor is $\sqrt{1-e^2}$ in this case, since that leads to $b = a\sqrt{1-e^2}$ for the semi-minor axis.

Expressing cos E and cos f in (2.2.27) in terms of tan $E/2$ and tan $f/2$, we find

$$\tan f/2 = \sqrt{\frac{1+e}{1-e}}\tan E/2. \tag{2.2.29}$$

Elimination of f from (2.2.27) and (2.2.28) by squaring and adding leads to the equation of the ellipse

$$r = a(1-e\cos E). \tag{2.2.30}$$

If we differentiate this with respect to t, we have

$$\dot{r} = ae\dot{E}\sin E, \tag{2.2.31}$$

which corresponds to (2.2.14) in terms of the eccentric anomaly. Using (2.2.14), we get

$$\dot{E} = \sqrt{\frac{\mu}{a^3(1-e^2)}}\frac{\sin f}{\sin E}, \tag{2.2.32}$$

from which we eliminate $\sin f/\sin E$ by (2.2.28) to find

$$\dot{E} = \sqrt{\frac{\mu}{a}}\frac{1}{r}. \tag{2.2.33}$$

Substituting for r from (2.2.30), we obtain

$$\dot{E}(1-e\cos E) = \sqrt{\mu/a^3},$$

which may be integrated at once to

$$E-e\sin E = \sqrt{\mu/a^3}\,(t-\tau), \tag{2.2.34}$$

where τ is a constant of integration. Equation (2.2.34) is known as *Kepler's equation.* Since $t = \tau$ for $E = 0$ it follows that τ represents the time of pericenter passage. We may note here a few alternative forms in which Kepler's equation is sometimes written. Using (2.2.23), Eq. (2.2.34) becomes

$$E-e\sin E = n(t-\tau),$$

where n is the mean angular motion. The quantity $n(t-\tau)$ is frequently written M and called the *mean anomaly*. The product of $n\tau$ is often written as a single constant $(-\chi)$, which has certain advantages. In this case, Kepler's equation becomes

$$E-e\sin E = nt+\chi. \tag{2.2.35}$$

Kepler's equation affords an example of the relations of position angle (true or eccentric anomaly) to time. Generally, these relations involve mixed transcendental functions (angle argument *and* trigonometric function of the angle) for f or E. Dependence of r on t exhibits the same awkwardness. In most cases it is much simpler to express time as a function of the position coordinate. For dependence on f we utilize (2.2.9) in the form

$$dt = \frac{r^2}{\sqrt{\mu a(1-e^2)}}df.$$

Employing (2.2.1), we find

$$t-\tau = \int_0^f \frac{a^2(1-e^2)^2}{\sqrt{\mu a(1-e^2)}}\frac{1}{(1+e\cos f)^2}df \tag{2.2.36}$$

$$= \sqrt{\frac{a^3}{\mu}}\left[2\tan^{-1}\left(\sqrt{\frac{1-e}{1+e}}\tan\frac{f}{2}\right)-e\sqrt{1-e^2}\,\frac{\sin f}{1+e\cos f}\right]_0^f. \tag{2.2.37}$$

Equation (2.2.37) is merely an alternative statement of Kepler's equation, from which it could have been derived (without integration) by judicious substitution of (2.2.1), (2.2.28), and (2.2.29).*

An expression for the time in terms of radial distance follows from (2.2.17), which can be written as

$$\dot{r} = \pm\sqrt{\frac{\mu}{a}}\frac{[2ar-a^2(1-e^2)-r^2]^{1/2}}{r}, \tag{2.2.38}$$

introducing a sign indeterminacy which has yet to be resolved. Thus

$$t_2-t_1 = \pm\sqrt{\frac{a}{\mu}}\int_{r_1}^{r_2}\frac{r\,dr}{[2ar-a^2(1-e^2)-r^2]^{1/2}}, \tag{2.2.39}$$

which can be evaluated in the form

$$t_2-t_1 = \pm\sqrt{\frac{a}{\mu}}\left\{a\cos^{-1}\frac{a-r}{ae}-[2ar-a^2(1-e^2)-r^2]^{1/2}\right\}_{r_1}^{r_2}. \tag{2.2.40}$$

The $\pm$ sign has the following significance: when the true anomalies f_1 and f_2 (corresponding to the values r_1 and r_2) lie in the first or the second quadrant ($\dot{r}>0$), the positive sign is to be used; when f_1 and f_2 lie in the third or the fourth quadrant ($\dot{r}<0$), the negative sign is used. When the radius vector r_1 lies on one side of the

*An alternative form of (2.2.37) employs $\sin^{-1}\left(\frac{\sqrt{1-e^2}\sin f}{1+e\cos f}\right)$ instead of $2\tan^{-1}\left(\sqrt{\frac{1-e}{1+e}}\tan\frac{f}{2}\right)$ in the brackets.

major axis of the ellipse and r_2 on the other, it is simplest to compute the *time of flight* from r_1 to q or Q and then separately from q or Q to r_2. A variety of computing algorithms may be introduced here to guard against sign errors.

An alternative to (2.2.40) can be found by changing the arc-cosine term to an arc-tangent:

$$t_2 - t_1 = \pm\sqrt{\frac{a}{\mu}}\left\{2a\tan^{-1}\sqrt{\frac{r-a(1-e)}{a(1+e)-r}} - \left[2ar - a^2(1-e^2) - r^2\right]^{1/2}\right\}_{r_1}^{r_2}. \tag{2.2.41}$$

For circular orbits ($r = a$, $e = 0$), Eq. (2.2.39) reduces to

$$t - \tau = \sqrt{\frac{a^3}{\mu}}\,f, \tag{2.2.42}$$

while both (2.2.40) and (2.2.41) become indeterminate. More will be said about time equations for e approaching zero in Section 6.

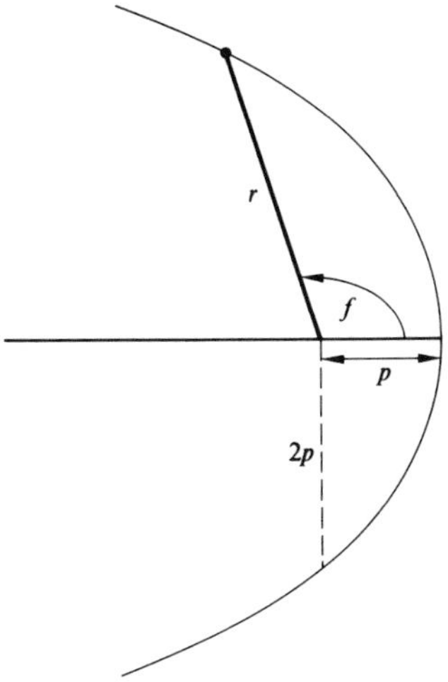

Figure 2.3

3. THE PARABOLIC ORBIT

The polar equation of a parabola with the origin at the focus (Fig. 2.3) is

$$r = 2p/(1+\cos f), \tag{2.3.1}$$

which we recognize as the limiting form of (2.2.1) as e approaches unity and the semi-major axis approaches infinity in such a way that $a(1-e^2)$ remains determinate and has the value of $2p$. Equation (2.3.1) may also be written

$$r = p\sec^2(f/2). \tag{2.3.2}$$

In view of (2.2.3) and (2.2.5) we have

$$\frac{1}{2}v_0^2 - \frac{\mu}{r_0} = \mathscr{E} = 0, \tag{2.3.3}$$

which distinguishes the parabolic trajectory as the *zero-energy* case among Keplerian orbits. Noting from (2.2.8) and (2.2.9) that

$$2p = a(1-e^2) = \frac{r_0^2 v_0^2 \cos^2 \gamma_0}{\mu},$$

we have, in view of (2.3.3),

$$p = r_0 \cos^2 \gamma_0. \tag{2.3.4}$$

We may note that (2.3.4) is an alternative form of the equation of the parabola when written as $p = r \cos^2 \gamma$; using (2.3.2), we find a third representation,

$$\gamma = f/2. \tag{2.3.5}$$

From (2.3.1) it is obvious that the closest point of approach is obtained at $f = 0$ (where $q = p$) and that Q is infinite. Transition of (2.2.9) from the elliptic to the parabolic case follows immediately and we have

$$r^2 \dot{f} = \sqrt{2p\mu}. \tag{2.3.6}$$

Similarly, the expressions (2.2.14) and (2.2.17) for $\dot{r}(f)$ and $\dot{r}(r)$ can be rewritten without difficulty by letting $a(1-e^2) \rightarrow 2p$ and $e \rightarrow 1$. From the conservation of $\mathscr{E} = 0$, according to (2.2.6), it follows that

$$v^2 = 2\mu/r \tag{2.3.7}$$

for parabolic trajectories.

Combining (2.3.2) and (2.3.6), we obtain $p^2 \sec^4(f/2)df = \sqrt{2p\mu}dt$, which may be written as

$$\left(\sec^2\frac{f}{2} + \sec^2\frac{f}{2}\tan^2\frac{f}{2}\right)\frac{df}{2} = \sqrt{\mu/2p^3}\, dt.$$

This can be integrated at once to

$$\tan\frac{f}{2} + \frac{1}{3}\tan^3\frac{f}{2} = \sqrt{\mu/2p^3}\,(t-\tau). \tag{2.3.8}$$

One can also derive statements analogous to Kepler's laws. The first of these would read: a possible orbit around the sun is a parabola with the sun situated at the focus. (Certain comets come very close to fulfilling this law.) Kepler's second law carries over directly, since it merely states the conservation of angular momentum. The third law must be reinterpreted since the motion here is not periodic. Consider the time of flight of the body as it travels from point (r_1, f_1) to (r_2, f_2). This interval is obtained by differencing two equations of the type (2.3.8), thus

$$t_2 - t_1 = \sqrt{2p^3/\mu}\left[\tan\frac{f_2}{2} + \frac{1}{3}\tan^3\frac{f_2}{2} - \tan\frac{f_1}{2} - \frac{1}{3}\tan^3\frac{f_1}{2}\right]. \tag{2.3.9}$$

If, for all parabolas, we take particular values of f_2 and f_1, the term in the brackets in the equation above has some fixed number. For convenience we take $f_1 = 3\pi/2$ and $f_2 = \pi/2$, i.e., the points on the parabola where it is intersected by the *latus rectum*.

Then, $t_2 - t_1 \equiv T_f = \sqrt{2p^3/\mu}(1.64992)$, or $p^3/T_f^2 = 0.18367\mu$; that is, the ratio of the cube of the pericenter distance and the square of the time of flight between particular values of the true anomaly is a constant for all parabolic orbits. This is the analog to Kepler's third law.

We have already derived the time-angle relation in (2.3.9). The time-distance relation can be obtained directly from this by substitution of (2.3.2). The result is

$$t_2 - t_1 = \pm\sqrt{\frac{2p^3}{\mu}}\left[\left(\frac{r}{p} - 1\right)^{1/2} + \frac{1}{3}\left(\frac{r}{p} - 1\right)^{3/2}\right]_{r_1}^{r_2}, \tag{2.3.10}$$

where the same conditions apply to the use of the $\pm$ sign as for the ellipse. Since (2.3.9) and (2.3.10) express the same cubic equation, the inverse relations for $f(t)$ and $r(t)$ follow readily from the solution of the equation. We find

$$\begin{aligned} f = 2\tan^{-1}&\left\{\left[\frac{3}{2}\sqrt{\frac{\mu}{2p^3}}(t_2 - t_1) + \left(\frac{9\mu}{8p^3}[t_2 - t_1]^2 + 1\right)^{1/2}\right]^{1/3}\right. \\ &\left. + \left[\frac{3}{2}\sqrt{\frac{\mu}{2p^3}}(t_2 - t_1) - \left(\frac{9\mu}{8p^3}[t_2 - t_1]^2 + 1\right)^{1/2}\right]^{1/3}\right\} \\ \equiv 2\tan^{-1}&F(t) \end{aligned} \tag{2.3.11}$$

and

$$r = p[F^2(t) + 1]. \tag{2.3.12}$$

4. THE HYPERBOLIC ORBIT

The polar equation of a hyperbola with the origin at one focus (Fig. 2.4) may be written as

$$r = \frac{a(e^2 - 1)}{1 + e\cos f}, \tag{2.4.1}$$

where now $e > 1$. We see from (2.2.3) that we require $v^2/2 - \mu/r > 0$; i.e., the total

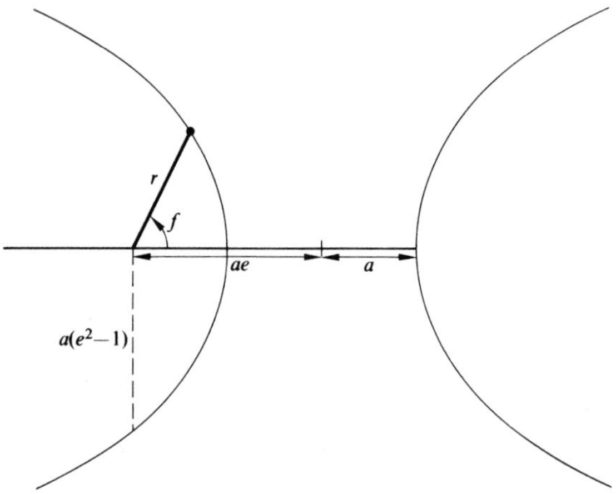

Figure 2.4

energy of motion is positive. Solving $a(e^2-1) = r_0^2 v_0^2 \cos^2 \gamma_0/\mu$ with the help of (2.2.3), we have

$$a = \mu r_0/(r_0 v_0^2 - 2\mu). \tag{2.4.2}$$

From (2.4.1) we deduce that

$$q = a(e-1). \tag{2.4.3}$$

If we ask the value of r at $f = \pi$, (2.4.1) yields $r = -a(e+1)$, which brings us to the other branch of the hyperbola; on any one branch we have $Q = \infty$.

The angular momentum equation (2.2.9) exhibits (e^2-1) in place of $(1-e^2)$, namely,

$$r^2\dot{f} = \sqrt{\mu a(e^2-1)}. \tag{2.4.4}$$

Similarly (2.2.14) becomes

$$\dot{r} = \sqrt{\frac{\mu}{a(e^2-1)}}\, e \sin f\,; \tag{2.4.5}$$

and (2.2.17) can be rewritten in an analogous way. The combination of (2.4.4) and (2.4.5) yields, after elimination of $\sin f$ by (2.4.1),

$$v^2 = 2\mu/r + \mu/a. \tag{2.4.6}$$

An angle that plays the role of the eccentric anomaly can be found by constructing a "standard" hyperbola with $e^2-1 = 1$ or $e = \sqrt{2}$; this curve fulfills the mission that the circle does for the ellipse. The construction is as follows (Fig. 2.5). Given a hyperbola with a semi-major axis a and eccentricity e, we draw a standard hyperbola ($e = \sqrt{2}$) with the same semi-major axis. For a particular value f of the true anomaly, we then construct a perpendicular to the major axis from the intersection of the radius vector and the hyperbola of eccentricity e. A line joining the center to the intersection of the perpendicular and the standard hyperbola encloses the shaded area A of Fig. 2.5.

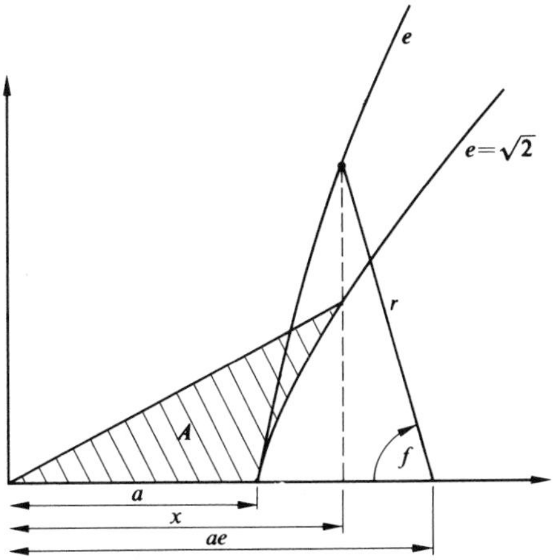

Figure 2.5

It can be seen that $r\cos f = ae - x$, where x is the value of the abscissa at the intersection point. This may be written as $r\cos f = a(e - x/a)$, but the quantity x/a has the value defined by the hyperbolic cosine of the argument $F = 2A/a^2$. Consequently,

$$r\cos f = a(e - \cosh F). \tag{2.4.7}$$

It can also be shown that

$$r\sin f = a\sqrt{e^2 - 1}\,\sinh F \tag{2.4.8}$$

and

$$\tan\frac{f}{2} = \sqrt{\frac{e+1}{e-1}}\tanh\frac{F}{2}. \tag{2.4.9}$$

From (2.4.7) and (2.4.8) we get the alternative expression for the hyperbola:

$$r = a(e\cosh F - 1). \tag{2.4.10}$$

Differentiating this with respect to t, we get $r = ae\,\dot{F}\sinh F$ and, using (2.4.5) and then (2.4.8) again, we get $(e\cosh F - 1)\dot{F} = \sqrt{\mu/a^3}$, or

$$e\sinh F - F = \sqrt{(\mu/a^3)}(t - \tau), \tag{2.4.11}$$

where τ is again the time of passage through the closest point of approach to the focus. Equation (2.4.11) is analogous to Kepler's equation for the ellipse.

Statements analogous to Kepler's laws can also be made with respect to the hyperbola. However, since they are quite similar to those derived for the parabola, they will not be given here.

Use of (2.4.1) in (2.4.4) allows us to find

$$t-\tau = \sqrt{\frac{a^3}{\mu}}\left\{e\sqrt{e^2-1}\,\frac{\sin f}{1+e\cos f}-2\tanh^{-1}\sqrt{\frac{e-1}{e+1}}\tan\frac{f}{2}\right\}_0^f, \qquad (2.4.12)$$

or the equivalent form

$$t_2-t_1 = \pm\sqrt{\frac{a}{\mu}}\left\{[2ra+r^2-a^2(e^2-1)]^{1/2}-2a\tanh^{-1}\left[\frac{r+a(1-e)}{r+a(1+e)}\right]^{1/2}\right\}_{r_1}^{r_2}. \qquad (2.4.13)$$

5. ORIENTATION OF CONIC-SECTION ORBITS IN SPACE

So far, we have considered the plane geometry of conic-section orbits and the time equations giving instantaneous positions along these trajectories in the form $t = t(E)$, $t(f)$, or $t(r)$. To specify the position of a moving body completely in a three-dimensional reference frame, we must give the orientation of the conic trajectory in space. This is accomplished by describing, relative to some Cartesian frame, the plane of the orbit and the orientation of the line to pericenter within that plane. Figure 2.6 illustrates the three quantities required, which correspond to the classical Euler angles:

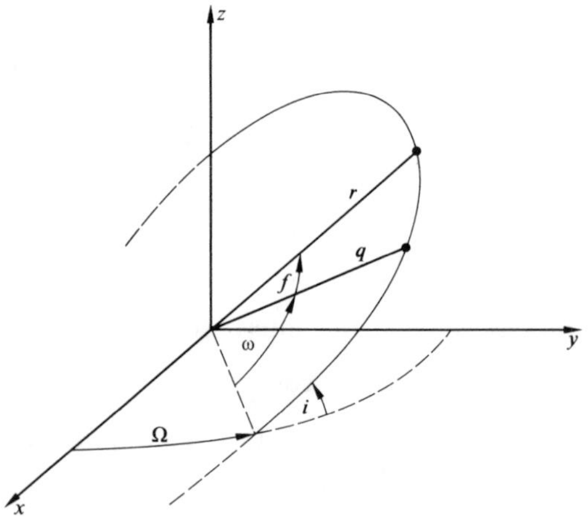

Figure 2.6

1. Ω, the nodal angle, measured from the x axis to the intersection between the orbit plane and the xy plane. We usually refer to that half of the line of nodes where the moving body goes from $z<0$ to $z>0$ as the *ascending node*;

2. i, the inclination of the orbit plane to the xy plane;
3. ω, the *argument of pericenter*, which locates that point in the orbit plane relative to the node.

Together with a, e, and τ these parameters represent one of the most frequently used sets of *orbit elements*; all are constants for Keplerian (conic-section) orbits. Along with f and E, one often uses $\theta = f+\omega$, the *argument of latitude*, to mark an instantaneous position. Note that the exact nature of the x, y, z system need not be discussed at this point; this is treated at length in Chapter 3. The same set of elements is applicable to hyperbolic trajectories, while parabolic ones require us to replace $a(1-e^2)$ by $2p$.

Certain forms of geometric degeneracy must now be considered which require a redefinition of some elements. Clearly ω and τ become ill-determined as e approaches zero. We may then use the set $a, i, \Omega, \bar{\mu} = e\sin(\omega+\Omega)$, $\bar{\nu} = e\cos(\omega+\Omega)$, and $\bar{\chi} = -n\tau+\omega = \chi+\omega$. For additional brevity one sometimes uses $\bar{\omega} = \omega+\Omega$, the *longitude of pericenter*. One encounters no difficulty with this set for small eccentricities. Note that θ, the argument of latitude, can be used with an ill-defined pericenter.

When the inclination angle approaches zero, the node becomes ill-determined. It is then appropriate to adopt the elements a, e, $\upsilon = \sin i \sin \Omega$, $\vartheta = \sin i \cos \Omega$, $\bar{\omega} = \omega+\Omega$, and τ. Now we should also use the modified argument of latitude $\tilde{\theta} = \theta+\Omega = f+\bar{\omega}$, known as the *true orbital longitude*.

For the case of low-eccentricity, low-inclination orbits a suitable set of elements is the union of the previous two: a, $\mu = e \sin \bar{\omega}$, $\nu = e \cos \bar{\omega}$, $\upsilon = \sin i \sin \Omega$, $\vartheta = \sin i \cos \Omega$ and $\varepsilon = \chi+\bar{\omega}$, the last quantity being referred to as the *longitude at epoch.*

6. SPECIAL TIME EQUATIONS; EXPANSIONS FOR CONIC TRAJECTORIES

We have seen that the time equations for conic trajectories are generally transcendental and cannot be inverted to obtain expressions for $r(t)$, $f(t)$, $E(t)$ or (what amounts to the same thing) $r(M)$, $f(M)$, $E(M)$, where M is the mean anomaly. The traditional approach has resorted to approximations obtainable by more or less elaborate expansions. They take the form of Fourier series whose independent variable is M and whose coefficients are of ascending order in the small quantities e or $(1-e)$. For the reader who requires a complete treatment of this subject, the literature is rich in detailed explanations [1 through 5]. Some of these series are particularly useful when e lies near zero or unity and they will be needed for the perturbation methods of Chapter 8. We therefore consider briefly a few formal manipulations required for these purposes.

Let us consider the time equation (2.2.37) as the elliptic orbit approaches circularity. The most elementary and strictly formal approach consists of developing the integrand of (2.2.36) as a binomial series in powers of e and integrating term by term. We find

$$M = n(t-\tau) = f - 2e\sin f + \left(\frac{3}{4}e^2 + \frac{1}{8}e^4\right)\sin 2f$$

$$+\frac{1}{3}e^3\sin 3f + \frac{5}{32}e^4\sin 4f + 0(e^5). \tag{2.6.1}$$

A more useful result, since it provides position in terms of time rather than *vice versa*, is an expansion for E in terms of M. We let $E - M = u$. Then Kepler's equation becomes

$$u = e\sin(M+u). \tag{2.6.2}$$

Now we assume that u can be found in the form

$$u = u_1 e + u_2 e^2 + \cdots + u_n e^n, \tag{2.6.3}$$

where the coefficients u_n are expressible in terms of trigonometric functions of M. They are determined in a straightforward manner by substituting (2.6.3) into (2.6.2), so that

$$u_1 e + u_2 e^2 + \cdots = e\sin M\cos u + e\cos M\sin u$$

$$= e\sin M\left[1 - \frac{1}{2!}(u_1 e + u_2 e^2 + \cdots)^2 + \frac{1}{4!}(u_1 e + u_2 e^2 + \cdots)^4 - \cdots\right]$$

$$+ e\cos M\left[(u_1 e + u_2 e^2 + \cdots) - \frac{1}{3!}(u_1 e + u_2 e^2 + \cdots)^3 + \cdots\right].$$

Equating powers of e, we obtain a set of algebraic equations in u_n whose solutions are

$$u_1 = \sin M; \qquad u_2 = \frac{1}{2}\sin 2M; \qquad u_3 = \frac{3}{8}\sin 3M - \frac{1}{8}\sin M; \qquad \ldots$$

Substituting this into the defining equation for u, we ultimately find

$$E = M + e\left(1 - \frac{e^2}{8} + \frac{e^4}{192}\right)\sin M + \frac{e^2}{2}\left(1 - \frac{e^2}{3} + \frac{e^4}{24}\right)\sin 2M$$

$$+ e^3\left(\frac{3}{8} - \frac{27}{218}e^2\right)\sin 3M + \cdots \tag{2.6.4}$$

It is interesting to note that the general term of this expansion is of the form $0(e^k)\sin kM$; i.e., the order of magnitude of each coefficient corresponds to the order of the Fourier component to which it belongs. Astronomers call this *d'Alembert's principle*; it holds for many series expansions in celestial mechanics.

Now we can use (2.6.4) to derive an expansion for $f(M)$. From (2.2.6) we have

$$dM = \frac{(1-e^2)^{3/2}}{(1+e\cos f)^2}df.$$

Since from (2.2.1) and (2.2.30), $(1-e^2)/(1+e\cos f) = 1-e\cos E$, we obtain

$$df = \frac{(1-e^2)^{1/2}}{(1-e\cos E)^2}dM. \tag{2.6.5}$$

But differentiation of (2.2.34) yields $dE/dM = 1/(1-e\cos E)$, so that (2.6.5) becomes

$$df = (1-e^2)^{1/2}(dE/dM)^2 dM. \tag{2.6.6}$$

Developing the square root by the binomial theorem, substituting for dE/dM from (2.6.4), and integrating (2.6.6), we eventually find

$$f = M + e\left(2 - \frac{e^2}{4} + \frac{5e^4}{96}\right)\sin M + e^2\left(\frac{5}{4} - \frac{11}{24}e^2 + \frac{17}{192}e^4\right)\sin 2M$$
$$+ e^3\left(\frac{13}{12} - \frac{129}{192}e^2\right)\sin 3M + \cdots \tag{2.6.7}$$

The trigonometric terms in (2.6.7), representing $f-M$, are known as the *equation of the center*. This result can also be derived by inverting the expression (2.6.1) for $M(f)$. A well-known theorem due to Lagrange was developed to facilitate such series inversions [3 p. 161; 4 through 8]. In its simplified form, it states that if

$$\zeta = z + e\phi(\zeta), \tag{2.6.8}$$

where $e \ll 1$, then

$$\zeta = z + \sum_{m=1}^{\infty} \frac{e^m}{m!}\frac{d^{m-1}}{dz^{m-1}}[\phi(z)]^m. \tag{2.6.9}$$

The reader may care to verify for himself that these manipulations will reduce (2.6.1) to (2.6.7). When $\phi(z)$ consists of trigonometric terms, as in this case, the use of (2.6.8) leads to powers of trigonometric functions which must subsequently be converted to multiple arguments. We can circumvent some of the tedium by taking

$$\sin kM = \frac{1}{2i}[\exp(ikM) - \exp(-ikM)],$$

$$\cos kM = \frac{1}{2}[\exp(ikM) + \exp(-ikM)],$$

where $i = \sqrt{-1}$, and performing the manipulations in terms of the exponentials.

Besides expressing the anomalies as functions of time, we should also be able to do this for r. We already noted in connection with (2.2.40) and (2.2.41) that these expressions become ill-defined as e approaches zero and are awkward to invert into $r(M)$. One might think of starting with (2.2.30), introducing a power series for $\cos E$, and expressing each term with the help of (2.6.4); while this is straightforward, it is certainly laborious. An alternative would be to start from the basic equations of motion in polar coordinates [3, p. 172], assume a series solution for r in terms of M, and solve for its coefficients. Since there is likely to be need for series expansions of quantities of the form

$$\left(\frac{r}{a}\right)^k \begin{Bmatrix}\sin\\ \cos\end{Bmatrix}(jf) \quad \text{and} \quad \left(\frac{r}{a}\right)^k \begin{Bmatrix}\sin\\ \cos\end{Bmatrix}(jE)$$

in terms of M, any technique restricted to very special cases does not seem particularly attractive; instead, we examine a general procedure which copes with a variety of series developments encountered in celestial mechanics.

Consider, for example, $k = -1$ and $j = 0$. The Fourier series for this case is

$$\frac{a}{r} = \frac{1}{\pi}\int_0^\pi \frac{a}{r} dM + \frac{2}{\pi}\sum_{l=1}^{\infty} \cos lM \int_0^\pi \frac{a}{r} \cos lM\, dM, \tag{2.6.10}$$

where $\sin lM$ terms are absent due to the symmetry of r about $M = 0$. Noting from (2.2.34) that $dE = (a/r)dM$ and using Kepler's equation in the second integrand of (2.6.10), we have

$$\frac{a}{r} = \frac{1}{\pi}\int_0^\pi dE + \frac{2}{\pi}\sum_{l=1}^{\infty} \cos lM \int_0^\pi \cos(lE - le \sin E) dE. \tag{2.6.11}$$

It is convenient to define the second integral as the special function

$$J_l(le) = \frac{1}{\pi}\int_0^\pi \cos(lE - le \sin E) dE. \tag{2.6.12}$$

Historically speaking, it was precisely for this astronomical application that the Bessel functions of the first kind, with integer orders l and real arguments le, had been defined. Equation (2.6.11) becomes

$$\frac{a}{r} = 1 + 2\sum_{l=1}^{\infty} J_l(le) \cos lM. \tag{2.6.13}$$

We do not need to develop here the theory of Bessel functions; the reader will find further information relative to their application to orbits in the references [1, 4, 5].

Suffice it to record a few explicit expressions for some low-order J_l and typical Fourier expansions obtainable with Bessel coefficients:

$$J_0(\xi) = 1 - \frac{\xi^2}{4} + \frac{\xi^4}{64} - \frac{\xi^6}{2304} + \cdots,$$

$$J_1(\xi) = \frac{\xi}{2}\left[1 - \frac{\xi^2}{8} + \frac{\xi^4}{192} - \frac{\xi^6}{9216} + \cdots\right],$$

$$J_2(\xi) = \frac{\xi^2}{8}\left[1 - \frac{\xi^2}{12} + \frac{\xi^4}{384} - \cdots\right],$$

$$J_3(\xi) = \frac{\xi^3}{48}\left[1 - \frac{\xi^2}{16} + \frac{\xi^4}{640} - \cdots\right].$$

For example, (2.6.4) can now be recast in the form

$$E = M + 2\sum_{l=1}^{\infty} \frac{1}{l} J_l(le) \sin lM. \tag{2.6.14}$$

Furthermore

$$\cos E = -\frac{e}{2} + 2\sum_{l=1}^{\infty} \frac{1}{l} J_l'(le) \cos lM, \tag{2.6.15}$$

and

$$\frac{r}{a} = 1 - e\cos E = 1 + \frac{e}{2} - 2e\sum_{l=1}^{\infty} \frac{1}{l} J_l'(le) \cos lM, \tag{2.6.16}$$

where $J'(\xi) = dJ/d\xi$. Also,

$$\frac{r}{a}\cos f = \cos E - e = -\frac{3e}{2} + 2\sum_{l=1}^{\infty} \frac{1}{l} J_l'(le) \cos lM. \tag{2.6.17}$$

A discussion of convergence properties for these expansions will be found in Plummer [5, p. 46] and elaborate explicit tabulations for geometric quantities like

$$\left(\frac{r}{a}\right)^k \begin{Bmatrix}\sin\\ \cos\end{Bmatrix}(jf) \quad \text{and} \quad \left(\frac{r}{a} - 1\right)^k \begin{Bmatrix}\sin\\ \cos\end{Bmatrix}(jf)$$

may be found in Cayley's and Newcomb's tables [9, 10].

Before closing this section we consider the time relation for near-parabolic trajectories, i.e., for e approaching unity. When e becomes large there is a loss of accuracy in expressions like (2.2.37). Furthermore, in practical applications one would like to use a time equation that holds for all near-parabolic trajectories, be they elliptic or hyperbolic. An obvious approach consists of rearranging (2.2.37) in such a way that it can be expanded in terms of the small quantity $(1-e)$. Thus we find

$$\frac{\sin f}{1+e\cos f}=\tan\frac{f}{2}\left[\frac{1+e}{2}+\frac{1-e}{2}\tan^2\frac{f}{2}\right]^{-1}=\frac{2\tan f/2}{1+e}\left[1+\sum_{n=1}^{\infty}\left(\frac{e-1}{e+1}\tan^2\frac{f}{2}\right)^n\right]$$

by binomial expansion. Furthermore, a Taylor series for the arctangent term yields

$$\tan^{-1}\left(\sqrt{\frac{1-e}{1+e}}\tan\frac{f}{2}\right)=\sqrt{\frac{1-e}{1+e}}\sum_{n=0}^{\infty}\left(\frac{e-1}{e+1}\right)^n\frac{\tan^{2n+1}f/2}{2n+1}.$$

Combining these results and giving the first two terms of the resulting series explicitly, we have

$$t_2-t_1=4\sqrt{\frac{2p^3}{\mu}}\frac{1}{(1+e)^3}\left[(1+e)\tan\frac{f}{2}+\left(e-\frac{1}{3}\right)\tan^3\frac{f}{2}\right.$$
$$\left.+\sum_{n=2}^{\infty}\left(e-1+\frac{2n}{2n+1}\right)\left(\frac{e-1}{e+1}\right)^{n-1}\tan^{2n+1}\frac{f}{2}\right]_{f_1}^{f_2}. \quad (2.6.18)$$

This converges for $\tan^2 f/2<|(e+1)/(e-1)|$. Thus the formula is useful for a significant portion of the trajectory near pericenter. It is arranged so that the first two terms tend to (2.3.9) as $e\to 1$.

One common drawback of the time relations involving the true anomaly on near-parabolic orbits is their inherent loss of accuracy for the remote parts of the trajectory, where f changes very little with the passage of time and the vehicle performs a near-asymptotic motion. Clearly r is a more appropriate independent variable for these cases, but the necessary formal manipulations are again quite obvious and will not be developed here.

REFERENCES

1. D. Brouwer and G. M. Clemence, *Methods of Celestial Mechanics*, Academic Press, New York, 1961.
2. J. M. A. Danby, *Fundamentals of Celestial Mechanics*, Macmillan, New York, 1962.
3. F. R. Moulton, *Introduction to Celestial Mechanics*, Macmillan, New York, 1914.
4. W. M. Smart, *Celestial Mechanics*, Longmans-Green, London, 1953.
5. H. C. Plummer, *An Introductory Treatise on Dynamical Astronomy* (reprint), Dover, New York, 1960.
6. E. T. Whittaker and G. N. Watson, *Introduction to Modern Analysis*, Cambridge University Press, Cambridge, 1950, p. 133.
7. P. S. Laplace, *Mecanique Celeste*, translated by N. Bowditch, Hilliard, Gray, Little, and Wilkins, Boston, 1829, p. 362.
8. E. W. Brown and C. A. Shook, *Planetary Theory* (reprint), Dover, New York, 1964.

9. A. Cayley, "Tables of the Developments of Functions in the Theory of Elliptic Motion," *Mem. Roy. Astron. Soc., London,* **29,** 1861.

10. S. Newcomb, "Development of the Perturbation Function in Cosines of Multiples of the Mean Anomalies and of Angles between the Perihelia and Common Node and in Powers of the Eccentricities and Mutual Inclination," *Astron. Papers Amer. Ephemeris,* **5,** 1, 1895.

Chapter three

POSITION IN SPACE

1. INTRODUCTION

In this chapter, we develop more fully the concepts, nomenclature, and notation describing the position of an orbiting body, deal with traditional astronomic conventions for coordinate systems and time, and discuss the interpretation of standard ephemerides. Methods of converting one coordinate system to another and one time system to another are explained in detail, with illustrative examples. The reader may find it helpful to consult references 1 and 10 for numerous points beyond the scope of the chapter and for an introduction to the specialized literature.

Although the subject matter is not analytically profound at the level adopted here, it sometimes proves confusing to the professional without an astronomical background. Definitions, computational procedures, and terminologies that are perfectly consistent and logical at the time of their inception may lose these qualities in subsequent refinement. Thus certain interpretations and adjustments of ephemeris data, as well as various details connected with the time scales, can be rendered plausible only by appealing to history. However, rather than use history as a logical outline for this chapter, we have attempted to arrange the material on a conceptual basis.

2. INERTIAL SYSTEMS

In the first two chapters we introduced various coordinate systems without asking how any such frame might be established in practice, i.e., to what it should be referred geometrically and what precision do the equations of motion that we formulate provide. Let us obtain a preliminary view of the difficulties involved by reexamining the two-body problem. When we wrote the equations of motion for this case, we tacitly assumed that the universe consisted of nothing but these two bodies. We then introduced a nonrotating coordinate frame whose origin was at the center of mass of the system. In this reference frame the acceleration of the particle m_2 due to attraction by the particle m_1 was Gm_1/r^2 and we found that the two particles described conic-section paths about the origin and also about each other.

Alternatively, we could have put the origin of coordinates at the center of m_1. To arrive at the same result, we would have had to write the acceleration of m_2 as $(Gm_1 + Gm_2)/r^2$. This disagrees with the form of the acceleration term as derived by Newton's second law and inverse-square attraction and is due to the fact that our new origin of coordinates, at body m_1, is being accelerated by the action of m_2. We speak of such a coordinate system as *noninertial.*

However, even choosing the center of mass of the two-body system (or of any n-body system) as our origin of coordinates, we must admit that this cannot be considered a strictly inertial reference so long as we cannot deny the existence of other masses in the universe. There are two ways of observing the *noninertial* qualities of a coordinate frame: first, we may observe that the motion of its origin is not unaccelerated within the universe or, second, we may note the apparent departures from Newton's law of gravitation as we have done in the two-body example above.

So far, we have not mentioned the *nonrotational* quality of inertial coordinate systems. Now, on the one hand, an angular velocity of the reference frame would introduce centrifugal and Coriolis forces into the equations of motion but, on the other hand, there is no sure way of establishing the angular rates of a coordinate frame, since all visible references, like the stars, are themselves moving. The only fact we can state is that in a coordinate frame *considered* as "inertial" (and hence nonrotating) the inverse-square law of attraction is encountered empirically and what ultimately matters is that motion in a system rotating *relative* to what we consider an inertial reference may be successfully explained by our notions of centrifugal and Coriolis forces.

With our earlier remark that a strictly inertial origin of coordinates could be established only by taking into account all the mass particles in the universe, we have already implied that the practical analyst and the purist will be parting ways in their recognition of inertial systems. In practice we are forced to adopt what we may call *pseudo-inertial* systems. In so doing, we ignore certain noninertial and rotational manifestations of our reference frame because (1) they may be too small to be noticeable with present-day instruments or (2) they may be negligible for the required accuracy of our analysis. Thus, the flight of a bullet is usually so short that we may neglect the rotation of the earth in studying its trajectory; i.e., even though we know the earth rotates on its axis, thereby giving rise to Coriolis and centrifugal forces, the accuracy by which we can measure *or care to measure* the trajectory of the bullet is not affected by these forces. However, when the time of flight is so long that the integrated accelerations from these forces amount to (relatively) substantial displacements, they must be accounted for. Hence, in ballistic-missile flight, we must include the effect of earth's rotation in the equations of motion; we can, however, neglect the accelerations exerted by the missile on the earth (see Chapter 1) and ignore the relatively slow rate of the earth's motion round the sun. This may also be the case for near satellites when we compare positions in successive revolutions. The earth's orbital motion must be taken into account for flights to the moon and the planets, but in these we can still ignore the motion of the solar system in the galaxy. Thus, until man journeys beyond the solar system, two coordinate systems will suffice for our purposes: a geocentric frame and a heliocentric one.

When the origin of a coordinate system has been selected, one still needs to specify the directions of coordinate axes about this point. That is usually done by taking a *fundamental* plane and an angular reference in it which constitutes the first coordinate axis. The second lies in the plane and is perpendicular to the first, while the third is normal to both and follows the right-hand rule. Two natural choices exist for the fundamental plane, that of the earth's equator, and that of the earth's orbit about the sun, known as the *ecliptic*. Since these two planes are inclined to one another at an angle of 23.5°, their intersection forms a convenient choice for the angular reference in either plane. This intersection is called the *line of equinoxes*, and passes through the sun only twice a year (Fig. 3.1). We may take a line parallel to it, intercepting the sun, as the reference direction in the heliocentric system.

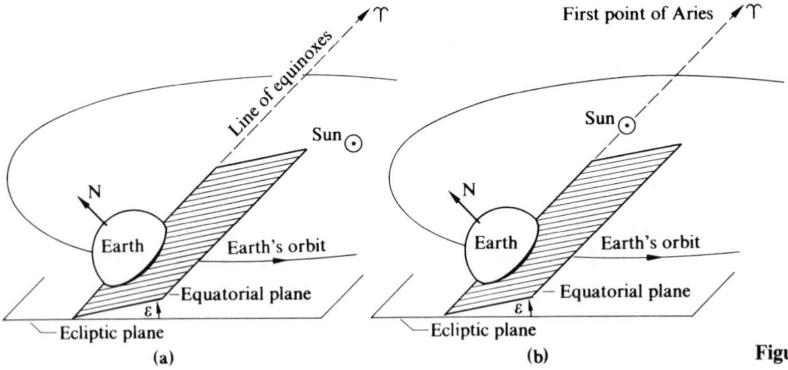

Figure 3.1

When the line of equinoxes does pass through the sun, that body also lies in the earth's equator, thus making day and night of equal length. This occurs on or about March 21 and September 23 each year. The positive sense of the axis, for angular reference, is taken from earth to sun during the March equinox.* The position of the line of equinoxes on a sphere of infinite radius centered on the earth, the celestial sphere, is called the *first point of Aries* and has the symbol ♈.

*Also called the vernal equinox. Since observers in the southern hemisphere are then welcoming autumn, we prefer the designation used in the text.

This point marks the extension of the line of equinoxes beyond the sun (Fig. 3.1b) to the "fixed" stars.

Since the distance to the stars is extremely great, the same point located amongst them may serve as a directional reference for the line of equinoxes in both the geocentric and heliocentric systems. The position of ♈ is not invariant, however. Both the equatorial and the ecliptic planes are continually shifting their orientations and the stars exhibit some motion of their own. As a result, in the course of time the first point of Aries has separated by nearly 30° from the constellation from which it originally took its name. This rate of angular displacement (in the order of one minute of arc per year) requires the introduction of a specified equinox (identified by a certain *epoch* or instant in time) for the tabulation of celestial positions in a geo- or heliocentric reference frame. This will be discussed later in this chapter.

3. ORBIT ELEMENTS

In Chapter 2 we introduced the elements Ω, i, ω to give the orientation of a Keplerian orbit in space. We shall briefly reexamine these elements to relate them more specifically to the notions introduced in the previous section. They are defined as follows (Fig. 3.2). We draw a perpendicular to the fundamental plane (which can be the ecliptic or the equator) at the origin and call *north* that segment which coincides most closely with the earth's north pole. Considering the nodal line between the orbit and the fundamental plane, we call the point of intersection at which the object passes from south to north the ascending node. The inclination, i, is the angle between these planes, and is taken counterclockwise when standing at the ascending node and looking toward the origin. Obviously, $0° \leq i \leq 180°$. The *longitude of the node** or, simply, node angle, Ω, is measured eastward along

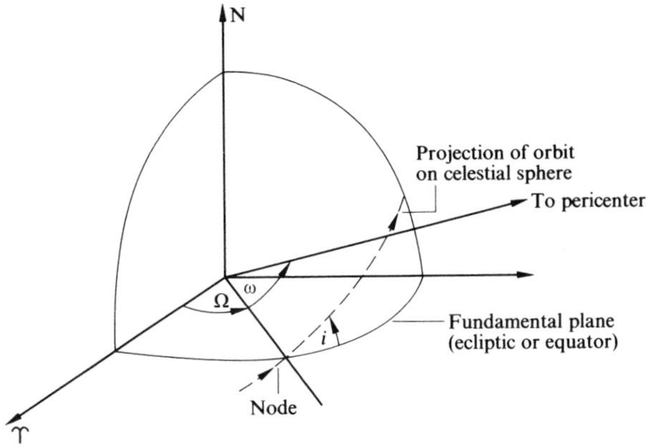

Figure 3.2

*The adjective *ascending* is frequently dropped and used only when ambiguity is possible. Here, when we use *node* we mean *ascending node*.

the arc of the fundamental plane from the invariant line (the first point of Aries) to the node; it varies from 0° to 360°. The argument of pericenter, ω, is the angle subtended at the origin by the line to the node and the line to pericenter (this last forming one branch of what is often called the *line of apsides*). It is measured in the direction of motion of the orbiting object and varies from 0° to 360°.

In the present context it is also possible to introduce different definitions for the orbital period. In Chapter 2 we used the symbol T for the time interval between successive pericenter passages; this is known as the *anomalistic* period. If nodal crossings are used as a reference, we speak of the *draconitic* period, whereas successive crossings of the meridian of ♈ define the *sidereal* period. For Keplerian orbits, these three intervals are identical; only when perturbations act do they differ numerically.

4. THE ORBIT IN RECTANGULAR AND SPHERICAL COORDINATES; HELIOCENTRIC AND GEOCENTRIC SYSTEMS

In Section 2 of this chapter we considered various matters concerning the origin and the fundamental plane of a coordinate system and in Section 3 we discussed classical orbit elements, which might be called an orbital reference frame. In the present section, we shall show the connection of this system to the more conventional Cartesian and spherical ones.

In the plane of the orbit the calculation of rectangular coordinates is simple enough. Let the origin be at the occupied focus, which implies that it is at or very near the center of the most massive body. Let the ξ axis point toward pericenter and the η axis be perpendicular to it, positive when taken in the same direction as the motion of the object at pericenter (Fig. 3.3). Obviously,

$$\xi = r\cos f; \qquad \eta = r\sin f. \tag{3.4.1}$$

Using Eqs. (2.2.27) and (2.2.28), we may also write

$$\xi = a(\cos E - e); \qquad \eta = a\sqrt{1-e^2}\sin E. \tag{3.4.2}$$

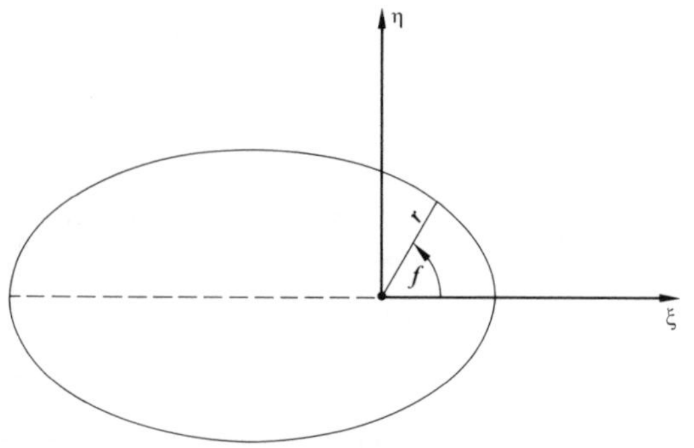

Figure 3.3

For the connection of these coordinates to a three-dimensional frame, consider a rectangular system at the same origin. Let the x axis be in the direction of ♈ (and consequently in the fundamental plane); let the z axis be taken perpendicular to the fundamental plane, positive in the northward sense (Fig. 3.4). When the object is at a distance r from the origin and an angle f from the ξ axis, we may write $z = r \sin \varphi$. But $\sin \varphi = \sin i \sin (\omega+f)$ or, from (3.4.1), $z = \xi \sin \omega \sin i + \eta \cos \omega \sin i$. Similarly, the application of spherical trigonometry leads to expressions for x and y in terms of ξ, η, ω, i, Ω. The complete array of transformations is most simply written as

$$x = l_1\xi+l_2\eta; \qquad y = m_1\xi+m_2\eta; \qquad z = n_1\xi+n_2\eta, \tag{3.4.3}$$

where

$$\begin{aligned} l_1 &= \cos\Omega\cos\omega - \sin\Omega\sin\omega\cos i, \\ m_1 &= \sin\Omega\cos\omega + \cos\Omega\sin\omega\cos i, \\ n_1 &= \sin\omega\sin i, \end{aligned} \tag{3.4.4}$$

and

$$\begin{aligned} l_2 &= -\cos\Omega\sin\omega - \sin\Omega\cos\omega\cos i, \\ m_2 &= -\sin\Omega\sin\omega + \cos\Omega\cos\omega\cos i, \\ n_2 &= \cos\omega\sin i. \end{aligned} \tag{3.4.5}$$

The orbit elements being given, the position of a body may be found for any value of f or E. Tabulation against time is somewhat more difficult since it involves the application of Kepler's equation or its equivalents (2.2.34, 2.2.37, 2.2.40). We noted in Chapter 2 that the orbit elements had to be redefined for special cases, such as $e \to 0$ and $i \to 0$, in order to retain accuracy in numerical computations. Corresponding modifications can then be made in (3.4.4) and (3.4.5) for the calculation of Cartesian coordinates.

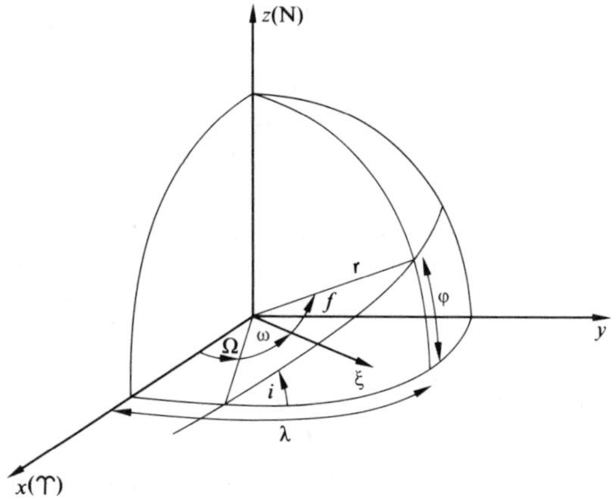

Figure 3.4

In a spherical coordinate system, the notation and customary terminology depend on the fundamental plane used. When using the equator, we speak of a *declination* angle, δ ($\pm$ for north or south of the equator) and *right ascension*, α, positive eastward from the ♈ axis, usually measured in hours, minutes, and seconds along the equator ($24^h = 360°$). (For some uses it is convenient to refer celestial objects to the observer's meridian by a longitude-like angle, the *local hour angle* of the object. This is measured westward from the local meridian and ranges between 0° to 360°. The connection between this angular coordinate and the ♈ axis is given by the observer's right ascension.) In reference to the ecliptic, the angle φ is called the celestial latitude and λ the celestial longitude, taken positive eastward from the ♈ axis.* For illustrative purposes, it suffices to demonstrate the relations between one of these spherical systems and the corresponding Cartesian frame. Obviously

$$\sin\varphi = z/r; \qquad \cos\varphi = \sqrt{x^2+y^2}/r \tag{3.4.6}$$

and

$$\sin\lambda = y/\sqrt{x^2+y^2}; \qquad \cos\lambda = x/\sqrt{x^2+y^2}. \tag{3.4.7}$$

The reader will find occasional references to the so-called astrometric right ascension and declination. This is essentially a spherical system, but the numerical coordinate values are adjusted for certain physical effects, as explained later, which make them similar to the information given in star catalogs.

5. RELATIONS BETWEEN THE HELIOCENTRIC ECLIPTIC AND THE GEOCENTRIC EQUATORIAL SYSTEMS

As the reader may suspect, certain combinations of fundamental planes and origins of coordinates have become preferred choices in the astronomical tradition. Thus, in a heliocentric frame, one frequently takes the ecliptic as a fundamental plane, whereas in a geocentric system the equatorial plane is preferred. In this section we will discuss some of the relations between these systems.

In the ephemerides [2, 3, 4] one may find the positions of the planets tabulated in terms of Cartesian or spherical sets of heliocentric coordinates where, in the latter case, the heliocentric distance may be given in terms of the astronomical unit,† which is essentially the mean distance from earth to sun. This quantity is called the *radius vector* in astronomic terminology. We have already indicated that the orientations of any of the customary fundamental planes and the ♈ axis are not exactly invariant relative to a *truly* inertial set of axes; hence most coordinate values are subject to certain corrections to be discussed in Section 8.

*This notation should not be confused with terrestrial latitude and longitude. There is a tendency to describe the positions of low-altitude satellites in terms of the geocentric latitude and longitude; these are discussed in Section 6.

†The subject of physical units in dynamical astronomy warrants a separate discussion. We shall comment on it in Sections 7.2 and 8.

If the position of a planet is tabulated by means of the heliocentric ecliptic system in terms of celestial longitude, celestial latitude, and radius vector, the conversion to a rectangular frame follows from the inverse of (3.4.6) and (3.4.7), that is,

$$x = r\cos\varphi\cos\lambda; \qquad y = r\cos\varphi\cos\lambda; \qquad z = r\sin\varphi. \tag{3.5.1}$$

In general, the heliocentric ephemerides do not include positions of the earth; instead, the geocentric ephemerides include positions of the sun, which constitutes equivalent information. Thus, for example, the heliocentric latitude and longitude of the earth may be obtained from the corresponding geocentric coordinates of the sun as

$$\varphi_E = -\varphi_S \quad \text{and} \quad \lambda_E = \lambda_S + 180°, \tag{3.5.2}$$

where, for the sake of convenience, we have replaced the traditional astronomic subscripts ⊕ for the earth by E and ⊙ for the sun by S.*

As stated, in the geocentric equatorial system we refer to the latitude type angle as *declination*, symbol δ, and the longitude-like angle as *right ascension*, symbol α. This last is also measured from the line of equinoxes eastward, but along the equator. Right ascension is ordinarily expressed in units of time; tables for conversion of time to arc and *vice versa* are given in the *American Ephemeris and Nautical Almanac* [2] here abbreviated as AENA. For the planets, AENA also lists distances from earth at convenient time intervals. If we designate, according to astronomic tradition, the Cartesian coordinates of a body relative to the earth's center by X, Y, Z, we have (compare Eqs. 3.5.1)

$$X = r\cos\delta\cos\alpha; \qquad Y = r\cos\delta\sin\alpha; \qquad Z = r\sin\delta. \tag{3.5.3}$$

The solar ephemeris in geocentric coordinates is given in AENA not only in the equatorial spherical and Cartesian systems but also with reference to the ecliptic, as we have mentioned. The sun's distance from the earth is tabulated in two ways. The more direct consists of giving the ratio of the instantaneous earth-sun distance to the mean value of this dimension, the astronomical unit. The second method consists of giving the so-called *equatorial horizontal parallax* of the sun, p_h. This is the angle subtended by the earth's equatorial radius at the center of the sun. From the geometry of Fig. 3.5 it follows that $R_{ES} = R/\sin p_h$. Since p_h amounts to less than 9″ of arc, we can usually replace $\sin p_h$ by its argument without causing

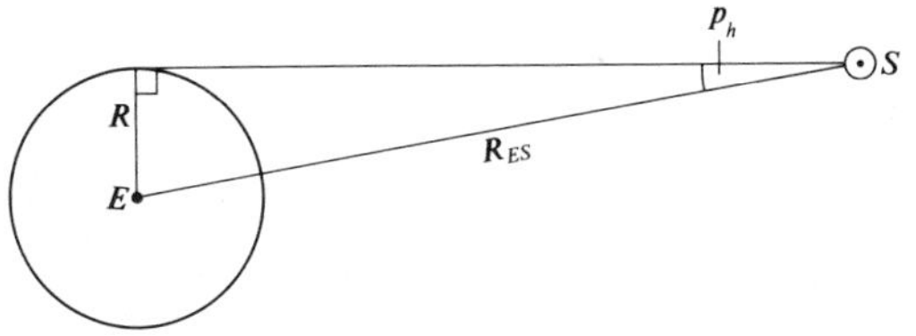

Figure 3.5

*Similarly, we propose to use M instead of ☾ for the moon.

noticeable error. The tables of the moon, finally, are also given in both equatorial and ecliptic geocentric spherical systems. Lunar distance is represented by the equatorial horizontal parallax in complete analogy to the definition of this quantity for the solar tables.

Conversion of coordinates from the heliocentric ecliptic frame to the geocentric equatorial one is most easily accomplished in the Cartesian systems (Fig. 3.6). Let us first perform a rotation about the x axis by the obliquity ε. We have

$$x' = x; \qquad y' = y \cos \varepsilon - z \sin \varepsilon; \qquad z' = y \sin \varepsilon + z \cos \varepsilon, \tag{3.5.4}$$

where x', y', z' are now parallel to the X, Y, Z axes. Then, by a simple translation,

$$X = x' + X_S; \qquad Y = y' + Y_S; \qquad Z = z' + Z_S, \tag{3.5.5}$$

we complete the transformation. As mentioned, the coordinates of the sun are tabulated directly in AENA; the obliquity of the ecliptic is also given there.

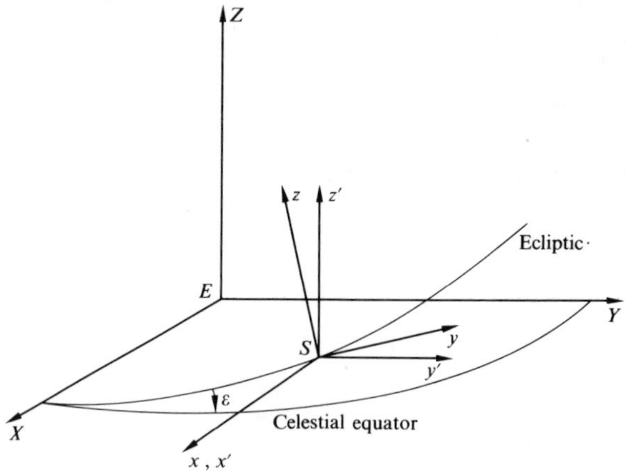

Figure 3.6

6. OBSERVER'S POSITION ON EARTH; THE TOPOCENTRIC SYSTEM

Since most observations of an object are made from the surface of the earth, conversions to and from a system with origin there are required. Thus, some specification of the observer's position in relation to the equator and line of equinoxes is necessary. Because the earth is nonspherical and is rotating relative to ♈, such a specification is not trivial. We need for this not only some knowledge of the shape of the earth but also a means of obtaining the angular departure of the observer's meridian from the line of equinoxes. Since the latter involves certain definitions of time, we choose to relegate it to the next section.

The shape of the earth can be closely approximated by that of an oblate spheroid, i.e., by an ellipse rotated about its minor axis. The means by which the dimensions of the spheroid are found are beyond the scope of this discussion and the reader is referred to treatises on surveying geodesy for details [5–8]. Much of the current literature in this field concerns the geodetic uses of artificial satellites. As a result, the numerical constants for the figure of the earth are updated almost on a monthly basis and considerable detail on the processing of satellite observations may be found in the appropriate periodicals. Suffice it here to give a brief exposition on concepts and nomenclature.

6.1. The Geopotential, the Geoid, and the Co-geoid

Suppose we select some place on the surface of the earth and measure the direction and magnitude of the force exerted on a unit mass there, this force being the resultant of that of gravity and of the earth's rotation and arising from what is known as the *geopotential.* At any other place both the direction and magnitude of the force due to the geopotential will differ from those of the first selected site, partly because we have moved relative to the center of attraction and partly because the local distribution of mass density immediately below the earth's surface is not the same in each spot. We may move (up or down) along the local force vector until we reach a point where the geopotential has the same magnitude as at the initial place.

It is customary to choose this initial place to coincide in elevation with mean sea level, since the mean surfaces of the oceans, in the absence of winds and abnormal mass distributions beneath, would conform to those described by equal values of the geopotential. With such a choice, we would, for a point on land, generally have to proceed *down* along the local force vector, i.e., below the surface, to reach the point of equi-geopotential. If, in so proceeding, we take account of the fact that the mass of earth above (between us and the actual surface of the earth) has a gravitational effect, the point reached where the (resultant) geopotential is the same as that at mean sea level lies on a surface called the *geoid* to which the local force vector is normal; if we do not account for this diminution of gravity, the point lies on a surface called the *co-geoid.*

It is evident that the geoid and co-geoid are much more regular surfaces than is the actual profile of the earth. This is because neighboring force vectors cannot differ appreciably from one another due to local mass distributions, since these local masses play only a small role (in determining the normals to the geopotential) relative to the mass of the rest of the earth. As might be suspected, both the geoid and co-geoid coincide with the surface of the (mean) ocean reasonably far from land. Otherwise, they generally lie below ground level, with the geoid closer to the actual surface. The distinction between these two imaginary surfaces need not concern us further; indeed, Jeffreys [8, p. 192] claims that since the gravitational compensation required for finding the geoid can never actually be accomplished, the concept of geoid "leads only to many needless complications." However, less pragmatic geodesists do use the word, although they may, in the final analysis, settle for the physically realizable [8, p. 131] co-geoid in any actual case. We shall follow their practice here.

The geoid itself is the surface which can be approximated quite well by an oblate spheroid, i.e., an ellipse rotated about its minor axis. The "best" figure is chosen by selecting the major and minor axes in such a way that the average excursions of the geoid are minimized in some sense. Naturally, these values may vary from land mass (continent) to land mass; the one adopted by astronomers for the whole earth is the so-called International Ellipsoid, defined by a semi-major axis, $a = 6{,}378{,}388$ m, and a *flattening* or *ellipticity*, $f^* = 1/297.0$. From

$$f^* = (a-b)/a, \tag{3.6.1}$$

we find the semi-minor axis $b = 6{,}356{,}912$ m. The semi-minor axis of this figure coincides with the rotational axis of the earth; the so-called *wandering of the pole* is of such a small magnitude as to be of no significance [6, p. 384]. Thus the plane perpendicular to the minor axis can be taken as the earth's equator.

Recent work using satellites as geodetic tools has resulted in the values $a = 6{,}378{,}166$ m and $f^* = 1/298.3$. While these have not been accepted by astronomers yet, one may find them used more and more in the aerospace sciences. Additional detail on current activity in this field is available [7].

6.2. Geodetic and Geocentric Coordinates

Any point on a meridian† may be specified uniquely by identifying it with the normal (to the ellipsoid) which passes through it. This normal will not, generally, coincide with the local force vector, owing to the undulations of the geoid. The difference between these two is called the *deflection of the vertical*; we will discuss this in more detail later.

Because of the ellipticity of the spheroid, the normal will, in general, not intersect the center of the earth. It will strike the equatorial plane at an angle φ, the geodetic (or geographic) latitude (Fig. 3.7). The geodetic latitude of a place is the latitude actually recorded on a map; it is reckoned from 0° to 90° and is positive if north. The corresponding angle to the equator made by a line from a point on the surface of the ellipsoid to its center is called the geocentric latitude, φ_s'. The relation between φ_s' and φ is most simply found by writing the equation of a meridional cross section of the earth as

$$x^2/a^2 + y^2/b^2 = 1, \tag{3.6.2}$$

where the x axis lies in the equatorial plane and the y and polar axes are colinear. Then the slope at (x, y) is $dy/dx = -b^2x/a^2y$ and the slope of the normal is $\tan\varphi = a^2y/b^2x$. But $y/x = \tan\varphi_s'$ and, using (3.6.1), $b/a = 1-f^*$. Thus,

$$\tan\varphi_s' = (1-f^*)^2 \tan\varphi. \tag{3.6.3}$$

†Since the ellipsoid has a circular cross-section through its equator, corrections for ellipticity are restricted to latitude type angles.

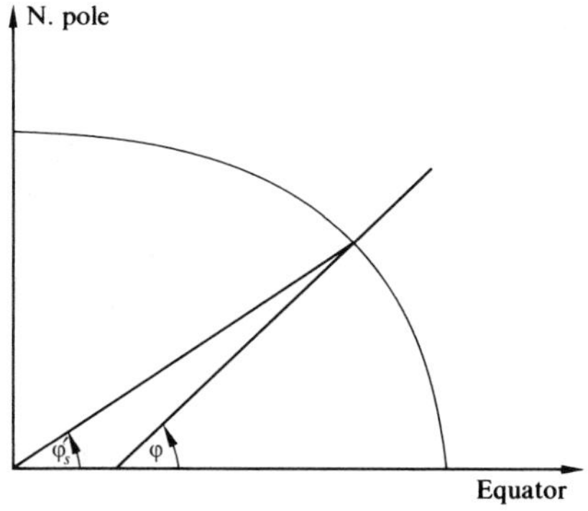

Figure 3.7

Similar considerations lead to the distance of the point on the surface from the center as

$$R'_s = \frac{a(1-f^*)}{\sqrt{(1-f^*)^2 \cos^2 \varphi'_s + \sin^2 \varphi'_s}}. \tag{3.6.4}$$

Since height is always measured perpendicular to the surface, a point at an altitude h has the same geodetic latitude as a position on the surface directly under it (Fig. 3.8). However, this is not true of its geocentric angle. We find that the geocentric distance of a point above the surface at an altitude h, say the eye level of an observer, is given by

$$r^2 = h^2 + R'^2_s + 2hR'_s \cos(\varphi - \varphi'_s) \tag{3.6.5}$$

and the latitude of such a point by

$$\varphi' = \varphi'_s + \sin^{-1}\left[\frac{h}{r}\sin(\varphi - \varphi'_s)\right]. \tag{3.6.6}$$

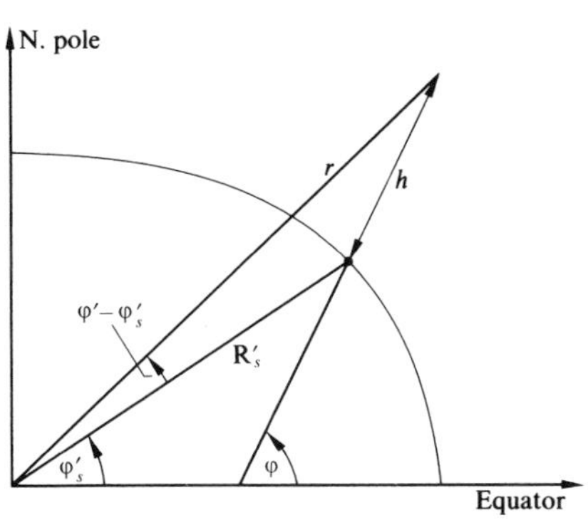

Figure 3.8

6.3. Topocentric-Geodetic Coordinates

Anticipating the material of the next section, let us assume that we have a way of establishing the instantaneous right ascension α_0 of the observer's meridian. Then we are in a position to specify the coordinates of a heavenly body relative to an observer using a topocentric, i.e. local, coordinate system. The most common of these is the so-called *horizon* system, which takes, as its fundamental plane, one which is tangent* to the ellipsoid at the observer's position. Since the point directly overhead (the zenith) lies on the normal to the ellipsoid, i.e. along the line which defines the geodetic latitude, the horizon plane is also normal to this line.

If we extend the plane of the local meridian until it intersects the horizon plane, we can take that segment of the intersection line which proceeds from the observer's position toward local north as the primary coordinate axis in the horizon system. Now let us pass a plane, perpendicular to that of the horizon, through the observer's position and the body being observed (Fig. 3.9). We call the angle between the primary (north) axis and the intersection of these last two planes the azimuth, A, of the body. We shall take azimuth as being measured clockwise from north (looking down from the zenith) from zero through 360°.

In the vertical plane, we shall define the distance from the observer to the body as the slant range, D, and the angle between the horizon to the line joining observer and body as the elevation angle, E. This last we take as positive when measured from the horizon toward the zenith from zero to 90°. The elevation angle is called the *altitude* in astronomical terminology; the complement of elevation angle is called *zenith distance.*

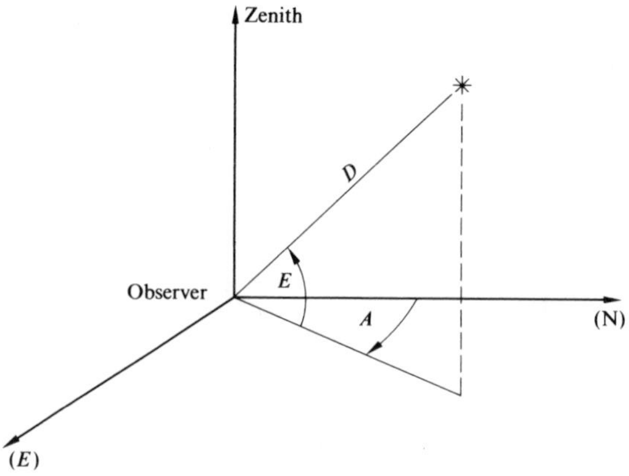

Figure 3.9

*This cannot easily be accomplished due to the presence of *deflections of the vertical* or local anomalies due to the variations of the true earth relative to the approximating ellipsoid. These are normally very small and can be accounted for; see Sections 8.3 and 8.4.

For conversion from the body's geocentric equatorial coordinates (X, Y, Z) to those in the horizon system, we may first rotate the coordinate frame about the Z axis by the angle α_0 between the observer's meridian and the line of equinoxes. If we designate this system by the subscript 1, we find that

$$X_1 = X \cos \alpha_0 + Y \sin \alpha_0; \qquad Y_1 = -X \sin \alpha_0 + Y \cos \alpha_0; \qquad Z_1 = Z. \qquad (3.6.7)$$

Translating the origin of this system from the earth's center to the observer's position, we have

$$X_2 = X_1 - r_0 \cos \varphi'_0; \qquad Y_2 = Y_1; \qquad Z_2 = Z_1 - r_0 \sin \varphi'_0, \qquad (3.6.8)$$

where φ'_0 and r_0 are the geocentric latitude and distance of the observer. Finally, a rotation about the Y_2 axis by $\pi/2 - \varphi_0$ results in

$$X_3 = X_2 \sin \varphi_0 - Z_2 \cos \varphi_0; \qquad Y_3 = Y_2; \qquad Z_3 = X_2 \cos \varphi_0 + Z_2 \sin \varphi_0, \qquad (3.6.9)$$

where φ_0 is the geodetic latitude of the observer. We note that X_3 points south, Y_3 east, and Z_3 toward the zenith. Conversion to polar coordinates is accomplished by using

$$\begin{aligned} D^2 &= X_3^2 + Y_3^2 + Z_3^2, \\ E &= \tan^{-1}(Z_3/\sqrt{X_3^2 + Y_3^2}), \qquad (3.6.10) \\ A &= \sin^{-1}(Y_3/\sqrt{X_3^2 + Y_3^2}) = \cos^{-1}(-X_3/\sqrt{X_3^2 + Y_3^2}). \end{aligned}$$

If the object for which we wish to compute these coordinates is extremely far from earth's center, so that the parallax in the transition from a geocentric to a topocentric origin becomes negligible, or if we wish to allow for parallax by one of the standard formulas to be given later, then the transformation we have just discussed may be formulated entirely in terms of the right ascension and declination of the object. Imagine that the position of this object is given by a unit vector in the direction of α, δ. Then the rotation from the X, Y, Z system through the observer's right ascension, α_0, yields

$$X_1 = \cos \delta \cos (\alpha - \alpha_0); \qquad Y_1 = \cos \delta \sin (\alpha - \alpha_0); \qquad Z_1 = \sin \delta. \qquad (3.6.11)$$

Next, the rotation about the Y_1 axis through $\pi/2 - \varphi_0$ results in

$$X_3 = X_1 \sin \varphi_0 - Z_1 \cos \varphi_0; \quad Y_3 = Y_1; \quad Z_3 = X_1 \cos \varphi_0 + Z_1 \sin \varphi_0. \qquad (3.6.12)$$

Thus, finally

$$E = \sin^{-1} Z_3$$

and (3.6.13)

$$A = \sin^{-1}[Y_3(X_3^2 + Y_3^2)^{-1/2}] = \cos^{-1}[-X_3(X_3^2 + Y_3^2)^{-1/2}].$$

7. TIME

As the reader knows, astrodynamic theories endeavor to give the positions of celestial bodies as functions of time. The quantity t, measured on a suitable chronometric scale, constitutes the independent variable for the resulting expressions. In the present section we undertake a description of the time systems most commonly employed in astronomy. As an introduction, we review some elementary features of time scales and illustrate these by executing a standard computation for the instantaneous hour angle (or right ascension) of an earthbound observer, which we temporarily postponed in the preceding section.

7.1. Elementary Notions of Time

The earth rotates to the eastward about its polar axis, completing a cycle in a time unit we may call, rather vaguely, a day. At the same time, the earth is traveling in its orbit about the sun and the geocentric line of equinoxes translates with it. For this reason, one rotation relative to ♈ is completed before the corresponding one relative to the sun. The situation is depicted in Fig. 3.10. At (a) the *upper branch* of the Greenwich meridian happens to coincide with ♈, thus marking 0 hours relative to the line of equinoxes.*

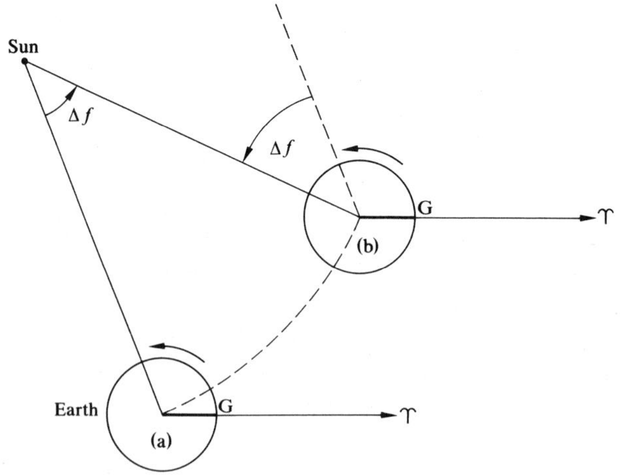

Figure 3.10

At (b) the earth has moved in its orbit while completing one revolution of the Greenwich meridian relative to ♈. On the other hand, the position of the sun, as seen from the earth, has moved ahead by the angle Δf due to the earth's displacement along its orbit. Relative to the sun, the earth has yet to rotate through Δf

*Astronomers take a meridian to be bisected by the earth's axis into an *upper* and a *lower* branch, the upper branch containing the station in question. While 0 hours relative to ♈ is marked by the crossing of the upper branch, 0 hours relative to the sun is given by lower-branch crossings to avoid a change of date during daylight hours.

to complete a revolution. We call complete revolutions relative to the sun *solar days* and relative to the stars *sidereal days.*

As will be explained later in this chapter, we find it convenient to replace the apparent (real) sun by a fictitious body, the mean sun; we also speak of the mean and true line of equinoxes. The word "mean" signifies a suitably averaged value which keeps the orbital and diurnal motions reasonably uniform. We designate a certain kind of mean solar time as *Universal Time* (U.T.).

If we take roughly $365\frac{1}{4}$ mean solar days as one year, then in one day the earth moves through an average central angle of about 360/365.25 degrees. But this is also the angle through which the earth must turn to complete a mean solar day after completing a mean sidereal day. The fractional angle amounts to about 4 minutes of time; i.e., the mean solar day is about 4 minutes longer than the mean sidereal day. However, by convention, we choose to retain the equality: $24^h = 360°$, so that both solar and sidereal time run from zero to 24 hr. The difference is compensated for by making the solar unit somewhat longer than the sidereal one.

Thus, if both solar midnight and sidereal 0^h were to occur at the same instant on a given day, a clock keeping mean sidereal time would soon be ahead of one keeping mean solar time (U.T.). In one mean solar year, the two clocks would again agree, since during that interval the sidereal clock would have gained exactly one day over the solar one; i.e., a mean sidereal year contains one more day than the mean solar year. Between the beginning and end of such a year, we must prorate the gain in sidereal time over solar time. In AENA [2], the sidereal time at Greenwich at the instant of mean solar midnight (0^h U.T.) is tabulated for each day of the year. Thus, some of this prorating is done for us; we must account only for that portion of the day elapsed since midnight. For this we also find a table in AENA.

Since we wish ultimately to relate the observer's meridian to the constellations as they actually appear for a given time (e.g., for observations in the topocentric system) we must convert from mean sidereal to apparent sidereal time; the physical implications of this conversion are discussed in some detail later. This adjustment

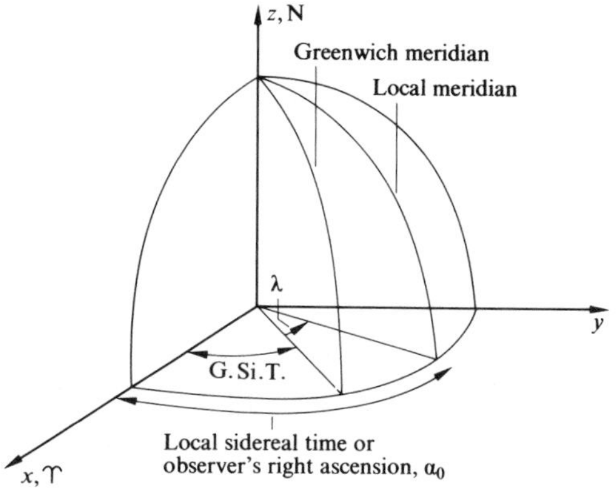

Figure 3.11

is found in AENA as the *Equation of Equinoxes* and is defined as apparent sidereal time minus mean sidereal time.

Since we reckon local sidereal time from transit of ♈ over the upper branch of our meridian, it is the local sidereal time which gives us the angle westward from the observer's meridian to the equinox, which is, as it were, the observer's right ascension, α_0 (Fig. 3.11). For conversion of time to angular measure and *vice versa* another set of tables is given in AENA.

The foregoing is somewhat involved; in addition, the references to tables in AENA should be clarified. For this purpose, we shall attempt a more detailed illustrative example, listing the tables to be used. In referring to AENA, we restrict ourselves to editions embracing the format introduced in 1960. Suppose we wish to find the angle α_0 (Fig. 3.11) of a specific longitude λ, say 74° 11′ 13.42″ west, at a particular time expressed in U.T., say $09^h43^m12\overset{s}{.}700$ on July 7, 1961. The procedure is as follows.

a) Find the Greenwich mean sidereal time (G.M.SI.T.) at 0^h U.T. of date. This is tabulated in AENA under *Universal and Sidereal Times*. For the present case we find that 0^h U.T. July 7, 1961 = $18^h58^m53\overset{s}{.}433$ G.M.SI.T.

b) Convert the time elapsed since 0^h U.T. from mean solar to mean sidereal units. This is done by adding to the U.T. of observation the corrections to be found in AENA, Table IX, *Conversion of Mean Solar into Sidereal Time*. We have the following corrections. For 09^h43^m: $1^m35\overset{s}{.}772$; for $12\overset{s}{.}700$: $0\overset{s}{.}035$.
Thus, time elapsed at Greenwich since 0^h U.T. in sidereal units is

$$\begin{array}{r} 09^h43^m12\overset{s}{.}700 \\ 1^m35\overset{s}{.}772 \\ 0\overset{s}{.}035 \\ \hline 09^h44^m48\overset{s}{.}507 \end{array}$$

c) Add the sidereal time elapsed since 0^h U.T. to the Greenwich mean sidereal time for 0^h U.T. This yields the Greenwich mean sidereal time at the moment of observation:

$$\begin{array}{r} 18^h58^m53\overset{s}{.}433 \\ +09^h44^m48\overset{s}{.}507 \\ \hline 04^h43^m41\overset{s}{.}940 \end{array} \quad (\textit{modulo } 24 \text{ hr}).$$

d) Convert the G.M.SI.T. to apparent sidereal time to find the true angle between the Greenwich meridian and ♈. We accomplish this by applying the Equation of Equinoxes from the table on *Universal and Sidereal Times*. We find

$$\text{Equation of Equinoxes, July 7, } 0^h = -0\overset{s}{.}516$$
$$\text{Equation of Equinoxes, July 8, } 0^h = -0\overset{s}{.}515.$$

In situations where linear interpolation for the fractional day since midnight would affect the last digit of the tabular values, one first converts U.T. of observation to the decimal fraction of a day by using AENA, Table X, *Conversion of Hours, Minutes, and Seconds to Decimals of a Day*. Thus

$$\begin{array}{rl} 09^h43^m & = 0\overset{d}{.}404861 \\ 12\overset{s}{.}700 & = 0\overset{d}{.}000147 \\ \hline 09^h43^m12\overset{s}{.}700 & = 0\overset{d}{.}405008 \end{array}$$

In our example, this fraction of a day will not change the Equation of the Equinoxes from its value of $-0\overset{s}{.}516$. Adding this to the result of (c), we get

$$\begin{array}{lll} \text{G.M.SI.T. of observation} & = & 04^h43^m41\overset{s}{.}940 \\ \text{Equation of Equinoxes} & = - & 0\overset{s}{.}516 \\ \hline \text{G.A.SI.T. of observation} & = & 04^h43^m41\overset{s}{.}424 \end{array}$$

e) Convert the result of (d) to units of arc ($24^h = 360°$) by means of AENA, Table XI, *Conversion of Time to Arc*. We have

$$\begin{array}{rl} 04^h43^m & = 70°\ 45' \\ 41\overset{s}{.} & = \quad 10'\ 15'' \\ 0\overset{s}{.}424 & = \qquad 6\overset{''}{.}36 \\ \hline 04^h43^m41\overset{s}{.}424 & = 70°\ 55'\ 21\overset{''}{.}36 \end{array}$$

This is the angle between the *true* line of equinoxes and the Greenwich meridian at the time of observation.

f) The value of the observer's apparent sidereal hour angle differs from the result of (e) only by the longitude of his local meridian. Conventionally, we designate longitudes east as positive and west as negative. Thus, the local apparent sidereal time (in units of arc) is found by

$$\begin{array}{lll} \text{G.A.SI.T. of observation} & = & 70°\ 55'\ 21\overset{''}{.}36(+360°) \\ \text{Local longitude} & = & -74°\ 11'\ 13\overset{''}{.}42 \\ \hline \text{L.A.SI.T. of observation} & = & 356°\ 44'\ 07\overset{''}{.}94 \end{array}$$

This is the angle measured westward from the local meridian to the true equinox. Of course, it is also the value of the angle α_0, the observer's right ascension (Fig. 3.11), measured eastward from ♈ to the local meridian.

As the reader may imagine, for actual observations one can establish the time by a chronometer or by observations of those celestial bodies whose local hour angles can be correlated with local apparent sidereal time. Thus, one might pre-compute a set of lunar positions to mark instants of time during an interval of observation. (The same kind of computation is involved in calibrating telescopes and antennas for boresight errors. In this case we test the instrument settings from such calculations against actual lunar or stellar positions at specified chronometer readings.) As an example, let us compute the moon's local hour angle for the instant of time considered above.

The apparent lunar right ascension at $09^h43^m12\overset{s}{.}700$ of July 7, 1961, is obtained from the lunar tables in AENA.* The entries in these tables are given for every hour and the adjustments for fractional hours must be computed from the first differences that are listed in these tables in seconds. At $9^h0^m0^s$, $\alpha_M = 02^h46^m44\overset{s}{.}803$. By interpolation for $0^h43^m12\overset{s}{.}700$, $\Delta\alpha_M = 127\overset{s}{.}173 \times (2592\overset{s}{.}700/3600\overset{s}{.}000) = 1^m44\overset{s}{.}307$. Thus, $\alpha_M = 02^h48^m29\overset{s}{.}110$. With the help of AENA, Table XI, the value of α_M in units of arc becomes

$$\begin{array}{rcl} 02^h48^m & = & 42^\circ\ 00' \\ 29^s & = & 07'\ 15'' \\ 0\overset{s}{.}11 & = & 1\overset{''}{.}65 \\ \hline 02^h48^m29\overset{s}{.}11 & = & 42^\circ\ 07'\ 16\overset{''}{.}65 \end{array}$$

Since the local hour angle of a celestial body is measured westward from the observer's meridian to the object, it follows that the moon's local hour angle is the local apparent sidereal time (L.A.SI.T.) minus α_M:

$$\begin{array}{lcl} \text{L.A.SI.T.} & = & 356^\circ\ 44'\ 07\overset{''}{.}94 \\ \alpha_M & = & 42^\circ\ 07'\ 16\overset{''}{.}65 \\ \hline \text{Moon's local hour angle} & = & 314^\circ\ 36'\ 51\overset{''}{.}29 \end{array}$$

7.2. Limitations of Chronometric Systems

Having reviewed some elementary notions regarding timekeeping, we now examine some difficulties encountered in establishing a precise chronometric system.

First, the reader will observe that the distinctions between solar and sidereal time and mean and apparent time reflect the search for a suitable reference mark on the celestial sphere. We need this reference to measure the progress of any timing mechanism, which in the last section was the earth's diurnal motion. Preferably, such a reference mark should yield a nonrotating line in space, and we recall the problematic nature of this undertaking from earlier remarks.

A second consideration in defining a time scale is the question of validity of our model of the universe. In particular, we must ask ourselves whether the physical phenomena to be timed, as well as the timing mechanism, are adequately described by their mathematical representation in terms of not only the gravitational forces involved, but also such phenomena as electromagnetic effects, changes in the figures of celestial bodies, and whatever non-Newtonian features may be of importance. As we shall see, some very basic distinctions between time systems rest on this question of physical validity.

Closely related to the mathematical models of different motions is the need for employing their fundamental constants to the same accuracy or, rather, the

*We note that the lunar tables list their entries against what is called Ephemeris Time (E.T.) rather than Universal Time. This distinction will be explained later and a method will be given for making the necessary corrections. At present, let us consider E.T. = U.T.

uncertainties within their units should be allocated in exactly parallel fashion for the different motions. To be more specific, let us consider two planets whose mean rates are given by the relations

$$n_1^2 = \frac{G(m_S + m_1)}{a_1^3} \quad \text{and} \quad n_2^2 = \frac{G(m_S + m_2)}{a_2^3},$$

where n, m, and a are the mean motion, mass, and semi-major axis of each planet and m_S is the sun's mass. Certainly, the anomalistic period and hence n of a celestial body may be established with greater accuracy than any of the quantities on the right-hand sides of the above expressions. For convenience, astronomers have chosen not to change the value of the universal gravitational constant G since the days of Gauss; and if we also adopt a standard value for the solar mass, we are left with trying to distinguish between the probable errors of m and a in each of the right-hand sides. This inquiry would be unnecessary if we never wanted to calculate anything but n_1 and n_2 from tabulated values for G, m_S, a_1, m_1, a_2, and m_2. However, as soon as we strive to correlate the detailed motions of planets 1 and 2 in the course of establishing a time scale, we must consider their mutual perturbations. For planet 1 this effect is proportional to m_2/m_S and *vice versa*. In order to make an effective comparison between the theories of the motion of 1 and 2, one requires a statistical "error allocation" between the constants m_1, m_2, and m_S that makes them mutually consistent in some sense.

Finally, there is the question whether a time scale which serves as independent variable in several related astrodynamic theories is "uniform." This turns out to lack meaning. Uniformity implies an invariant phase relation between the time scale in question and some independent master standard. It is not clear what this standard might be and it would not matter if it did prove our time scale "nonuniform." All we really need is that our chronometric variable, if inserted into the astrodynamic theories, furnishes predictions that agree with observations. In other words, the physical mechanism from which this variable is derived must be theoretically understood to the same level as the phenomena to be timed. In fact, our chronometric reference is often a physical motion belonging to the same group as the ones to be clocked, with the sole distinction that its progress may be more easily and continually observed than that of the others. As the reader might gather, the selection of a chronometric standard cannot be done once and considered valid for eternity, for, in the course of scientific progress, measurements as well as mathematical theories are constantly being refined. Hence, we may expect that our time standard will have to be revised whenever such refinement occurs.

A survey of the historical sequence in which astronomers have moved from one chronometric system to another, always in search of an improvement but never finding one that was universally and forever applicable, would serve no useful purpose here. Instead, we shall merely examine existing time systems, first giving a preliminary description of each; later we shall introduce more formal definitions.

7.3. Ephemeris Time

We begin with a description of the time system which at present appears to fulfill the prerequisites of the preceding section to the greatest extent. It is currently adopted by dynamical astronomers but is not well suited for observations. In fact, to anticipate a little, it is the need for observational accessibility that generates our interest in the connection between this "dynamical time" and the less accurate systems that we have already touched upon, based on the earth's diurnal rotation.

In recent years, it has become apparent that the earth's rotation rate is not quite constant. For some trends a promising theory is beginning to emerge but others remain essentially unexplained and unpredictable. It is for this reason that astronomers have been forced to use a system which is less desirable from the point of view of simplicity.

Most quantitative astrodynamic theories deal with the orbital motions of the planets and their satellites. Our present model of this system considers solar and interplanetary gravitation, and includes relativistic effects where significant, but neglects features such as gravitational interference from the rest of the galaxy, etc. Thus, our mathematical theories assume the center of mass of the solar system to be an inertial origin and, under the specifications given, they describe planetary motion which matches the accuracy of our measurements. We shall not attempt to document the strong evidence in favor of this statement, but merely observe that much has accumulated from study of past data. As a result, it is orbital motion, not diurnal motion, that we look upon as more completely understood, and the independent variable in our planetary theories, which is also the argument of the planetary tables, is the presently accepted time standard called Ephemeris Time (E.T.). More specifically, the orbital motion of the earth has been adopted as the primary timekeeper in this system. The fundamental unit of Ephemeris Time is the tropical year, to be defined presently.

It is evident, considering that the earth's annual motion is now the "clock," that it is not possible to make a precise determination of E.T. at any one moment. Many observations must be made and elaborate statistics must be employed in their reduction to find the instant when the observed configuration of planets agrees with that computed in the ephemerides. Although the earth's orbital motion serves as a basis for the definition of E.T., lunar motion with its shorter period is more conveniently used for actual measurements of E.T. It can be related to the earth's motion with the necessary accuracy. Other auxiliary timekeepers must also be employed; it may require several years of observational data to derive the relations between them and E.T. accurately. It is convenient to use mean solar time as one of these auxiliaries.

7.4. Solar Time

As we have seen, it seems natural to measure the diurnal rotation in relation to the sun. However, if we really were to observe the solar disc in order to clock this motion, the solar positions, as seen by an observer on earth, would be subject to a variety of optical effects. These will be explained more fully later; suffice it to say that it is difficult to observe accurately any sizeable, luminous object such as the sun. We prefer to define the *apparent* solar positions as coordinates from which all optical effects have been excluded. This time scale is known as *apparent solar time.*

In spite of these idealizations, which divorce apparent solar time from direct observation, this time scale is highly nonuniform in comparison with other existing systems. Fortunately, most of the nonuniformities can be explained by our theory of the solar system. Major contributions come from the eccentricity of the earth's orbit and the inclination (obliquity) between the ecliptic and equatorial planes. Furthermore, planetary interference perturbs the earth's anomalistic motion and causes the ecliptic to change its attitude. Finally, the earth's equatorial plane is perturbed because of solar and lunar attractions on the equatorial bulge.

We may account for most of the nonoptical effects mentioned above by planetary theory, and find a more uniform time scale than apparent solar time. This is known as *mean solar time* and, in essence, may be visualized as representing a dynamic system consisting of a spherical uniformly rotating earth, whose equatorial and ecliptic planes are coincident and which is moving in a circular orbit about the sun. It is also thought of as describing the motion of a fictitious *mean sun* about the earth. The difference between apparent and mean solar time is called the Equation of Time; it is defined as the former minus the latter.

As has been mentioned, the change of date on the (mean or apparent) solar time scale occurs when the sun crosses the lower branch of the meridian in question. When referring to elapsed mean solar time reckoned from the crossings of the lower branch of the Greenwich meridian (180° longitude), we have universal time (U.T.). It is occasionally also referred to as Greenwich mean time (G.M.T.), Greenwich civil time (G.C.T.), or Weltzeit. To mark a daily 24-hour cycle everywhere throughout the world, the globe has been subdivided by meridians, 15° apart, which establish a system of *local standard times* with one-hour phase differences. The one-hour zones extend generally $7\frac{1}{2}°$ in longitude to either side of the standard meridians. In some cases, e.g., parts of the International Date Line (180° longitude), the zone limits depart from their precise longitude for local administrative reasons. The reader may also be aware of *summer* or *daylight saving* times, defined as one hour ahead of local standard time.

The drawback of mean solar time relative to ephemeris time is that vagaries in the earth's rate of rotation and some related geophysical effects have not been accounted for; these have become measurable in the last few decades but cannot be fully explained at present. In an attempt to compensate partially for geophysical effects, some modifications have been applied to universal time, which in its unmodified form is designated U.T.0. Thus, U.T.1 is defined as U.T.0 compensated for the wandering of the earth's geographic poles relative to the astronomic ones. A second refinement includes the effects of seasonal and tidal variations in the earth's diurnal rate. This modification is known as U.T.2 and represents the current form of mean solar time used in international civil timekeeping.

7.5. Sidereal Time

When using the earth's rotation for chronometric purposes, astronomers find it more convenient, in terms of observations, to take the stars as a reference. However, every star has a motion of its own, and some difficulties in establishing nonrotating lines of reference for geocentric coordinates have already been mentioned. A natural choice is, of course, ♈. The line of equinoxes is subject to the attitude changes of the ecliptic and equatorial planes caused by the various gravitational effects described earlier.

If the earth's rotation is measured relative to the *true*, i.e., actual, line of equinoxes, thereby is established what is known as *apparent sidereal time*. Again, as in the case of the apparent sun, the definition of the *true equinox* excludes all optical effects of observation but includes all perturbations acting on the ecliptic and equatorial planes. These are of two kinds; those that grow monotonically as time goes on, and those periodic in nature. Although physically their causes cannot be distinguished, it is tradition to call the periodic motion a *nutation* and the cumulative or *secular* motion a *precession*. In the long run, the effects of precession predominate since nutation averages out. Hence, if we omit the periodic terms from the definition of ♈, we go from the true equinox to the so-called *mean equinox*. If we refer our time scale to the mean equinox, we speak of *mean sidereal time*. In particular, the successive passages of the mean equinox across the upper branch of the Greenwich meridian mark *Greenwich mean sidereal time* (G.M.SI.T.). The difference between apparent and mean sidereal time is called the Equation of Equinoxes and, as stated earlier (Section 7.1), is defined as the former minus the latter.

In conclusion, we note that both kinds of sidereal time are subject to vagaries in the diurnal rate of rotation which again constitutes a disadvantage relative to Ephemeris Time.

7.6. Calendars and Years

Before proceeding to formal definitions of time systems, it is convenient to introduce some notions of calendars and years. This is essential for the subsequent definitions and some of the conversions between time scales. Moreover, it is needed for some corrective formulas that must be applied to ephemeris data as described in the final section of this chapter.

The two basic Western calendars are the Julian and the Gregorian. The former allows for successive transits of the sun through the equinox requiring approximately $365\frac{1}{4}$ days, by giving the standard year 365 days and making every fourth year a leap year of 366 days. Additional precision was obtained in the Gregorian calendar when no year ending in two zeros was counted as a leap year unless it was integrally divisible by 400. Thus, a Julian century has exactly 36525 days, while a Gregorian century has 36524.25 days.

For record keeping, astronomers often use a *Julian day* (which has no relation to the Julian calendar). The Julian day is reckoned from Greenwich mean noon and a continuous count of Julian days is kept from Greenwich mean noon of January 1, 4713 B.C. (which is Julian date zero) to yield the Julian dates found in the ephemerides opposite conventional dates. It is also common to designate the time elapsed since the start of a day by decimal notation. As already pointed out, this conversion is simplified by use of AENA, Table X. When conventional dates are used, the part of the day elapsed is added to the date expressed in the usual way. Thus 18 hours, May 4 = May 4.75; 12 hours, April 30 = April 30.5 = May 0.5. When Julian dates are used, it must be remembered that the Julian day starts at mean noon; thus 18 hours, May 4, 1961 = 2437423.25.

We conclude this discussion with a brief series of definitions of the sorts of years in common use. We have already indicated the fact that the Julian and Gregorian years are specified without direct reference to a real physical period. On the other hand, the *tropical year* is taken as the period between successive passages of the mean sun through the mean equinox; the *sidereal year* marks the return of the earth to the same position among the stars, as seen from the sun; the *anomalistic year* is the period between successive passages of the earth through perihelion. If T represents the number of Julian ephemeris centuries since the epoch January 0.5, 1900 (also known as *Julian epoch* 1900.0), we have:

$$\begin{aligned}
\text{tropical year} &= 365^{\text{d}}.242{,}198{,}79 - 0^{\text{d}}.000{,}006{,}14T \\
\text{sidereal year} &= 365^{\text{d}}.256{,}360{,}42 + 0^{\text{d}}.000{,}000{,}11T \\
\text{anomalistic year} &= 365^{\text{d}}.259{,}641{,}34 + 0^{\text{d}}.000{,}003{,}04T
\end{aligned}$$

where d is measured in ephemeris days. Additional definitions such as the Besselian year and the eclipse year may be found in the literature [9, 10]. There also exist several definitions of the month involving different reference marks on the lunar orbit.

7.7. Formal Definitions of the Time Systems; Computation of Time; Atomic Clocks

In the preceding sections we surveyed the astronomical time scales for their general characteristics and the consistency with which they represent the dynamics of the solar system. At the outset we stated that the formal definitions of astronomical time were to be left to the last, as this is the information on which the computation of a particular instant (or *epoch*) on a time scale is based. In essence, this process amounts to obtaining a "fix" on the time in a given chronometric system. We have already seen some of these computations in Section 7.1. To make the transition from one chronometric system to another, we must have the value for a certain epoch in terms of each of the time scales. We also need to know the relations between their units in order to proceed to other points on either scale.

From earlier sections, it should have become clear to the reader that a listing of the chronometric systems in order of their accessibility to observations would run: sidereal, solar, ephemeris time. In fact, the only computations (other than elimination of optical effects) required for deduction of sidereal time from telescopic observations concern the location of the true or mean equinox among the fixed stars. The slow changes of the equator and the equinox, as predicted from our theories of the equator and the ecliptic, may be expressed in terms of changes of stellar right ascensions and declinations of the form

$$\theta = at + bt^2 + \cdots$$

$$+ \sum_j S_j \sin j\alpha t + \sum_k C_k \cos k\beta t, \tag{3.7.1}$$

where a, b, S_j C_k, α, and β are constants; the first line represents the precession and the second line the nutation. Knowing the values of the constants in (3.7.1) and assuming that the proper motion of the stars can be allowed for, one succeeds in locating ♈ relative to the stars. In particular, the *annual rate of precession in right ascension* is

$$\begin{aligned} m &= a + bT \\ &= 46''.0850 + 0''.000279T \\ &= 3^s.07234 + 0^s.0000186T, \end{aligned} \tag{3.7.2}$$

where T is measured in tropical years from 1900.0. Equation (3.7.2) describes the motion of the mean equinox relative to its right ascension at 1900.0 and defines the point whose transit over a local meridian provides a daily fix for local mean sidereal time. The mean sidereal day, which is marked by these transits, is equipartitioned into 86400 seconds. As already shown, the corresponding observations on the true equinox, yielding apparent sidereal time, are related to mean sidereal time by the Equation of Equinoxes. This quantity, defined as apparent minus mean sidereal time, is computed from the nutational terms in (3.7.1) and given in the table of *Universal and Sidereal Times* in AENA.

Sidereal time bears the closest relation to observable meridian transits; mean solar time is one step further removed by way of computations. A quantitative representation relating mean solar and mean sidereal times is derived from Newcomb's expression for the right ascension of the mean sun [11]; we obtain for the mean sidereal time at 0^hU.T.:

$$6^h 38^m 45^s.836 + 8{,}640{,}184^s.542T + 0^s.0929T^2, \tag{3.7.3}$$

where T is measured in Julian ephemeris centuries from January 0.5, 1900. This gives the practical correlation between the two time scales and is presented for each day in the table *Universal and Sidereal Times* of AENA. A division of the mean solar day by 86400 yields a standard for the mean solar second. Knowing the ratio of the mean solar to the mean sidereal unit, we may generate Tables VIII and IX in AENA, which provide for the conversion between the two systems at any time of day. Finally, it should be recalled that the relation between apparent and mean solar time is given by the Equation of Time. This takes into account the idealizations that went into computing mean solar time and is given in the solar tables of AENA.

Separating ourselves by another step from the observations of meridian crossings, we proceed from mean solar time to Ephemeris Time, and here the correlation is at present empirical.

As an independent concept and based solely on our theory of the earth's orbital motion, Ephemeris Time appears as the independent variable in Newcomb's formula [11] for the geocentric mean longitude of the sun:

$$L = 279^\circ\,41'\,48''.04 + 129602768''.13T + 1''.089T^2, \tag{3.7.4}$$

where T is measured in Julian ephemeris centuries from January 0.5, 1900. In fact, at the epoch $T = 0$, we have E.T. = 12 hours, January 0, 1900. Since the basic unit of Ephemeris Time is the year, it is convenient to derive an ephemeris second for computation of smaller time intervals. To this end, we adopt the tropical year (the time elapsed between two successive passages of the mean sun through the mean equinox) based on the solar mean motion given by (3.7.4) for $T = 0$. The ephemeris second is then defined as 1/31556925.9747 of the tropical year and, in effect, is the average of the mean solar second over the last 200 years.

While (3.7.4) yields a formal definition of Ephemeris Time, auxiliary devices are needed for the practical determination of E.T. As was mentioned, Universal Time is one such auxiliary—though the relation between it and Ephemeris Time is empirical in the last analysis. Curves have been fitted to the data for $\Delta T =$ E.T. − U.T. and yearly corrections of this kind are tabulated on one of the first pages in AENA. The accuracy of this information decreases as we extrapolate ΔT toward the present.

Since the curve fitting for ΔT is strictly empirical [12, 13], the search continues for more satisfactory means of obtaining an up-to-date value for ΔT. From our current understanding of physics it is felt that the time provided by a device like the cesium clock should correlate with Ephemeris Time to the extent that it can provide acceptable extrapolations for E.T. over a longer range than is presently possible.

This device consists of a quartz crystal which keeps a cumulative cycle count and an atomized cesium beam for intermittent calibration of the crystal frequency. The time scale established is known as A1 and has the fiducial epoch $0^h\,0^m\,0^s$A1 = $0^h\,0^m\,0^s$ U.T.2 on January 1, 1958. The standard frequency, to current precision, is 9 192 631 770 ± 20 cycles per ephemeris second. On the grounds of general relativity theory one seems to expect a difference between A1 and E.T. of 0.001 sec/yr^2. Experimental verification of this point is under way to establish the relation between atomic and gravitational time.

The results of high-precision timekeeping by means of frequency standards and observations of meridian transits are made available to the general public by time signals from various radio stations of the National Bureau of Standards and the U.S. Navy. The proper use of these signals requires that certain precautions be taken, particularly in allowing for transmission delays and tuning errors. For further details, the reader is referred to the literature [14].

8. ADJUSTMENT OF EPHEMERIDES

We have seen that various effects, both astronomical and geophysical, enter into discussions of coordinate and time systems. In this section, we provide a description of these effects and the means by which they may be taken into account. We may establish three groups, according to their physical causes:

a) *Astrodynamical.* Perturbations of the fundamental planes by precession and nutation, and difficulties in establishing inertial references due to proper motion of the stars

b) *Observational.* Variations between observed and predicted position due to parallax, aberration, refraction, and irradiation

c) *Geophysical.* Variations in time and observer's position due to the recently discovered changes in the earth's figure and rotation; these include wandering of the poles, variations of the vertical, and vagaries of the diurnal rotation.

Before proceeding to a detailed discussion, we should clarify the distinction between *mean*, *true*, and *apparent* place as used in astronomical terminology with regard to these perturbations. The *true* coordinates of a celestial object are given with respect to the true equator and equinox (including precession and nutation) at a standard epoch; i.e., they include the effects of group (a) (except for proper motion), but none of (b) or (c), and constitute the object's actual, instantaneous geometric position. The *mean* place eliminates the effects of nutation but resembles the true coordinates in all other respects. The *apparent* place is referred to the true equator and equinox of date and is subject to geocentric aberration (i.e., all aberration except that due to the earth's diurnal motion, which is station-dependent. For the same reason it does not include parallax or refraction). It should be noted that the definitions of apparent solar and sidereal times, in contrast to the apparent place, do not include aberration (or other optical effects).

At this point it is also appropriate to comment on the basic purpose of an ephemeris and its fundamental system of units. Clearly, the astronomical tables have been traditionally provided for use with optical instruments and achieve their highest accuracy in the angular coordinates. For aerospace applications one would like to know the geocentric or heliocentric position and velocity of an object with about equal accuracy in all components. With this in mind, the general perturbation theories of major interest, namely, Brown's lunar and Newcomb's planetary theories, were reexamined and reevaluated [15, 16]. In so doing, the residual inaccuracies from the theories, the numerical computations, and the reference observations were redistributed in a fashion that differed from the traditional astronomical procedure. This matter has been touched upon in the specific context of chronometry (Section 7.2). It involves a reallocation of the uncertainties in the basic units of length and mass and in the ratios of the masses and semi-major axes of the planets. A thorough discussion of this subject is beyond the scope of this chapter. Suffice it here to repeat that the updating of error allocations in the fundamental constants is a never-ending process, as documented in the literature [2, 9, 17–21].

8.1. Astrodynamical Effects

As mentioned, rather elaborate theories exist for the slight changes in orientation of the equatorial and ecliptic planes. For the equator we distinguish between secular terms known as precession and periodic terms known as nutations. Changes in the equatorial plane are due to the earth's asphericity which gives rise to gravitational torques because of the moon's and the sun's attraction. The earth's orbital plane, the ecliptic, is subject to perturbations from planetary influence. The reader is referred to the literature for derivations of the following equations [9, 10].

Precession. To convert the mean position of an object in terms of the coordinate frame at one epoch to that at another epoch, we must account for the *luni-solar precession*, Ψ, due to attraction of the sun and of the moon on the figure of the earth and *planetary precession*, λ', reflecting the perturbation of the ecliptic plane. If we define

$$m = \Psi \cos \varepsilon - \lambda'; \qquad n = \Psi \sin \varepsilon, \tag{3.8.1}$$

where ε is the angle of obliquity, then, in geocentric equatorial coordinates,

$$\begin{aligned} \alpha_1 &= \alpha_0 + m + n \sin \alpha_0 \tan \delta_0, \\ \delta_1 &= \delta_0 + n \cos \alpha_0. \end{aligned} \tag{3.8.2}$$

Here α_0 and δ_0 are the right ascension and declination of the object at the initial epoch; m and n are tabulated in AENA for conversions between integral years. Fractional years may be accommodated by linear interpolation. Analogous formulas to (3.8.2) exist for updating ecliptic spherical coordinates subject to precession.

Conversion of Cartesian equatorial coordinates from one mean reference frame to another may be performed by use of the matrix elements [4]:

$$\begin{matrix} X_x, Y_x, Z_x \\ X_y, Y_y, Z_y \\ X_z, Y_z, Z_z. \end{matrix}$$

For reduction to a standard epoch such as 1950.0, we have

$$\begin{aligned} x_1 &= X_x x_0 - Y_x y_0 - Z_x z_0, \\ y_1 &= -X_y x_0 + Y_y y_0 + Z_y z_0, \\ z_1 &= -X_z x_0 + Y_z y_0 + Z_z z_0. \end{aligned} \tag{3.8.3}$$

The conversion from a standard epoch to some other is given by

$$
\begin{aligned}
x_1 &= X_x x_0 + Y_x y_0 + Z_x z_0, \\
y_1 &= X_y x_0 + Y_y y_0 + Z_y z_0, \\
z_1 &= X_z x_0 + Y_z y_0 + Z_z z_0,
\end{aligned}
\tag{3.8.4}
$$

using again the established meaning for the subscripts 1 and 0.

Nutation. To establish the true position of an object at any epoch within a particular year, we start with α_1 and δ_1 relative to the mean equator at the nearest integral year. If we designate $\Delta\psi$ and $\Delta\varepsilon$ as the nutation in longitude and obliquity, respectively, we find

$$
\begin{aligned}
\alpha_2 &= \alpha_1 + (\tau + \Delta\psi/\Psi)(m + n \sin\alpha_1 \tan\delta_1) + \lambda'\Delta\psi/\Psi - \Delta\varepsilon \cos\alpha_1 \tan\delta_1, \\
\delta_2 &= \delta_1 + (\tau + \Delta\psi/\Psi) n \cos\alpha_1 + \Delta\varepsilon \sin\alpha_1,
\end{aligned}
\tag{3.8.5}
$$

where α_2 and δ_2 are the required true right ascension and declination, and τ is the fraction of a year from the epoch of α_1, δ_1. For convenience, the functions

$$
A = (\tau + \Delta\psi/\Psi)n; \qquad B = -\Delta\varepsilon; \qquad E = \lambda'\Delta\psi/15\Psi, \tag{3.8.6}
$$

are tabulated at daily intervals in AENA, as *Besselian day numbers.*

Proper Motion. The proper motion of a star is its angular rate of displacement, as seen from the sun. This phenomenon plays an important role in efforts to establish truly invariant directional references on the celestial sphere. In an attempt to clarify understanding of the motions of the equatorial and ecliptic planes, precession, nutation, and proper motion are examined by a statistical treatment of the observed movement of ♈ against the background stars. This work is closely connected with the construction of star catalogs and a current effort aims at including a large group of stars as *near-inertial* references, choosing those whose proper motion is considerably less than that of some large-magnitude stars previously included in such catalogs. Data on the proper motion are listed with each star in the catalogs and their use in deriving the up-to-date coordinates of a star is described in the literature [9].

8.2. Observational Effects

Parallax. Parallax is known as the difference between the coordinates of an object given in a heliocentric or geocentric frame and those apparent to an observer who is not located at the origin of the reference frame. Relative to positions given in heliocentric coordinates the observer finds himself "off-center" by the dimensions of the earth's orbit and relative to positions given in a geocentric frame by those of the earth's figure. In the former case we speak of *annual* or *stellar*, and in the latter, of *diurnal* parallax. Adjustments for annual parallax amount to a change from heliocentric to geocentric coordinates and their magnitudes depend on the time of the year. If, on the other hand, the distance to a stellar object is unknown, one may compute it, in terms of the astronomical unit, from observations of annual parallactic effects. The method is similar to that already illustrated for computation of distances between the earth and the sun or the moon. In this case, the procedure may be useful for distances within our own galaxy.

Diurnal parallax is dependent on the time of day and the observer's geographic location and, as has been shown, may be used to compute distances within the solar system. Let φ' be the observer's geocentric latitude and H the local hour angle of the object, i.e., the geocentric angle between the observer's meridian and that of the body (its hour circle) measured westward from the former along the equator.* Then

$$\tan \Delta H = -\tan \Delta\alpha = Q \frac{\sin H \cos \varphi'}{\cos \delta - Q \cos H \cos \varphi'} \tag{3.8.7}$$

and

$$\frac{\tan \delta + S}{1 - S \tan \delta} = \frac{\cos H (\sin \delta - Q \sin \varphi')}{\cos \delta \cos H - Q \cos \varphi'}, \tag{3.8.8}$$

where Q is the ratio of the earth's local radius and the geocentric distance to the object and $S = \tan \Delta\delta$ [9]. If we denote $\alpha' = \alpha + \Delta\alpha$ and $\delta' = \delta + \Delta\delta$, the "primed" quantities include parallactic effects and represent coordinates as they appear to an observer.

Aberration. The effects of aberration stem from the fact that light travels with finite velocity. First, a remote object will move a certain distance during the time it takes the optical signal to reach an observer. The latter must update all observed coordinates for such an object to their values corresponding to the time of light reception. Since this correction is necessitated by motion of the observed object, which can be computed for planets but not for stars, one speaks of *planetary aberration* in this case. A second kind, the *stellar aberration,* is caused by motion of the observer himself. Here the vector addition of the velocity of the incoming light and that of the observer results in an incident light ray, as seen by the observer, whose direction differs from the geometrically correct orientation of the body. The terrestrial observer's total motion in the solar system may be looked upon as consisting of annual and diurnal components.

The customary procedure is to perform the reduction for the annual and diurnal parts of stellar aberration first, and then to apply corrections for the planetary aberration [9]. If the primed symbol for a coordinate be its observed value, subject to aberration, and the unprimed symbol be its value after eliminating the aberration, we have the following relations.

---

*We may find the local hour angle by $H = \lambda + \text{G.A.SI.T.} - \alpha$, where λ is the observer's longitude positive eastward), G.A.SI.T. is the Greenwich apparent sidereal time of observation, and α is the body's true right ascension at that time.

For the annual aberration in equatorial coordinates, neglecting the earth's orbital eccentricity,

$$\alpha = \alpha' + \kappa \sec \delta' (\cos \alpha' \cos \lambda_S \cos \varepsilon + \sin \alpha' \sin \lambda_S)$$

$$\delta = \delta' + \kappa \cos \lambda_S \cos \varepsilon(\tan \varepsilon \cos \delta' - \sin \alpha' \sin \delta') + \kappa \cos \alpha' \sin \delta' \sin \lambda_S, \quad (3.8.9)$$

where λ_S is the sun's longitude and ε the obliquity of the ecliptic. The quantity κ is the aberrational constant with a value of $20''.47$.

For the diurnal aberration in equatorial coordinates we have

$$\begin{aligned} H &= H' + 0''.32 \cos \varphi' \cos H' \sec \delta', \\ \delta &= \delta' - 0''.32 \cos \varphi' \sin H' \sin \delta', \end{aligned} \quad (3.8.10)$$

where H' and H are the observed and actual hour angle and φ', as before, is the geocentric latitude.

Having corrected the observation for stellar aberration, we may adjust for the planetary effect if the distance between the object and earth is known. This is tabulated in AENA for the major bodies in the solar system (or can be derived, as for the moon); also given are the daily rates of change of right ascension and declination, say $\dot{\alpha}$ and $\dot{\delta}$. Thus, this correction takes the simple form

$$\alpha = \alpha' + \dot{\alpha}(r/c^*); \qquad \delta = \delta' + \dot{\delta}(r/c^*), \quad (3.8.11)$$

where r is the distance in question (usually given in astronomic units) and c^* is the velocity of light in corresponding units of length per day.

At this point, we may introduce, for completeness, the so-called *astrometric coordinates*. These coordinates are applied to the minor planets and to Pluto and constitute apparent coordinates minus the annual (stellar) aberration. They are also the coordinates used in the star catalogs.

Refraction. The reader may be familiar with the refraction caused by the atmosphere on incoming light rays. This causes a deviation of the light ray toward the earth's center. In a topocentric coordinate system, involving azimuth and elevation, we expect no influence on the azimuth. The actual elevation, E, is to be computed from the optically observed value E' by the relation

$$E = E' - 58''.2 \cot E'. \quad (3.8.12)$$

This formula has to be abandoned in favor of empirical refraction measurements for $E < 15°$ and when electromagnetic radiation of frequency less than that in the visible band is used, the constant in (3.8.12) no longer holds. In a topocentric equatorial system we have

$$\delta = \delta' - 58''.2k^* \cot E', \quad (3.8.13)$$

where

$$k^* = (\sin \varphi' - \sin \delta' \sin E')/\cos \delta' \cos E', \quad (3.8.14)$$

φ' is the observer's geocentric latitude, and δ' is the declination calculated from E', A, and φ'. Also

$$\alpha = \alpha' \pm 58''.2 \cot E' \sec \delta' \sqrt{1-k^{*2}}, \tag{3.8.15}$$

where α' is calculated from E', A, and φ'. The minus sign in (3.8.15) is chosen if the observer, when facing the object, finds the north pole (at a zenith distance $<\pi$) toward his right and the plus sign if it is on his left [9].

Irradiation. While refraction is a physical effect of the atmosphere, irradiation seems to be a subjective effect on the human observer. The results are an apparent enlargement of luminous objects such as the sun, the moon, and the higher-magnitude stars; this makes an accurate determination of eclipses and meridian crossings of these objects impossible but does not affect any observations concerned with the center of a visible disc. Since we have no exact understanding of the phenomenon, no fully satisfactory method of compensation for irradiation exists.

8.3. Geophysical Effects

We close this discussion with a brief consideration of the slow changes in the earth's figure and the vagaries of its rigid body motion. The three effects, wandering of the poles, deflections of the vertical, and diurnal vagaries, cannot be easily separated from each other in the observational material, nor from a few other effects such as proper motion of the stars and instrumentation errors. Most of the raw data are generated from the work on star catalogs and chronometric observations.

Polar Wandering. Wandering of the poles consists of a slow shift of the earth's figure, i.e., the geographic poles, relative to its axis of rotation, the astronomic poles [22, 23]. Plots of this motion show a secular trend, but also a strong cyclic component known as the *Chandler term*, whose period is approximately 14 months, and another component with an annual period.

The geographic (or geodetic) pole has been taken to coincide with the mean astronomic pole of the period from 1900 to 1905; i.e., the mean position of the astronomic pole during that period has been defined as a reference on the earth's surface; its separation from the astronomic pole at any other time constitutes the wandering. The instantaneous displacement of the latter is usually given in two components: x along the Greenwich meridian and y along the meridian 90°W. The secular trend just mentioned is estimated at 0''.0032/year along the meridian 60°W.

To convert the displacement of the pole to corrections for the longitude and latitude so as to obtain these angles relative to the astronomic axis, one may show that

$$\Delta\varphi = x \cos\lambda - y \sin\lambda \tag{3.8.16}$$

and

$$\Delta\bar{\lambda} = (x \sin\lambda + y \cos\lambda) \tan\varphi. \tag{3.8.17}$$

Since it is convenient to maintain the Greenwich longitude as the zero-meridian, we must write

$$\Delta\lambda = \Delta\bar{\lambda} - y \tan \varphi_G \tag{3.8.18}$$

for the net correction in longitude due to polar wandering. The basic data (x and y) are usually made available by the International Time Service with a delay of about one year (due to data smoothing).

Deflections of the Vertical. Deflections of the vertical are the local differences between the normal to the true equipotential surface of the earth (see Section 6.1) and the normal to the approximating ellipsoid. Thus they are the differences between the direction of the actual gravitational force and the geographic (or geodetic) vertical. These deflections are usually specified in terms of two components: the *deflection in the meridian*, ξ^*, and the *deflection in the prime vertical*, η^*, i.e., along the circle of latitude.

If we imagine that the direction of the actual gravity vector marks a point on the celestial sphere (the zenith), we may associate with this point the so-called astronomic longitude λ_A and astronomic latitude φ_A. The astronomic zenith direction at the geodetic point of observation does not in general pass through the earth's axis. In order to retain the geometric significance of λ_A and φ_A on the surface of the ellipsoid, one must imagine that an appropriate offset is applied to the location of the point at which λ_A and φ_A were observed. This brings us to the *astronomic position* of the observer on the ellipsoid; defined as the point where φ and λ of the latter agree with φ_A and λ_A. On the other hand, let us identify the actual observer's position on the ellipsoid by λ_G and φ_G. (Note that φ_G is the angle that was denoted up to this point by φ.) The components of the deflection are then defined as

$$\xi^* = \varphi_A - \varphi_G; \qquad \eta^* = (\lambda_A - \lambda_G) \cos \varphi_G. \tag{3.8.19}$$

For most applications one treats the deflections of the vertical as time-invariant. Whatever trends exist essentially reflect changes in the earth's figure, its internal density distribution, and glaciation on a geological time scale. These trends are currently estimated to be much less than one second of arc per century. Additional information on gravitational anomalies may be found in the literature [5, 24, 25, 26].

Changes in Rotation Rate. Finally, the vagaries in the earth's rotation are perhaps the most intriguing effect in this group and, as pointed out, are responsible for the introduction of Ephemeris Time in preference to Universal Time. Modern data on this phenomenon have accumulated since the turn of the century and have been interpreted by numerous workers. It is possible to recognize periodic terms due to tidal action and the effects of seasonal surface changes on atmospheric drag. The former is correlated with a corresponding perturbation in the moon's orbital motion, as expected. The remaining diurnal vagaries consist of secular terms due to tidal dissipation and changes in the earth's moment of inertia as well as apparently random terms. The latter two phenomena are the result of currently inexplicable changes of global structure. A surprising aspect about the random variations is that they consist of a succession of approximately linear trends with sudden breaks between. These symptoms point toward a sequence of cumulative processes, such as the drift of continents, and sudden releasing mechanisms like stress relief along surface faults. The corroboration of this hypothesis by correlating seismic events with the sudden breaks in $\Delta T =$ E.T.—U.T. has scarcely begun. The complete explanation of ΔT by means of geophysical theories is an undertaking of the first magnitude and will require many years of fundamental work [27, 28]. In the meanwhile, only empirical expressions for ΔT exist (see 7.7).

8.4. Example

To illustrate the use of the corrective equations given in this section, we set ourselves the task of reducing the coordinates of the moon, as found in the illustrative example of Section 7.1, to azimuth-elevation information at the location $\lambda = 74°\ 11'\ 13''.42$ W and $\varphi = 40°\ 18'\ 16''.47$ N. To distinguish between these pointing angles, which allow for all effects discussed, and the apparent coordinates, as defined by astronomers, we might refer to the former as *actual apparent co-ordinates*.

a) Apparent right-ascension, hour angle, and declination of the moon at $09^h 43^m 12^s.700$ U.T. on July 7, 1961
From our previous computations we have, for the moon's right ascension and hour angle at the given time, $\alpha_M = 42°\ 07'\ 16''.65$ and $H_M = 314°\ 36'\ 51''.29$. From the lunar tables in AENA we obtain the corresponding declination as $\delta_M = 11°\ 00'\ 13''.18$. These coordinates allow for precession and nutation and contain the effects of planetary and annual aberration but not those of diurnal aberration, nor do they allow for diurnal parallax.

b) Correction for diurnal aberration
Using Eqs. (3.8.10) for the present case, we obtain a sufficiently accurate inversion in the form $H'_M = H_M - 0''.32 \cos\varphi \cos H_M \sec\delta_M$ and δ'_M and $\delta'_M = \delta_M + 0''.32 \cos\varphi \sin H_M \sin\delta_M$. Substituting the values for H_M and δ_M, we have $H'_M = 314°\ 36'\ 51''.11$ and $\delta'_M = 11°\ 00'\ 13''.14$.

c) Correction for diurnal parallax
The parallactic corrections in H_M and δ_M follow from (3.8.7) and (3.8.8) as $\Delta H_M = -32''.57$ and $\Delta\delta_M = -23''.44$. Hence, $H'_M = 314°\ 36'\ 18''.54$ and $\delta'_M = 10°\ 59'\ 49''.70$. Applying the corrections of H_M from (b) and (c) with reversed sign to the moon's right ascension, we have $\alpha'_M = 42°\ 07'\ 49''.40$.

d) Correction for ΔT
At this point we must allow for the difference between ephemeris time and universal time in using the lunar table. As we have seen, the tabular data are listed against E.T. Until now, we have treated these tables as if they were based on U.T. To be as rigorous as possible, we use α_M, δ_M for the instant E.T. = U.T. +

ΔT, taking ΔT for July 1961 as $\Delta T \simeq 34$ seconds. Thus we may find the correction to the right ascension and declination by multiplying ΔT by the hourly change of α_M or δ_M divided by 3600. We obtain $\Delta\alpha_M = 17''.93$ and $\Delta\delta_M = 5''.02$. Hence, $\alpha'_M = 42°\ 08'\ 07''.33$ and $\delta'_M = 10°\ 59'\ 54''.72$.

e) Perturbations of the topocentric axes

In order to locate the observer's reference frame accurately in geocentric space, we should consider the remaining geophysical factors and include their effects on the observer's longitude and latitude.

For the location in question, a special survey, conducted in 1903, yielded $\varphi_A - \varphi_G = -2''.92$ and $\lambda_A - \lambda_G = +1''.54$. Strictly speaking, these data are valid for the time the survey of the position was made. For the sake of illustration let us update them for wandering of the poles. We find the displacement of the astronomic pole at the required time as $x = -0''.091$, $y = +0''.220$ [23]. With the help of (3.8.16), (3.8.17), and (3.8.18), we get $\Delta\lambda = +0''.06$ and $\Delta\varphi = +0''.19$. These corrections are now used to obtain the actual latitude and right ascension that orient the observer's topocentric axes. Thus

	40°	48′	16″.47
+	0	0	0″.19
−	0	0	2″.92
$\varphi_0 =$	40°	48′	13″.74

and

	356°	44′	07″.94	(observer's right ascension)
+	0	0	0″.06	
+	0	0	1″.54	
$\alpha_0 =$	356°	44′	9″.54	

f) Transformation to azimuth-elevation coordinates

With the help of (3.6.11) through (3.6.13) we convert the right ascension and declination of the moon to azimuth and elevation angles. In so doing, we use the results of (e) for the observer's latitude and right ascension. We obtain $A = 113°\ 38'\ 44''.73$ and $E = 40°\ 16'\ 2''.90$.

g) Allowance for refraction

At this point we must introduce the modifications caused by atmospheric refraction in the topocentric coordinates.

An adequate inversion of (3.8.12) is $E' = E + 58''.2 \cot E$, which yields $E' = 40°\ 17'\ 11''.61$. The azimuth angle, as stated earlier, is unaffected.

h) Irradiation and proper motion

As a final adjustment, one would have to allow for irradiation, if a precise compensation were known and if an observation of the lunar limb were intended. For the purpose of pointing at the center of the lunar disc, however, this effect may be ignored. In closing, we also observe that the proper motion of the stars never entered our computations explicitly. Since, however, the measurements of mean sidereal time from stellar observations and the position of ♈ used in the lunar tables allow for this phenomenon, its contribution has already been included.

To summarize, the final and actual values of the pointing angles from the ground observer to the moon's center are $A = 113°38'44''.73$ and $E = 40°17'11''.61$. We must emphasize again that several corrections used in arriving at these results are of no practical importance if one considers the accuracy of most present-day instruments. Their inclusion in these calculations was only for illustrative purposes.

REFERENCES

1. Nautical Almanac Offices of the U.K. and the U.S., *Explanatory Supplement to the Ephemeris*, H.M. Stationery Office, London, 1961.
2. Nautical Almanac Office, U.S. Naval Observatory, *American Ephemeris and Nautical Almanac*, U.S. Government Printing Office, Washington, D.C., published annually.
3. Nautical Almanac Office, U.S. Naval Observatory, *Coordinates of the Five Outer Planets, 1653–2060, Astronomical Papers of American Ephemeris*, Vol. XII, U.S. Government Printing Office, Washington, D.C., 1951.
4. H.M. Nautical Almanac Office, *Planetary Coordinates 1960–1980*, H.M. Stationery Office, London, 1958.
5. W. A. Heiskanen and F. A. Vening Meinesz, *The Earth and Its Gravity Field*, McGraw-Hill, New York, 1958.
6. G. Bomford, *Geodesy*, Clarendon Press, Oxford, 1952.
7. a) W. M. Kaula, "Celestial Geodesy," in *Advances in Geophysics*, Vol. 9, Academic Press, New York, 1962.
   b) I. I. Mueller, *Introduction to Satellite Geodesy*, Frederick Ungar, New York, 1964.
8. H. Jeffries, *The Earth*, 4th ed., Cambridge University Press, Cambridge, 1959.
9. W. M. Smart, *Textbook on Spherical Astronomy*, Cambridge University Press, Cambridge, 1956.
10. E. W. Woolard and G. M. Clemence, *Spherical Astronomy*, Academic Press, New York, 1966.
11. S. Newcomb, *Tables of the Motion of the Earth on Its Axis and around the Sun, Astronomical Papers of American Ephemeris,* Vol. VI, part 1, Nautical Almanac Office, U.S. Naval Observatory, U.S. Government Printing Office, Washington, D.C., 1898.
12. D. Brouwer, "A Study of the Changes in the Rate of Rotation of the Earth," *Astron. J.*, **37,** 125, 1952.
13. D. A. Rice, "Ephemeris Time and Universal Time," *Surveying and Mapping*, **19,** 367, 1959.
14. a) Circular No. 49, U.S. Naval Observatory, Washington, D.C., March 8, 1954.
    b) Time Service Notices (especially nos. 5, 6, 7, and 8), U.S. Naval Observatory, Washington, D.C.
    c) W. Markowitz, "Accurate Timing of Artificial Observations on a World-Wide Basis," in Proceedings of Symposium on Geodesy in Space Age, Columbus, Ohio, 1961, p. 168.

15. N. Block, *The Brown Improved Lunar Theory*, T.R. no. 32–590, Jet Propulsion Laboratory, Pasadena, California, 1964.

16. N. Block, *Ephemerides of Mercury, Venus, and Earth-Moon Barycenter, Evaluated from Newcomb's Theories*, T.R. no. 32–591, Jet Propulsion Laboratory, Pasadena, California, 1964.

17. C. W. Allen, *Astrophysical Quantities*, Athlone Press, London, 1955.

18. G. M. Clemence, "On the System of Astronomical Constants," *Astron. J.*, **53,** 169, 1948.

19. M. W. Makemson, R. M. L. Baker, Jr., and G. B. Westrom, "Analysis and Standardization of Astrodynamic Constants," *J. Astron. Sci.*, **8,** 1, 1961.

20. D. Brouwer, "An Assessment of the Present Accuracy of the Value of the Astronomical Unit," *Navigation*, **9,** 206, 1962.

21. D. O. Muhleman, *Relationship between the System of Astronomical Constants and the Radar Determinations of the Astronomical Unit*, T.R. no. 32–477, Jet Propulsion Laboratory, Pasadena, California, 1964.

22. W. Markowitz, "Latitude and Longitude and the Secular Motion of the Pole," in *Methods and Techniques in Geophysics*, Interscience, London, 1960.

23. W. Markowitz, N. Stoyko, and E. P. Fedorov, "Longitude and Latitude," in *Research in Geophysics*, Vol. 2, M.I.T. Press, Cambridge, 1964.

24. W. M. Kaula, "Determination of the Earth's Gravitation Field," *Reviews of Geophysics*, **1,** 507, 1963.

25. J. A. Duerkson, *Deflections of the Vertical in the United States*, Special Publication no. 229, U.S. Department of Commerce, Coast and Geodetic Survey, U.S. Government Printing Office, Washington, D.C., 1941.

26. H. G. Baussus, *A Unified Isostatic and Statistical Theory of Gravity Anomalies and Its Significance*, Pres. Int. Ass'n Geodesy XII Assy, IUGG, Helsinki, 1960.

27. W. deSitter, "On the Secular Accelerations and the Fluctuations of the Longitudes of the Moon, the Sun, Mercury, and Venus," *Bull. Astron. Inst. of Neth.*, **4,** 21, 1927.

28. H. Spencer-Jones, "The Rotation of the Earth and the Secular Accelerations of the Sun, Moon, and Planets," *M.N.R.A.S.*, **99,** 541, 1938–39.

Chapter four

THE DETERMINATION OF ORBITS

1. GENERAL CONSIDERATIONS

Classically, the problem of orbit determination requires us to find the orbit elements valid at some specific time, given certain observations of the orbiting body. We choose here to extend the problem beyond this definition. In particular, we shall examine means for finding subsequent effects of inaccuracies in our observations of position and velocity or of small but known variations of these quantities at the moment of injection into orbit.

As for treatment of observations, there are at least as many methods for finding some representation of the orbit as there are means of observing it. The classical problem, utilizing only (telescopic) angle measurements of the body, has received extensive study over the last century and at least two main methods (each with several variations) have been recorded [1–6]. With the advent of pulse radar, techniques have been derived which utilize both range and angle observations. Other methods, devised recently, have been based on the availability of range-only data, range-rate data, and on various types of measurements from instruments carried on the orbiting body. In each case, the observations must be corrected for various physical effects (as discussed in Chapter 3) and transformed to the proper coordinates. The relations between the observed quantities and the characteristics of the orbit constitute a separate problem for each type of data. Thus, if a guidance record furnishes us with vehicle position and velocity at the start of ballistic flight, we can consider these as the initial conditions and determine the orbit elements accordingly. If, on the other hand, measurements are made at different points along the orbit, both the number of observations required and the relations used to compute a set of elements depend on the nature of the quantities being measured. We assume here that just the minimum number of observations is available to determine a set of orbit parameters, a situation referred to by the astronomers as *preliminary orbit determination*. We concentrate on cases where the measurements are made by terrestrial observers and are used to determine the orbit of a body in geocentric or heliocentric coordinates. The extension of these methods to cases where measurements are made elsewhere, such as on board a space vehicle, is reasonably straightforward.

Once a set of algebraic equations for the elements has been formulated for a situation, the techniques employed in the solution form a subject in their own right. Since some of these equations are transcendental and nonlinear, we are forced to use numerical iterations and suitable auxiliary variables. In Chapter 2 we indicated how some orbit parameters have to be redefined for low- or high-eccentricity orbits to offset certain geometric degeneracies; special attention also had to be given to the time equations for these cases. The numerous conditions of measurement encountered in orbit-determination problems leave much room for ingenuity in manipulating the governing algebraic equations; we shall not elaborate on that here.

Another subject omitted from the present discussion is the statistical processing of redundant sets of data for refinement of preliminary orbits. Since no single piece of tracking data is ever given with ideal accuracy, we always need a certain amount of "excess" information to establish the orbit with some confidence in the statistical sense. The validity of the resulting elements depends not only on the accuracy of the observing equipment, the amount of data, and the time sequence in which the data were acquired, but also on the way in which the observations are combined. The classical technique for this purpose involves *differential corrections*; descriptions of this method are to be found in the available literature [see especially references 3 and 4]. In its usual form it entails the employment, and consequently the storage, of a large amount of past observations. To avoid this in "real-time" operations, especially with earth satellites, several investigators have developed techniques for the combination of observational data, sometimes in the form of more or less statistically independent sets of orbit elements, which do not require extensive computer storage.* Once the elements have been established to sufficient accuracy by any of these methods, they are taken to represent the *refined* or *definitive* orbit.

In this chapter we shall not discuss the extensive subject of statistical estimates for orbit determination and recursive filtering of tracking data. We restrict ourselves to a discussion of the purely geometric relations between observables and orbit elements leading to *minimum data methods* in that they do not provide any more equations than are required algebraically.

Now as to various definitions of orbit elements, we note that while position and velocity do in principle determine the orbit, in themselves they fail to tell us much about the geometry of the orbit. We cannot decide at a glance whether the

---

*See references 7 through 10 for some early literature on batch processing of orbital tracking data.

trajectory is elliptical, parabolic, or hyperbolic. The conic-section parameters of Chapter 2 indicate this in a more satisfactory way. It should be kept in mind that these orbit elements are constants only when we consider the classical two-body problem with a central-gravity force; the effect of any other force is to cause departures from Keplerian motion. We have noted that the additional forces are often quite small and techniques exist that account for these effects; we may choose to express the elements themselves as (slowly varying) functions of time (Chapter 6). Consequently, a determination of the elements, valid at some instant, provides us with the first step necessary for evaluation of the orbit and for predictions of future positions (to be used for later observations, studies, etc.).

Our knowledge of the orbit elements is affected not only by random errors but also by systematic errors (e.g., instrument bias) introduced at the time of determination. Thus, a study of the relations between such errors in the observations and the orbit elements is a very necessary adjunct to the problem of orbit determination. Again, we will not in this chapter pursue the statistical approach, but content ourselves with an examination of the geometric effects induced by errors of a given type and magnitude. These relations are also known as *orbit sensitivities* and have a further significance. Since there is no way of distinguishing mathematically between apparent deviations in position and velocity due to measurement error and those actually introduced in the vehicle's motion (intentionally or otherwise), the latter interpretation of these relations is of great help in the synthesis of man-made orbits. They indicate what changes must be effected in the position and the velocity at the end of powered flight of a rocket to alter the orbit in some desired way. Manipulations of this kind are encountered in designing a trajectory for a satellite orbit, for a rendezvous, or transfer between two orbits, as well as in "splicing" or "targeting" the segments of a trajectory for impact on or circumnavigation of a celestial body. Such computations usually consist of numerical iterations based on the orbit sensitivities to be derived here.

2. COMPUTATION OF THE ORBIT ELEMENTS FROM INERTIAL POSITION AND VELOCITY

In the preceding section we indicated that we can often think of the orbit as being determined by the position and velocity vector taken at a known time. Indeed, several orbit-determination techniques follow this approach. In this section we examine detailed computations leading from a known position, velocity, and time to a set of orbit parameters. Here we restrict ourselves to elliptic orbits, but the calculations for parabolic and hyperbolic orbits may be accomplished with no essential changes in methodology. The basic relations we are about to derive may be used in any "pseudo-inertial" reference frame with a central mass at its origin. However, to make the following discussion specific, we concern ourselves with earth-centered flight. Adaptation of the method to a heliocentric frame will be obvious.

2.1. Orbit Elements from Spherical Coordinates

We use the equator as the invariant plane and the intersection of the meridian plane of the observer and the equator, at the time of observation, as the invariant line. We consider this frame to be fixed or "locked" in space and assume that the position and velocity of the object have been determined relative to it. (The observer is moving with respect to this system since he is rotating with the earth.) We choose to "lock" this frame at the moment $t = t_0$, at which time the following have been determined (Fig. 4.1):

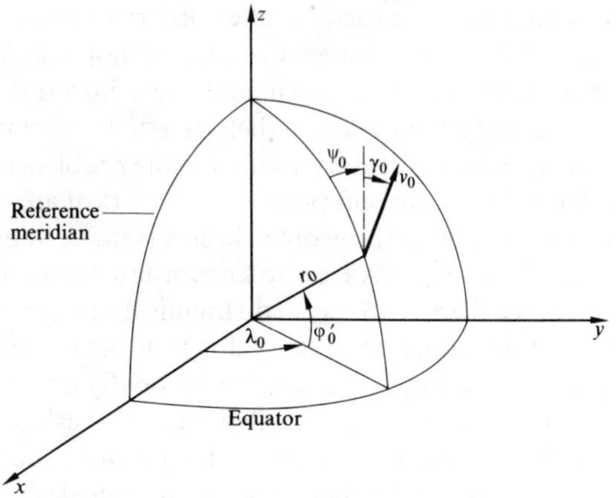

Figure 4.1

r_0, the distance from earth's center to the object;

φ_0', the latitude of the object;

λ_0, the inertial longitude of the object relative to the meridian of observation;

v_0, the magnitude of the inertial velocity of the object;

γ_0, the angle of the velocity vector above the local horizontal (the *flight path angle*);

ψ_0, the angle between the horizontal projection of the velocity vector and the local north, i.e., the course of the object at $t = t_0$ (the *flight path azimuth*).

We have already seen how to compute two of the orbit elements. Equation (2.2.4) is

$$a = \frac{\mu r_0}{2\mu - r_0 v_0^2}, \tag{4.2.1}$$

where μ is the product of the universal gravitational constant and the mass of the earth. Equation (2.2.3) yields

$$e = \frac{1}{\mu}(\mu^2 - 2\mu r_0 v_0^2 \cos^2 \gamma_0 + r_0^2 v_0^4 \cos^2 \gamma_0)^{1/2}. \tag{4.2.2}$$

From the equation of the ellipse, (2.2.30), we have

$$e \cos E_0 = 1 - r_0/a, \tag{4.2.3}$$

where E_0 is the value of the eccentric anomaly at $t = t_0$. If we eliminate $\dot{E}$ in (2.2.32) by using (2.2.33) we obtain

$$r_0 \dot{r}_0/\sqrt{\mu a} = e \sin E_0, \tag{4.2.4}$$

but, by definition, $\dot{r}_0 = v_0 \sin \gamma_0$, thus

$$e \sin E_0 = r_0 v_0 \sin \gamma_0/\sqrt{\mu a}. \tag{4.2.5}$$

Since the eccentricity, e, is always positive, we can determine the quadrant in which E lies, and its magnitude is

$$E_0 = \tan^{-1}\left[\sqrt{\frac{a}{\mu}} \frac{r_0 v_0 \sin \gamma_0}{a - r_0}\right]. \tag{4.2.6}$$

Using Kepler's equation (2.2.34), we get

$$\tau = t_0 - \sqrt{a^3/\mu}(E_0 - e \sin E_0). \tag{4.2.7}$$

We note that the time of perigee passage, τ, is given in terms of t_0. Equation (4.2.7) will yield a τ which may be positive or negative and refers to the time of next or last perigee passage, respectively. In this case, $t = t_0$ is referred to as *the epoch.*

The calculations leading to angular position and time of perigee passage relative to the epoch may also be carried out in terms of the true anomaly. If we substitute (4.2.1) and (4.2.2) into the equation of the conic-section orbit and solve for $\cos f_0$ we obtain

$$\cos f_0 = \frac{[r_0 v_0^2 \cos^2 \gamma_0 - \mu]}{(\mu^2 - 2\mu r_0 v_0^2 \cos^2 \gamma_0 + r_0^2 v_0^4 \cos^2 \gamma_0)^{1/2}}. \tag{4.2.8}$$

From this we may write formally

$$\sin f_0 = \pm\sqrt{1 - \cos^2 f_0} \equiv \frac{r_0 v_0^2 \cos \gamma_0 \sin \gamma_0}{(\mu^2 - 2\mu r_0 v_0^2 \cos^2 \gamma_0 + r_0^2 v_0^4 \cos^2 \gamma_0)^{1/2}}, \tag{4.2.9}$$

where a little consideration shows that $\sin f_0$ must have the same algebraic sign as $\sin \gamma_0$.

To compute the time of perigee passage in terms of f or r, one may use Eqs. (2.2.37) or (2.2.40) with the lower limits being $f = 0$ or $r = a(1-e)$. Even before e approaches unity close enough to necessitate the use of (2.2.41) one gains numerical accuracy by using (2.2.40) instead of (2.2.37) if f_0 is in the second or third quadrant.

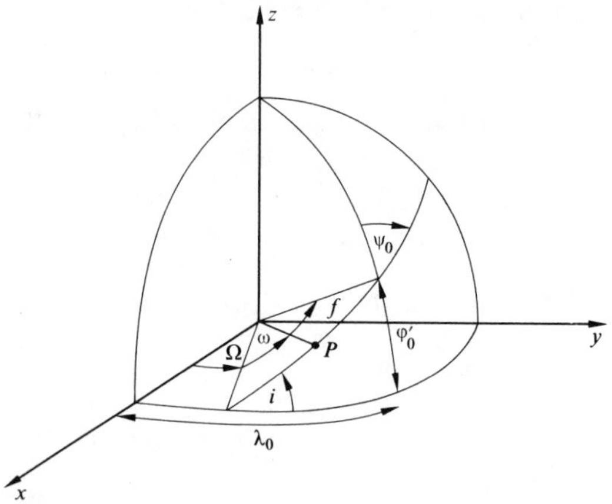

Figure 4.2

To compute the other three orbit elements, it is simplest to examine the track of the orbit on a nonrotating earth (Fig. 4.2). From the laws for right spherical triangles, we get

$$\cos i = \cos \varphi_0' \sin \psi_0, \tag{4.2.10}$$

and, since by definition i is never greater than 180°,

$$\sin i = \sqrt{1-\cos^2 \varphi_0' \sin^2 \psi_0}. \tag{4.2.11}$$

Then

$$\sin(\lambda_0-\Omega) = \tan \varphi_0' \cot i; \qquad \cos(\lambda_0-\Omega) = \cos \psi_0/\sin i, \tag{4.2.12}$$

and

$$\sin(\omega+f_0) = \sin \varphi_0'/\sin i; \qquad \cos(\omega+f_0) = \cos(\lambda_0-\Omega)\cos \varphi_0'. \tag{4.2.13}$$

Since λ_0 is known,* the node angle, Ω, can be determined from (4.2.12) and, assuming that f_0 has been found from (4.2.8) and (4.2.9) or by (4.2.6) and (2.2.29), we can obtain ω from (4.2.13).

2.2. Orbit Elements from Rectangular Coordinates

It is sometimes more convenient to express the position and velocity of the orbiting object in terms of the (x, y, z) coordinate frame. The computation of the orbit elements can be performed as follows, if we are given x_0, y_0, z_0, $\dot{x}_0$, $\dot{y}_0$, $\dot{z}_0$. We assume that these are taken with respect to an inertial frame which may be oriented as shown in Figs. 4.1 and 4.2, although this is not necessary. It is standard (Chapter 3) to consider the x-y plane as coincident with the equator and the x axis as

---

*Because λ_0 is measured relative to the observer's position, it follows that the Ω obtained from (4.2.12) is also. We simply add the geographic longitude of the observer to find Ω relative to Greenwich at t_0, or the right ascension of the observer at t_0 to obtain Ω relative to ♈.

containing the inertial meridian of observation or pointing toward ♈. We have, of course,

$$r_0 = (x_0^2+y_0^2+z_0^2)^{1/2}; \qquad v_0^2 = \dot{x}_0^2+\dot{y}_0^2+\dot{z}_0^2, \tag{4.2.14}$$

from which we may obtain the semi-major axis by use of (4.2.1). Equation (4.2.4) may be written as

$$e \sin E_0 = \frac{1}{\sqrt{\mu a}}(x_0\dot{x}_0+y_0\dot{y}_0+z_0\dot{z}_0); \tag{4.2.15}$$

if, now, we find $e \cos E$ by (4.2.3), the eccentricity can be determined, using (4.2.3) and (4.2.15), by

$$e^2 = (e \sin E_0)^2+(e \cos E_0)^2. \tag{4.2.16}$$

The eccentric anomaly E_0 is obtained by again applying (4.2.3) and (4.2.15):

$$E_0 = \tan^{-1}[e \sin E_0/e \cos E_0], \tag{4.2.17}$$

where its quadrant is determined by the algebraic signs of $e \sin E$ and $e \cos E$. The time of perigee passage can now be computed, as before, by (4.2.7).

If we set up unit vectors $\mathbf{a}_x$, $\mathbf{a}_y$, $\mathbf{a}_z$ along the x, y, z axes, respectively, we may write

$$\mathbf{r}_0 = \mathbf{a}_x x_0+\mathbf{a}_y y_0+\mathbf{a}_z z_0,$$

and (4.2.18)

$$\mathbf{v}_0 = \mathbf{a}_x \dot{x}_0+\mathbf{a}_y \dot{y}_0+\mathbf{a}_z \dot{z}_0.$$

Now $(\mathbf{r}_0 \times \mathbf{v}_0)$ is a vector perpendicular to the orbit plane and of magnitude $r_0 v_0 \cos \gamma_0$; thus

$$\cos \gamma_0 = \frac{(r\dot{f})_0}{v_0} = \frac{|\mathbf{r}_0 \times \mathbf{v}_0|}{r_0 v_0} = \frac{\sqrt{\mu a(1-e^2)}}{r_0 v_0}, \tag{4.2.19}$$

and, if we wish at this point to compute the time of perigee passage in terms of true anomaly, we may proceed by way of Eqs. (4.2.8) and (4.2.9) as before, where we must remember that the sign of γ_0 is that of $\mathbf{r}_0 \cdot \mathbf{v}_0$. Further

$$(\mathbf{r}_0 \times \mathbf{v}_0) \cdot \mathbf{a}_z = r_0 v_0 \cos \gamma_0 \cos i, \tag{4.2.20}$$

and, performing the vector multiplication indicated, we obtain

$$\cos i = \frac{x_0\dot{y}_0-y_0\dot{x}_0}{\sqrt{\mu a(1-e^2)}}, \tag{4.2.21}$$

where we have used (4.2.18) and (4.2.20). Again, $\sin i = +\sqrt{1-\cos^2 i}$. Now the vector $\mathbf{a}_z \times (\mathbf{r}_0 \times \mathbf{v}_0)$ lies in both equatorial and orbit planes, i.e., along the line of nodes; a little consideration indicates that it points toward the ascending node.

Then $[\mathbf{a}_z \times (\mathbf{r}_0 \times \mathbf{v}_0)] \cdot \mathbf{a}_y = r_0 v_0 \cos \gamma_0 \sin i \sin \Omega$, or

$$\sin \Omega = \frac{y_0 \dot{z}_0 - z_0 \dot{y}_0}{\sqrt{\mu a(1-e^2)} \sin i}, \tag{4.2.22}$$

and, similarly,

$$\cos \Omega = \frac{x_0 \dot{z}_0 - z_0 \dot{x}_0}{\sqrt{\mu a(1-e^2)} \sin i}. \tag{4.2.23}$$

Finally, we may use the first equation of (4.2.13) to find $\sin(\omega + f_0)$ since $\sin \varphi_0' = z_0/r_0$, that is,

$$\sin(\omega + f_0) = z_0/r_0 \sin i. \tag{4.2.24}$$

To find $\cos(\omega + f_0)$ we note, as an alternative for the second equation of (4.2.13), that $[\mathbf{a}_z \times (\mathbf{r}_0 \times \mathbf{v}_0)] \cdot \mathbf{r}_0 = r_0^2 v_0 \cos \gamma_0 \sin i \cos(\omega + f_0)$, or

$$\cos(\omega + f_0) = \frac{y_0(y_0 \dot{z}_0 - z_0 \dot{y}_0) - x_0(z_0 \dot{x}_0 - x_0 \dot{z}_0)}{r_0 \sin i \sqrt{\mu a(1-e^2)}}. \tag{4.2.25}$$

3. ORBIT DETERMINATION FROM CLOSELY SPACED OBSERVATIONS

3.1. Observations Include Range and Two Angles

The calculations of the preceding section suggest orbit-determination techniques that rely on the actual knowledge of vehicle position and velocity at some instant, or on ready inference of them from tracking data. In practice, this will be the case with various ascent guidance "packages" which monitor the powered flight of a rocket by the use of ground-based and on-board sensors and a suitable computer so as to yield the dynamic state variables of the vehicle at engine cutoff.

As another example, we might obtain closely spaced vehicle positions from successive measurements of radar angles and slant range so that finite-difference schemes applied to the position data might produce an acceptable estimate of the velocity vector. The most elementary scheme of this sort would run as follows. Let the observer's geographic position be given by h, φ_G, λ_G, i.e., height above the spheroid, geodetic latitude, and geodetic longitude, respectively. His geocentric distance and latitude can then be found by using Eqs. (3.6.3) through (3.6.6). If t_1 represents the time of the first measurement, and t_2 that of the second, and the corresponding observables are slant range (D_1, D_2), elevation angle (E_1, E_2), and azimuth (A_1, A_2), the crudest form of combination yields

$$D = (D_1 + D_2)/2; \qquad E = (E_1 + E_2)/2; \qquad A = (A_1 + A_2)/2, \tag{4.3.1}$$

$$\dot{D} = (D_2 - D_1)/(t_2 - t_1); \qquad \dot{E} = (E_2 - E_1)/(t_2 - t_1); \qquad \dot{A} = (A_2 - A_1)/(t_2 - t_1), \tag{4.3.2}$$

which are presumed valid at $t = (t_1 + t_2)/2$. An obvious combination of these quantities with the observer's position and his diurnal velocity (according to Chapter 3) yields the geocentric inertial position and velocity of the vehicle at t. In practice many more than two sets of tracking data are usually available, so that the position and velocity of the vehicle can be deduced more reliably by "smoothing" techniques. The resulting information can serve as the starting point for an orbit determination according to Section 2.

3.2. Observations Include Angles Only. The Method of Laplace

If the observing instruments cannot provide range measurements, we can devise a method involving finite-difference schemes to estimate $\mathbf{r}$ and $\mathbf{v}$, but this requires a minimum of three closely spaced "angle-only" observations. Naturally, this case has been thoroughly examined by astronomers; we restrict our discussion to its essentials.*

Suppose we operate in a geocentric or heliocentric cartesian frame where the instantaneous position of the object is given by $\mathbf{r} = \mathbf{R} + \mathbf{D}$, the vector $\mathbf{R}$ representing the observer's position (assumed calculable) and $\mathbf{D}$ that of the object relative to the observer. Further, let us write the components of these vectors as $\mathbf{R}:(X, Y, Z)$ and $\mathbf{D}:(Da, Db, Dc)$, where a, b, c are the direction cosines of the line of sight, i.e., combinations of trigonometric functions of the azimuth, the elevation angle, the right ascension, and the declination of the body (see Chapter 3). D is the magnitude of $\mathbf{D}$. Hence,

$$x = Da + Y; \qquad y = Db + Y; \qquad z = Dc + Z. \tag{4.3.3}$$

Now we assume that the data a, b, c have been obtained at three instants of time t_1, t_2, t_3 sufficiently close together to permit reliable numerical estimates of $\dot{a}, \dot{b}, \dot{c}, \ddot{a}, \ddot{b}, \ddot{c}$ at the time t_2 by finite-difference schemes. If $t_3 - t_2 = t_2 - t_1$, we obtain such expressions as

$$\dot{a}_2 \simeq \frac{a_3 - a_1}{t_3 - t_1} \quad \text{and} \quad \ddot{a}_2 \simeq \frac{4(a_3 - 2a_2 + a_1)}{(t_3 - t_1)^2}.$$

For unequal spacings of t_1, t_2, t_3 similar expressions are available; we shall not proceed further into the subject of numerical differentiation at this point.

If we are operating in a heliocentric frame, then that part of the observer's position (X, Y, Z) which depends on the location of the earth's center is read from the tables of the sun in AENA and the time derivatives we need must also be obtained from finite-difference expressions. The additional part of $\mathbf{R}$ (or, if we are working in a geocentric frame, the sole part of X, Y, Z and their derivatives) is given by the obvious expressions for the observer's position relative to the center of the earth and must include diurnal rotation.

If we knew D and $\dot{D}$ at t_2 we would have the necessary information to compute

*For additional detail, see, for example, reference 1, p. 195.

the orbit elements since Eq. (4.3.3) gives us the position of the object, and its velocity follows from

$$\dot{x} = \dot{D}a + D\dot{a} + \dot{X}; \qquad \dot{y} = \dot{D}b + D\dot{b} + \dot{Y}; \qquad \dot{z} = \dot{D}c + D\dot{c} + \dot{Z}. \tag{4.3.4}$$

To determine D and $\dot{D}$, we have recourse to the differential equations of the two-body problem:

$$\ddot{x} = -\mu x/r^3; \qquad \ddot{y} = -\mu y/r^3; \qquad \ddot{z} = -\mu z/r^3.$$

Substitution of (4.3.3) on both sides of these equations leads to

$$\begin{aligned} a\ddot{D} + 2\dot{a}\dot{D} + \left(\ddot{a} + \frac{\mu a}{r^3}\right)D &= -\left(\ddot{X} + \frac{\mu X}{r^3}\right), \\ b\ddot{D} + 2\dot{b}\dot{D} + \left(\ddot{b} + \frac{\mu b}{r^3}\right)D &= -\left(\ddot{Y} + \frac{\mu Y}{r^3}\right), \\ c\ddot{D} + 2\dot{c}\dot{D} + \left(\ddot{c} + \frac{\mu c}{r^3}\right)D &= -\left(\ddot{Z} + \frac{\mu Z}{r^3}\right). \end{aligned} \tag{4.3.5}$$

The unknowns in this system are the four quantities D, $\dot{D}$, $\ddot{D}$, and r. The problem becomes determinate if we remember the cosine law which must prevail in the triangle of observation between the vectors $\mathbf{R}$ and $\mathbf{D}$:

$$r^2 = R^2 + D^2 - 2DR\cos v, \tag{4.3.6}$$

where the angle v $(= E + \pi/2)$ is given by $\mathbf{R}$ and the known direction of $\mathbf{D}$, that is,

$$\cos v = \frac{-(a, b, c)\cdot\mathbf{R}}{R}.$$

We eliminate $\dot{D}$ and $\ddot{D}$ from (4.3.5) to obtain a second equation in the two unknowns r and D. The left-hand sides lead to the determinant

$$\Delta = 2\begin{vmatrix} a & \dot{a} & \ddot{a} + \dfrac{\mu a}{r^3} \\ b & \dot{b} & \ddot{b} + \dfrac{\mu b}{r^3} \\ c & \dot{c} & \ddot{c} + \dfrac{\mu c}{r^3} \end{vmatrix},$$

which immediately reduces to

$$\Delta = 2\begin{vmatrix} a & \dot{a} & \ddot{a} \\ b & \dot{b} & \ddot{b} \\ c & \dot{c} & \ddot{c} \end{vmatrix}. \tag{4.3.7}$$

Thus, we find

$$D = \frac{1}{\Delta}\left[\Delta_1 + \frac{1}{r^3}\Delta_2\right], \tag{4.3.8}$$

where

$$\Delta_1 = -2\begin{vmatrix} a & \dot{a} & \ddot{X} \\ b & \dot{b} & \ddot{Y} \\ c & \dot{c} & \ddot{Z} \end{vmatrix} \quad \text{and} \quad \Delta_2 = -2\mu\begin{vmatrix} a & \dot{a} & X \\ b & \dot{b} & Y \\ c & \dot{c} & Z \end{vmatrix}. \tag{4.3.9}$$

If, in a heliocentric frame, the motion of the terrestrial observer about the sun be taken as given by the two-body approximation, one may substitute $\ddot{X} = -\mu X/R^3$, etc., in (4.3.9). The simultaneous solution of (4.3.6) and (4.3.8) may be obtained by numerical iteration.

Eliminating $\ddot{D}$ and D from (4.3.5), one finds

$$\dot{D} = \frac{1}{\Delta}\left[\Delta_3 + \frac{1}{r^3}\Delta_4\right], \tag{4.3.10}$$

where

$$\Delta_3 = -\begin{vmatrix} a & \ddot{X} & \dot{a} \\ b & \ddot{Y} & \dot{b} \\ c & \ddot{Z} & \dot{c} \end{vmatrix} \quad \text{and} \quad \Delta_4 = -\mu\begin{vmatrix} a & X & \ddot{a} \\ b & Y & \ddot{b} \\ c & Z & \ddot{c} \end{vmatrix}. \tag{4.3.11}$$

Having obtained $\dot{D}$, the velocity vector follows from (4.3.4) and the determination of the orbit elements proceeds as in (4.2.14) to (4.2.25).

Thus, the procedure of orbit determination according to Laplace is rather straightforward. Its weakest point is the numerical estimation of $\dot{a}$, $\dot{b}$, $\dot{c}$, $\ddot{a}$, $\ddot{b}$, $\ddot{c}$, at least if we restrict ourselves to three observations and use the most primitive finite-difference expressions. Another consideration is the possibility of a vanishingly small determinant Δ. This occurs whenever the observer is located near the orbital plane; we shall see more of this later.

4. ORBIT DETERMINATION FROM WIDELY SPACED OBSERVATIONS

In many situations we do not enjoy the advantage of having closely spaced observations from which the position and the velocity of the vehicle can be reliably deduced for an epoch. Rather, we may obtain data from widely separated points of the orbit. Indeed, in astronomical orbit determination we may deal with telescopic angle readings separated in time by several years. In the case of satellites or space probes, individual observations may have been gathered from different sections of the orbit or even during different anomalistic periods. The data may consist of angles, ranges, range rates, or any combination of these, depending on the instruments used. In the light of such possibilities it is helpful to summarize the basic relations that connect the measured quantities with the orbit elements in each case.

We begin our summary by fixing the notation. The equation for a conic can be written as

$$r = r(p, e, \omega, \theta), \tag{4.4.1}$$

where $p = \frac{1}{2}a(1-e^2)$ and $\theta = f+\omega$. We adopt p to circumvent the singularity in the semi-major axis for parabolic orbits. The vector components of $\mathbf{r}(x,y,z)$ are

$$\begin{pmatrix} x \\ y \\ z \end{pmatrix} = \begin{pmatrix} l_1 & l_2 \\ m_1 & m_2 \\ n_1 & n_2 \end{pmatrix} \cdot \begin{pmatrix} r\cos(\theta-\omega) \\ r\sin(\theta-\omega) \end{pmatrix}, \tag{4.4.2}$$

where

$$l_1 = l_1(\omega, i, \Omega), \ldots, n_2 = n_2(\omega, i), \tag{4.4.3}$$

are the direction cosines of the major and minor axes. They are functions of ω, i, and Ω defined in (3.4.4) and (3.4.5). Thus we may write $x = x(p, e, \omega, i, \Omega, \theta)$, etc.. and also

$$\dot{x} = \dot{x}\,(p, e, \omega, i, \Omega, \theta), \text{ etc.} \tag{4.4.4}$$

Finally, we can represent the time relations for any conic, e.g. (2.2.37) or (2.2.40), in the form

$$t = t(p, e, \tau, \omega, \theta) \quad \text{or} \quad t = t(p, e, \tau, r). \tag{4.4.5}$$

Let the observer's position be denoted by

$$\mathbf{R} : X, Y, Z, \tag{4.4.6}$$

and the information from a radar be

$$\mathbf{D} : D_x, D_y, D_z \tag{4.4.7}$$

in the event azimuth and elevation angles and slant range are measured and converted into components in the x, y, z frame. If range alone is measured we designate it

$$D = |\mathbf{D}|, \tag{4.4.8}$$

and if only angles are furnished we use

$$\rho = a/c \quad \text{and} \quad \sigma = b/c, \tag{4.4.9}$$

where a, b, c are the unit vector components of $\mathbf{D}$ introduced in Section 3. Finally, if range rate is measured (by the Doppler effect), we shall use

$$\dot{D} = \frac{d}{dt}\,|\mathbf{D}|\,. \tag{4.4.10}$$

It is assumed that time will be recorded with every observation. With the help of these definitions, let us find out how to determine the six orbit elements from various combinations of tracking data.

If angles and range are furnished we need to observe two points on the orbit and the associated times; the governing algebraic system turns out to be

$$\mathbf{R}_j+\mathbf{D}_j = \mathbf{r}_j(p, e, \omega, i, \Omega, \theta_j), \qquad j = 1, 2, \tag{4.4.11}$$

$$t_j = t_j(p, e, \omega, \tau, \theta_j), \qquad j = 1, 2, \tag{4.4.12}$$

where, for the case of elliptic orbits, the time equations are (2.2.37) evaluated between the limits ω and θ_j. Equations (4.4.11) and (4.4.12) are merely of symbolic significance in that they exhibit a system of eight conditions (six components of Eq. 4.4.11 and two time equations) for the eight unknowns (six orbit elements, θ_1, and θ_2). In practice we rely on geometric insight and the specific structure of the right-hand sides to suggest an effective procedure for solving these equations.

Starting from the given vector quantities $\mathbf{R}_j+\mathbf{D}_j = \mathbf{r}_j$, we compute the normal to the orbit plane

$$\frac{\mathbf{r}_1\times\mathbf{r}_2}{|\mathbf{r}_1\times\mathbf{r}_2|} = \mathbf{N},$$

and then

$$\cos i = \mathbf{N}\cdot\mathbf{a}_z = \frac{x_1y_2-x_2y_1}{|\mathbf{r}_1\times\mathbf{r}_2|}, \tag{4.4.13}$$

where $\mathbf{a}_z$ is the unit vector along the earth's polar axis and i lies in the first or second quadrant. As with (4.2.22) and (4.2.23)

$$\begin{aligned} \sin\Omega &= \frac{y_1z_2-y_2z_1}{|\mathbf{r}_1\times\mathbf{r}_2|\sqrt{1-\cos^2 i}}, \\ \cos\Omega &= \frac{x_1z_2-x_2z_1}{|\mathbf{r}_1\times\mathbf{r}_2|\sqrt{1-\cos^2 i}}. \end{aligned} \tag{4.4.14}$$

Now from

$$\frac{|\mathbf{r}_1\times\mathbf{r}_2|}{r_1r_2} = \sin(\theta_2-\theta_1) \quad \text{and} \quad \frac{\mathbf{r}_1\cdot\mathbf{r}_2}{r_1r_2} = \cos(\theta_2-\theta_1) \tag{4.4.15}$$

we find $\theta_2-\theta_1$. We also obtain

$$\sin\theta_1 = \frac{z_1}{r_1\sqrt{1-\cos^2 i}}, \tag{4.4.16}$$

and

$$\cos\theta_1 = \frac{y_1(y_1z_2-z_1y_2)-x_1(z_1x_2-x_1z_2)}{r_1|\mathbf{r}_1\times\mathbf{r}_2|\sqrt{1-\cos^2 i}}.$$

Next we can write

$$r_1 = \frac{2p}{1+e\cos(\theta_1-\omega)}, \tag{4.4.17}$$

$$r_2 = \frac{2p}{1+e\cos(\theta_2-\omega)}, \tag{4.4.18}$$

and t_2-t_1 by (2.2.37) taken between the limits $\theta_1-\omega$ and $\theta_2-\omega$. Here an allowance may have to be made for the number of integral periods elapsed between t_1 and t_2. One approach to the numerical solution of the last three equations might start from a combination of (4.4.17) and (4.4.18) yielding

$$e = \frac{r_2-r_1}{r_1\cos(\theta_1-\omega)-r_2\cos(\theta_2-\omega)} = e(\omega). \tag{4.4.19}$$

For any trial value of ω one can find $e(\omega)$ and $p(\omega)$ from (4.4.19) and (4.4.17). Iterations in ω are used to satisfy the expression for t_2-t_1. After that, τ is found from (2.2.37) written for t_1 or t_2.

An iterative numerical solution of the above equations accomplishes the same as Lambert's theorem. The latter represents a standard approach in the astronomical literature to the efficient computation of an orbit from two positions relative to the central mass and the associated times [2(a) p.50; 2(b) p.141]. Since modern high-speed computers render the differences between equivalent formulations of secondary importance (barring cases with pathological convergence) we shall not pursue this matter further in the present discussion. Instead, we briefly review several other combinations of observational data and the geometric arguments by which they yield orbit elements.*

If only angle data are observed we find in general that three sightings suffice to determine a set of elements; i.e., the data

$$\mathbf{R}_j,\ \rho_j,\ \sigma_j, \qquad j = 1,2,3 \tag{4.4.20}$$

determine three lines of sight in space. To utilize this information one notes that the orbit plane can be written as

$$z = \tan i(-x\sin\Omega + y\cos\Omega), \tag{4.4.21}$$

in terms of the (yet unknown) parameters i and Ω. The intersections between this plane and the lines of sight will mark positions on the conic. They can be found in a straightforward manner as follows.

*Throughout this section we assume that full use is being made of the information contained in every set of observations. Departing from that principle, we might have added to (4.4.11), for example, the partial condition $|\mathbf{R}_3+\mathbf{D}_3| = |\mathbf{r}_3(p, e, \omega, i, \Omega, \theta_3)|$ from a third observation and retained only one equation (4.4.12). There is practically no limit to the possibilities one might consider. The use of such "partial" observations arises most naturally in recursive statistical orbit refinement and will not be pursued further in this section.

Let the equations of the sight line from an observer be denoted

$$c+gx = y; \qquad d+hx = z. \tag{4.4.22}$$

For an earth-centered orbit the coefficients c, d, g, h are expressible in terms of the observer's latitude, instantaneous right ascension, and the azimuth and elevation angles at which the object appeared to him at the time. This may be done by means of the coordinate transformations given in Chapter 3. By inverting (3.6.7) through (3.6.10), we find

$$g = \{\sin\alpha_0[\sin\varphi_0 \sin E - \cos\varphi_0 \cos E \cos A] + \cos\alpha_0 \cos E \sin A\}$$
$$\times\{\cos\alpha_0[\sin\varphi_0 \sin E - \cos\varphi_0 \cos E \cos A] - \sin\alpha_0 \cos E \sin A\}^{-1}, \tag{4.4.23}$$

$$h = \{\sin\varphi_0 \cos E \cos A + \cos\varphi_0 \sin E\}$$
$$\times\{\cos\alpha_0[\sin\varphi_0 \sin E - \cos\varphi_0 \cos E \cos A] - \sin\alpha_0 \cos E \sin A\}^{-1}, \tag{4.4.24}$$

$$c = R\cos\varphi_0'(\sin\alpha_0 - g\cos\alpha_0), \tag{4.4.25}$$

$$d = R(\sin\varphi_0' - h\cos\varphi_0'\cos\alpha_0). \tag{4.4.26}$$

(If Eq. 4.4.22 is meant to represent heliocentric coordinates, the appropriate expressions in place of Eqs. 4.4.23 through 4.4.26 are easily found.)

Manipulation of (4.4.21) and (4.4.22) yields the cartesian coordinates of the point of intersection of a line of sight with the orbit plane as

$$x = \frac{d - c\cos\Omega\tan i}{(g\cos\Omega\tan i - \sin\Omega\tan i - h)},$$

$$y = \frac{dg - c\sin\Omega\sin i - ch}{(g\cos\Omega\tan i - \sin\Omega\tan i - h)}, \tag{4.4.27}$$

$$z = \frac{dg\cos\Omega\tan i - d\sin\Omega\tan i - ch\cos\Omega\tan i}{(g\cos\Omega\tan i - \sin\Omega\tan i - h)}.$$

In order to refer these cartesian coordinates to the geometry of the conic section, let us define the unit vectors

$$\mathbf{a}_R : (\cos\Omega, \sin\Omega, 0),$$

and (4.4.28)

$$\mathbf{a}_S : (-\cos i\sin\Omega, \cos i\cos\Omega, \sin i),$$

where $\mathbf{a}_R$ points to the node and $\mathbf{a}_S$ lies in the orbit plane—separated from $\mathbf{a}_R$ by $\pi/2$ in the direction of anomalistic motion. If we denote the position of a point of intersection (4.4.27) as $\mathbf{r} : (x,y,z)$, the central angle between it and the node is, as we have seen before,

$$\theta = \cos^{-1}\frac{(\mathbf{r}\cdot\mathbf{a}_R)}{|r|} = \sin^{-1}\frac{(\mathbf{r}\cdot\mathbf{a}_S)}{|r|} = \theta(\Omega, i), \tag{4.4.29}$$

and of course

$$|r| = [x^2+y^2+z^2]^{1/2} = r(\Omega, i). \tag{4.4.30}$$

Considering the r, θ associated with the three sightings and the corresponding clock readings, we may now use the following relations for Keplerian orbits,

$$r_j = \frac{2p}{1+e\cos(\theta_j-\omega)}, \qquad j = 1,2,3, \tag{4.4.31}$$

and the corresponding three versions of (2.2.37).

Equation (4.4.31) and the three time conditions constitute six equations in terms of the orbit parameters; these must be solved by iteration. An effective means of accomplishing this consists of using two of the radial distances, say r_1 and r_3, as trial variables and solving for tentative values of i and Ω from (4.4.30). From the same equations r_2 follows immediately and the θ_j's are found from (4.4.29). Using these values, we can obtain p,e,ω (by algebraic elimination) from (4.4.37). Thereafter a value for τ is calculated from one of the time conditions in a straightforward manner; this completes a tentative set of elements. The residuals found in the other two time conditions, after substitution of these elements, are the criteria for a revision of r_1 and r_3 and the start of the next iteration.

If it should happen that all values of $\mathbf{R}_j$ and $\mathbf{D}_j$ lie in or near the same plane, i.e., the orbit plane, any assumed values for r_1 and r_3 will lead to an indeterminate (or at least very inaccurate) result for r_2 via (4.4.30). This is because (4.4.30) is based on the intersections between the sight lines and the orbit plane.

Once such an in-plane case is recognized, a different approach has to be adopted; four sight lines are required for an orbit determination. Figure 4.3 illustrates typical triangles of observation, which lie entirely in the orbit plane. The notation is as

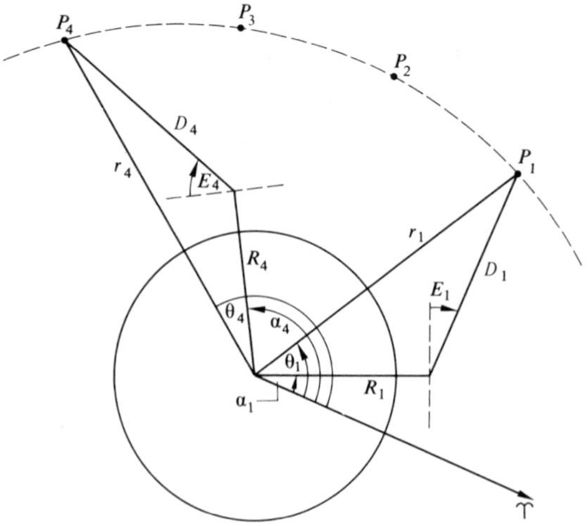

Figure 4.3

before, except that α_j is introduced as an observer's coordinate. Of the sight lines and the observer's position angles, any two will suffice for a determination of i and Ω by existing formulas. (We could, for example, use two $\mathbf{R}_j$'s in place of $\mathbf{r}_1$ and $\mathbf{r}_2$ in Eqs. 4.4.13 and 4.4.14.) To establish the remaining four elements, we note that, for each triangle of observation,

$$r_j = R_j \frac{\cos E_j}{\cos(\theta_j - \alpha_j + E_j)} = \frac{2p}{1 + e\cos(\theta_j - \omega)}. \tag{4.4.32}$$

The time of each observation is again given by (2.2.37). This is our system of eight equations in the unknowns p,e,ω,τ, and the θ_j's. It still would be very awkward to solve such a system as it stands, but, in line with the preceding case, we can adopt two of the r_j's, say r_1 and r_4, as trial variables. This leads to tentative results for p,e,ω,τ by a procedure analogous to (4.4.15) through (4.4.19). With these we can compute θ_2 and θ_3 from (4.4.32) which, if substituted into the time conditions, yield a pair of residuals that serve to initiate the next iteration in r_1 and r_4.

One might observe about angle-only observations in general that if two stations make simultaneous sightings of the orbiting body they establish a complete "fix." Two such fixes permit a solution analogous to (4.4.13) through (4.4.19). In situations where terrestrial base lines between stations are adequate such triangulation seems very appealing; but since most often one cannot rely on simultaneous sightings entirely, it is preferable to retain a general formulation of the angle-only case which takes advantage of simultaneous observations implicitly when they do occur, without being based explicitly on triangulation.

In situations where $R_j/r_j \ll 1$, i.e., where the observer's parallax is negligible, Eqs. (4.4.32) degenerate. Actually, they are unnecessary, since we are, in effect, measuring the θ_j's directly. Thus, only the time equations remain to determine the four orbit elements.

Observational data consisting of six range measurements with their corresponding times represent, at least conceptually, another fundamental situation for orbit determination. As an exercise in analytic geometry, one can write down the equation for the orbit plane (with as yet unknown coefficients), the six circles representing its intersections with the six given "ranging spheres," and proceed with a six-point iteration to find the intersections of a conic trajectory with the six circles that satisfy the six time equations. In its most general form, this analysis does not lead to an algorithm that is attractive for preliminary orbit determination, nor is it relevant from a practical point of view, since every known ranging device also yields at least some crude angle measurements. These lead to a tentative orbit more rapidly than the strict "range-only" case. However, the special situation involving two simultaneous triplets of ranges from different observers is convenient to use and of some practical significance. Each simultaneous triplet of range measurements results in three equations of the form

$$D_j = |\mathbf{r}_j - \mathbf{R}_j| = [(x_j - X_j)^2 + (y_j - Y_j)^2 + (z_j - Z_j)^2]^{1/2}, \tag{4.4.33}$$

and can be solved for x,y,z. Thus two positions and times on the orbit are obtained, from which the orbit parameters can be determined according to (4.4.13) through (4.4.19).

It remains to consider the use of range-rate information, $\dot{D}_j$, derivable from Doppler measurements. As in the case of range readings, one needs, in principle, six Doppler observations for an orbit determination. The formal exercise of writing the dot products between the velocities at six positions in orbit, given by θ_j ($j = 1, \ldots, 6$), and the corresponding sight lines is straightforward. These expressions, together with the time equations, constitute the determining equations for the orbit parameters and θ_j's. Again, the twelve-dimensional iterative algorithm leading to the numerical solution turns out to be quite awkward and of limited practical significance since Doppler measuring equipment also yields some angular data in most instances.

The preliminary orbit determinations encountered in practice often involve a heterogeneous collection of partial observations, e.g., a cutoff velocity measurement, the crossing of a radar fence, and a few Doppler data from Minitrack-type stations. Another typical situation is the determination of remote satellite orbits, e.g., around the moon or a planet, from earth-based trackers. Here the angle data are practically worthless while range and range-rate data are usually available. In that event the above approaches based on observations of D_j and $\dot{D}_j$ must be combined in a suitable *ad hoc* manner.

5. THE METHOD OF GAUSS

In the preceding section we showed the governing conditions for several types of orbit-determination problems. They give an indication of the approaches one might implement on modern computers. We also indicated that a special effort was made by classical astronomers to reduce the orbit determination from two positions to an efficient computing algorithm by virtue of Lambert's theorem. For completeness, we outline a similar effort on behalf of the "angle-only" case, known as Gauss' method.* It has been the prototype of numerous ingenious procedures for calculating orbits from telescopic sightings. Since the available literature on this method is extensive, we content ourselves with a survey of its essentials.

Gauss utilized the geometry of conics as well as the dynamics of motion in a central force field to obtain the solution. First, the planar character of the orbit leads us to relations among the unknown distances D_1, D_2, D_3, i.e., the ranges of the object from the observer, at times t_1, t_2, t_3. Next, the equations of motion provide us with approximations allowing an estimate of D_2 and thence of D_1 and D_3. Then, knowing two points on the orbit in terms of any two of the ranges D_j, associated sight angles and times, we have access to all the orbit elements. Gauss performed this calculation by using the relations between the orbit sectors de-

*Cf. especially reference 5, p. 121, and reference 1, p. 199.

limited by r_1, r_2, r_3 and Kepler's equation. His entire formulation was designed for hand computations but retains some general interest.

Since the orbit lies in a plane passing through the origin, we require that

$$\mathbf{r}_1\cdot\mathbf{N} = \mathbf{r}_2\cdot\mathbf{N} = \mathbf{r}_3\cdot\mathbf{N} = 0, \tag{4.5.1}$$

where $\mathbf{N}: A, B, C$ is the unit normal to the orbit. For a nontrivial solution of the algebraic system (4.5.1) we must have

$$\begin{vmatrix} x_1 & y_1 & z_1 \\ x_2 & y_2 & z_2 \\ x_3 & y_3 & z_3 \end{vmatrix} = 0. \tag{4.5.2}$$

Arranging the expression for this determinant in three alternate forms we obtain

$$\begin{aligned} x_1[y_2z_3 - z_2y_3] - x_2[y_1z_3 - z_1y_3] + x_3[y_1z_2 - z_1y_2] &= 0, \\ y_1[z_2x_3 - x_2z_3] - y_2[z_1x_3 - x_1z_3] + y_3[z_1x_2 - x_1z_2] &= 0, \\ z_1[x_2y_3 - y_2x_3] - z_2[x_1y_3 - y_1x_3] + z_3[x_1y_2 - y_1x_2] &= 0. \end{aligned} \tag{4.5.3}$$

These equations will become independent if we can acquire independent information on the various bracketed terms. We note for example that $y_2z_3 - z_2y_3 = \mathbf{a}_x\cdot[\mathbf{r}_2 \times \mathbf{r}_3] = [r_2r_3]\cos(N, x)$, where $\mathbf{a}_x$ is a unit vector along the x axis, $[r_2r_3]$ denotes twice the area of the triangle delineated by $\mathbf{r}_2$ and $\mathbf{r}_3$, and $\cos(N, x)$ is the direction cosine between the x axis and the normal to the orbit plane. Reinterpreting all the bracketed terms of (4.5.3) in this fashion and noting that each equation may be divided through by $\cos(N, x)$, $\cos(N, y)$, or $\cos(N, z)$ respectively, we find

$$n_1x_1 - x_2 + n_3x_3 = 0; \qquad n_1y_1 - y_2 + n_3y_3 = 0; \qquad n_1z_1 - z_2 + n_3z_3 = 0, \tag{4.5.4}$$

where $n_1 = [r_2r_3]/[r_1r_3]$ and $n_3 = [r_1r_2]/[r_1r_3]$. Now, no matter what coordinate system an observer uses, his sightings may be represented (by the standard transformations of Chapter 3) as $D_j = D_j(a_j, b_j, c_j)$ where a_j, b_j, c_j are the direction cosines of his sight lines in the x, y, z system. At the times of observation, let us denote the position of the observer with respect to the origin by X_j, Y_j, Z_j. Then

$$x_j = a_jD_j + X_j; \qquad y_j = b_jD_j + Y_j; \qquad z_j = c_jD_j + Z_j, \tag{4.5.5}$$

and substitution into (4.5.4) yields

$$\begin{aligned} a_1n_1D_1 - a_2D_2 + a_3n_3D_3 &= -n_1X_1 + X_2 - n_3X_3, \\ b_1n_1D_1 - b_2D_2 + b_3n_3D_3 &= -n_1Y_1 + Y_2 - n_3Y_3, \\ c_1n_1D_1 - c_2D_2 + c_3n_3D_3 &= -n_1Z_1 + Z_2 - n_3Z_3. \end{aligned} \tag{4.5.6}$$

This may be solved for D_2 in the form

$$\Delta D_2 = d = n_1d_1 - d_2 + n_3d_3. \tag{4.5.7}$$

In this expression we have

$$\Delta = \begin{vmatrix} a_1 & a_2 & a_3 \\ b_1 & b_2 & b_3 \\ c_1 & c_2 & c_3 \end{vmatrix},$$

and

$$d = \begin{vmatrix} a_1 & n_1X_1 - X_2 + n_3X_3 & a_3 \\ b_1 & n_1Y_1 - Y_2 + n_3Y_3 & b_3 \\ c_1 & n_1Z_1 - Z_2 + n_3Z_3 & c_3 \end{vmatrix};$$

$$d_1 = \begin{vmatrix} a_1 & X_1 & a_3 \\ b_1 & Y_1 & b_3 \\ c_1 & Z_1 & c_3 \end{vmatrix}; \quad d_2 = \begin{vmatrix} a_1 & X_2 & a_3 \\ b_1 & Y_2 & b_3 \\ c_1 & Z_2 & c_3 \end{vmatrix}; \quad d_3 = \begin{vmatrix} a_1 & X_3 & a_3 \\ b_1 & Y_3 & b_3 \\ c_1 & Z_3 & c_3 \end{vmatrix}.$$

Were n_1 and n_3 known quantities, we could solve (4.5.7) for D_2, if $\Delta \neq 0$. This last means that the three sight lines $\mathbf{D}_1$, $\mathbf{D}_2$, $\mathbf{D}_3$, taken as vectors in x, y, z space, must not lie in one plane, i.e., that the observer must not be situated in the orbit plane. The case with $\Delta = 0$ requires special attention and we shall return to it later. Assuming for the moment that (4.5.7) is not degenerate, we must determine the independent means by which n_1 and n_3 are to be computed.

For this purpose we use the time relations between r_1, r_2, r_3. As a first step one writes series expansions of the type

$$x_3 = x_2 + \dot{x}_2 T_1 + \frac{1}{2!}\ddot{x}_2 T_1^2 + \cdots, \tag{4.5.8}$$

where $T_1 = t_3 - t_2$. Next, we make use of the differential equations of motion $\ddot{x} = -\mu x/r^3$, $\ddot{y} = -\mu y/r^3$, and $\ddot{z} = -\mu z/r^3$, to eliminate all but the first-order derivatives from the expansions (4.5.8). Substitution of these results, for example, into the expression for $[r_2 r_3] \cos(N,x)$ yields

$$x_2 y_3 - y_2 x_3 = \left[-T_3 + \frac{\mu T_3^2}{6r_2^3} + \frac{\mu T_3^4}{4r_2^4}\dot{r}_2 + \cdots \right] \left[x_2 \dot{y}_2 - y_2 \dot{x}_2 \right],$$

where $T_3 = t_2 - t_1$. Further manipulations of such expressions lead to the results

$$n_1 = \frac{[r_2 r_3]}{[r_1 r_3]} = \frac{T_1}{T_2}\left\{1 + \frac{\mu T_3(T_2 + T_1)}{6r_2^3} + \frac{\mu T_3(T_3^2 + T_1 T_3 - T_1^2)}{4r_2^4}\dot{r}_2 + \cdots \right\},$$

$$n_3 = \frac{[r_1 r_2]}{[r_1 r_3]} = \frac{T_3}{T_2}\left\{1 + \frac{\mu T_1(T_2 + T_3)}{6r_2^3} - \frac{\mu T_1(T_1^2 + T_1 T_3 - T_3^2)}{4r_2^4}\dot{r}_2 + \cdots \right\}, \tag{4.5.9}$$

where $T_2 = t_3 - t_1$.

Inspection of (4.5.9) reveals that the terms in $\dot{r}_2$ are obviously inconvenient. Any procedure for estimating this derivative by finite differences would introduce the weaknesses of Laplace's method. Fortunately one can neglect the $\dot{r}_2$ terms without excessive loss of accuracy in many applications of Gauss' method. Let us, therefore, proceed to use (4.5.9) with only two terms in each bracket and refine it later, if necessary. Substitution into (4.5.7) yields

$$D_2 = \frac{1}{\Delta}\left[d_1(T_1/T_2) - d_2 + d_3(T_3/T_2)\right] + (T_1T_3/6T_2\Delta)\left[d_1(T_2+T_1) + d_3(T_2+T_3)\right]\frac{1}{r_2^3}, \tag{4.5.10}$$

which now contains the unknowns D_2 and r_2. From the triangle of observation at t_2 we remember that there also exists the geometric relation

$$r_2^2 = R_2^2 - 2R_2D_2 \cos v_2 + D_2^2, \tag{4.5.11}$$

where the angle $v_2(=E_2+\pi/2)$ is a known quantity and determined by the vectors $\mathbf{R}_2$ and $\mathbf{D}_2$. After solution of (4.5.10) and (4.5.11) for r_2 and D_2 we can evaluate n_1 and n_3 by (4.5.9). Thereupon, D_1 and D_3 follow from (4.5.6) and $\mathbf{r}_1$, $\mathbf{r}_2$, $\mathbf{r}_3$ from (4.5.5).

To eliminate the approximations introduced in truncating (4.5.9), Gauss showed that since a conic section is defined by three vectors from the focus, one can also give the relations between the areas of the triangles $[r_1r_2]$, $[r_2r_3]$, $[r_1r_3]$ and the corresponding sectors of the Kepler orbit in closed form. Since the areas of the latter are related to time by Kepler's law of areas, this ultimately permits one to relate n_1 and n_3 to T_1, T_2, T_3 in a precise fashion and without such errors as we introduced in (4.5.9). Thus, a refinement of our first set of results for $\mathbf{r}_1$, $\mathbf{r}_2$, $\mathbf{r}_3$ is possible.

There is nothing in the preceding discussion that implies a restriction to a particular type of orbit. One would expect that special precautions are necessary with observations in the remote parts of highly eccentric orbits (e.g., cometary orbits or earth-escape trajectories in a geocentric frame) and we remember that the case $\Delta = 0$ requires special treatment. Gauss and his successors have devoted considerable attention to the existence, accuracy, and checks of solutions for (4.5.10) and (4.5.11) under various conditions. Thereupon, the final task of calculating orbit elements from any two of $\mathbf{r}_1$, $\mathbf{r}_2$, $\mathbf{r}_3$ was based essentially on Lambert's theorem.

6. A SELF-ADAPTIVE METHOD

We have seen in Section 4 that the standard angle-only methods fail when the observer is situated in the orbit plane, i.e., if all three lines of sight are contained in that plane. We also demonstrated how an extension to four observations suffices for orbit determinations in that case. The same geometric degeneracy manifests itself in the Gauss method by a vanishing of the determinant Δ; in practice, this determinant will become very small if all the sight lines are close to the orbit plane. Indeed, astronomers have had every reason to be concerned with near-degenerate cases since a terrestrial observer of the planets spends most of his time near their orbit planes. Consequently, there exists a modification of Gauss' method to cope with this condition.

In modern practice it turns out that the lines of sight to artificial celestial bodies, especially satellites, swing in and out of the orbit plane rather frequently. With automatic computing routines it is awkward to switch between various formulations and computing algorithms as a consequence of varying geometric conditions. In an effort to avoid this, a method has been devised which always utilizes four sightings, but which makes only partial use of the information obtainable from two of these for the *out-of-plane* case. It does this in such a way that the procedure automatically reduces to that explained in conjunction with Fig. 4.3 if all lines of sight coincide with the orbit plane.*

As in that earlier discussion, we adopt two of the ranges, say D_1 and D_4, as intermediate variables. These establish a tentative orbit according to the two-point method of orbit determination. Now let us find the normal projections of the other two lines of sight on the orbit plane and their intersections with this tentative orbit (Fig. 4.4). They will mark the two radii $\mathbf{r}_2$ and $\mathbf{r}_3$ whose angles relative to $\mathbf{r}_1$ (and $\mathbf{r}_4$) must be compatible with the observed time differentials $t_3 - t_1$ and $t_2 - t_1$. To the extent that they are not, the assumed values of r_1 and r_4 (i.e., D_1 and D_4) must be revised until, by a process of repeated trials, this compatibility is established. At this stage the points of intersection between the orbit and the projections $\tilde{D}_2$,

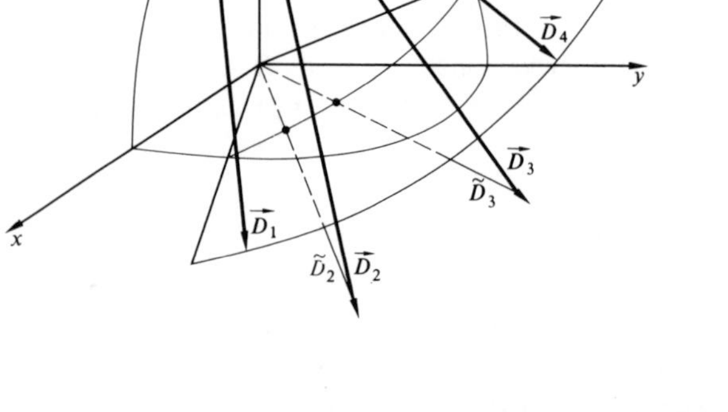

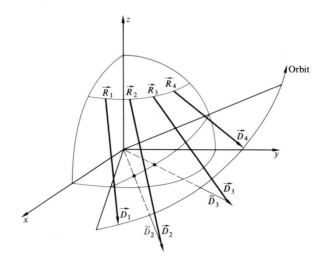

Figure 4.4

*To the writers' knowledge this is a novel (or at least independent) approach, published in reference 11. The formulation in that publication differs slightly from the one given here; the reader may imagine numerous variants of the basic idea.

$\tilde{D}_3$ of $\mathbf{D}_2$ and $\mathbf{D}_3$ on the orbit plane should also be the intersections of the vectors $\mathbf{D}_2$ and $\mathbf{D}_3$ themselves with the orbit plane. This assumes that the observational data are strictly self-consistent. If all the lines of sight approach coincidence with the orbital plane, it is obvious that $\mathbf{D}_2$ and $\mathbf{D}_3$ tend to merge with their projections on this plane and the task of orbit determination passes continuously to the "in-plane" procedure of Section 3 without any change of computational procedure.

The detailed calculations are as follows. With the assumed values of D_1 and D_4 we find

$$\mathbf{r}_1 :(X_1+D_1a_1,\ Y_1+D_1b_1,\ Z_1+D_1c_1); \qquad \mathbf{r}_4 :(X_4+D_4a_4,\ Y_4+D_4b_4,\ Z_4+D_4c_4), \tag{4.6.1}$$

where the quantities X_j, Y_j, Z_j, a_j, b_j, c_j follow as usual from the observations. With this information on $\mathbf{r}_1$, $\mathbf{r}_4$, and t_1, t_4 we can determine a tentative orbit according to Eqs. (4.4.13) through (4.4.19). This results in preliminary values for the orbit elements.

Next we find the normal to this orbit

$$\mathbf{N} = \frac{\mathbf{r}_1 \times \mathbf{r}_4}{|\mathbf{r}_1 \times \mathbf{r}_4|}. \tag{4.6.2}$$

Now let $\mathbf{I}_1$ be the unit vector corresponding to $\mathbf{r}_1$ and form $\mathbf{I}_2 = \mathbf{N} \times \mathbf{I}_1$. In the orthogonal orbital reference frame ($\mathbf{I}_1$, $\mathbf{I}_2$, $\mathbf{N}$), the equation of the projection of $\mathbf{D}_2$ on the orbit reads

$$i_2 = \mathbf{R}_2 \cdot \mathbf{I}_2 + (i_1 - \mathbf{R}_2 \cdot \mathbf{I}_1)\frac{\mathbf{D}_2 \cdot \mathbf{I}_2}{\mathbf{D}_2 \cdot \mathbf{I}_1}, \tag{4.6.3}$$

where i_1 and i_2 are coordinate values along $\mathbf{I}_1$ and $\mathbf{I}_2$. To obtain the intersection between this line and the orbit, we use the angle θ_2 as an independent variable for the iteration. Thus

$$i_1 = \frac{a(1-e^2)\cos(\theta_2-\theta_1)}{1+e\cos(\theta_2-\omega)}, \tag{4.6.4}$$

and, using this expression with (4.6.3), the quantity

$$\left[i_2 - \frac{a(1-e^2)\sin(\theta_2-\theta_1)}{1+e\cos(\theta_2-\omega)}\right] \tag{4.6.5}$$

must be driven to zero by successive trials in $\theta_2-\theta_1$. This establishes the desired intersection. Having repeated this procedure for $\mathbf{D}_3$ we now possess tentative values for the two angles θ_2 and θ_3 which are to be associated with our current results for the elements. However, these angles must also yield the times of observation t_2 and t_3 upon substitution into (2.2.37) or other appropriate time expressions.

In general this will not be the case in a first trial and the quantities

$$\Delta_2 t = t_2 - \tau - \sqrt{\frac{a^3}{\mu}}\,[2.2.37]_{\omega}^{\theta_2}$$

and (4.6.6)

$$\Delta_3 t = t_3 - \tau - \sqrt{\frac{a^3}{\mu}}\,[2.2.37]_{\omega}^{\theta_3}$$

must be driven to zero by successive corrections in D_1 and D_4. In these equations, $[2.2.37]_{\omega}^{\theta}$ stands for the corresponding bracketed term in (2.2.37).

This then is the "outer loop" of this iterative method—the "inner" one having been the determination of a tentative orbit according to (4.4.13) through (4.4.19) from assumed values for D_1 and D_4. (In both operations the numerical search procedure must be designed with some care to result in a practical implementation.) These iterations become more significant when one realizes that no quadruplet of actual observations is exactly self-consistent with respect to the geometric conditions of the orbit. Measurements are always subject to errors from the various causes discussed in Chapter 3 (and from a great variety of instrument errors) so that after (4.6.6) has been made to vanish, the sight lines $\mathbf{D}_2$ and $\mathbf{D}_3$ do not intersect the orbital plane exactly on the orbit path.* It is characteristic of this method that it throws all of this inconsistency into $\mathbf{D}_2$ and $\mathbf{D}_3$ but none of it into $\mathbf{D}_1$ and $\mathbf{D}_4$. More could be said about this aspect from a data-processing point of view but we will not discuss it further here.

7. ORBIT ELEMENT SENSITIVITY: SERIES EXPANSIONS OF PARAMETERS

Up to this point we have treated the observed values of a position and the velocity vector as if they had been determined with absolute accuracy, though of course this is never the case. As noted earlier, data-reduction routines must be applied to the information obtained from tracking apparatus or to the orbital elements derived from actual observations, which are always contaminated by errors. In this section and the next we shall consider the case where a position and velocity vector of the vehicle are established at time t_0 and where we would like to know the effects on the orbit elements of small changes in these quantities. In other words, we would like to know how sensitive an orbit parameter is to the conditions at t_0. Such a study is referred to as *sensitivity analysis*.

This technique is of value from several points of view. First, it gives the variation to be expected in the orbit when observational errors at t_0 can be estimated; thus, the effect of instrument bias on the orbit elements resulting from some of the

*In practice, one may not care to restrict these inconsistencies entirely to an out-of-plane component by permitting the projections $\tilde{D}_2$ and $\tilde{D}_3$ to intersect the orbit at points whose times are slightly different from t_2 and t_3. The successive trials with D_1 and D_4 could then aim at minimizing the sum of the squares of the tangential and transverse residuals at points 2 and 3.

methods in Section 4 through Section 6 can be judged. Second, sensitivity analysis tells us how guidance errors during the powered flight portion of a trajectory and the resulting small changes in the injection conditions will affect the final orbit; e.g., in a "targeting" or "splice" problem, as mentioned in Section 1, one might be concerned with the displacements of the terminal point or changes at the splice points resulting from changes of the injection conditions. Third, we can use the sensitivities for "trajectory shaping" during the planning phase of a project; a preliminary orbit can be based on accurate computations from tentative values of the controlling parameters, and the significance of small changes can be roughly gauged by a sensitivity analysis. As regards the last, this approach avoids a full-scale, time-consuming, parameter study—i.e., a numerical optimization—and the consequent differencing of large numbers to obtain small changes. A typical example is the compromise between the perigee altitude, orbit inclination, and spin orientation for a satellite with given payload, all of which can be controlled by the magnitude and direction of its injection velocity.

We restrict our analysis to elliptic orbits and begin by establishing the sensitivities of the six basic orbit parameters. Assume that we have established the "smoothed" radius vector r_0, the velocity v_0, and the flight path angle γ_0 for an orbiting object. Assume further that these quantities are subject to errors Δr, Δv, and $\Delta\gamma$ which are very small compared to the gross values of r_0, v_0, and γ_0. If we denote the true values by a *prime*, then $r' = r_0 \pm \Delta r$, or if we absorb the sign in Δr, we have $r' = r_0(1+\Delta r/r_0)$ where $\Delta r/r_0 \ll 1$, and corresponding forms for v' and γ'. One way of establishing orbit sensitivities makes use of the expressions for orbit parameters in terms of the position and velocity at the initial point, which were derived in Section 2. In the present section we use these to form Taylor series expansions in powers of Δr, Δv, $\Delta\gamma$, etc., and truncate these series as needed for a satisfactory estimate of the sensitivities.

Let us simplify the notation by dropping the subscript zero from the initial values for r, v, γ, etc. From (4.2.1) we find for the first-order sensitivities of the semi-major axis

$$\partial a/\partial r = 2a^2/r^2,$$

and

$$\partial a/\partial v = 2a^2 v/\mu,$$

so that

$$a' - a \equiv \Delta a \simeq 2a^2\left(\frac{\Delta r}{r^2} + \frac{v}{\mu}\Delta v\right). \tag{4.7.1}$$

The next terms in the Taylor series expansion are of order $(\Delta r/r)^2$ and $(\Delta v/v)^2$ and will be neglected here. The absence of γ in the expression for the semi-major axis is worthy of note. A family of elliptic orbits with equal major axes may be generated by launching from a radial distance r with a fixed velocity but firing at different angles. The complete family of orbit shapes will range from an ellipse with minimum eccentricity (horizontal injection) to a straight line through the center of the earth and of length $2a$.

For the sensitivities of e, we find from (4.2.2)

$$\begin{aligned}\Delta e = {} & e_1 \cos^2\gamma \frac{1}{e}\frac{\Delta r}{r} + 2e_1 \cos^2\gamma \frac{1}{e}\frac{\Delta v}{v} - e_2 \sin\gamma \cos\gamma \frac{1}{e}\Delta\gamma \\ & + \left[\frac{v^4 r^2}{2\mu^2}\cos^2\gamma \frac{1}{e} - \frac{1}{2} e_1 \cos^4\gamma \frac{1}{e^3}\right]\left(\frac{\Delta r}{r}\right)^2 \\ & + \left[e_3 \cos^2\gamma \frac{1}{e} - 2e_1 \cos^4\gamma \frac{1}{e^3}\right]\left(\frac{\Delta v}{v}\right)^2 \\ & + \left[-\frac{1}{2} e_2 \cos^2\gamma \frac{1}{e} + \frac{1}{2}(e_2 \sin\gamma \cos\gamma)^2 \frac{1}{e^3}\right](\Delta\gamma)^2 \\ & + \left[e_4 \cos^2\gamma \frac{1}{e} - (e_1 \cos^2\gamma)^2 \frac{1}{e^3}\right]\frac{\Delta r}{r}\frac{\Delta v}{v} \\ & + \left[-\frac{1}{2} e_1 \sin 2\gamma \frac{1}{e} + \frac{1}{2} e_1 e_2 \cos^3\gamma \sin\gamma \frac{1}{e^3}\right]\frac{\Delta r}{r}\Delta\gamma \\ & + \left[e_1 \sin 2\gamma \frac{1}{e} + e_1 e_2 \cos^3\gamma \sin\gamma \frac{1}{e^3}\right]\frac{\Delta v}{v}\Delta\gamma + \cdots \end{aligned} \tag{4.7.2}$$

Here we included second-order terms for reasons that will appear presently. In (4.7.2) we have

$$e_1 = [v^2 - \mu/r](v^2 r^2/\mu^2); \qquad e_2 = [v^2 - 2\mu/r](v^2 r^2/\mu^2);$$

$$e_3 = [3v^2 - \mu/r](v^2 r^2/\mu^2); \qquad e_4 = [2v^2 - \mu/r](v^2 r^2/\mu^2).$$

If injection occurs at perigee, as is frequently the case, we have $\gamma = 0$; hence $e = 1 - rv^2/\mu$ and the above expression simplifies considerably:

$$\begin{aligned}\Delta e = {} & \frac{v^2 r}{\mu}\frac{\Delta r}{r} + \frac{2v^2 r}{\mu}\frac{\Delta v}{v} \\ & + \left[\frac{v^4 r}{2\mu}\frac{1}{\left[v^2 - \frac{\mu}{r}\right]} - \frac{v^2\mu}{2r}\frac{1}{\left[v^2 - \frac{\mu}{r}\right]^2}\right]\left(\frac{\Delta r}{r}\right)^2 \\ & + \left[\frac{v^2 r}{\mu}\frac{3v^2 - \frac{\mu}{r}}{v^2 - \frac{\mu}{r}} - \frac{2v^2\mu}{r}\frac{1}{\left[v^2 - \frac{\mu}{r}\right]^2}\right]\left(\frac{\Delta v}{v}\right)^2 - \frac{v^2 r}{2\mu}\frac{v^2 - \frac{2\mu}{r}}{v^2 - \frac{\mu}{r}}(\Delta\gamma)^2 \\ & + \left[\frac{v^2 r}{\mu}\frac{2v^2 - \frac{\mu}{r}}{v^2 - \frac{\mu}{r}} - \frac{v^4 r}{\mu}\frac{1}{v^2 - \frac{\mu}{r}}\right]\left(\frac{\Delta r}{r}\right)\left(\frac{\Delta v}{v}\right) + \cdots \end{aligned} \tag{4.7.3}$$

While no difficulty arises in applying (4.7.2) to orbits of high, or even moderate, eccentricity, one observes that for given errors Δr, Δv, $\Delta\gamma$ we might easily have a value of e small enough to render the expansion (4.7.2) inaccurate (no matter how many terms we include in the series). This indicates that for near-circular orbits a power series expansion for Δe is not a suitable approach. This difficulty is not peculiar to the way in which we approach the limit $e = 0$ and cannot be avoided by taking $\lim_{v^2\to\mu/r} \Delta e$, with $\gamma(v)$ a function that vanishes only as $e\to 0$. We shall see a way around this obstacle in the next section.

A similar situation exists with regard to the sensitivities of f_0, the true anomaly at t_0, where $0<f_0<2\pi$. From (4.2.8) and (4.2.9) we deduce

$$f_0 = \tan^{-1}\frac{rv^2 \sin 2\gamma}{2(rv^2\cos^2\gamma-\mu)}. \tag{4.7.4}$$

The leading term of the Taylor series for Δf_0 reads

$$\Delta f_0 \simeq \left\{4\left(\cos^2\gamma - \frac{\cos 2\gamma}{rv^2}\right)\Delta\gamma - \left(\frac{4\mu}{rv^3}\sin 2\gamma\right)\Delta v - \left(\frac{2\mu}{r^2v^2}\sin 2\gamma\right)\Delta r\right\}$$
$$\times\left[4\left(\cos^2\gamma - \frac{\mu}{rv^2}\right)^2 + \sin^2 2\gamma\right]^{-1}. \tag{4.7.5}$$

If $0<(v^2-\mu/r)\ll 1$ and $|\gamma| \ll \pi/2$, the higher-order terms of the series expansion become appreciable and, as $v^2\to\mu/r$ and $\gamma\to 0$ (the circular case), all coefficients of the expansion exhibit singularities; one must establish a suitable asymptotic expansion for this case or use the closed forms of the next section.

We now consider the time of perigee passage. From Chapter 2 we recall that $\tau = t_0 - \sqrt{a^3/\mu}\,[2.2.37]_0^{f_0}$, where [2.2.37] stands for the corresponding bracketed term in (2.2.37). If we formally generate a series expansion for this to first-order terms, we find

$$\Delta\tau = \Delta t_0 + \frac{3}{2}\sqrt{\frac{a}{\mu}}\left[\frac{e\sqrt{1-e^2}\sin f_0}{1+e\cos f_0} - 2\tan^{-1}\left(\sqrt{\frac{1-e}{1+e}}\tan\frac{f_0}{2}\right)\right]\Delta a$$
$$+\sqrt{\frac{a^3}{\mu}}\frac{\sqrt{1-e^2}\sin f_0\,(2+e\cos f_0)}{(1+e\cos f_0)^2}\Delta e - \sqrt{\frac{a^3}{\mu}}\frac{(1-e^2)^{3/2}}{(1+e\cos f_0)^2}\Delta f_0, \tag{4.7.6}$$

where Δa, Δe, and Δf_0 are given by (4.7.1), (4.7.2), and (4.7.5) respectively. Needless to say, this expression for $\Delta\tau$ exhibits the same difficulties that we have already noted with Δe and Δf_0 as $e\to 0$.

We can investigate Ω, i, and ω by the spherical trigonometry of Fig. 4.2. Since $\cos i = \sin\psi\cos\varphi'$, we find

$$\Delta i \simeq \frac{1}{\sin i}[(\sin\psi\sin\varphi')\,\Delta\varphi' - (\cos\psi\cos\varphi')\Delta\psi]. \tag{4.7.7}$$

Similarly, we obtain from the second part of (4.2.12)

$$\Delta\Omega = \frac{-1}{\sin i \sin(\lambda - \Omega)} [(\sin\psi)\,\Delta\psi + (\cos\psi \cot i)\Delta i] + \Delta\lambda$$

$$= \frac{1}{\sin^3 i \sin(\lambda - \Omega)} [(\cos i \cos^2\psi \cos\varphi' - \sin^2 i \sin\psi)\Delta\psi$$

$$-\tfrac{1}{2}(\sin 2\psi \sin\varphi' \cos i)\,\Delta\varphi'] + \Delta\lambda. \tag{4.7.8}$$

From the first part of (4.2.13) we write

$$\Delta\omega = \frac{1}{\cos(\omega + f_0)\sin i} [(\cos\varphi')\,\Delta\varphi' - (\cot i \sin\varphi')\,\Delta i] - \Delta f_0$$

$$= \frac{1}{\cos(\omega + f_0)\sin^3 i} [(\sin^2 i \cos\varphi' - \cos i \sin^2\varphi' \sin\psi)\Delta\varphi'$$

$$+\tfrac{1}{2}(\sin 2\varphi' \cos i \cos\psi)\,\Delta\psi] - \Delta f_0, \tag{4.7.9}$$

which gives the sensitivity of the argument of perigee. Since this expression contains Δf_0, it diverges for $e \to 0$. Moreover, we note that (4.7.7), (4.7.8), and (4.7.9) diverge as i tends to zero. In such cases the longitude of the node becomes poorly defined and this manifests itself in these sensitivities. One alternative is to utilize suitable redefined elements, as discussed in Chapter 2, but we will not pursue this here.

Error estimates for a few derived parameters follow quite simply from the sensitivities already calculated. Since the pericenter and apocenter distances are $q = a(1-e)$ and $Q = a(1+e)$, we have

$$\Delta q = \Delta a(1-e) - a\Delta e, \tag{4.7.10}$$

and

$$\Delta Q = \Delta a(1+e) + a\Delta e, \tag{4.7.11}$$

where (4.7.1) and (4.7.2) are to be substituted into these equations. From (2.2.24) we have, for the anomalistic period of the orbit, $T = 2\pi(a^3/\mu)^{1/2}$, and thus

$$\Delta T = 3\pi(a/\mu)^{1/2}\Delta a. \tag{4.7.12}$$

To demonstrate the utility of some of the foregoing expressions for the orbit sensitivities, consider the following example.

Suppose that in an attempt to launch a satellite, we have obtained, with the flight path angle $\gamma = 5.0403°$, a velocity $v = 7.714 \times 10^3$ m/sec in the nonrotating geocentric frame and a burnout altitude of $h = 1.2995 \times 10^6$ m. We ask the following. Is this a satellite orbit? If so, what will be the effect on the apogee distance, the eccentricity, and the period if an error of 0.3 m/sec in velocity and a 30 m error in altitude had been made at burnout? If no errors occurred in v and h, but the flight path angle was off by 0.05°, what effect would this have on the eccentricity and on altitude, location, and passage of perigee?

Assuming a value of 6.3795×10^6 m for the earth's radius, we have $r = 7.6790 \times 10^6$ m. From (4.2.1) and (4.2.2), we find $a = 8.998 \times 10^6$ m, $e = 0.1744$, and, from (2.2.11), $q = 7.418 \times 10^6$ m. Thus, we have an elliptic orbit which does not intersect the earth. From (4.2.8) and (4.2.9) we obtain $f_0 = 38.22°$. Considering first the possible errors in h and v, we compute from (4.7.1) that the error in altitude induces a change of 73.8 m in the semi-major axis; similarly, the effect due to Δv is 955.2 m. Thus, if we had underestimated h and v ($\Delta r > 0$, $\Delta v > 0$), the total adjustment in a would have to be $\Delta a = 1029$ m; an underestimate of h and an overestimate of v yields $\Delta a = -881.4$ m, etc. Further, (4.7.2) yields $\Delta e = 3.795 \times 10^{-6}$ due to Δh and $\Delta e = 7.554 \times 10^{-5}$ for Δv; in this case the second-order terms in Δe can be ignored. If both measurements had been underestimated, then, according to (4.7.11), the change in apogee could amount to $\Delta Q = 1936$ m, and from (4.7.12) $\Delta T = 1.471$ sec.

If the cutoff errors consisted only of $\Delta\gamma = (+)0.05°$ we would find that $\Delta e = 4.591 \times 10^{-4}$, where this time the third term of (4.7.2) made the chief contribution. With $\Delta a = 0$ we find from (4.7.10) that $\Delta q = -4176$ m. Finally, one obtains from (4.7.5) and (4.7.6), $\Delta f_0 = 0.293°$ and $\Delta\tau = -11.11$ sec.

It is worth pointing out that expressions of this type may be used for certain orbit refinement schemes. In fact, they form the basis for the method of *differential corrections* mentioned in Section 1. We give here a much simplified application. We assume that a satellite has been launched into orbit and we have only very crude injection data for an estimate of the orbit parameters. Before the regular tracking operation gets under way from which we can collect "smoothed data," it may be expected that some post-launch observations, not too precise in character, become available. We would like to know what use can be made of such information to effect a preliminary improvement of the orbit parameters.

Suppose a station registers a meridian crossing of the vehicle at the time t_1. On the basis of launch parameters this would correspond to the value f_1 in true anomaly. Suppose a second observing station possesses a low-grade instrument whose readings can be reduced to another pair of data f_2, t_2. Now the observed time difference $\delta t = t_2 - t_1$ will usually disagree with that interval computed from the injection parameters and corresponding to $f_2 - f_1$. We would like to know the extent to which this discrepancy $\Delta(\delta t)$ reflects the inaccuracies in the various orbit parameters and how it should be used to rectify them.

In analogy to (4.7.6) we may derive

$$\Delta(\delta t) = \frac{3}{2}\sqrt{\frac{a}{\mu}}\left[2\tan^{-1}\left(\sqrt{\frac{1-e}{1+e}}\tan\frac{f}{2}\right) - \frac{e\sqrt{1-e^2}\sin f}{1+e\cos f}\right]_{f_1}^{f_2}\Delta a$$

$$-\sqrt{\frac{a^3}{\mu}}\left[\frac{\sqrt{1-e^2}\sin f(2+e\cos f)}{(1+e\cos f)^2}\right]_{f_1}^{f_2}\Delta e$$

$$+\sqrt{\frac{a^3}{\mu}}\frac{(1-e^2)^{3/2}}{(1+e\cos f_2)^2}\Delta f_2 - \sqrt{\frac{a^3}{\mu}}\frac{(1-e^2)^{3/2}}{(1+e\cos f_1)^2}\Delta f_1. \tag{4.7.13}$$

Here Δa and Δe represent errors in the orbit parameters due to inaccuracies of the injection conditions, Δf_1 and Δf_2 represent errors in the anomalies at t_1 and t_2, which are partly due to Δf_0 at injection (since f_0 enters into the computation of f_1 and f_2 from the sight angles at t_1 and t_2) and are partly due to observational errors in the sight angles themselves. The expression (4.7.13) shows us immediately that if we can select observations such that $f_2 - f_1$ is large, the secular term in the first brackets magnifies the contribution from Δa beyond all others. Therefore such a pair of observations, where each consists essentially of a single angle and time, lends itself to a revision of the semi-major axis or, what amounts to the same thing, of the period.

8. ORBIT ELEMENT SENSITIVITY. MOTION RELATIVE TO THE NOMINAL ORBIT

In the preceding section we noticed that the truncated series for orbit sensitivities became inaccurate as the eccentricity approached zero. On the other hand, an extension to higher-order terms soon makes these expressions excessively awkward. As an alternate approach we introduce the idea of using the nominal (i.e., the planned or desired) orbit of the satellite as a locus of reference for the variations. With respect to this reference one may express the actual motion of the satellite as a function of its velocity and position errors at t_0. Since we shall discuss this approach more fully in Chapters 5 and 7, in relation to several perturbation methods, we merely state the equations of motion in this section by inspection and intuition. They will be specialized to nominally circular orbits. In Fig. 4.5, point O' marks the nominal satellite position in the nominal orbit. It is located by the distance r from E and by the central angle θ measured from the node, whose initial value is θ_0. The point O' serves as an origin for the ξ, η, ζ coordinates where ξ is positive in the radially outward direction, η is normal thereto in the nominal orbit plane, positive in the direction of increasing θ, and ζ is perpendicular to the orbit plane, completing a right-handed system. We assume that the departures (ξ, η, ζ)

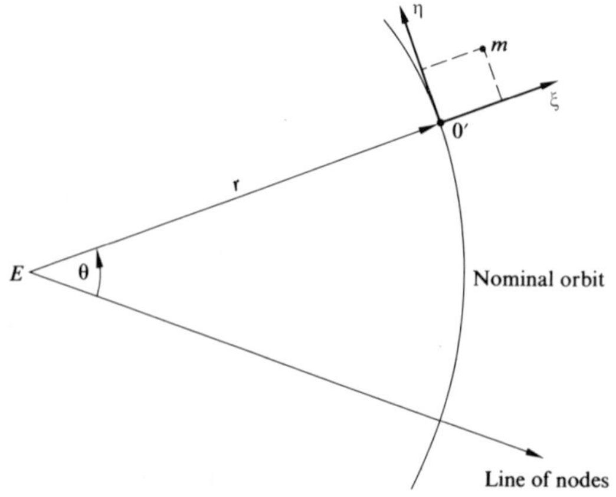

Figure 4.5

from nominality are small compared to r, hence we ignore terms of order $(\xi/r)^2$, $(\eta/r)^2$, $(\zeta/r)^2$, and the equations of motion of the satellite about O' may be written as follows:

$$-m(\ddot{r}+\ddot{\xi})+m(r+\xi)\dot{\theta}^2+m\eta\ddot{\theta}+2m\dot{\eta}\dot{\theta}-\mu m/(r+\xi)^2 = 0, \tag{4.8.1}$$

$$-m\ddot{\eta}+m\eta\dot{\theta}^2-m(r+\xi)\ddot{\theta}-2m(\dot{r}+\dot{\xi})\dot{\theta}-\mu m\eta/(r+\xi)^3 = 0, \tag{4.8.2}$$

$$-m\ddot{\zeta}-\mu m\zeta/(r+\xi)^3 = 0. \tag{4.8.3}$$

Wherever the distance from E to m occurred it was simplified from $[(r+\xi)^2+\eta^2+\zeta^2]^{1/2}$ to $(r+\xi)$.

The significance of the terms in (4.8.1) through (4.8.3) becomes evident if we examine their physical interpretation. Following the term-by-term sequence in which they are written, we have in the first (second) equation:

inertial reaction against rectilinear acceleration along the $\xi(\eta)$ axis;
inertial reaction against centripetal acceleration along the $\xi(\eta)$ axis;
inertial reaction against the $\xi(\eta)$ component of rotary acceleration of the ξ, η, ζ system;
inertial reaction against the $\xi(\eta)$ component of Coriolis acceleration;
$\xi(\eta)$ component of gravitational attraction;
and in (4.8.3):
inertial reaction against rectilinear acceleration along ζ axis;
ζ component of gravitational attraction.

This last equation describes the satellite's rectilinear motion normal to the orbit plane.

We now expand $(r+\xi)^{-2}$ and $(r+\xi)^{-3}$, retaining terms of $0(\xi/r)$, etc.; we observe that all terms containing r or its derivatives in the numerator describe the motion in the nominal orbit and therefore equilibrate among themselves. Thus we have

$$\ddot{\xi}-2\dot{\eta}\dot{\theta}-\eta\ddot{\theta}-\xi(2\mu/r^3+\dot{\theta}^2) = 0; \qquad \ddot{\eta}+2\dot{\xi}\dot{\theta}+\xi\ddot{\theta}+\eta(\mu/r^3-\dot{\theta}^2) = 0;$$
$$\ddot{\zeta}+\zeta\,\mu/r^3 = 0. \tag{4.8.4}$$

For the circular case, $\dot{\theta}^2 = n^2 = \mu/r^3$ and $d(\ )/dt = \sqrt{\mu/r^3}\, d(\ )/d\theta$. Hence

$$\xi''-2\eta'-3\xi = 0; \qquad \eta''+2\xi' = 0; \qquad \zeta''+\zeta = 0, \tag{4.8.5}$$

where the "primes" denote derivatives with respect to θ. The solution of (4.8.5) is

$$\xi = 2\dot{\eta}_0/n+4\xi_0-[2\dot{\eta}_0/n+3\xi_0]\cos\bar{f}+\dot{\xi}_0\sin\bar{f}/n,$$
$$\eta = \eta_0-2\dot{\xi}_0/n-3[\dot{\eta}_0/n+2\xi_0]\bar{f}+2[2\dot{\eta}_0/n+3\xi_0]\sin\bar{f}+2\dot{\xi}_0\cos\bar{f}/n,$$
$$\zeta = \dot{\zeta}_0\sin\bar{f}/n+\zeta_0\cos\bar{f}, \tag{4.8.6}$$

where $\bar{f} = \theta-\theta_0$ and the subscript 0 denotes the values of ξ, η, ζ at t_0. The values

ξ_{max} and ξ_{min} from this result mark the apogee and perigee of the orbit. One easily finds that these points are located at

$$\bar{f}_{q,Q} = \tan^{-1}\frac{-\dot{\xi}_0}{(2\dot{\eta}_0+3n\xi_0)}, \quad \text{where} \quad \bar{f}_q = \omega-\theta_0 \quad \text{and} \quad \bar{f}_Q = \omega-\theta_0+\pi. \tag{4.8.7}$$

A brief inspection of the geometry of an ellipse in polar coordinates will determine how to assign quadrants to $\bar{f}_q$ and $\bar{f}_Q$ and reveals the following behavior of the line of apsides.

	$2\dot{\eta}_0+3n\xi_0>0$	$2\dot{\eta}_0+3n\xi_0=0$	$2\dot{\eta}_0+3n\xi_0<0$
$\dot{\xi}_0>0$	$\bar{f}_q$ in 4th quad. $\bar{f}_Q$ in 2nd quad.	$\bar{f}_q=3\pi/2$ $\bar{f}_Q=\pi/2$	$\bar{f}_q$ in 3rd quad. $\bar{f}_Q$ in 1st quad.
$\dot{\xi}_0<0$	$\bar{f}_q$ in 1st quad. $\bar{f}_Q$ in 3rd quad.	$\bar{f}_q=\pi/2$ $\bar{f}_Q=3\pi/2$	$\bar{f}_q$ in 2nd quad. $\bar{f}_Q$ in 4th quad.

If we use (4.8.7) and (4.8.6), the maximum and minimum excursions from the circular orbit turn out to be

$$\xi_{\substack{max\\min}} = \frac{2}{n}\dot{\eta}_0+4\xi_0 \pm \frac{1}{n}\left[(2\dot{\eta}_0+3n\xi_0)^2+\dot{\xi}_0^2\right]^{1/2}. \tag{4.8.8}$$

Now, of course, $\Delta q = \xi_{min}$ and $\Delta Q = \xi_{max}$, hence

$$\Delta a = \tfrac{1}{2}(\xi_{max}+\xi_{min}) = \frac{2}{n}\dot{\eta}_0+4\xi_0, \tag{4.8.9}$$

and

$$e = \frac{1}{2r}(\xi_{max}-\xi_{min}) = \frac{1}{nr}\left[(2\dot{\eta}_0+3n\xi_0)^2+\dot{\xi}_0^2\right]^{1/2}. \tag{4.8.10}$$

To find the sensitivities of various characteristic times of the orbit, we must examine the expression for η in (4.8.6). We note that η_0 represents an error in the original observation of the satellite's central angle which is carried along unchanged in all predicted positions; η_0 enters into no other term of (4.8.6) and merely causes the constant error $-\eta_0/rn$ for all future times of observation at positions specified in terms of $\bar{f}$. Now let us examine the variations that the secular term of η produces in the period, and in the times of nodal and perigee passage. In general, the quantity $\eta(f)$ at any point represents a circumferential lead in the actual motion of m over the nominal anomalistic motion so that the time correction for passage through the point takes the form $\Delta t = -\eta(\bar{f})/rn$. Setting $\bar{f} = 2\pi$ as the argument in η, we get

$$\Delta T = -\frac{\eta(2\pi)}{rn} = \frac{6\pi}{rn^2}(\dot{\eta}_0+2n\xi_0). \tag{4.8.11}$$

Similarly, we observe the following sensitivity of the nodal passage

$$\Delta t_N = -\left[\frac{\eta}{rn}\right]_{\bar{f}=(2j\pi-\theta_0)} = -\frac{1}{n^2 r}\Big[n\eta_0 - 2\dot{\xi}_0 - 3(\dot{\eta}_0 + 2n\xi_0)(2j\pi - \theta_0)$$

$$-2(2\dot{\eta}_0 + 3n\xi_0)\sin\theta_0 + 2\dot{\xi}_0\cos\theta_0\Big], \tag{4.8.12}$$

where j is the number of the revolutions for which the passage is to be predicted. We note that (4.8.7), (4.8.10), and (4.8.12) constitute simple and useful expressions for sensitivity analyses of orbits with vanishingly small nominal eccentricity, the case which caused us trouble in the preceding section. When expressing the present results in the notation of that section, one observes that, due to the rotation of the frame (ξ, η, ζ), we have

$$\Delta v = \dot{\eta}_0 + n\xi_0 \quad \text{and} \quad \Delta\gamma = (\dot{\xi}_0 - n\eta_0)/rn. \tag{4.8.13}$$

In this notation* we find, for the case where all deviations except $\dot{\xi}_0$ vanish, that

$$\bar{f}_{q^{\circ}Q} = \mp\pi/2, \quad e = \Delta\gamma, \quad \text{and} \quad \Delta t_N = 2\left(\frac{r^3}{\mu}\right)^{1/2}[1-\cos\theta_0]\Delta\gamma.$$

Finally, we observe that sensitivities for Ω and i may also be calculated from (4.8.6):

$$\Delta\Omega = -\left[\frac{\zeta}{r\sin i}\right]_{\bar{f}=2\pi-\theta_0} = \frac{1}{nr\sin i}[\dot{\zeta}_0\sin\theta_0 - n\zeta_0\cos\theta_0] \tag{4.8.14}$$

and

$$\Delta i = \left[\frac{\zeta'}{r}\right]_{\bar{f}=2\pi-\theta_0} = \frac{1}{nr}[\dot{\zeta}_0\cos\theta_0 + n\zeta_0\sin\theta_0]. \tag{4.8.15}$$

In order to show an application of the equations in this section, assume that we wish to establish a satellite in a circular orbit of altitude $h = 1.300\times10^6$ m. The nominal orbit is to have an inclination of 50° to the equatorial plane. A typical rocket engine cutoff point within the capabilities of the ascent vehicle might be at the latitude $\varphi_0' = 38°$ and the right ascension $\alpha_0 = 105°$. We ask: what azimuth ψ_0

*Note that, in terms of these deviations in an inertial coordinate system, we obtain

$$\xi = 2\Delta v/n + 2\Delta r - (2\Delta v/n + \Delta r)\cos\bar{f} + r\Delta\gamma\sin\bar{f}.$$

Such an expression for the circular orbit may also be obtained by the simple expansion

$$r = \frac{C_1^2/\mu}{1+e\cos(\bar{f}+f_0)} \simeq \frac{C_1^2}{\mu}[1 - e\cos\bar{f}\cos f_0 + e\sin\bar{f}\sin f_0],$$

where $C_1 = (v+\Delta v)(r+\Delta r)$ and, from (4.2.8) and (4.2.9), $\cos f_0 = [(r+\Delta r)(v+\Delta v)^2 - \mu]/\mu e$, and $\sin f_0 = (r+\Delta r)(v+\Delta v)nr\Delta\gamma/\mu e$.

will be required to establish this orbit and where will the ascending node be located? If an error of (+)0.05° is committed in the flight-path angle at burnout and of (+)0.30 m/sec in the cutoff velocity, what will be the apogee and perigee distances of the resulting orbit and its eccentricity, where will perigee be located, and when will the first nodal passage occur? If the reading for ψ_0 was accurate to 0.05° and φ_0 to 0.01°, what are the maximum uncertainties in i, Ω, and ω?

Equation (4.2.10) yields $\psi_0 = 54.66°$ and, from (4.2.12),

$$\Omega = \alpha_0 - \sin^{-1}(\tan\varphi_0 \cot i) = 64.04°.$$

The circular velocity is $v = (\mu/r_0)^{1/2} = 7.193\times 10^3$ m/sec and the nominal angular velocity is $n = 9.367\times 10^{-4}$ rad/sec. If an error of $\Delta\gamma = 0.05°$ is made at burnout, this, according to (4.8.13), corresponds to a radial velocity component of $\dot{\xi}_0 = 6.276$ m/sec. Substituting this, together with $\dot{\eta}_0 = 0.30$ m/sec into (4.8.9), we obtain $q = r_0 + \Delta q = 7.671\times 10^6$ m; $Q = r_0 + \Delta Q = 7.685\times 10^6$ m. Also from (4.8.10), $e = 8.337\times 10^{-5}$ and from (4.8.7), $\bar{f}_q = -84\overset{\circ}{.}45$.

We find with an obvious change of notation in (4.2.13) that $\theta_0 = 53.49°$ and with the help of (4.8.12), the time to the first nodal passage is $t_N = (2\pi - \theta_0)/n - \eta(2\pi - \theta_0)/rn = 5711 + 2.6 \simeq 5714$ sec. If the uncertainty in the launch azimuth is $\Delta\psi_0 = \pm 0\overset{\circ}{.}05 = \pm 8.72\times 10^{-4}$ rad, $\dot{\zeta}_0 = v\Delta\psi_0 = \pm 6.276$ m/sec and if $\Delta\varphi_0 = \pm 0.01°$, then $\zeta_0 = r_0\Delta\varphi_0 \sin\psi_0 = \pm 1093$ m. Thus, with the help of (4.8.14) and (4.8.15), the maximum uncertainties in node and inclination are found to be $\Delta\Omega = 9.214\times 10^{-4}$ rad, and $\Delta i = 2.603\times 10^{-4}$ rad. Finally, from (4.7.9), $\Delta\omega = 2.707\times 10^{-3}$ rad.

There are other uses for (4.8.6) besides computation of simple orbit sensitivities. For example, we may apply these equations to study the release of objects from a satellite already in orbit. The path of every ejected particle may be expressed in terms of ξ, η, ζ as a motion relative to the nominal orbit, which in this case is the trajectory of the container from which the particle was released. Let us assume that there are no other perturbations than those due to the conditions at injection. Since all particles start from the same point, we have $\xi_0 = \eta_0 = \zeta_0 = 0$, but $\dot{\xi}_0, \dot{\eta}_0, \dot{\zeta}_0$ will have various values depending on the mechanism of expulsion from the capsule.

Let us examine the case of a single container explosion by which a cloud of particles is to be distributed around the orbit. Then the instantaneous position of the jth particle may be written as

$$\begin{aligned} \xi_j &= -\kappa_j \sin\alpha_j + \kappa_j \sin(\alpha_j + f), \\ \eta_j &= -2\kappa_j \cos\alpha_j + (\tfrac{3}{2}\kappa_j \sin\alpha_j) f - 2\kappa_j \cos(\alpha_j + f), \\ \zeta_j &= \lambda_j \sin f \end{aligned} \qquad (4.8.16)$$

where

$$\alpha_j = \tan^{-1}\left(\frac{-2\dot{\eta}_0}{\dot{\xi}_0}\right)_j; \qquad \kappa_j = \frac{1}{n}\left[4\dot{\eta}_0^2 + \dot{\xi}_0^2\right]_j^{1/2}; \qquad \lambda_j = \left(\frac{\dot{\zeta}_0}{n}\right)_j.$$

The distribution of these amplitude and phase parameters is a function of the distribution of the ejection velocities from the dispenser.

The most effective term for spreading the particles around the orbit is the nonperiodic part of η_j. Since its coefficient is proportional to sin α_j, gradual spreading does not occur if $\dot{\eta}_0 = 0$. As one should expect, the particles ejected at right angles to the orbital velocity do not contribute to a spreading of the cloud in a circumferential direction. We also note that ξ_j and ζ_j will vanish periodically for all particles. This means that the width and depth of the belt of particles will show a null twice during each orbital period. Such a null can be avoided only by ejecting the total mass of particles continuously around the orbit.

Another application of (4.8.6) is in design of corrective maneuvers to achieve satellite rendezvous. Let us consider the following rudimentary example. Suppose one space vehicle has been brought into the vicinity of another. Two measurements, at different times, of the position vector $\boldsymbol{\chi}(\xi, \eta, \zeta)$ between the vehicles will, in principle, suffice to yield the constants in (4.8.6). Then the auxiliary rockets of the ship may be caused to deliver one velocity impulse $-\boldsymbol{\chi}_1/\Delta t$ at a time t_1 and another one, $(\boldsymbol{\chi}_1/\Delta t)-\dot{\boldsymbol{\chi}}_1$, at $t_1+\Delta t$, where Δt is to be a small interval in terms of the period so that the space ship can be assumed to follow a straightline path in the ξ, η, ζ frame. This double-impulse maneuver will then improve the agreement between the orbits. It will not, in general, bring about a perfect rendezvous. A more general solution of this problem would consist of a succession of impulse corrections with some constraint imposed, e.g. minimizing the propellant consumption.

Of course one could say more about trajectory sensitivities and their application to guidance and control procedures. An extension of (4.8.6) to elliptic, parabolic, or hyperbolic orbits is given in Chapter 7. Rather elaborate *ad hoc* schemes have been developed for various situations where the form of the required sensitivities depends on the specific mission and the geometry at terminus. Such calculations usually involve numerical iterations based on the equations derived for conic-section orbits in this chapter. Since the detailed procedures may lean on the theory of trajectory optimization and usually reflect the structure of the necessary computer simulations, it seems appropriate to withhold further comments here.

REFERENCES

1. F. R. Moulton, *Introduction to Celestial Mechanics*, Macmillan, New York, 1914.
2. a) H. C. Plummer, *An Introductory Treatise on Dynamic Astronomy*, Dover, New York, 1960.
   b) J. M. A. Danby, *Fundamentals of Celestial Mechanics*, Macmillan, New York, 1962.
3. P. Herget, *The Computation of Orbits*, published by the author, 1948.
4. D. Brouwer and G. M. Clemence, *Methods of Celestial Mechanics*, Academic Press, New York, 1961.
5. A. D. Dubyago, *The Determination of Orbits*, Macmillan, New York, 1961.
6. T. E. Sterne, *An Introduction to Celestial Mechanics*, Interscience, New York, 1960.

7. R. B. Blackman, "Methods of Orbit Refinement," *Bell System Technical Journal*, **43**, 885, 1964.

8. P. Swerling, "First Order Error Propagation in a Stagewise Smoothing Procedure for Satellite Observations," *J. Astronautical Sci.*, **6**, 46, 1959.

9. S. F. Schmidt, "The Application of State Space Methods to Navigation Problems," Philco, WDL, Tech. Rep. No. 4, October 1963.

10. R. E. Kalman, "A New Approach to Linear Filtering and Prediction Problems," *J. of Basic Engineering*, 35–45, March 1960.

11. A. J. Claus, R. B. Blackman, E. G. Halline, and W. C. Ridgway, "Orbit Determination and Prediction, and Computer Programs," The Telstar Experiment, Part 2, *Bell System Technical Journal*, **42**, 1357, 1963.

Chapter five

FUNDAMENTALS OF PERTURBATION THEORY

1. INTRODUCTION

We have seen that the classical two-body problem has solutions which can be written in *closed form* when either the true or the eccentric anomaly is used as the independent variable.* The solutions provide us with planar motion in a conic section; we generally refer to such behavior as Keplerian.

If an additional force acting on either of the two bodies is introduced, the resulting equations of motion usually no longer have closed-form solutions. When the magnitude of such a force is small compared to the central gravity term, the force is called a *perturbation*. Then, as might be expected, the resulting orbit does not depart appreciably from its Keplerian counterpart, at least at first; these departures† are also termed perturbations. The terms *disturbing force*, *disturbed motion*, etc., are also used.

Under certain circumstances, it is possible to make analytic approximations to the effects of the perturbing forces, though a precise solution cannot be obtained. Means of obtaining these approximations will form the subject of this and the next few chapters. Generally, the methods consist in determining the exact equations of motion and then assuming that their solution does not depart appreciably from that which would be valid if the extraneous small forces were not present. We can, in any practical case, obtain only an indication of the actual motion of the body. "Precise" solutions can be found for specific initial conditions by numerical integration techniques, but these afford little insight on the dependence of the motion

*We remind the reader that if time is selected as the independent variable these solutions cannot, in general, be expressed in closed form but must be written as infinite series.

†We note that these arise from a force which acts continuously along the orbit; this is in distinction to the departures we considered in the preceding chapter which were due to (virtual) deviations induced at one point in the path.

on the parameters of the disturbing force. An understanding of these dependencies is frequently far more important than a precise set of numbers and, for this reason, we restrict ourselves here to the analytic approach. However, it can be shown that in many cases the approximations are quite good and may exceed the precision of numerical methods if we wish to predict the effects for a reasonably long time into the future.*

In this chapter we begin by examining some fundamental physical effects in order to familiarize ourselves with the basic phenomena and geometric relations characterizing each situation. For concreteness, we will discuss several significant disturbing forces and their gross effects on orbits. Thereafter we will proceed to a more systematic treatment of perturbation theory.

2. ELEMENTARY ANALYSIS OF PERTURBATIONS

As a first attempt to understand disturbed orbital behavior, we recall two basic physical principles: (1) The rate of change of angular momentum is equal to the torque exerted by the perturbative forces on the body in the orbit; and (2) the change in kinetic energy of the orbiting body is equal to the work done on it by the external forces.

These provide the means for an illuminating, though elementary, analysis of (1) the effect of the disturbing force on the plane of motion, and (2) the effect in the undisturbed orbit plane. For this initial examination, we restrict ourselves to studying orbits which, in the absence of perturbations, would have been circular. Other illustrative or qualitative discussions of satellite perturbations may be found in the literature, such as the graphical treatment in Chapter 9 of reference 1.

2.1. Perturbative Effects on the Orbit Plane

Let us consider first the motion of the orbit plane itself. The angular momentum vector, $\mathbf{L}$, of the orbit is normal to the instantaneous plane of the motion, and is given by

$$\mathbf{L} = \mathbf{r} \times m\mathbf{v}, \tag{5.2.1}$$

where m is the satellite's mass, and $\mathbf{r}$, $\mathbf{v}$ are its instantaneous radius and velocity vectors, respectively. Now the torque is

$$d\mathbf{L}/dt = \mathbf{r} \times \mathbf{F}, \tag{5.2.2}$$

where $\mathbf{F}$ is the force applied; obviously if $\mathbf{F}$ lies along $\mathbf{r}$ there is no change in $\mathbf{L}$.

When $\mathbf{F}$ does not coincide with $\mathbf{r}$, the change in angular momentum is

$$\Delta\mathbf{L} = \int (\mathbf{r} \times \mathbf{F})dt, \tag{5.2.3}$$

*For cases where there is no clear dominance of any one force, there often is no substitute for numerical integration to produce acceptable results.

where the integral will be evaluated over some appropriate time interval. Now we may write

$$dt = \frac{d\theta}{\dot{\theta}},$$

where $\dot{\theta}$ is the angular rate of motion in the unperturbed orbit, that is,

$$\dot{\theta}^2 = \mu/r_0^3,$$

with r_0 being the radius of the assumed circular undisturbed orbit. Hence (5.2.3) becomes

$$\Delta\mathbf{L} = \frac{1}{\dot{\theta}}\int(\mathbf{r}\times\mathbf{F})d\theta. \tag{5.2.4}$$

Equation (5.2.4) suggests that, as a first approximation, we express **r** and **F** in terms of the unperturbed position angle of the orbit; the errors so committed are obviously small relative to the effects we are calculating, as long as those effects themselves remain within bounds.

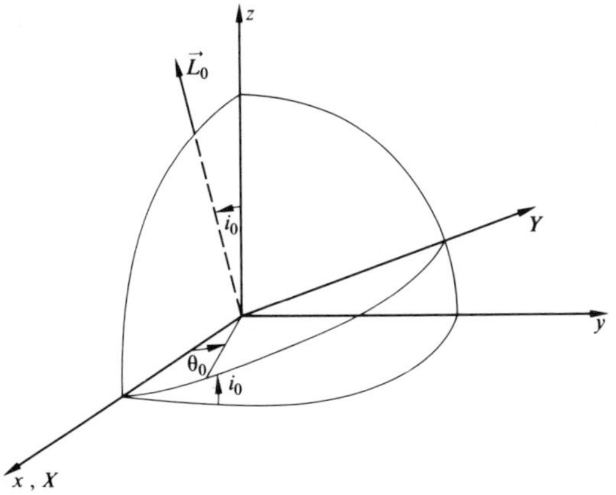

Figure 5.1

The components of $\Delta\mathbf{L}$ indicate the change in the orientation of the orbit. Let us set, in this case, the x axis along the unperturbed line of nodes. (See Fig. 5.1.) Then it is easy to show that

$$L\cos i = \mathbf{a}_z\cdot\mathbf{L}; \qquad L\sin i\sin\Omega = |(\mathbf{a}_z\times\mathbf{L})\times\mathbf{a}_x|; \qquad L\sin i\cos\Omega = \mathbf{a}_z\times\mathbf{L}\cdot\mathbf{a}_x, \tag{5.2.5}$$

where $\mathbf{a}_x$, $\mathbf{a}_y$, $\mathbf{a}_z$ are unit vectors along the inertial axes. For a given $\Delta\mathbf{L}$ we can write

$$\mathbf{L} = \mathbf{a}_x(\Delta L_x) + \mathbf{a}_y(-L_0\sin i_0+\Delta L_y) + \mathbf{a}_z(L_0\cos i_0+\Delta L_z).$$

Carrying out the operations indicated in (5.2.5), setting $i = i_0 + \Delta i$, $L = L_0 + \Delta L$, $\Omega = \Delta\Omega$, and assuming Δi, ΔL, $\Delta\Omega$ are small,* we obtain

$$\Delta L = \Delta L_z \cos i_0 - \Delta L_y \sin i_0,$$

$$\Delta i = -\frac{\Delta L_y \cos i_0 + \Delta L_z \sin i_0}{L_0}, \tag{5.2.6}$$

$$\Delta\Omega = \frac{\Delta L_x}{L_0 \sin i_0}. \tag{5.2.7}$$

Equations (5.2.6) and (5.2.7) relate the changes in angular momentum to the changes in orientation of the orbit plane. The $\mathbf{\Delta L}$ may be found by (5.2.4), where, for example, we may integrate over one revolution†, i.e., from $\theta = 0$ to $\theta = 2\pi$.

2.2. Perturbative Effects in the Undisturbed Orbit Plane

Now let us look at the motion of the satellite as projected on its initial orbit plane. Since we are interested in the departures from circularity, it is convenient to employ the relative coordinate system ξ, η, ζ we introduced in Chapter 4. We have (see Figs. 5.1 and 5.2),

$$X = (r_0 + \xi)\cos\theta - \eta \sin\theta, \qquad Y = (r_0 + \xi)\sin\theta + \eta\cos\theta,$$

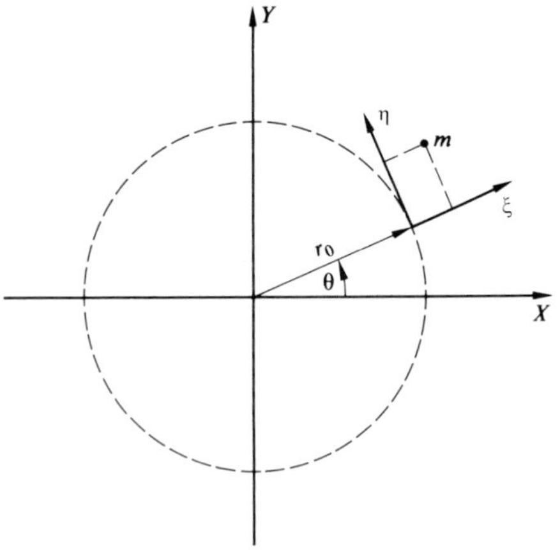

Figure 5.2

*As mentioned, if the perturbing forces are small, the changes in these elements over a reasonable period should also be small.

†By calculating ΔL for one revolution and dividing the results for Δi and $\Delta\Omega$ by the period T we obtain mean rates of change in i and Ω. The notion of *averaging* perturbations over one period is intuitively obvious; a more formal treatment of this idea, leading to so-called averaging methods, is a separate subject.

and, thus, in the X,Y plane, the kinetic energy of the satellite is

$$W = \frac{m}{2}(\dot{X}^2+\dot{Y}^2)$$

$$= \frac{m}{2}\left\{\dot{\theta}^2\left[(r_0+\xi)^2+\eta^2\right]+\dot{\xi}^2+\dot{\eta}^2+2\dot{\theta}[(r_0+\xi)\dot{\eta}-\eta\dot{\xi}]\right. , \tag{5.2.8}$$

where m is the satellite's mass, r_0 is the radius of the unperturbed orbit, and $\dot{\theta}$ is the (mean) motion in the unperturbed orbit.

Now the work done by a force over some arc of the orbit is $\Delta W = \int \mathbf{F}\cdot d\mathbf{s}$, where $d\mathbf{s}$ is the linear displacement of the satellite. This relation can also be written

$$\dot{W} = \mathbf{F}\cdot\mathbf{v}. \tag{5.2.9}$$

The total force $\mathbf{F}$ may be resolved into that arising from central gravity and that arising from other causes. We have

$$F_X = -\frac{\mu m X}{[(r_0+\xi)^2+\eta^2]^{3/2}} + \tilde{F}_X, \qquad F_Y = -\frac{\mu m Y}{[(r_0+\xi)^2+\eta^2]^{3/2}} + \tilde{F}_Y,$$

where $\tilde{F}$ is the perturbation; in place of $\tilde{F}_X$ and $\tilde{F}_Y$, it is better to use

$$F_r = \tilde{F}_X \cos\theta + \tilde{F}_Y \sin\theta, \qquad F_t = -\tilde{F}_X \sin\theta + \tilde{F}_Y \cos\theta, \tag{5.2.10}$$

where F_r is the radial component of the perturbing force, and F_t is the tangential component. Utilizing (5.2.8) and (5.2.9) yields

$$m\{\dot{\theta}^2[(r_0+\xi)\dot{\xi}+\eta\dot{\eta}] + \dot{\xi}\ddot{\xi} + \dot{\eta}\ddot{\eta} + \dot{\theta}[(r_0+\xi)\ddot{\eta}-\eta\ddot{\xi}]\}$$

$$= -\frac{\mu m[(r_0+\xi)\dot{\xi}+\eta\dot{\eta}]}{[(r_0+\xi)^2+\eta^2]^{3/2}} + F_r[\dot{\xi}-\dot{\theta}\eta] + F_t[(r_0+\xi)\dot{\theta}+\dot{\eta}], \tag{5.2.11}$$

remembering that $\dot{r}_0 = \ddot{\theta} = 0$, and $\dot{\theta}^2 = \mu/r_0^3$. We again change to θ as the independent variable by virtue of

$$d/dt = \dot{\theta}\, d/d\theta, \tag{5.2.12}$$

and further note the expansion

$$\frac{1}{m\dot{\theta}^2}\frac{\mu m}{[(r_0+\xi)^2+\eta^2]^{3/2}} = 1 - 3\frac{\xi}{r_0} + 6\frac{\xi^2}{r_0^2} - \frac{3}{2}\frac{\eta^2}{r_0^2} + \cdots$$

$$\equiv 1 + \Delta,$$

where Δ is a small quantity as long as the departures (ξ, η) from circularity are small compared to r_0. Then (5.2.11) becomes

$$(r_0+\xi+\eta')\left[\eta'' - \frac{F_t}{\dot{\theta}^2} + \xi'(2+\Delta)\right] = (\eta-\xi')\left[\xi'' - \frac{F_r}{\dot{\theta}^2} - \eta'(2+\Delta)\right], \tag{5.2.13}$$

where a prime denotes differentiation with respect to θ.

Now, from (5.2.1),

$$L_Z = m[(r_0+\xi)(r_0\dot{\theta}+\xi\dot{\theta}+\dot{\eta}) - \eta(\dot{\xi}-\eta\dot{\theta})]; \tag{5.2.14}$$

from this, using (5.2.2) and (5.2.12), we obtain

$$(r_0+\xi)(\eta''-F_t/\dot{\theta}^2+2\xi') = \eta(\xi''-F_r/\dot{\theta}^2-2\eta'). \tag{5.2.15}$$

Considering (5.2.13) and (5.2.15) as simultaneous equations in ξ'', η'', we find

$$\xi'' - 2\eta' - F_r/\dot{\theta}^2 = -(r_0+\xi)\Delta, \qquad \eta'' + 2\xi' - F_t/\dot{\theta}^2 = -\eta\Delta.$$

Now $-(r_0+\xi)\Delta = 3\xi - 3\xi(\xi/r_0) + 3/2\eta(\eta/r_0) - \cdots$; the second and succeeding terms on the right-hand side, being quite small compared to ξ, may be ignored in this elementary analysis. Further, $-\eta\Delta = 3\eta(\xi/r_0) - \cdots$ yields terms similarly negligible. Thus,

$$\xi'' - 2\eta' - 3\xi = r_0^3F_r/\mu m, \tag{5.2.16}$$

$$\eta'' + 2\xi' = r_0^3F_t/\mu m. \tag{5.2.17}$$

We note that if $F_r = F_t = 0$, these become the first two of (4.8.5). In terms of the x, y, z components of the perturbing force, we have

$$\begin{aligned} F_r &= F_x \cos\theta + (F_y \cos i + F_z \sin i)\sin\theta; \\ F_t &= -F_x \sin\theta + (F_y \cos i + F_z \sin i)\cos\theta. \end{aligned} \tag{5.2.18}$$

3. AN EXAMINATION OF VARIOUS PERTURBING FORCES

To illustrate the use of the method outlined in Section 2, we now turn to some concrete examples of disturbing forces. Since we shall use these forces repeatedly in examples of perturbation techniques, we discuss each in some detail, applying the results of Section 2.

3.1. Perturbation by Third Ponderable Body

The Force. The most celebrated of perturbing forces, at least in classical astronomy, is that due to the gravitational effect of bodies other than the central mass. If we consider an artificial earth satellite, then the third body could be the moon, sun, or any of the other planets. Corresponding problems of classical astronomy involve the theory of lunar motion, subject to solar and planetary perturbations, and the theories for each of the planets subject to perturbations from all the others.

We have derived the equations of motion for the n-body problem in Chapter 1, and repeat one of these here with a slight change in notation, for convenience.

$$m_i\ddot{X}_i = -\sum_{j\neq i} \frac{Gm_i m_j(X_i - X_j)}{r_{ij}^3}, \tag{5.3.1}$$

where m_i is the mass of the ith body, X_i is one of its coordinates, G is the universal gravitational constant, and

$$r_{ij}^2 = (X_i - X_j)^2 + (Y_i - Y_j)^2 + (Z_i - Z_j)^2. \tag{5.3.2}$$

Now if m_j is a particular body of interest in the system, we may choose to express the motions of the other bodies in reference to its position.* Thus, let

$$\left.\begin{aligned} x_i &= X_i - X_j, \\ y_i &= Y_i - Y_j, \\ z_i &= Z_i - Z_j. \end{aligned}\right\} \quad (i\neq j). \tag{5.3.3}$$

Equation (5.3.1) can be written in the form

$$\ddot{X}_i = -Gm_j\frac{X_i - X_j}{r_{ij}^3} - G\sum_{k\neq i,j} m_k\frac{X_i - X_k}{r_{ik}^3},$$

and, similarly,

$$\ddot{X}_j = -Gm_i\frac{X_j - X_i}{r_{ij}^3} - G\sum_{k\neq i,j} m_k\frac{X_j - X_k}{r_{jk}^3}.$$

Using (5.3.3)

$$\ddot{X}_i = -Gm_j\frac{x_i}{r_{ij}^3} - G\sum_{k\neq i,j} m_k\frac{x_i - x_k}{r_{ik}^3}, \qquad \ddot{X}_j = Gm_i\frac{x_i}{r_{ij}^3} + G\sum_{k\neq i,j} m_k\frac{x_k}{r_{jk}^3}.$$

If we subtract the second of these equations from the first, and note that $\ddot{x}_i = \ddot{X}_i - \ddot{X}_j$,

$$\ddot{x}_i + G(m_i + m_j)\frac{x_i}{r_{ij}^3} = -G\sum_{k\neq i,j} m_k\left(\frac{x_i - x_k}{r_{ik}^3} + \frac{x_k}{r_{jk}^3}\right). \tag{5.3.4}$$

---

*We have already seen that if $m_j \gg m_i$, the center of mass will lie very close to the position of the jth body and this body is a preferred choice for the origin of coordinates.

Equation (5.3.4) with its y and z counterparts represents the equations of motion of the ith body referred to the position of the jth.

In order to express the perturbation due to other masses in the preferred classical form we note that $r_{ik}^2 = (x_i - x_k)^2 + (y_i - y_k)^2 + (z_i - z_k)^2$, and thus,

$$\frac{\partial}{\partial x_i}\left(\frac{1}{r_{ik}}\right) = -\frac{1}{r_{ik}^3}(x_i - x_k). \tag{5.3.5}$$

Further,

$$\frac{\partial}{\partial x_i}\left(\frac{x_i x_k}{r_{jk}^3}\right) = \frac{x_k}{r_{jk}^3},$$

or, more generally,

$$\frac{\partial}{\partial x_i}\left(\frac{x_i x_k + y_i y_k + z_i z_k}{r_{jk}^3}\right) = \frac{x_k}{r_{jk}^3}. \tag{5.3.6}$$

Equation (5.3.4) may then be cast into the form

$$\ddot{x}_i + G(m_i + m_j)x_i/r_{ij}^3 = \partial\tilde{R}/\partial x_i, \tag{5.3.7}$$

where the corresponding equations in y_i and z_i are analogous and

$$\tilde{R} = G \sum_{k \neq i,j} m_k \left(\frac{1}{r_{ik}} - \frac{x_i x_k + y_i y_k + z_i z_k}{r_{jk}^3}\right). \tag{5.3.8}$$

$\tilde{R}$ is known as the *disturbing function* since it contributes the terms in (5.3.4) that are not present in the two-body problem. Note that $\partial\tilde{R}/\partial x_i$ plays the role of the x component of the perturbing force (per unit mass); we may thus interpret $\tilde{R}$ as the negative of the perturbing potential (per unit mass).

Now the magnitude of the partial derivatives of $\tilde{R}$ is of the order $Gm_p r/r_p^3$ (where we have simplified the notation so that r denotes the distance of the perturbed body from the primary mass and r_p the distance of the perturbing body from the primary). The ratio of the perturbing force to the central gravity term is then

$$\frac{Gm_p r/r_p^3}{Gm_E/r^2} = \frac{m_p}{m_E}\frac{r^3}{r_p^3},$$

where m_E is the mass of the primary. Considering the case of an artificial earth satellite, let us assume that r is of the order 3.7×10^4 km (approximately the value for a 24-hour satellite). The relative importance of all extraterrestrial attractions on such a satellite is shown in the following table.

Perturbing body	m_p/m_E	r_p(km); [min]	$m_p r^3/m_E r_p^3$; [max]
Moon	1.2×10^{-2}	3.9×10^5	1.1×10^{-5}
Sun	3.3×10^5	1.5×10^8	2.9×10^{-6}
Mercury	5.4×10^{-2}	9.3×10^7	3.4×10^{-12}
Venus	8.1×10^{-1}	4.3×10^7	5.5×10^{-10}
Mars	1.1×10^{-1}	7.2×10^7	1.8×10^{-11}
Jupiter	3.2×10^2	6.3×10^8	6.4×10^{-11}
Saturn	9.5×10	1.3×10^9	2.2×10^{-12}
Uranus	1.4×10	2.8×10^9	3.3×10^{-14}
Neptune	1.7×10	4.3×10^9	1.1×10^{-14}
Pluto	8.3×10^{-1}	5.6×10^9	2.4×10^{-16}

The values of these ratios become smaller as the satellite is taken nearer the earth. (The figures given in this table are approximate and intended only to exhibit order-of-magnitude relations.)

The Effect on a Nominally Circular Orbit. In view of the simplifications used in Section 2, we will restrict ourselves here to investigation of the effect of the perturbing mass over a time interval equivalent to a few revolutions of an earth satellite. In such a case, we may consider the disturbing body as stationary in its orbit. Taking its mass as m_p, we have from (5.3.8)

$$\tilde{R} = Gm_p\left\{\frac{1}{[(x-x_p)^2 + (y-y_p)^2 + (z-z_p)^2]^{1/2}} - \frac{xx_p+yy_p+zz_p}{r_p^3}\right\},$$

where x, y, z are the coordinates of the satellite and $r_p^2 = x_p^2 + y_p^2 + z_p^2$. Then

$$F_x = m\frac{\partial \tilde{R}}{\partial x} = -Gmm_p\left\{\frac{x-x_p}{[r^2 - 2(xx_p+yy_p+zz_p) + r_p^2]^{3/2}} + \frac{x_p}{r_p^3}\right\},$$

with similar expressions for F_y and F_z. Now, $r \ll r_p$, so that we obtain

$$F_x \simeq -\frac{Gmm_p}{r_p^3}\left\{x - 3x_p\frac{xx_p+yy_p+zz_p}{r_p^2}\right\}. \tag{5.3.9}$$

It is evident that perturbing effects depend only on the relative positions of disturbed and disturbing bodies; thus, to simplify the analysis, let us choose $z_p = 0$. We can then consider different initial inclinations of the satellite orbit in order to investigate various relative geometries. Thus we set (Fig. 5.3)

$$x_p = r_p \cos\alpha; \qquad y_p = r_p \sin\alpha. \tag{5.3.10}$$

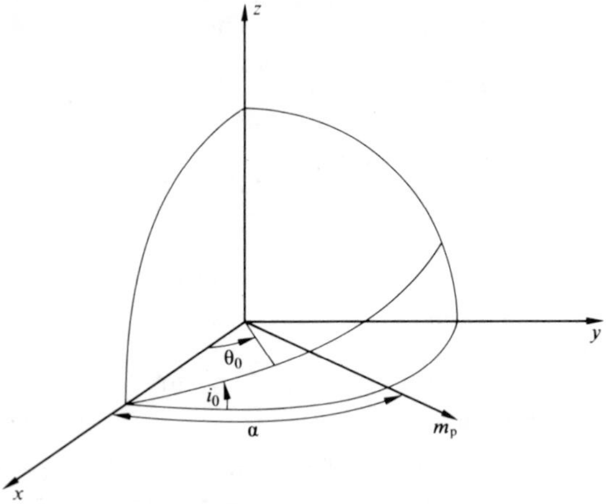

Figure 5.3

Further, we have

$$\begin{aligned} x &= (r_0+\xi)\cos\theta - \eta\sin\theta; \\ y &= [(r_0+\xi)\sin\theta+\eta\cos\theta]\cos i_0 - \zeta\sin i_0; \\ z &= [(r_0+\xi)\sin\theta+\eta\cos\theta]\sin i_0 + \zeta\cos i_0, \end{aligned} \tag{5.3.11}$$

where ξ, η, ζ express the departure from circularity due to the perturbation. However, over the interval of investigation we expect these deviations to be so small that they do not truly affect the magnitude of the perturbing force, which is itself small. For the coordinates as they enter the force expression we may use

$$x \simeq r_0\cos\theta; \qquad y \simeq r_0\sin\theta\cos i_0; \qquad z \simeq r_0\sin\theta\sin i_0. \tag{5.3.12}$$

Equation (5.3.9) then becomes, to good approximation,

$$F_x = -\frac{Gmm_p}{r_p^3}r_0\{(1-3\cos^2\alpha)\cos\theta - 3\cos i_0\sin\alpha\cos\alpha\sin\theta\}.$$

Similarly,

$$F_y = -\frac{Gmm_p}{r_p^3}r_0\{(1-3\sin^2\alpha)\cos i_0\sin\theta - 3\sin\alpha\cos\alpha\cos\theta\},$$

and

$$F_z = -\frac{Gmm_p}{r_p^3}r_0\{\sin i_0\sin\theta\}.$$

As a result

$$(\mathbf{r}\times\mathbf{F})_x = -\frac{3Gmm_pr_0^2}{r_p^3}\sin i_0\sin\alpha\{\cos i_0\sin^2\theta + \cos\alpha\sin\theta\cos\theta\}.$$

From (5.2.4), integrating from $\theta = \theta_0$ to $\theta = \theta_0 + 2\pi$,

$$\Delta L_x = -\frac{3Gmm_p r_0^2}{\dot{\theta} r_p^3} \pi \sin i_0 \cos i_0 \sin^2\alpha.$$

Likewise

$$\Delta L_y = \frac{3Gmm_p r_0^2}{\dot{\theta} r_p^3} \pi \sin i_0 \cos i_0 \sin\alpha \cos\alpha,$$

and

$$\Delta L_z = \frac{3Gmm_p r_0^2}{\dot{\theta} r_p^3} \pi \sin^2 i_0 \sin\alpha \cos\alpha.$$

Since $L_0 = m\dot{\theta} r_0^2$, we obtain from (5.2.6)

$$\Delta i \equiv i_{2\pi} - i_0 = -\frac{3m_p r_0^3}{m_E r_p^3} \pi \sin i_0 \sin\alpha \cos\alpha, \qquad (5.3.13)$$

where m_E is the mass of the earth. From (5.2.7)

$$\Delta\Omega = -\frac{3m_p r_0^3}{m_E r_p^3} \pi \cos i_0 \sin^2\alpha. \qquad (5.3.14)$$

We will pause here to examine these results, which express the change in the orientation of the orbit plane after one complete revolution of the satellite. As might have been expected, (5.3.13) predicts no change in inclination if the perturbing body lies in the plane of the orbit ($i_0 = 0$); moreover, when $i_0 \neq 0$, we see that the inclination decreases if α lies in the first and third quadrants but increases otherwise. Since, in fact, the perturbing body is in motion and α will, in time, take on all values between zero and 2π, we can expect that the changes in i will largely cancel over long intervals of time.

On the other hand, (5.3.14) shows that the longitude of the node changes without limit as time goes on unless, of course, $i_0 = 90°$. Indeed, averaging $\sin^2\alpha$ over the range $\alpha = 0$ to $\alpha = 2\pi$ yields

$$\Delta\Omega_{av} = -\frac{3m_p r_0^3}{2m_E r_p^3} \pi \cos i_0;$$

and thus the mean rate of this precession is* $\dot{\Omega}_{av} = \Delta\Omega_{av}/T = -3\sqrt{\mu r_0^3}\cos i_0/4r_p^3 m_E$. As an example, let us consider a synchronous satellite ($T = 24$ h) at an inclination of 20° to the equator; if we take the perturbing body to be the moon at declination

*One can visualize this regression easily by considering a simple geometry like $\alpha = \pi/2$ and observing that the *net torque* exerted by the body P on the satellite orbit is counterclockwise about the (positive) x axis. Thence, the counterclockwise precession of the momentum vector L about the (positive) y axis, and hence the regression of the nodes, follows immediately.

zero, then $\Delta\Omega_{\max} = -1.4 \times 10^{-5}$ radian per revolution, while $\dot{\Omega}_{av} = -4.2 \times 10^{-10}$ rad/sec. The effect of the sun is somewhat less and that of the planets still smaller.

Turning now to the effect in the initial orbit plane, (5.2.16) and (5.2.17) yield, using (5.2.18),

$$\xi = \frac{m_p r_0^4}{m_E r_p^3}\{A \cos 2\theta - \frac{3}{2} B \sin 2\theta - C\} + 2K_1 + K_2 \cos\theta + K_3 \sin\theta, \tag{5.3.15}$$

$$\eta = \frac{m_p r_0^4}{m_E r_p^3}\{\frac{1}{4} A\,(3\theta - \frac{11}{2}\sin 2\theta) - \frac{9}{4} B \cos 2\theta + 2C\theta\}$$
$$-3K_1\theta - 2K_2 \sin\theta + 2K_3 \cos\theta + K_4, \tag{5.3.16}$$

where

$$A = \cos^2 i_0 \sin^2\alpha - \cos^2\alpha; \qquad B = \cos i_0 \sin\alpha \cos\alpha; \qquad C = 1 - 3\cos^2 i_0 \sin^2\alpha; \tag{5.3.17}$$

and K_1, K_2, K_3, K_4 are constants of integration. The terms involving these constants are recognized as the complementary solution discussed in Chapter 4 and represent the effects of the initial conditions. We may imagine these are chosen such that $K_1 = K_2 = K_3 = K_4 = 0$ and that we have only the particular solution in (5.3.15) and (5.3.16) to consider. To appreciate the geometric features of this solution, let $i = 0$ and $\alpha = \pi/2$. Then

$$\xi = \frac{m_p r_0^4}{m_E r_p^3}\{\cos 2\theta + 2\}, \qquad \eta = \frac{m_p r_0^4}{m_E r_p^3}\{-\frac{13}{4}\theta - \frac{11}{8}\sin 2\theta\}.$$

The ξ equation shows that the perturbing body, which is located on the y axis (see Fig. 5.3), causes the satellite orbit to be elongated in the x direction, i.e., normal to the direction to m_p, and foreshortened in the y direction. The radial response of the orbiting body is reminiscent of a linear oscillator, since the maximum outward acceleration experienced by the body on the y axis is coincident with the maximum inward displacement there, etc. For a synchronous satellite, the periodic perturbations due to the moon have amplitudes in the order of 2 km.

In the tangential direction, η has a cumulative term which grows without limit. These same effects also arise if we let $i \neq 0$ and permit the perturbing body to move, but such refinements take us beyond the scope of the present discussion. We must also keep in mind that our entire approach is based on the conditions $\xi/r_0 \ll 1$, $\eta/r_0 \ll 1$, and that as soon as either of these no longer holds, our linearizations cease to be valid.

3.2. Perturbation by Primary Body's Asphericity

The Force. Most natural celestial bodies are not precisely spherical. As a consequence, further terms appear in the gravitational potential of such bodies, in addition to the fundamental term representing spherically symmetric attraction. For example, if we consider the earth, which is approximated reasonably well by an oblate spheroid, the gravitational potential can be expressed as

$$V = -\frac{\mu}{r}\left[1 + \frac{J_2}{2}\frac{R^2}{r^2}(1-3\sin^2\varphi') + \frac{J_3}{2}\frac{R^3}{r^3}(3\sin\varphi' - 5\sin^3\varphi') + \frac{J_4}{8}\frac{R^4}{r^4}(3-30\sin^2\varphi' + 35\sin^4\varphi') + \cdots\right], \tag{5.3.18}$$

where r and φ' are the radial distance and geocentric latitude, respectively, of the point in question and R, J_2, J_3, J_4 are constants. A good survey of research concerning the earth's figure and potential field, including an extensive bibliography, is given in [2]. A set of values for the governing constants widely accepted at this time is the following:

$$R = 6.3381778 \times 10^6 \text{ m (equatorial radius of earth)},$$
$$J_2 = 1.08260 \times 10^{-3},$$
$$J_3 = -2.500 \times 10^{-6},$$
$$J_4 = 1.800 \times 10^{-6}.$$

The force (per unit mass) is given by the appropriate derivative of (5.3.18); the first term leads to μ/r^2. The next yields an additional force of order $J_2\mu R^2/2r^4$. The ratio of these terms is $J_2R^2/2r^2$, which always has a value less than J_2, since $r > R$. Corresponding ratios of terms involving J_3 and J_4 are smaller still.

The Effect on a Nominally Circular Orbit. The predominant gravitational term arising from the nonspherical character of the earth gives rise to the following perturbing force:

$$F_x = -m\frac{\partial V}{\partial x} = -\frac{3J_2\mu R^2 mx}{2r^5}\left(1 - \frac{5z^2}{r^2}\right),$$
$$F_y = -\frac{3J_2\mu R^2 my}{2r^5}\left(1 - \frac{5z^2}{r^2}\right), \tag{5.3.19}$$
$$F_z = -\frac{3J_2\mu R^2 mz}{2r^5}\left(3 - \frac{5z^2}{r^2}\right),$$

where we have used $\sin\varphi' = z/r$. Substituting (5.3.12) and employing (5.2.4), we find, integrating from $\theta = \theta_0$ to $\theta_0 + 2\pi$,

$$\Delta L_x = -3\pi J_2\mu R^2 m \sin i_0 \cos i_0/\dot{\theta} r_0^3, \qquad \Delta L_y = \Delta L_z = 0.$$

Then (5.2.6) and (5.2.7) yield

$$\Delta i = 0, \qquad \Delta\Omega = -\frac{3\pi J_2 R^2 \cos i_0}{r_0^2}. \tag{5.3.20}$$

This last expresses the well-known *regression of the nodes*; the mean rate of this negative precession is given by

$$\dot{\Omega}_{av} = \frac{\Delta\Omega}{T} = -\frac{3J_2R^2}{2}\sqrt{\frac{\mu}{r_0^7}}\cos i_0,$$

and we shall see later that this is indeed the dominating term in nodal perturbations obtained from more elaborate analyses.*

As an example, let us consider the effects on orbits with $r_0 = R+185$ and $R+1850$ km both inclined at 45° to the equator. For the former we find $\dot{\Omega} = -1.4\times10^{-6}$ rad/sec, and for the latter $\dot{\Omega} = -5.9\times10^{-7}$ rad/sec. The time for a complete revolution of the nodes amounts to 54 days for the lower orbit and to 123 days for the other case.

The in-plane perturbations for this case may be found in a straightforward manner by (5.2.16) through (5.2.18). Since they apply to nominally-circular orbits, no apsidal precession is exhibited; we shall not display the results here.

3.3. Perturbation by Atmospheric Resistance

The Force. The force (per unit mass) due to the resistance of the air to the passage of a vehicle of mass m can be written as

$$F_D = -C_D A\rho v_a^2/2m. \tag{5.3.21}$$

Here, C_D is the nondimensional *drag coefficient*, A is the cross-sectional area of the vehicle in the direction of motion, ρ is the atmospheric density, and v_a is the speed of the vehicle relative to the atmosphere.

At satellite speeds and altitudes, a recommended value of C_D is about 2; for a tumbling, nonspherical vehicle A may be approximated by $A_T/4$, where A_T is the total surface area [3]. A more recent study is reported in [4].

The quantity ρ may be expressed as an exponential function of the altitude, h, in question. A reasonable form is

$$\rho = \bar{\rho}\exp\left[-B\frac{h}{1+h/R}\right], \tag{5.3.22}$$

where $\bar{\rho}$ and B are constants in a given altitude band and R is the earth's equatorial radius. Various density profiles exist; a reasonable but by no means most recent one has been compiled by the Air Research and Development Command of the U.S. Air Force [5] into what has become known as the "ARDC 1959 Atmosphere" for which a fit of the form (5.3.22) leads to the values of $\bar{\rho}$ and B given in the table below. For an alternative, consult [6].

---

*Once again the geometric interpretation of this effect follows from the counterclockwise torque about the x axis resulting from the integral of (5.2.4) over one period. **L** precesses about the z axis in a counterclockwise direction, giving rise to the nodal regression.

Altitude Band (m)	$\bar{\rho}$ (kg/m^3)	B (m^{-1})
3×10^4—1.2×10^5	2.2	1.6×10^{-4}
1.2×10^5—1.8×10^5	4.3×10^{-6}	5.3×10^{-5}
1.8×10^5— 3×10^5	2.2×10^{-8}	2.1×10^{-5}
3×10^5—7.5×10^5	4.1×10^{-9}	1.5×10^{-5}
7.5×10^5—	2.3×10^{-11}	7.9×10^{-6}

The representation of atmospheric density by a time-invariant, spherically symmetric form such as (5.3.22) is admittedly an idealization, especially since we recognize such effects as the oblateness of the atmosphere, the effects of solar heating and of convective currents, as well as transient phenomena due to solar activity. However, quantitative information on these features is yet quite fragmentary [7]; moreover, the motion of a satellite carries it through the day and night sides of the earth, and the summer and winter hemispheres (if the orbit is inclined) each period. If (5.3.22) represents an "average" over such conditions, it tends to provide a useful estimate; at this stage, our ignorance of the dynamics of the atmosphere precludes asking for more.

The quantity v_a of (5.3.21), as noted, denotes the speed of the vehicle relative to the atmosphere, presumed rotating with the earth. If we indicate the earth's rotational rate by σ, the velocity of the atmosphere, always directed eastward, is given by

$$V = r\sigma \cos \varphi', \tag{5.3.23}$$

where r and φ' are the geocentric distance and latitude of the point in question. Here we ignore the possibility that the atmosphere at higher altitudes may "fall behind" the earth's rotation. In fact, one may often neglect the atmospheric rotation altogether, in which case v_a represents the satellite's inertial velocity. By so doing, we rarely cause errors in F_D exceeding 10%.

It should also be noted that the second-power drag law used in (5.3.21) is not beyond criticism. Some investigators believe that the drag force, in the highly rarefied strata of the atmosphere, may be more nearly proportional to the first power of v_a. At present general consensus favors (5.3.21).

If the inertial velocity of the satellite is denoted by $\mathbf{v}$, then $\mathbf{v}_a = \mathbf{v} - \mathbf{V}$ and the unit vector in a sense opposite $\mathbf{v}_a$ is $(\mathbf{V}-\mathbf{v})/|\mathbf{V}-\mathbf{v}|$, which indicates the direction of the drag force in inertial space. To express (5.3.21) as a vector, we write

$$\mathbf{F}_D = \frac{C_D A}{2m}\rho\,|\mathbf{V}-\mathbf{v}|\,(\mathbf{V}-\mathbf{v})$$

$$\simeq \frac{C_D A}{2m}\rho v(\mathbf{V}-\mathbf{v}), \tag{5.3.24}$$

where the latter form is a reasonable approximation, since usually $|V| \ll |v|$.

For purposes of numerical evaluation, let us take a satellite in a circular orbit at 160 km altitude. We find $\rho \simeq 7.7 \times 10^{-10}$ kg/m^3. The satellite velocity is of the order of 7.9×10^3 m/sec and the maximum value of the speed of the air ($\varphi' = 0$) is about 4.9×10^2 m/sec, using $\sigma = 7.29212 \times 10^{-5}$ rad/sec. For an aluminized balloon of the type used in Project Echo, which has about the greatest area-to-mass ratio obtainable, we find $C_D A/2m \simeq 13$ m^2/kg. Thus $F_D \simeq 0.53$ m/sec^2, whereas $\mu/r^2 \simeq 8.8$ m/sec^2. The ratio of forces is about 0.06; this will be even less for satellites with smaller A/m or for those at greater altitudes.

The Effect on a Nominally Circular Orbit. In terms of the geometry of Fig. 5.4, the relative velocity is given by $v_a^2 = (\dot{x} - \dot{X})^2 + (\dot{y} - \dot{Y})^2 + \dot{z}^2$, where $\dot{x}, \dot{y}, \dot{z}$ may be determined from Eq. (5.3.12) and $\dot{X}$ and $\dot{Y}$ are the components of **V**, that is, $\dot{X} = -r_0 \sigma \cos i_0 \sin \theta$, $\dot{Y} = r_0 \sigma \cos \theta$. We then have

$$v_a^2 = r_0^2 \dot{\theta}^2 - 2 r_0^2 \dot{\theta} \sigma \cos i_0 + r_0^2 \sigma^2 (\cos^2 i_0 \sin^2 \theta + \cos^2 \theta).$$

However, as we have pointed out, the ratio $\sigma/\dot{\theta}$ is normally very small, and thus

$$v_a \simeq r_0 \dot{\theta} (1 - \sigma \cos i_0 / \dot{\theta}), \tag{5.3.25}$$

where $\dot{\theta} = \sqrt{\mu / r_0^3}$.

Equation (5.3.24) thus leads to

$$\begin{aligned} F_x &= \frac{C_D A}{2} \rho r_0^2 \dot{\theta}^2 \left(1 - 2 \frac{\sigma}{\dot{\theta}} \cos i_0 \right) \sin \theta, \\ F_y &= -\frac{C_D A}{2} \rho r_0^2 \dot{\theta}^2 \left[\cos i_0 - \frac{\sigma}{\dot{\theta}} \left(1 + \cos^2 i_0 \right) \right] \cos \theta, \\ F_z &= -\frac{C_D A}{2} \rho r_0^2 \dot{\theta}^2 \sin i \left(1 - \frac{\sigma}{\dot{\theta}} \cos i_0 \right) \cos \theta. \end{aligned} \tag{5.3.26}$$

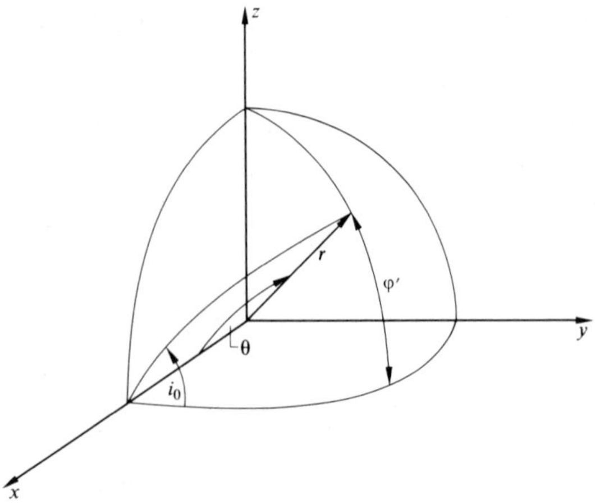

Figure 5.4

The atmospheric density may, in this case, be treated as constant since, for (5.3.22), we have $h = r-R = r_0+\xi-R \simeq r_0-R = h_0$. Equations (5.2.6) and (5.2.7) then yield

$$\Delta i = -\frac{C_D A}{2m}\rho\pi r_0 \frac{\sigma}{\dot{\theta}}\sin i_0, \qquad \Delta\Omega = 0, \tag{5.3.27}$$

as the changes per revolution. We see that the tendency is to reduce the inclination of the orbit,* although this is a very small effect since it depends on $\sigma/\dot{\theta}$.

The solutions of (5.2.16) and (5.2.17) provide us with

$$\xi = -\frac{C_D A}{m}\rho r_0^2\left(1-2\frac{\sigma}{\dot{\theta}}\cos i_0\right)\theta,$$

$$\eta = \frac{C_D A}{m}\rho r_0^2\left(1-2\frac{\sigma}{\dot{\theta}}\cos i_0\right)\left(\frac{3}{4}\theta^2-2\right),$$

where again we have set the constants of integration to zero. It is easy to see the significance of the equation for ξ: the radial departure grows (negatively) as time goes on. This is the well-known "spiral decay" of orbits acted on by drag. The term involving θ^2 in the η equation is also interesting; the rapid increase in η indicates that, although atmospheric resistance acts to retard the satellite, the result is a "speeding up" of the body. This seeming paradox is also well known.

3.4. Perturbation by Solar Radiation Pressure

The Force. When photons impinge on a surface they impart a pressure, or force per unit area, on the surface. A simple way to compute this force is as follows. The *solar constant*, defined as the amount of radiant energy intercepted by a unit area per unit time at the earth's distance from the sun, has a value of about two calories per square centimeter per minute, or about 1.4×10^3 joules m^{-2}sec^{-1}. Since the radiation travels outward from the sun with (essentially) spherical symmetry, we may write the expression for the energy per unit area per second as $E_p = K/4\pi r_S^2$, where r_S is the distance from the sun and K is chosen so that E_p has the proper value at one astronomic unit. We find

$$E_p = 4\times10^{30}/4\pi r_S^2 \text{ joules/m}^2\text{sec}.$$

Now the momentum carried per unit area per unit time in such a case is simply E_p/c, where c is the velocity of light. When photons strike a surface, some may be absorbed and the remaining fraction reflected; if we represent that fraction by β, then the total momentum per second received by a unit surface placed normal to the radiation is $(1+\beta)E_p/c$, where β is called the *reflectivity*. The time

*This time the "net torque" resulting from (5.2.4) is clockwise about the (positive) z axis, tending to align **L** with that axis and thus decreasing the inclination.

rate of change of momentum being the force, this is also the radiation pressure. The total force acting on a given body must, strictly speaking, follow from the appropriate surface integral. However, for a simple approximation, one may use

$$F_p/A = (1+\beta)E_p/c, \tag{5.3.28}$$

where A is the total area of the surface normal to the direction of radiation and F_p the resultant pressure force. The latter is, finally,

$$F_p = 4\times 10^{33}(1+\beta)A/4\pi c r_S^2 = 4.7\times 10^{-18}(1+\beta)A \text{ Newtons}, \tag{5.3.29}$$

if A is in m^2.

For a perfectly reflecting surface $\beta = 1$. We find the pressure of radiation on such a surface, placed at one astronomical unit from the sun, to be about 1×10^{-10} atmosphere; thus, radiation effects are indeed small.

The value of the gradient of the radiation force, at the earth's orbit, is $dF_p/dr_S = -2F_p/r_S$. While not truly linear, we may write this as

$$\Delta F_p/F_p = -2\Delta r_S/r_S, \tag{5.3.30}$$

from which we can derive that a change of 1 % in F_p (about the accuracy with which we know the solar constant) requires a displacement radially of approximately 7.5×10^8 m—i.e., about twice the distance from earth to moon.

If the reflecting surface were displaced tangentially to the earth's orbit by this 7.5×10^8 m, the component of force in the direction of sun-to-earth would be diminished by a factor of less than 10^{-5}. The component perpendicular to the line from sun-to-earth would have a magnitude of about $5\times 10^{-3}F_p$.

Thus, we may treat this force as constant in both magnitude and direction for satellites in orbits between the earth and moon. We shall do this, taking the magnitude as that to be obtained at one astronomic unit and the direction as that pointing from sun's to earth's center.

Although we may treat the radiation force as constant wherever the object intercepts sunlight, we must take account of the fact that the satellite may pass through the earth's shadow. If we treat the sun's rays as if they were perfectly collimated, the geometric conditions stating that the satellite is in the shadow zone are

$$|\mathbf{r}\times\mathbf{r}_S| < Rr_S,$$

and (5.3.31)

$$\mathbf{r}\cdot\mathbf{r}_S < 0,$$

where $\mathbf{r}$ signifies the geocentric position vector of the satellite and $\mathbf{r}_S$ that of the sun. R is the earth's radius.

The Effect on a Nominally-Circular Orbit. As with the gravitational effect of an extraterrestrial mass, let us select our "geometry" so the sun lies in the xy plane at an angle α from the x axis (Fig. 5.3). We then have $F_x = -F_p\cos\alpha$, $F_y = -F_p\sin\alpha$, and $F_z = 0$, where F_p is given by (5.3.29) or (5.3.30). To allow for the shadow effect we will assume quite generally the satellite is eclipsed at $\theta = \theta_1$ and emerges into sunlight again at $\theta = \theta_2$. Then we find

$$\Delta i = -\frac{F_p \sin\alpha \sin i_0}{\dot{\theta}^2 m r_0}(\sin\theta_2 - \sin\theta_1),$$

$$\Delta\Omega = \frac{F_p \sin\alpha}{\dot{\theta}^2 m r_0}(\cos\theta_2 - \cos\theta_1). \tag{5.3.32}$$

Examining the case in which the sun and satellite lie in the same plane, we find $\Delta i = 0$; further (Fig. 5.5) $\theta_1 = \alpha + \pi/2 + \cos^{-1} R/r_0$, $\theta_2 = \alpha + \pi + \sin^{-1} R/r_0$. Then $\cos\theta_2 - \cos\theta_1 = 2(R/r_0)\sin\alpha$, or $\Delta\Omega = 2F_p R \sin^2\alpha/\dot{\theta}^2 m r_0^2$. For an Echo type satellite in an 1850 km high orbit, we would find $\Delta\Omega = 3.1 \times 10^{-5}\sin^2\alpha$ rad/sec.

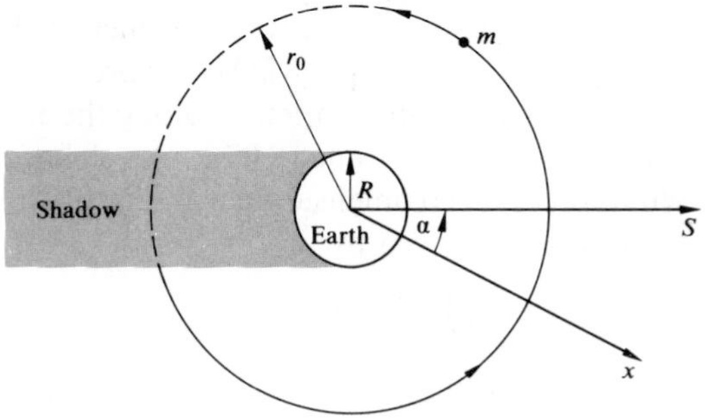

Figure 5.5

The effect in the undisturbed orbit plane is given by

$$\xi = -\frac{r_0^3 F_p}{\mu m}\left\{\cos\alpha\left(2\cos\theta + \frac{3}{2}\theta\sin\theta\right) + \sin\alpha\cos i_0\left(\frac{3}{2}\sin\theta - \frac{3}{2}\theta\cos\theta\right)\right\} + 2K_1 + K_2\cos\theta + K_3\sin\theta,$$

and

$$\eta = -\frac{r_0^3 F_p}{\mu m}\left\{\cos\alpha(3\theta\cos\theta - 6\sin\theta) + \sin\alpha\cos i_0(3\theta\sin\theta + 5\cos\theta)\right\} - 3K_1\theta - 2K_2\sin\theta + 2K_3\cos\theta + K_4,$$

where the need for retaining the complementary solution arises as follows. We note that this solution is to be used only when the satellite is illuminated by the sun. In fact, obtaining a clear idea of the behavior over one complete cycle entails "patching" three sets of such equations: the first with $F_p \neq 0$ being applicable from $\theta = \theta_0$ to $\theta = \theta_1$. These results should then be used as initial conditions for the interval $\theta_1 < \theta < \theta_2$ with $F_p = 0$; finally the complete solution should be used again, this time with initial conditions as obtained at $\theta = \theta_2$. The details would carry us too far beyond our present discussion.

The really significant thing about the behavior of ξ and η is the appearance of the periodic terms which have θ as a coefficient, i.e., have increasing amplitudes. These terms allow the departures to return to zero periodically, but cause the maximum inward and outward amplitudes of ξ to increase without limit as time goes on. For a simple geometry such as $\alpha = \pi/2$ and $i = 0$ one finds that the entire (circular) orbit is shifted at right angles to the earth-sun line. Again we must remind the reader that when θ grows to such size that ξ and η are no longer small compared with r_0, the present approach loses its validity.

3.5. Perturbation by Geomagnetic Deflection

The Force. We finally consider, very crudely, a force which is of occasional interest. It arises from the interaction of the earth's magnetic field and any electric charge an orbiting body may acquire [4, 8]. We approximate the former by assuming it stems from a magnetic dipole oriented along the earth's axis, positive south. In fact, this model is a very poor one [9], but the elaboration necessary to form a better representation is not commensurate with this preliminary discussion.

We may take the force to be given by

$$\mathbf{F}_e = q_e \mathbf{v} \times \mathbf{B}, \tag{5.3.33}$$

where q_e is the charge acquired by the satellite, $\mathbf{v}$ is its velocity, and $\mathbf{B}$ is the magnetic induction of the earth's field. In MKS units,

$$\mathbf{B} = \nabla \times \mathbf{A}, \tag{5.3.34}$$

where the vector potential [10] is

$$\mathbf{A} = \frac{\mu_0}{4\pi} \mathbf{M} \times \nabla(1/r). \tag{5.3.35}$$

$\mathbf{M}$ is the magnetic moment of the earth, and μ_0 is the permeability of free space.

Carrying out the operations indicated in (5.3.33) through (5.3.35), we obtain

$$\frac{|F_e|}{m} \simeq \frac{q_e \mu_0 M}{4\pi m r^2} \frac{v}{r}, \tag{5.3.36}$$

and the ratio of this to μ/r^2 is

$$(q_e \mu_0 M / 4\pi m \mu) v/r.$$

Now the magnitude of M is about 8.1×10^{22} amp-m^2 [11] and μ_0 has the value 4×10^{-7}. Moreover, if the satellite is spherical, its capacitance is $(R_s/9) \times 10^{-9}$ farads where R_s is the satellite radius. Thus $q_e \mu_0 M / 4\pi m \simeq 9 \times 10^5 \, R_s V_e / m$, where V_e is the voltage on the satellite (relative to infinity). It has been deduced [8] that, at an altitude of about 500 km, a satellite may obtain an electric potential of about 60 V. Thus, at this altitude, $(q_e\mu_0 M/4\pi m\mu)v/r \simeq 3\times 10^{-10}\, R_s/m$. Again R_s/m has, taking a practical maximum for the Echo satellite, a value of less than about 0.3 m/kg, so that the ratio of disturbing to central gravity force is of the order of 10^{-10}. This will, of course, be smaller still for most satellites.

The Effect on a Nominally-Circular Orbit. Utilizing (5.3.12), we find

$$F_x = F_M \cos\theta \cos i_0; \quad F_y = F_M \sin\theta(1-3\sin^2 i_0); \quad F_z = F_M(3\sin\theta \sin i_0 \cos i_0), \tag{5.3.37}$$

where

$$F_M = -\frac{q_e\mu_0 M}{4\pi}\sqrt{\frac{\mu}{r_0^5}}. \tag{5.3.38}$$

From this we obtain

$$\Delta i = 0; \qquad \Delta\Omega = -\frac{q_e\mu_0 M}{2\sqrt{\mu r_0^3}}\sin i_0; \tag{5.3.39}$$

thus, to this approximation, there is a regression of the node, except when $i = 0$, for which the node is undefined.

We also obtain

$$\xi = -\frac{q_e\mu_0 M}{4\pi m}\frac{\cos i_0}{\sqrt{\mu r_0}}; \qquad \eta = 2\frac{q_e\mu_0 M}{4\pi m}\frac{\cos i_0}{\sqrt{\mu r_0}}\theta, \tag{5.3.40}$$

again setting the constants of the complementary solution to zero. The effect under these circumstances is rather interesting: a fixed decrement in the radial component and a cumulative advance in the tangential direction.

4. FORMAL ASPECTS OF PERTURBATION THEORY

Having established some preliminary notions of the effects that various physical disturbances have on an orbit, we may note that, inasmuch as we started from fundamental principles, there is no inherent limitation which could keep this approach from being carried to greater accuracy. Before embarking upon an elaborate effort with the type of formulation such as in Section 2, however, we must make some remarks about perturbation techniques in general.

4.1. Orders of the Solution

We have noted that the entire problem of perturbations in a satellite orbit hinges on the appearance of small forces other than the central gravity term. If, then, we have such an additional force per unit mass, Φ, acting on the body in question, the equations of motion are

$$\ddot{x} = -\mu x/r^3 + \Phi_x, \qquad \ddot{y} = -\mu y/r^3 + \Phi_y, \qquad \ddot{z} = -\mu z/r^3 + \Phi_z, \tag{5.4.1}$$

where Φ_x, Φ_y, Φ_z are the components of Φ. If we rewrite (5.4.1) as

$$\ddot{x} = -\frac{\mu x}{r^3} + \kappa F_x, \qquad \ddot{y} = -\frac{\mu y}{r^3} + \kappa F_y, \qquad \ddot{z} = -\frac{\mu z}{r^3} + \kappa F_z, \tag{5.4.2}$$

where F expresses only the functional form of Φ and κ represents it magnitude, we see that the solutions of (5.4.2) must be dependent on κ in such a way that as it becomes smaller and smaller, the solutions approach nearer and nearer to the Keplerian (i.e., elliptic) coordinates x, y, z. At some specific time, say τ, we can expand the true solutions of (5.4.2) in power series of κ, that is

$$\begin{aligned} x(\tau) &= x_0 + x_1\kappa + x_2\kappa^2 + x_3\kappa^3 + \cdots, \\ y(\tau) &= y_0 + y_1\kappa + y_2\kappa^2 + y_3\kappa^3 + \cdots, \\ z(\tau) &= z_0 + z_1\kappa + z_2\kappa^2 + z_3\kappa^3 + \cdots, \end{aligned} \tag{5.4.3}$$

where $x_0, x_1, x_2, \ldots, y_0, y_1, \ldots, z_0, \ldots$ are constants. Obviously, from (5.4.2), when $\kappa = 0$, the x_0, y_0, z_0 must be the Keplerian values of x, y, z at time τ.

We can ask further, considering now a specific value of κ, if we cannot obtain solutions of (5.4.2) such that

$$\begin{aligned} x(t) &= x^{(0)}(t) + \kappa x^{(1)}(t) + \kappa^2 x^{(2)}(t) + \cdots, \\ y(t) &= y^{(0)}(t) + \kappa y^{(1)}(t) + \kappa^2 y^{(2)}(t) + \cdots, \\ z(t) &= z^{(0)}(t) + \kappa z^{(1)}(t) + \kappa^2 z^{(2)}(t) + \cdots, \end{aligned} \tag{5.4.4}$$

where the $x^{(0)}, x^{(1)}, \ldots$, are here functions of the independent variable, and, particularly, the $x^{(0)}$, $y^{(0)}$, $z^{(0)}$ are those obtained in Keplerian motion. If (5.4.4) holds, then the time derivatives of (5.4.4) must also, that is,

$$\dot{x}(t) = \dot{x}^{(0)}(t) + \kappa\dot{x}^{(1)}(t) + \cdots, \qquad \ddot{x}(t) = \ddot{x}^{(0)}(t) + \kappa\ddot{x}^{(1)}(t) + \cdots, \text{etc.}$$

Now,

$$\begin{aligned} r^2 &= x^2 + y^2 + z^2 \\ &= (x^{(0)} + \kappa x^{(1)} + \cdots)^2 + (y^{(0)} + \kappa y^{(1)} + \cdots)^2 + (z^{(0)} + \kappa z^{(1)} + \cdots)^2 \\ &= r^{(0)^2} + 2\kappa[x^{(0)}x^{(1)} + y^{(0)}y^{(1)} + z^{(0)}z^{(1)}] \\ &\quad + \kappa^2[x^{(1)^2} + y^{(1)^2} + z^{(1)^2} + \cdots] + \cdots \\ &= r^{(0)^2}\left[1 + 2\kappa\frac{x^{(0)}x^{(1)} + y^{(0)}y^{(1)} + z^{(0)}z^{(1)}}{r^{(0)2}}\right. \\ &\quad \left. + \kappa^2\frac{x^{(1)^2} + y^{(1)^2} + z^{(1)^2} + \cdots}{r^{(0)2}} + \cdots\right], \end{aligned} \tag{5.4.5}$$

Then

$$\frac{1}{r^3} = \frac{1}{r^{(0)^3}}\left[1 - 3\kappa\frac{x^{(0)}x^{(1)} + y^{(0)}y^{(1)} + z^{(0)}z^{(1)}}{r^{(0)^2}} + \kappa^2 \cdots\right]. \tag{5.4.6}$$

If (5.4.6) and the first of (5.4.4) be substituted in the first of (5.4.1), we find each side yields a power series in κ. Since κ can take any conceivable value, the coefficients of like powers on each side of the resulting equation must be equal. Thus for terms independent of κ, we find

$$\ddot{x}^{(0)} = -\mu x^{(0)}/r^{(0)^3}, \tag{5.4.7}$$

with similar expressions in $y^{(0)}$ and $z^{(0)}$. These obviously are precisely the Keplerian equations of motion; hence, $x^{(0)}$, $y^{(0)}$, $z^{(0)}$ are known.

The coefficients of κ to the first power provide us with

$$\begin{aligned}
\ddot{x}^{(0)} &= -\frac{\mu}{r^{(0)^3}}\left\{x^{(1)} - 3\frac{x^{(0)}}{r^{(0)^2}}\Xi\right\} + F_x^{(0)},\\
\ddot{y}^{(1)} &= -\frac{\mu}{r^{(0)^3}}\left\{y^{(1)} - 3\frac{y^{(0)}}{r^{(0)^2}}\Xi\right\} + F_y^{(0)},\\
\ddot{z}^{(1)} &= -\frac{\mu}{r^{(0)^3}}\left\{z^{(1)} - 3\frac{z^{(0)}}{r^{(0)^2}}\Xi\right\} + F_z^{(0)},
\end{aligned} \tag{5.4.8}$$

where

$$\Xi = x^{(0)}x^{(1)} + y^{(0)}y^{(1)} + z^{(0)}z^{(1)}, \tag{5.4.9}$$

and $F^{(0)}$ is the part of $F(x, y, z, \dot{x}, \dot{y}, \dot{z})$ which is independent of κ, i.e., depends only on $x^{(0)}$, $y^{(0)}$, $z^{(0)}$ or their derivatives. We note that (5.4.8) contain only $x^{(1)}$, $y^{(1)}$, $z^{(1)}$ as unknown functions and are independent of $x^{(2)}$, $y^{(2)}$, $z^{(2)}$, etc.

For the coefficients of κ^2,

$$\begin{aligned}
\ddot{x}^{(2)} = -\frac{\mu}{r^{(0)^3}}\Bigg\{x^{(2)} &- \frac{3x^{(1)}}{r^{(0)^2}}\Xi + \frac{15x^{(0)}}{r^{(0)^4}}\Xi^2\\
&- \frac{3x^{(0)}}{2r^{(0)^2}}\Big[x^{(1)^2} + y^{(1)^2} + z^{(1)^2} + 2x^{(0)}x^{(2)}\\
&+ 2y^{(0)}y^{(2)} + 2z^{(0)}z^{(2)}\Big]\Bigg\} + F_x^{(1)},
\end{aligned}$$

with similar expressions for $\ddot{y}^{(2)}$ and $\ddot{z}^{(2)}$. Here $F_x^{(1)}$, $F_y^{(1)}$, $F_z^{(1)}$ are the terms of the disturbing force involving $x^{(1)}$, $y^{(1)}$, and $z^{(1)}$ to the first power. Again, having previously obtained $x^{(0)}$, etc., $x^{(1)}$, etc., the equations of this last type can, in principle, be solved for $x^{(2)}$, etc. This process can be carried on indefinitely, or at least until patience is exhausted.

In grouping these "coefficients" of powers of κ, we call those independent of it the zero-order equations, those involving κ the first-order equations, those related to κ^2 the second-order equations, etc.

Obviously, the tedium involved both in isolating each higher-order part of the equations of motion and in solving them is a monotonic function of the order of perturbation desired. To be able to stop the procedure at a reasonable order in a practical case the perturbing force must be smaller than the central gravity term. Then succeeding orders of solution, since each enters (5.4.4) with a higher power of κ, tend to play a less and less significant role.* In many cases, κ is so small that only first-order terms need be found. This is indeed the position we took in Section 2, when we ignored terms of type $(\xi/r_0)^2$, etc.

4.2. Separation of Perturbing Effects

In any real situation, there is never only one perturbing force acting. We must account for several simultaneously, i.e., we would expect the displacement (from Keplerian motion) due to one perturbing force to change the magnitudes of any other forces acting, since these are dependent on the position and velocity of the perturbed body. Strictly speaking, this is true; however, if the individual perturbations are so small that a first-order method is sufficient, we can consider the effects separately. Their influence on each other can be shown to be of second or higher order and may be neglected.

In particular, suppose we have two such forces, F_1 and F_2. Thus, in place of the first of (5.4.3), we would have, say,

$$\begin{aligned} x = x^{(0)} &+ \kappa_1 x^{(1)} + \kappa_1^2 x^{(2)} + \cdots \\ &+ \kappa_2 \xi^{(1)} + \kappa_2^2 \xi^{(2)} + \cdots \\ &+ \kappa_1 \kappa_2 \chi^{(2)} + \cdots, \end{aligned} \tag{5.4.10}$$

where κ_1 is the perturbation parameter for F_1, κ_2 is that for F_2, and the terms involving the product of parameters express the dependence of one force on the effect of the other. It is clear that the product of the parameters has a magnitude less than either separately (if both κ_1 and κ_2 are less than unity) and its effect may be considered to be of second order. If we restrict ourselves to a first-order analysis, (5.4.10) leads to one set of equations of zero order as before, but two sets of first-order equations, one from equating coefficients of κ_1 and not containing any terms due to F_2, the other from equating coefficients of κ_2 and not containing any terms due to F_1. In this sense, perturbing forces are separable, and we may find $x^{(1)}$ and $\xi^{(1)}$ independently, writing for the coordinate $x = x^{(0)} + \kappa_1 x^{(1)} + \kappa_2 \xi^{(1)}$.

Indeed, this result is exactly what one might expect intuitively in such a case.

---

*There is, of course, the possibility of encountering a higher-order solution possessing a singularity. However, we usually expect equations reflecting behavior in the physical world (in distinction to the purely mathematical one) to be well-behaved. The question of uniform convergence of the present development will not be treated here.

The effect of the small force F_1 is to cause small departures from Keplerian motion, but these deviations can hardly give rise to large-scale changes in the effects of F_2. Similarly, the perturbations due to F_2, being small, cannot significantly alter the magnitude of F_1 or the geometry according to which it acts on the orbit.* From this point of view it should also be clear why we made an explicit distinction between the particular and the complementary solutions in the examples of Section 3. The particular solutions satisfy the nonvanishing right-hand sides of the first-order equations, where several such solutions may be necessary to reflect several perturbations. On the other hand, the complementary solution, which satisfies the homogeneous system, reflects only the effects of the initial conditions and is not connected intrinsically with any of the physical disturbances represented by the particular solutions. Though we may seem to belabor the obvious, this point is often missed when interpreting analytic results for practical applications.

5. PERTURBATION IN CARTESIAN COORDINATES

If we attempt to work directly with the effects of the disturbing force as they appear in x, y, z or any other direct representation of position, the method is called *perturbation in the coordinates*. This is in distinction to techniques based on variation of the elliptic elements or canonic constants discussed in later chapters. In addition, there are methods employing hybrid sets of variables, i.e., combinations of position coordinates and orbit parameters; a classical example in this category is Hansen's method. Again we must defer discussion of these. In this introductory chapter, we shall restrict our attention to obtaining the perturbations in the coordinates directly.

5.1. Rectangular Coordinates

If we wish to obtain the effects in terms of x, y, z we are led to Eqs. (5.4.8), which present difficulties at once due to the mixture of terms in $x^{(1)}$, $y^{(1)}$, and $z^{(1)}$ as given by (5.4.9). In general, it is not possible to separate these terms and also retain the basic rectangular coordinates.

A method due to Encke [13] circumvents this difficulty but only at the cost of additional labor. Instead of the development leading to (5.4.6), let us take the term x/r^3 of (5.4.2) and write

$$\frac{x}{r^3} = \frac{x^{(0)} + \kappa x^{(1)} + \cdots}{(r^{(0)} + \kappa r^{(1)} + \cdots)^3}, \tag{5.5.1}$$

where we have introduced the expansion

$$r = r^{(0)} + \kappa r^{(1)} + \kappa^2 r^{(2)} + \cdots \tag{5.5.2}$$

* Note that in all cases considered in this work, the effect of the perturbed body on the perturbing body is ignored. This can also be shown to be a higher-order effect.

But then

$$\frac{1}{r^3} = \frac{1}{r^{(0)3}} - 3\kappa \frac{r^{(1)}}{r^{(0)4}} + \cdots$$

or

$$\frac{x}{r^3} = \frac{x^{(0)}}{r^{(0)3}} - 3\kappa \frac{x^{(0)}r^{(1)}}{r^{(0)4}} + \kappa \frac{x^{(1)}}{r^{(0)3}} + \cdots,$$

which allows us to write the first-order part of (5.4.2) as

$$\begin{aligned} \ddot{x}^{(1)} + \mu \frac{x^{(1)}}{r^{(0)3}} &= 3\mu \frac{x^{(0)}r^{(1)}}{r^{(0)4}} + F_x^{(0)}, \\ \ddot{y}^{(1)} + \mu \frac{y^{(1)}}{r^{(0)3}} &= 3\mu \frac{y^{(0)}r^{(1)}}{r^{(0)4}} + F_y^{(0)}, \\ \ddot{z}^{(1)} + \mu \frac{z^{(1)}}{r^{(0)3}} &= 3\mu \frac{z^{(0)}r^{(1)}}{r^{(0)4}} + F_z^{(0)}. \end{aligned} \tag{5.5.3}$$

We note that each of (5.5.3) contains the unknown function $r^{(1)}$, for which we must find an appropriate expression.

Now

$$\frac{1}{2}\frac{d^2}{dt^2}(r^2) = x\ddot{x} + y\ddot{y} + z\ddot{z} + \dot{x}^2 + \dot{y}^2 + \dot{z}^2, \tag{5.5.4}$$

and

$$\frac{d}{dt}(\dot{x}^2 + \dot{y}^2 + \dot{z}^2) = 2(\dot{x}\,\ddot{x} + \dot{y}\,\ddot{y} + \dot{z}\,\ddot{z}),$$

or

$$(\dot{x}^2 + \dot{y}^2 + \dot{z}^2) = 2\int_{t_0}^{t} (\dot{x}\,\ddot{x} + \dot{y}\,\ddot{y} + \dot{z}\,\ddot{z})dt + v_0^2, \tag{5.5.5}$$

where v_0 is the velocity at $t = t_0$. Using this last and (5.4.2) and (5.5.4), we find

$$\begin{aligned} \frac{1}{2}\frac{d^2}{dt^2}(r^2) &= \kappa(xF_x + yF_y + zF_z) - \frac{\mu}{r} \\ &\quad + 2\kappa\int_{t_0}^{t} (\dot{x}F_x + \dot{y}F_y + \dot{z}F_z)dt + v_0^2 - 2\int_{t_0}^{t} \frac{\mu}{r^2}\dot{r}\,dt, \end{aligned} \tag{5.5.6}$$

where we have employed the fact that $r\dot{r} = x\dot{x} + y\dot{y} + z\dot{z}$. But

$$\mu\int_{t_0}^{t} \frac{\dot{r}}{r^2}\,dt = -\frac{\mu}{r} + \frac{\mu}{r_0}.$$

Thus

$$\frac{1}{2}\frac{d^2}{dt^2}(r^2) = \kappa(xF_x + yF_y + zF_z) + \frac{\mu}{r} + 2\kappa\int_{t_0}^{t}(\dot{x}F_x + \dot{y}F_y + \dot{z}F_z)\,dt + v_0^2 - 2\frac{\mu}{r_0}. \tag{5.5.7}$$

Since $r^2 = r^{(0)^2} + 2\kappa r^{(0)}r^{(1)} + \cdots$, (5.5.7) becomes

$$\frac{1}{2}\frac{d^2}{dt^2}\left(r^{(0)^2}\right) + \kappa\frac{d^2}{dt^2}(r^{(0)}r^{(1)}) + \cdots$$

$$= \kappa(xF_x + yF_y + zF_z) + 2\kappa\int_{t_0}^{t}(\dot{x}F_x + \dot{y}F_y + \dot{z}F_z)\,dt + v_0^2 - 2\frac{\mu}{r_0} + \frac{\mu}{r}. \tag{5.5.8}$$

However, (5.5.4) and (5.5.5) also yield, when the perturbing force vanishes,

$$\frac{1}{2}\frac{d^2}{dt^2}\left(r^{(0)^2}\right) = v_0^2 - \frac{2\mu}{r_0} + \frac{\mu}{r^{(0)}}.$$

Subtracting this from (5.5.8) and retaining only first-order terms, we obtain

$$\kappa\frac{d^2}{dt^2}(r^{(0)}r^{(1)}) = \kappa\left[x^{(0)}F_x^{(0)} + y^{(0)}F_y^{(0)} + z^{(0)}F_z^{(0)}\right] + 2\kappa\int_{t_0}^{t}\left[\dot{x}^{(0)}F_x^{(0)} + \dot{y}^{(0)}F_y^{(0)} + \dot{z}^{(0)}F_z^{(0)}\right]dt + \frac{\mu}{r} - \frac{\mu}{r^{(0)}}. \tag{5.5.9}$$

But

$$\frac{1}{r} = \frac{1}{r^{(0)}} - \kappa\frac{r^{(1)}}{r^{(0)^2}} + \cdots,$$

so that we finally get from (5.5.9)

$$\frac{d^2}{dt^2}(r^{(0)}r^{(1)}) + \frac{\mu r^{(0)}r^{(1)}}{r^{(0)^3}} = x^{(0)}F_x^{(0)} + y^{(0)}F_y^{(0)} + z^{(0)}F_z^{(0)} + 2\int_{t_0}^{t}\left[\dot{x}^{(0)}F_x^{(0)} + \dot{y}^{(0)}F_y^{(0)} + \dot{z}^{(0)}F_z^{(0)}\right]dt, \tag{5.5.10}$$

which we have written in this way to emphasize that (5.5.10) and each of (5.5.3) are all of the form

$$\ddot{u} + \frac{\mu u}{r^{(0)3}} = \tilde{R}(x^{(0)}, y^{(0)}, z^{(0)}). \tag{5.5.11}$$

We note that (5.5.10) involves only the unknown function $r^{(1)}$, which, when found, can then be used in (5.5.3). It is the additional labor of solving (5.5.10) which is the cost of simplifying equations (5.4.8). One must exercise care that the relation

$$[r^{(0)} + \kappa r^{(1)} + \cdots]^2 = [x^{(0)} + \kappa x^{(1)} + \cdots]^2 + [y^{(0)} + \kappa y^{(1)} + \cdots]^2 + [z^{(0)} + \kappa z^{(1)} + \cdots]^2, \tag{5.5.12}$$

and its derivative with respect to time are satisfied to the necessary order of approximation. Thus the two additional constraints of integration arising for $r(t)$ from the solution of (5.5.10) will be tied to those in $x(t)$, $y(t)$, $z(t)$ through (5.5.12) and their derivatives at each level of approximation.

5.2. Illustrative Example. Effect of Atmospheric Resistance on a Circular Orbit

We illustrate the method of the preceding section by investigating the perturbative effect of drag on an initially circular satellite orbit. We adopt the geometry of Fig. 5.6, in which θ_0 is the geocentric angle between the unperturbed line of nodes and the point at which the satellite is injected into its orbit. Utilizing (5.3.26) with $\dot{\theta} = n_0$ and $\theta = \theta_0 + n_0 t$, we choose

$$\kappa = \frac{C_D A}{2m}\rho_0, \tag{5.5.13}$$

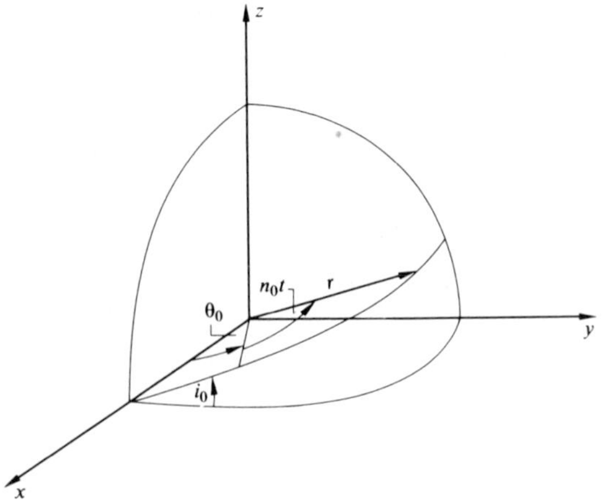

Figure 5.6

and, thus,

$$F_x^{(0)} = r_0^2 n_0^2\left(1 - 2\frac{\sigma}{n_0}\cos i_0\right)\sin(\theta_0+n_0 t),$$

$$F_y^{(0)} = -r_0^2 n_0^2\left[\cos i_0 - \frac{\sigma}{n_0}\left(1 + \cos^2 i_0\right)\right]\cos(\theta_0+n_0 t),$$

$$F_z^{(0)} = -r_0^2 n_0^2\left(1 - \frac{\sigma}{n_0}\cos i_0\right)\sin i_0\,\cos(\theta_0+n_0 t).$$

From these, we have immediately $x^{(0)}F_x^{(0)} + y^{(0)}F_y^{(0)} + z^{(0)}F_z^{(0)} = 0$, since

$$\begin{aligned} x^{(0)} &= r_0\cos(\theta_0+n_0 t);\\ y^{(0)} &= r_0\cos i_0\sin(\theta_0+n_0 t);\\ z^{(0)} &= r_0\sin i_0\sin(\theta_0+n_0 t). \end{aligned} \tag{5.5.14}$$

Further

$$\dot{x}^{(0)}F_x^{(0)} + \dot{y}^{(0)}F_y^{(0)} + \dot{z}^{(0)}F_z^{(0)} = -r_0^3 n_0^3\left(1-2\frac{\sigma}{n_0}\cos i_0\right),$$

so that (5.5.10) becomes

$$\frac{d^2}{dt^2}r^{(1)} + \mu r^{(1)}/r_0^3 = -2r_0^2 n_0^3(1-2\frac{\sigma}{n_0}\cos i_0)t,$$

where we have set $t_0 = 0$. This equation has the solution

$$r^{(1)} = -2r_0^2(1-2\frac{\sigma}{n_0}\cos i_0)n_0 t + K_1\cos(\theta_0 + n_0 t) + K_2\sin(\theta_0 + n_0 t). \tag{5.5.15}$$

We note the correspondence of $\kappa r^{(1)}$ obtained here and our earlier result (Section 3.3) for the radial perturbation due to drag. As an example let us choose the complementary solution in (5.5.15) such that the initial conditions, at $t = 0$, would yield a circular orbit in the absence of perturbations, i.e., $r^{(1)} = \dot{r}^{(1)} = 0$. Then

$$r = r_0 - \frac{C_D A}{m}\rho_0 r_0^2(1-2\frac{\sigma}{n_0}\cos i_0)(n_0 t - \sin n_0 t). \tag{5.5.16}$$

Utilizing (5.5.16), equations (5.5.3) lead to

$$\begin{aligned} x^{(1)} &= -r_0^2\left(1-2\frac{\sigma}{n_0}\cos i_0\right)\tilde{A},\\ y^{(1)} &= r_0^2\left\{\cos i_0\left(1-2\frac{\sigma}{n_0}\cos i_0\right)\tilde{B} + \frac{\sigma}{n_0}\sin^2 i_0\tilde{C}\right\},\\ z^{(1)} &= r_0^2\left\{\sin i_0\left(1-2\frac{\sigma}{n_0}\cos i_0\right)\tilde{B} - \frac{\sigma}{n_0}\sin i_0\,\cos i_0\tilde{C}\right\}, \end{aligned} \tag{5.5.17}$$

where

$$\begin{aligned}\tilde{A} &= \tfrac{3}{2} n_0^2 t^2 \sin(\theta_0 + n_0 t) + 2n_0 t \cos(\theta_0 + n_0 t) \\ &\quad - 4\sin(\theta_0 + n_0 t) + 2\sin\theta_0 + 2\cos n_0 t \sin(\theta_0 + n_0 t), \\ \tilde{B} &= \tfrac{3}{2} n_0^2 t^2 \cos(\theta_0 + n_0 t) - 2n_0 t \sin(\theta_0 + n_0 t) \\ &\quad - 4\cos(\theta_0 + n_0 t) + 2\cos\theta_0 + 2\cos n_0 t \cos(\theta_0 + n_0 t), \\ \tilde{C} &= \tfrac{1}{2}\left[n_0 t \sin(\theta_0 + n_0 t) - \sin\theta_0 \sin n_0 t\right].\end{aligned} \tag{5.5.18}$$

We have, of course, $x = x^{(0)} + \kappa x^{(1)}$, etc., to first order, where $x^{(0)}$ is given by (5.5.14) and κ by (5.5.13); also, $\sqrt{x^2+y^2+z^2}$ yields, to within the order of approximation, the same right-hand side as (5.5.16). The velocity components are obtained by differentiation.

For noncircular orbits the solution of the general equation (5.5.11) is not easily effected when utilizing time as the independent variable. The basic reason is the difficulty in solving Kepler's equation. If we insist on retaining t, the only alternative is to expand $x^{(0)}$, $y^{(0)}$, $z^{(0)}$, $r^{(0)}$ in some kind of series, e.g., as shown in Eq. (2.6.7). This inevitably leads to a very long awkward process; such methods are used in classical texts on celestial mechanics. More recently, some efforts have been made by Brouwer *et al* [12a] to facilitate this procedure by various changes of coordinates and by Danby *et al.* in a formulation using matrizants [12b].

Instead of using t as independent variable, it is often more convenient to change to the unperturbed true or eccentric anomaly since the expressions for $x^{(0)}$, $y^{(0)}$, $z^{(0)}$ and the disturbing function can then usually be given in closed form. We shall discuss this later in detail and make extensive use of such a transformation throughout the remainder of this work. It enables one to execute at least some low-order perturbation analyses entirely in closed form.

6. NONRECTANGULAR COORDINATE SYSTEMS

It is clear that there is nothing to restrict perturbation theory to rectangular coordinates. Indeed, adoption of a frame which utilizes the radial distance as a fundamental coordinate can lead us back to the case in which we need solve only three second-order equations of motion, rather than four as illustrated above. Encke [13, p. 393] proposed such an approach, which is one* of the several we discuss in the remainder of this chapter. Since all these formulations employ some form of spherical coordinate system, there is first the problem of selecting the fundamental plane for such an analysis. For most planetary theories the plane of the ecliptic is a natural choice. In lunar and earth satellite studies one might be

*Neither this nor the scheme already discussed is the well-known Encke method, which involves numerical integration and not analytic solution.

We easily find $X\dot{Y} - Y\dot{X} = r^2\dot{f}\cos^2\beta$, or, by up to first-order terms,

$$X\dot{Y} - Y\dot{X} = r^{(0)^2}\dot{f}^{(0)} + \kappa(r^{(0)^2}\dot{f}^{(1)} + 2r^{(0)}r^{(1)}\dot{f}^{(0)}),$$

where we have used (5.5.2). However, the equations of motion may be written as

$$\ddot{X} + \mu X/r^3 = \kappa F_X, \qquad \ddot{Y} + \mu Y/r^3 = \kappa F_Y, \qquad \ddot{Z} + \mu Z/r^3 = \kappa F_Z. \quad (5.6.6)$$

Multiplying the second of these by X, the first by Y, subtracting and integrating, we obtain

$$X\dot{Y} - Y\dot{X} = \kappa\int_{t_0}^{t} (XF_Y - YF_X)dt + C.$$

We thus have, to first order,

$$\frac{d}{dt}f^{(1)} = \frac{1}{r^{(0)2}}\int_{t_0}^{t} r^{(0)}\left[F_Y^{(0)}\cos f^{(0)} - F_X^{(0)}\sin f^{(0)}\right]dt - 2\frac{r^{(1)}}{r^{(0)}}\dot{f}^{(0)}, \qquad (5.6.7)$$

where we have recognized that $C = r^{(0)^2}\dot{f}^{(0)}$. The quantity $r^{(1)}$ is obtained by means of (5.5.10), with appropriate change of notation (x becoming X, etc.). The solution to Eq. (5.6.7) provides us with the perturbation to the anomaly, and (5.6.5) gives us what may be called the *disturbed true anomaly*.

The equation for β is obtained most simply by substituting the third of (5.6.3) into the last of (5.6.6). We have, again going only to first order,

$$\frac{d^2}{dt^2}(r^{(0)}\beta^{(1)}) + \frac{\mu}{r^{(0)3}}(r^{(0)}\beta^{(1)}) = F_Z, \qquad (5.6.8)$$

which is of the same form as (5.5.11).

Illustrative Example. Effect of Atmospheric Resistance on a Circular Orbit

The results of Section 5.2 are sufficiently complicated to warrant further examination in a different coordinate frame, namely, that discussed immediately above.* Since we are dealing with a nominally-circular orbit, we may take $\omega = \theta_0$ at $t = 0$ in (5.6.1) with no loss in generality; further, to conform to the geometry used in Section 5.2, we have $\Omega = 0$ (Fig. 5.8). Then

$$F_X = r_0^2 n_0^2\left(1 - 2\frac{\sigma}{n_0}\cos i_0\right)\sin n_0 t\ ;$$

$$F_Y = -r_0^2 n_0^2\left(1 - 2\frac{\sigma}{n_0}\cos i_0\right)\cos n_0 t;$$

$$F_Z = -r_0^2 n_0 \sigma \sin i_0 \cos(\theta_0 + n_0 t).$$

---

*The fact that spherical coordinates are more natural than Cartesian ones for this example seems fairly obvious and has been used in several publications [15].

Of course

$$X^{(0)} = r_0 \cos n_0 t,\ Y^{(0)} = r_0 \sin n_0 t,\ Z^{(0)} = 0, \text{ and } f^{(0)} = n_0 t.$$

Equation (5.5.10), rewritten as,

$$\frac{d^2}{dt^2}(r^{(0)}r^{(1)}) + \frac{\mu r^{(0)}r^{(1)}}{r^{(0)^3}} = X^{(0)}F_X^{(0)} + Y^{(0)}F_Y^{(0)} + Z^{(0)}F_Z^{(0)}$$

$$+ 2\int_{t_0}^{t} \left[\dot{X}^{(0)}F_X^{(0)} + \dot{Y}^{(0)}F_Y^{(0)} + \dot{Z}^{(0)}F_Z^{(0)}\right] dt,$$

has the same solution as we found in Section 5.2, namely,

$$r^{(1)} = -2r_0^2\left(1 - 2\frac{\sigma}{n_0}\cos i_0\right)(n_0 t - \sin n_0 t). \tag{5.6.9}$$

Then (5.6.7) yields

$$f^{(1)} = r_0\left(1 - 2\frac{\sigma}{n_0}\cos i_0\right)\left(\frac{3}{2}n_0^2 t^2 + 4\cos n_0 t - 4\right), \tag{5.6.10}$$

and (5.6.8) provides us with

$$\beta^{(1)} = -\frac{1}{2}r_0\frac{\sigma}{n_0}\sin i_0[n_0 t \sin(\theta_0 + n_0 t) - \sin\theta_0 \sin n_0 t]. \tag{5.6.11}$$

The spiral decay and the circumferential acceleration are evident from the secular terms in (5.6.9) and (5.6.10). The secular term in $\beta^{(1)}$ can be shown to yield the decrease in i due to atmospheric rotation. The reader may verify the equivalence of these results and those obtained in Section 5.2 by utilizing

$$\begin{aligned} x &= r\cos\beta\cos(\theta_0 + n_0 t), \\ y &= r[\cos\beta\sin(\theta_0 + n_0 t)\cos i_0 - \sin\beta\sin i_0], \\ z &= r[\cos\beta\sin(\theta_0 + n_0 t)\sin i_0 + \sin\beta\cos i_0], \end{aligned} \tag{5.6.12}$$

remembering that, to first order,

$$\theta = \theta^{(0)} + \kappa\theta^{(1)} = \theta_0 + f^{(0)} + \kappa f^{(1)},$$

(see also Fig. 5.7) and

$$\sin\theta = \sin\theta^{(0)} + \kappa\theta^{(1)}\cos\theta^{(0)}, \qquad \cos\theta = \cos\theta^{(0)} - \kappa\theta^{(1)}\sin\theta^{(0)}. \tag{5.6.13}$$

As a further exercise, the reader may treat the perturbation due to a third ponderable body in the present coordinate system and compare the results with those of Section 3.1.

6.2. Another Approach Using Spherical Coordinates

In order to write the equations of motion directly for spherical coordinates we may apply the formal procedure of Lagrangian mechanics.* Following this approach, we discuss some examples where the unperturbed orbit is noncircular.

With the coordinates of Fig. 5.7 the Lagrangian becomes

$$L = (m/2)(\dot{r}^2 + r^2\dot{\beta}^2 + r^2\dot{\theta}^2 \cos^2\beta) + \mu m/r - \tilde{V}, \tag{5.6.14}$$

where $\tilde{V}$ is the perturbing potential. If nonconservative forces are present the equations of motion become

$$\frac{d}{dt}\left[\frac{\partial L}{\partial(\dot{r},\dot{\theta},\dot{\beta})}\right] - \frac{\partial L}{\partial(r,\theta,\beta)} = Q_{r,\theta,\beta}, \tag{5.6.15}$$

where the meaning of the multiple symbols should be evident; Q represents a nonconservative force. Using (5.6.14) we have

$$\ddot{r} - r\dot{\beta}^2 - r\dot{\theta}^2 \cos^2\beta + \frac{\mu}{r^2} = -\frac{1}{m}\frac{\partial\tilde{V}}{\partial r} + \frac{1}{m}Q_r \equiv \kappa\tilde{R}_r(r,\theta,\beta), \tag{5.6.16}$$

$$\frac{d}{dt}(r^2\dot{\beta}) + r^2\dot{\theta}^2 \sin\beta\cos\beta = -\frac{1}{m}\frac{\partial\tilde{V}}{\partial\theta} + \frac{1}{m}Q_\beta \equiv \kappa\tilde{R}_\beta(r,\theta,\beta), \tag{5.6.17}$$

$$\frac{d}{dt}(r^2\dot{\theta}\cos^2\beta) = -\frac{1}{m}\frac{\partial\tilde{V}}{\partial\theta} + \frac{1}{m}Q_\theta \equiv \kappa\tilde{R}_\theta(r,\theta,\beta), \tag{5.6.18}$$

where κ represents the small parameter characterizing the perturbations.

In principle, we could substitute perturbation series for r, θ, β and proceed in a straightforward fashion. However, as pointed out, this often leads to intractable first-order equations. Frequently, we can extricate ourselves by making the well-known change of variables

$$1/r = u \quad \text{and} \quad r^2\dot{\theta} = p. \tag{5.6.19}$$

From the second of these we also have

$$\frac{d}{dt} = u^2 p \frac{d}{d\theta}, \tag{5.6.20}$$

which permits us to adopt θ, the central angle (Fig. 5.7), as the independent variable in place of the time. Two comments are appropriate. First, such a change turns t into a dependent variable for which a relation $t(\theta)$ must be found. Second, the θ

*A more detailed review of the Lagrangian procedure is given in Chapter 7 by way of introduction to Hamiltonian mechanics.

used here, related as it is to the disturbed values of r and p, is necessarily the perturbed value of the central angle, similar to the true anomaly defined in (5.6.5). We shall elaborate on both these points in Section 7.

With (5.6.19) and (5.6.20) the equations of motion become

$$\frac{d}{d\theta}\left(p\frac{du}{d\theta}\right) + up\left(\frac{d\beta}{d\theta}\right)^2 + up\cos^2\beta - \mu/p = \kappa\tilde{R}_r(u,p,\beta), \tag{5.6.21}$$

$$\frac{d}{d\theta}(p\cos^2\beta) = \kappa\tilde{R}_\theta(u,p,\beta), \tag{5.6.22}$$

$$\frac{d}{d\theta}\left(p\frac{d\beta}{d\theta}\right) + p\sin\beta\cos\beta = \kappa\tilde{R}_\beta(u,p,\beta). \tag{5.6.23}$$

We note that the system (5.6.21)–(5.6.23) has been reduced by one order by introducing the quantity p and adopting θ as independent variable. The sixth constant of integration is recovered in relating θ to t, as we shall see shortly. Now let

$$u = u^{(0)} + \kappa u^{(1)} + \cdots, \qquad p = p^{(0)} + \kappa p^{(1)} + \cdots, \qquad \beta = \beta^{(0)} + \kappa\beta^{(1)} + \cdots.$$

From the zero-order equations the obvious results follow:

$$\beta^{(0)} = 0, \qquad \frac{d\beta^{(0)}}{d\theta} = 0, \qquad p^{(0)} = p_0 = \sqrt{\mu a(1-e^2)}, \tag{5.6.24}$$

$$u^{(0)} = \frac{1 + e\cos(\theta-\omega)}{a(1-e^2)}, \tag{5.6.25}$$

which represent Keplerian motion. The unsubscripted quantities a, e, and ω represent parameters of the unperturbed orbit. The first-order equations then become

$$\frac{d^2u^{(1)}}{d\theta^2} + \frac{2}{p_0 a(1-e^2)}p^{(1)} - \frac{e\sin(\theta-\omega)}{p_0 a(1-e^2)}\frac{dp^{(1)}}{d\theta} + u^{(1)} = \tilde{R}_r, \tag{5.6.26}$$

$$\frac{dp^{(1)}}{d\theta} = \tilde{R}_\theta, \tag{5.6.27}$$

$$\frac{d^2\beta^{(1)}}{d\theta^2} + \beta^{(1)} = \tilde{R}_\beta. \tag{5.6.28}$$

It remains to find a relation between θ and t. From (5.6.20) we have $dt = d\theta/pu^2$. Expanding p and u in terms of κ, we find

$$\begin{aligned} t &= t_0 + \int_\omega^\theta \left[\frac{1}{p_0 u^{(0)2}} - \kappa\left(\frac{2u^{(1)}}{p_0 u^{(0)3}} + \frac{p^{(1)}}{p_0^2 u^{(0)2}}\right)\right] d\theta \\ &\equiv t_0 + \Delta t^{(0)} + \kappa\Delta t^{(1)}, \end{aligned} \tag{5.6.29}$$

where t_0 represents the sixth integration constant of the original system (5.6.16)–(5.6.18). The zero-order time differential $\Delta t^{(0)}$ has the Keplerian form when worked out in detail, but in terms of the perturbed angle θ. The first-order time perturbation $\Delta t^{(1)}$ represents the departure of the actual motion from Kepler's law, as given by (2.2.37) for the nominal orbit parameters a, e, ω.

Illustrative Example. Effect of the Geomagnetic Field on a Charged Satellite

If we use the perturbing function for the geomagnetic field as given in Section 3.5 we find

$$\begin{aligned}\tilde{R}_r &= -\frac{\cos i}{p_0 a^2(1-e^2)^2}[1+2e\cos(\theta-\omega) + e^2\cos^2(\theta-\omega)],\\ \tilde{R}_\theta &= -\frac{e\cos i}{p_0 a(1-e^2)}\sin(\theta-\omega),\\ \tilde{R}_\beta &= \frac{\sin i}{p_0 a(1-e^2)}\{2\sin\theta[1+e\cos(\theta-\omega)] + e\cos\theta\sin(\theta-\omega)\},\end{aligned} \tag{5.6.30}$$

where i is the unperturbed value of the inclination; the perturbation parameter turns out to be

$$\kappa = q_e\mu_0 M/4\pi m.$$

Then (5.6.27) yields

$$p^{(1)} = \frac{e\cos i}{a(1-e^2)}[\cos(\theta-\omega) - 1], \tag{5.6.31}$$

where we have chosen the integration constant so that $p^{(1)} = dp^{(1)}/d\theta = 0$ at $\theta = \omega$, representing perfect injection at perigee. Equation (5.6.26) leads to

$$\frac{d^2u^{(1)}}{d\theta^2} + u^{(1)} = -\frac{\cos i}{p_0 a^2(1-e^2)^2}[(1-e)^2+4e\cos(\theta-\omega)],$$

which has the solution

$$u^{(1)} = \frac{(1-e)^2\cos i}{p_0 a^2(1-e^2)^2}[\cos(\theta-\omega) - 1] - \frac{2e\cos i}{p_0 a^2(1-e^2)^2}(\theta-\omega)\sin(\theta-\omega), \tag{5.6.32}$$

with the conditions that $u^{(1)} = du^{(1)}/d\theta = 0$ at $\theta = \omega$, again, for injection at perigee. Finally (5.6.28) yields

$$\begin{aligned}\beta^{(1)} = \frac{\sin i}{p_0 a(1-e^2)}\{&[\sin\theta\cos(\theta-\omega) - \sin\omega - (\theta-\omega)\cos\omega]\cos(\theta-\omega)\\ &+ [\sin\theta\sin(\theta-\omega) + (\theta-\omega)\sin\omega]\sin(\theta-\omega)\\ &- e[\cos\theta - \cos\omega]\sin(\theta-\omega)\},\end{aligned} \tag{5.6.33}$$

with $\beta^{(1)} = d\beta^{(1)}/d\theta = 0$ at $\theta = \omega$.

We can see the effect of the geomagnetic field on the orbit plane immediately from (5.6.33). At $\theta = 2\pi j + \omega$, i.e., after j complete revolutions,

$$\Delta\beta_{2\pi j} = -\frac{q_e \mu_0 M}{2m} \frac{\sin i \cos \omega}{p_0 a(1-e^2)} j. \tag{5.6.34}$$

Thus, to first order, the satellite departs more and more from the initial orbit plane as time goes on, except when $i = 0$ or when perigee lies 90° away from the plane of the magnetic equator and the perturbations consequently act symmetrically on the orbit.

The perturbation in radius can be found by

$$r = \frac{1}{u} = \frac{1}{u^{(0)} + \kappa u^{(1)}}$$
$$\simeq \frac{1}{u^{(0)}} - \kappa \frac{u^{(1)}}{u^{(0)2}},$$

while for $\dot{r}$

$$\frac{d}{dt} r = -\frac{1}{u^2}\frac{du}{dt} = -\frac{1}{u^2}\left(pu^2 \frac{du}{d\theta}\right)$$
$$= -\frac{du^{(0)}}{d\theta} - \kappa\left(p_0 \frac{du^{(1)}}{d\theta} + p^{(1)} \frac{du^{(0)}}{d\theta}\right).$$

Examination of these expressions in the light of (5.6.32) shows that r and $\dot{r}$ experience oscillations of increasing amplitude. Likewise

$$\dot{\theta} = u^2 p = u^{(0)2} p_0 + \kappa\left(u^{(0)2} p^{(1)} + 2u^{(0)} u^{(1)} p_0\right),$$

and, here too, $u^{(1)}$ introduces a term of the form $(\theta - \omega)\sin(\theta - \omega)$. The perturbation in the angle-time relation follows from (5.6.29) as

$$\Delta t^{(1)} = \frac{\cos i}{\mu}\left\{\frac{(1-e)\sin(\theta-\omega)}{[1+e\cos(\theta-\omega)]^2} + \frac{(1-e^2)\sin(\theta-\omega)}{1+e\cos(\theta-\omega)} - \frac{2(\theta-\omega)}{[1+e\cos(\theta-\omega)]^2}\right\}, \tag{5.6.35}$$

where again we observe a secular term.

In principle, analyses like this one could be carried to higher order in a way that corresponds to Section 4.1. However, the algebra soon becomes unwieldy, although this example has been carried to third order under the simplifying assumptions $e = 0, i = 0$ [reference 16].

We note again the importance of the change of independent variables, from t to θ, illustrated in this section. It simplifies the differential equations but does so at the cost of leading to an inverse time relation $t = t_0 + \Delta t^{(0)}(\theta) + \kappa \Delta t^{(1)}(\theta)$. This is little or no inconvenience for practical applications since we are used to inverse relations like (2.2.38) for simple Keplerian motion anyway. In effect, θ serves as an intermediary between u, p, β on the one hand and time on the other; this approach has been generally useful in analyses such as illustrated here [17, 18].

6.3. The Lindstedt Transformation

In reviewing the previous examples we note that attention is invariably drawn to nonperiodic terms such as the ones in (5.6.10), (5.6.11), (5.6.33), and (5.6.35). Since these exhibit ever-increasing amplitudes or monotonic growth they quickly dominate the calculations of future positions in orbit and tend to limit the time interval over which the results of the theory are valid. Needless to say, considerable effort has been invested in the treatment of these terms. Typically, the attempt is to absorb these effects by suitable transformations so that they do not appear in the ultimate expressions for the perturbed motion. In this section we consider one device in this category which is commonly attributed to Lindstedt [19].

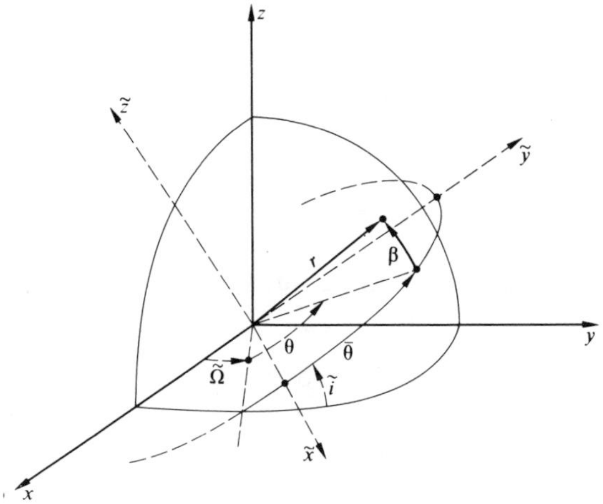

Figure 5.10

The rationale consists of anticipating a secular trend in some coordinate from simple physical considerations such as the ones displayed at the beginning of this chapter. One then provides the coordinate frame of reference with a motion to match this phenomenon, so that the remaining perturbations of the orbiting body relative to this reference frame are purely cyclic and of a relatively short period. In general, one may provide the coordinate system with the maximum number of independent angular rates, i.e., three, for matching secular trends and discard whichever motions are not needed for a particular problem.

Let us generalize the coordinate system of Fig. 5.8 to that of Fig. 5.10. X, Y, Z are now replaced by $\tilde{x}$, $\tilde{y}$, $\tilde{z}$; the nodal angle $\tilde{\Omega}$ and the inclination $\tilde{i}$ are taken as slowly varying quantities which can grow with time but obviously retain geometric meaning. Similarly the $\tilde{x}$ axis does not coincide with the node but gradually shifts away from it in the plane defined by $\tilde{\Omega}$ and $\tilde{\imath}$. These three slow changes correspond to variations of the three Euler angles by which a system like $\tilde{x}$, $\tilde{y}$, $\tilde{z}$ can be located relative to the inertial x, y, z coordinates; such monotonic changes are the new features of this approach. They have to be expressed in terms of the orbit geometry and the perturbing function under consideration to fulfill the ultimate purpose of eliminating secular trends. Generally, we could conceive them as polynomial functions of the time (or some other independent variable) but for a first-order analysis it turns out that linear expressions suffice.

To start from the beginning, the instantaneous satellite coordinates in the $\tilde{x}$, $\tilde{y}$, $\tilde{z}$ frame will be taken to be $\bar{\theta}$, β, r (Fig. 5.10). In relating these to the fundamental x, y, z frame, we must introduce the angle θ, which is measured in the same plane as $\bar{\theta}$ but reckoned from the instantaneous line of nodes; it differs from $\bar{\theta}$ by a quantity of at least first order which we will designate $\kappa\omega^{(1)}$, that is,

$$\theta - \bar{\theta} = \kappa\omega^{(1)}. \tag{5.6.36}$$

Analogously, let

$$\tilde{\Omega} = \Omega_0 + \kappa\Omega^{(1)},$$

and (5.6.37)

$$\tilde{\imath} = i_0 + \kappa i^{(1)},$$

where Ω_0 and i_0 designate the pertinent initial values, and $\omega^{(1)}$, $\Omega^{(1)}$, $i^{(1)}$ are as yet undetermined. Using

$$\begin{aligned} \tilde{x} &= r\cos\beta\cos\bar{\theta}; \\ \tilde{y} &= r\cos\beta\sin\bar{\theta}; \\ \tilde{z} &= r\sin\beta, \end{aligned} \tag{5.6.38}$$

we find

$$\begin{aligned} x &= r\cos\beta(\cos\theta\cos\tilde{\Omega} - \sin\theta\cos\tilde{\imath}\sin\tilde{\Omega}) + r\sin\beta\sin\tilde{\imath}\sin\tilde{\Omega}, \\ y &= r\cos\beta(\cos\theta\sin\tilde{\Omega} + \sin\theta\cos\tilde{\imath}\cos\tilde{\Omega}) - r\sin\beta\sin\tilde{\imath}\cos\tilde{\Omega}, \\ z &= r\cos\beta\sin\theta\sin\tilde{\imath} + r\sin\beta\cos\tilde{\imath}. \end{aligned} \tag{5.6.39}$$

From these we may derive the expression for the kinetic energy, namely,

$$\begin{aligned} T = \tfrac{1}{2}\{\dot{r}^2 &+ r^2[\dot{\beta} - \dot{\tilde{\Omega}}\sin\tilde{\imath}\cos\theta + \sin\theta\cdot d\tilde{\imath}/dt]^2 \\ &+ r^2[\dot{\theta}\cos\beta - \sin\beta\cos\theta\, d\tilde{\imath}/dt + \dot{\tilde{\Omega}}(\cos\beta\cos\tilde{\imath} - \sin\beta\sin\tilde{\imath}\sin\theta)]^2\}. \end{aligned}$$

The equations of motion become

$$\ddot{r} - r\dot{f}\cos^2\beta\left[\dot{f} + 2\kappa\left(\dot{\omega}^{(1)} + \dot{\Omega}^{(1)}\cos i_0\right)\right] + \frac{\mu}{r^2} = -\frac{\partial\tilde{V}}{\partial r}, \tag{5.6.40}$$

$$\frac{d}{dt}\left\{r^2\cos^2\beta\left[\dot{f} + \kappa\left(\dot{\omega}^{(1)} + \dot{\Omega}^{(1)}\cos i_0\right)\right]\right\} = -\frac{\partial\tilde{V}}{\partial f}, \tag{5.6.41}$$

$$\frac{d}{dt}\left\{r^2\left[\dot{\beta} - \kappa\left(\dot{\Omega}^{(1)}\sin i_0\cos\theta - \frac{di^{(1)}}{dt}\sin\theta\right)\right]\right\}$$
$$+ r^2\left[\dot{f}^2\sin\beta\cos\beta + \kappa\dot{f}\cos^2\beta\left(\dot{\Omega}^{(1)}\sin i_0\sin\theta + \frac{di^{(1)}}{dt}\cos\theta\right)\right] = -\frac{\partial\tilde{V}}{\partial\beta}, \tag{5.6.42}$$

where we have retained only first powers of κ, treated $\dot{\beta}$ and $\sin\beta$ as $O(\kappa)$, and used $\dot{\theta} = \dot{f} + \kappa\dot{\omega}^{(1)}$. This last implies $\theta = f + (\omega_0 + \kappa\omega^{(1)})$, with f representing the perturbed true anomaly.

Let us now adopt f as the independent variable and, as in the preceding section, employ $u = 1/r$, $p = r^2\dot{f}$, together with

$$u = u^{(0)} + \kappa u^{(1)}, \qquad p = p^{(0)} + \kappa p^{(1)}, \qquad \beta = \kappa\beta^{(1)}.$$

Further, we will restrict ourselves to values of $\omega^{(1)}$, $\Omega^{(1)}$, and $i^{(1)}$ which vary linearly with f; in particular, let

$$\omega^{(1)} = \hat{\omega}f, \qquad \Omega^{(1)} = \hat{\Omega}f, \qquad i^{(1)} = \hat{\imath}f. \tag{5.6.43}$$

These conditions provide us with new expressions for the equations of motion, the zero-order set again representing Keplerian motion in the plane $\beta^{(0)} \equiv 0$, with constant elements $a, e, \ldots$. The first-order system turns out to be

$$\frac{d^2u^{(1)}}{df^2} + u^{(1)} + \frac{2p^{(1)} + e\sin f\cdot dp^{(1)}/df}{\sqrt{\mu a^3(1-e^2)^3}} + \frac{2(1+e\cos f)}{a(1-e^2)}(\hat{\omega} + \hat{\Omega}\cos i_0)$$
$$= \frac{a(1-e^2)}{\mu(1+e\cos f)^2}\frac{1}{\kappa}\frac{\partial\tilde{V}}{\partial r}, \tag{5.6.44}$$

$$\frac{dp^{(1)}}{df} = -\sqrt{\frac{a^3(1-e^2)^3}{\mu}}\cdot\frac{1}{(1+e\cos f)^2}\frac{1}{\kappa}\frac{\partial\tilde{V}}{\partial f}, \tag{5.6.45}$$

$$\frac{d^2\beta^{(1)}}{df^2} + \beta^{(1)} + 2(\hat{\imath}\cos\theta + \hat{\Omega}\sin i_0\sin\theta) = -\frac{a(1-e^2)}{\mu(1+e\cos f)^2}\frac{1}{\kappa}\frac{\partial\tilde{V}}{\partial\beta}. \tag{5.6.46}$$

The additional degrees of freedom introduced by the Lindstedt functions $\hat{\omega}f$, $\hat{\Omega}f$, $\hat{\imath}f$ are now at our disposal and, in keeping with our original purpose, may be exploited to compensate for terms in (5.6.44)–(5.6.46) which give rise to the monotonic factors which motivated this approach. This compensation is obviously dependent on the exact form of $\tilde{V}$; hence, it is best to pursue this further by example. Before we do so, we remind the reader that the proper expression for time (see 5.6.29) must not be neglected; the Lindstedt device offers nothing new here so this question will not be considered at this point.

Illustrative Example. Effect of Earth's Oblateness on a Satellite*

From (5.3.18) we have, to first order ($J_2 \equiv \kappa$),

$$\frac{1}{J_2}\tilde{V} = -\frac{\mu R^2}{2r^3}(1-3\sin^2\varphi'),$$

so that, with the aid of some spherical trigonometry,

$$\frac{1}{J_2}\frac{\partial \tilde{V}}{\partial r} = \frac{3\mu R^2}{2r^4}\left(1-3\sin^2 i_0 \sin^2\theta\right),$$

$$\frac{1}{J_2}\frac{\partial \tilde{V}}{\partial f} = \frac{3\mu R^2}{r^3}\sin^2 i_0 \sin\theta\cos\theta,$$

$$\frac{1}{J_2}\frac{\partial \tilde{V}}{\partial \beta} = \frac{3\mu R^2}{r^3}\sin i_0 \cos i_0 \sin\theta.$$

Equation (5.6.45) becomes

$$\frac{dp^{(1)}}{df} = -\frac{3R^2\sin^2 i_0}{2}\sqrt{\frac{\mu}{a^3(1-e^2)^3}}(1+e\cos f)\sin\theta\cos\theta,$$

where we may now interpret θ as

$$\theta = f+\omega_0 = \bar{\theta}. \tag{5.6.47}$$

We then have $d/df = d/d\bar{\theta}$, and

$$p^{(1)} = -3R^2\sin^2 i_0\sqrt{\frac{\mu}{a^3(1-e^2)^3}} \cdot\left[\frac{1}{2}\sin^2\bar{\theta}+\frac{e}{3}\sin\omega_0\sin^3\bar{\theta}-\frac{e}{3}\cos\omega_0\cos^3\bar{\theta}\right]+C_1, \tag{5.6.48}$$

where $p = \sqrt{\mu a(1-e^2)} + J_2 p^{(1)}$, and C_1 is determined by the initial conditions, say $p^{(1)} = 0$ at $\bar{\theta} = \bar{\theta}_0$.

*Note also [20] for a treatment of first-order oblateness effects involving Lindstedt's technique.

Next, again using (5.6.47), (5.6.46) becomes

$$\frac{d^2\beta^{(1)}}{d\bar{\theta}^2} + \beta^{(1)} + 2(\hat{\imath}\cos\bar{\theta} + \hat{\Omega}\sin i_0 \sin\bar{\theta})$$

$$= -\frac{3R^2 \sin i_0 \cos i_0}{a^2(1-e^2)^2}\left(\sin\bar{\theta} + e\sin\omega_0 \sin^2\bar{\theta} + e\cos\omega_0 \sin\bar{\theta}\cos\bar{\theta}\right). \qquad (5.6.49)$$

Inspection of the right-hand side shows a "resonance" term, $\sin\bar{\theta}$, which would result in the form $\bar{\theta}\cos\bar{\theta}$ in β. It may be suppressed by choosing

$$\hat{\Omega} = -\frac{3R^2\cos i_0}{2a^2(1-e^2)^2},$$

or,

$$\tilde{\Omega} = \Omega_0 - \frac{3J_2R^2\cos i_0}{2a^2(1-e^2)^2}f. \qquad (5.6.50)$$

This last, interestingly enough, corresponds to the result obtained earlier (5.3.20) for the change in longitude of the node of a circular orbit ($e = 0$) over one revolution, i.e., $f = 2\pi$. As we shall see in the next chapter, this *regression of the nodes* is a well-known effect and can also be calculated through the application of Lagrange's planetary equations.

Since the right-hand side of (5.6.49) does not contain a term $\cos\bar{\theta}$ (which would generate another secular contribution to β), the Lindstedt parameter $\hat{\imath}$ is not needed for this problem and we set it equal to zero. We thus obtain, finally,

$$\beta = -\frac{3J_2R^2\sin i_0\cos i_0}{a^2(1-e^2)^2}\, e\cdot\left[\sin\omega_0\left(\frac{1}{3}\sin^4\bar{\theta} + \cos^2\bar{\theta} - \frac{1}{3}\cos^4\bar{\theta}\right)\right.$$

$$- \cos\omega_0\left(\frac{1}{3}\sin\bar{\theta}\cos^3\bar{\theta} + \frac{1}{3}\sin^3\bar{\theta}\cos\bar{\theta}\right)$$

$$\left. - C_2\cos\bar{\theta} + C_3\sin\bar{\theta}\right], \qquad (5.6.51)$$

where again C_2 and C_3 are to be chosen by appropriate initial conditions, for example, $\beta = d\beta/d\bar{\theta} = 0$ at $\bar{\theta} = \bar{\theta}_0$.

Equation (5.6.44), after substituting $\partial\tilde{V}/\partial r$ and equations (5.6.48) and (5.6.50), now can be solved. Again, terms in $\theta \sin\theta$ and $\theta \cos\theta$ may be avoided in its solution by choosing

$$\hat{\omega} = \frac{3R^2}{4a^2(1-e^2)^2}\left(4-5\sin^2 i_0\right); \tag{5.6.52}$$

we have

$$\begin{aligned} u^{(1)} = \frac{R^2}{a^3(1-e^2)^3}\Bigg\{&\sin^2 i_0\Big[\tfrac{7}{2} + \tfrac{1}{2}\sin^2\bar{\theta} - \sin^4\bar{\theta} + \tfrac{5}{2}e\sin\omega_0\sin^3\bar{\theta}(\tfrac{1}{2} - 3\sin^2\bar{\theta}) \\ &\quad + \tfrac{5}{4}e\cos\omega_0\sin^2\bar{\theta}\cos\bar{\theta} - \tfrac{1}{2}e^2\sin^2\omega_0(4 - 2\sin^2\bar{\theta} - \sin^4\bar{\theta}) \\ &\quad - e^2\cos^2\omega_0(1 - \tfrac{1}{2}\sin^2\bar{\theta} - \tfrac{9}{2}\sin^4\bar{\theta}) \\ &\quad + e^2\sin\omega_0\cos\omega_0\sin\bar{\theta}\cos\bar{\theta}\Big] \\ &- \tfrac{3}{2} + \tfrac{1}{2}e^2\cos^2\omega_0(1 + \sin^2\bar{\theta}) \\ &+ e^2\sin^2\omega_0(1 - \tfrac{1}{2}\sin^2\bar{\theta}) - e^2\sin\omega_0\cos\omega_0\sin\bar{\theta}\cos\bar{\theta}\Bigg\} \\ - \frac{2C_1}{\sqrt{\mu a(1-e^2)}} &+ C_4\sin\bar{\theta} + C_5\cos\bar{\theta}. \end{aligned} \tag{5.6.53}$$

Note that the expression (5.6.52) leads to

$$\tilde{\omega} = \omega_0 + \frac{3J_2R^2}{4a^2(1-e^2)^2}\left(5\cos^2 i_0 - 1\right)f. \tag{5.6.54}$$

which is also a well-known effect, the *precession of the apsides*.

The value of r is easily obtained by $r = 1/u \simeq r^{(0)} - J_2 u^{(1)}/u^{(0)2}$, but this result displays no behavior worth describing in detail. The constants C_4 and C_5 are also determined from initial conditions. The sixth constant will be obtained from the time equation as discussed earlier.

This completes our sketch of the Lindstedt approach. Observe that relative to the moving frame, the perturbed coordinates, as functions of f, exhibit purely periodic behavior. However, if the time equation (5.6.29) were executed in detail for this example, it would exhibit a secular term which cannot be avoided by the Lindstedt device as used here. More will be said about this "drift in epoch" in the next chapter.

In principle, the Lindstedt technique can be extended to eliminate a variety of effects, e.g., the spiral decay in r due to atmospheric drag could be "removed" by introducing a time dependent reference altitude. We also note that if several disturbing functions are to be treated simultaneously, their Lindstedt parameters are simply additive to first order; moreover, the Lindstedt procedure can be carried to higher orders by replacing equations such as (5.6.43) by nonlinear expressions. We may also remark that the moving reference frame $\tilde{x}$, $\tilde{y}$, $\tilde{z}$ and the Lindstedt variables themselves are conceptually related to such devices as Hansen's *auxiliary ellipse* (Chapter 9) and the "mean" variables or "averaged motions" encountered in several other astrodynamical techniques.

7. CHANGE OF INDEPENDENT VARIABLE

In this section we examine more closely the one transformation used in all the examples for noncircular orbits given above, namely, the change of independent variable from time to the true anomaly. In the foregoing, we used the actual, i.e., perturbed, value of the central angle. In general, we can also use the unperturbed true anomaly of the zero-order (Keplerian) orbit; we could even use the eccentric anomaly. In any case, the basic idea is to interpose a new independent variable between the time and the other coordinates like β, p, u, or r. The reason for this is the difficulty in solving Kepler's equation for noncircular orbits. If we insist on retaining t when the eccentricity is not zero, the only alternative is to expand the (unperturbed) coordinates in some kind of series, e.g., as shown in (2.6.17); then we are inevitably led to a long awkward process. As noted, such methods are used in classical celestial mechanics, but will not be followed in this chapter.

In transforming to one of the anomalies, care must be exercised to avoid losing the significance of time, which is now to be considered as a *dependent* variable. Indeed, the relation of time to angle is affected strongly by the choice of the new independent variable, i.e., not only whether we select true or eccentric anomaly, but also whether we wish to utilize the perturbed or unperturbed representation of that angle. This is sufficiently important to warrant illustration in some detail.

Use of the Unperturbed Anomaly. We return to the equations of motion for spherical coordinates derived in Section 6.1 and introduce the argument of latitude θ (Fig. 5.7) as in-plane angle. Using $r = r^{(0)} + \kappa r^{(1)} + \cdots$, $\theta = \theta^{(0)} + \kappa\theta^{(1)} + \cdots$, $\beta = \kappa\beta^{(1)} + \cdots$, the zero-order equations are

$$\ddot{r}^{(0)} - r^{(0)}\dot{\theta}^{(0)2} + \mu/r^{(0)2} = 0, \qquad \frac{d}{dt}\left[r^{(0)2}\dot{\theta}^{(0)}\right] = 0. \tag{5.7.1}$$

The last leads to

$$\dot{\theta}^{(0)} = p_0/r^{(0)2}; \tag{5.7.2}$$

it is this which allows us to make the transformation

$$\frac{d}{dt} \equiv \dot{\theta}^{(0)}\frac{d}{d\theta} = \frac{p_0}{r^{(0)2}}\frac{d}{d\theta^{(0)}},$$

and thus to solve the first of (5.7.1) in the form

$$r^{(0)} = \frac{p_0^2/\mu}{1 + C_1\cos(\theta^{(0)} - C_2)}. \tag{5.7.3}$$

We recognize (5.7.2) and (5.7.3) immediately as representing Keplerian motion. Further, the former provides us with

$$dt = \frac{r^{(0)2}}{p_0}\,d\theta^{(0)},$$

or

$$t = \frac{p_0^3}{\mu^2(1-C_1^2)}\left\{\frac{2}{\sqrt{1-C_1^2}}\tan^{-1}\left(\sqrt{\frac{1-C_1}{1+C_1}}\tan\frac{\theta^{(0)}-C_2}{2}\right) - \frac{C_1\sin(\theta^{(0)}-C_2)}{1+C_1\cos(\theta^{(0)}-C_2)}\right\} + C_3. \tag{5.7.4}$$

Thus we have time as a function of $\theta^{(0)}$; moreover, it is easily seen that (5.7.4) is no more than Kepler's equation (2.2.37).

The first-order equations, after transformation to $\theta^{(0)}$ as independent variable, are

$$\begin{aligned}
&\frac{d^2r^{(1)}}{d\theta^{(0)2}} - \frac{2}{r^{(0)}}\frac{dr^{(0)}}{d\theta^{(0)}}\frac{dr^{(1)}}{d\theta^{(0)}} - 2r^{(0)}\frac{d\theta^{(1)}}{d\theta^{(0)}} - r^{(1)} - \frac{2\mu}{p_0^2}r^{(0)}r^{(1)} = \frac{F_r^{(0)}}{p_0^2}r^{(0)4},\\
&\frac{d\theta^{(1)}}{d\theta^{(0)}} = -\frac{2r^{(1)}}{r^{(0)}} + \frac{1}{p_0^2}\int F_t^{(0)}r^{(0)2}\,d\theta^{(0)} + \frac{C_4}{p_0},\\
&\frac{d^2\beta^{(1)}}{d\theta^{(0)2}} + \beta^{(1)} = \frac{r^{(0)2}}{p_0^2}F_n.
\end{aligned} \tag{5.7.5}$$

Use of the Perturbed Anomaly. If we wish to transform the independent variable directly to θ, we use

$$\frac{d}{dt} = \dot\theta\frac{d}{d\theta} = \frac{1}{(dt/d\theta)}\frac{d}{d\theta}. \tag{5.7.6}$$

Then,

$$\frac{d^2r}{d\theta^2} - \frac{d^2t}{d\theta^2}\frac{1}{(dt/d\theta)}\frac{dr}{d\theta} - r\cos^2\beta - r\left(\frac{d\beta}{d\theta}\right)^2 + \frac{\mu}{r^2}\left(\frac{dt}{d\theta}\right)^2 = \kappa\left(\frac{dt}{d\theta}\right)^2F_r,$$

$$\frac{d}{d\theta}\left[\frac{r^2}{(dt/d\theta)}\cos^2\beta\right] = \kappa\frac{dt}{d\theta}F_t,$$

$$\frac{d}{d\theta}\left[\frac{r^2}{(dt/d\theta)}\frac{d\beta}{d\theta}\right] + \frac{r^2\sin\beta\cos\beta}{(dt/d\theta)} = \kappa\frac{dt}{d\theta}F_n.$$

This, of course, is familiar from Section 6.

Now, if we set

$$r = r^{(0)} + \kappa r^{(1)} + \cdots; \qquad \beta = \kappa\beta^{(1)} + \cdots; \qquad t = t^{(0)} + \kappa t^{(1)} + \cdots,$$

we obtain, as a zero-order set,

$$\begin{aligned} \frac{d^2r^{(0)}}{d\theta^2} - \frac{d^2t^{(0)}}{d\theta^2}\frac{1}{(dt^{(0)}/d\theta)}\frac{dr^{(0)}}{d\theta} - r^{(0)} + \frac{\mu}{r^{(0)2}}\left(\frac{dt^{(0)}}{d\theta}\right)^2 &= 0, \\ \frac{d}{d\theta}\left[\frac{r^{(0)2}}{(dt^{(0)}/d\theta)}\right] &= 0. \end{aligned} \tag{5.7.7}$$

This last gives us

$$dt^{(0)}/d\theta = \frac{1}{p'_0}\, r^{(0)2}, \tag{5.7.8}$$

where primes distinguish the integration constants belonging to the perturbed anomaly from those for the unperturbed anomaly. When substituted into the first of (5.7.7), this provides us with

$$\frac{d^2r^{(0)}}{d\theta^2} - \frac{2}{r^{(0)}}\frac{dr^{(0)}}{d\theta} - r^{(0)} + \frac{\mu}{p_0'^2}\, r^{(0)1} = 0,$$

which has the solution

$$r^{(0)} = \frac{p_0'^2/\mu}{1 + C'_1 \cos(\theta - C'_2)}; \tag{5.7.9}$$

compare (5.7.3). Then (5.7.8) yields

$$\begin{aligned} t^{(0)} = \frac{p_0'^3}{\mu^2(1-C'^2)}\Bigg\{\frac{2}{\sqrt{1-C_1'^2}}\tan^{-1}\left(\sqrt{\frac{1-C'_1}{1+C'_1}}\tan\frac{\theta - C'_2}{2}\right) \\ - \frac{C'_1 \sin(\theta - C'_2)}{1 + C'_1\cos(\theta - C'_2)}\Bigg\} + C'_3; \end{aligned} \tag{5.7.10}$$

compare (5.7.4).

The first-order equations are

$$\begin{aligned} &\frac{d^2r^{(1)}}{d\theta^2} - \frac{p'_0}{r^{(0)2}}\left[\frac{dr^{(0)}}{d\theta}\frac{d^2t^{(1)}}{d\theta^2} + \frac{dr^{(1)}}{d\theta}\frac{d^2t^{(0)}}{d\theta^2}\right] \\ &+ \frac{p_0'^2}{r^{(0)4}}\frac{dr^{(0)}}{d\theta}\frac{d^2t^{(0)}}{d\theta^2}\frac{dt^{(1)}}{d\theta} - r^{(1)} - \frac{2\mu}{p'_0}\left[\frac{r^{(0)}r^{(1)}}{p'_0} - \frac{dt^{(1)}}{d\theta}\right] = \frac{F_r^{(0)}}{p_0'^2}\, r^{(0)4}, \end{aligned} \tag{5.7.11}$$

$$\frac{dt^{(1)}}{d\theta} = \frac{2}{p_0'} r^{(0)} r^{(1)} - \frac{r^{(0)2}}{p_0'^3} \int F_\theta^{(0)} r^{(0)2}\, d\theta - \frac{C_4'}{p_0'^2} r^{(0)2},$$

$$\frac{d^2\beta^{(1)}}{d\theta^2} + \beta^{(1)} = \frac{r^{(0)2}}{p_0'^2} F_n^{(0)}. \tag{5.7.12}$$

Comparison of Results. It is worthwhile emphasizing that the choice of independent variable does not affect the results, only the means of obtaining them. That is to say, whether we select t, f or $f^{(0)}$, E or $E^{(0)}$, the final equations will be quantitatively identical, to the order desired.

To illustrate this, let us turn to our study of the effect of drag on a circular orbit, this time analyzing the motion by means of Eqs. (5.7.1) to (5.7.12). If the circular initial conditions $r = r_0, \dot{r} = 0, \dot{\theta} = \sqrt{\mu/r_0^3}$, apply at $\theta = \theta_0$, (5.7.2), (5.7.3), and (5.7.4) provide us with $p_0 = \sqrt{\mu r_0}, C_1 = 0, C_2 = \theta_0, C_3 = 0$, so that, of course,

$$r^{(0)} = r_0, \qquad \dot{\theta}^{(0)} = \sqrt{\mu/r^{(0)3}} = n_0, \qquad t = \frac{\theta^{(0)} - \theta_0}{n_0}. \tag{5.7.13}$$

Equations (5.3.26) then allow us to solve (5.7.5). We find

$$r^{(1)} = -2r_0^2\left(1-2\frac{\sigma}{n_0}\cos i_0\right)\left[\left(\theta^{(0)} - \theta_0\right) - \sin\left(\theta^{(0)} - \theta_0\right)\right],$$

$$\theta^{(1)} = r_0\left(1-2\frac{\sigma}{n_0}\cos i_0\right)\left[\frac{3}{2}\left(\theta^{(0)} - \theta_0\right)^2 + 4\cos\left(\theta^{(0)} - \theta_0\right) - 4\right], \tag{5.7.14}$$

$$\beta^{(1)} = -\frac{1}{2} r_0 \frac{\sigma}{n_0} \sin i_0 \left[\left(\theta^{(0)} - \theta_0\right)\sin\theta^{(0)} - \sin\theta_0 \sin\left(\theta^{(0)} - \theta_0\right)\right].$$

Substitution of the last of (5.7.13) and subsequent comparison with (5.6.9)–(5.6.11) indicates the equivalence of these approaches.

Turning now to the case where we used the perturbed true anomaly, (5.7.8)–(5.7.10) yield $C_0' = \sqrt{\mu r_0}$, $C_1' = 0$, $C_2' = \theta_0$, $C_3' = 0$ and

$$r^{(0)} = r_0, \; t^{(0)} = \frac{\theta - \theta_0}{n_0}. \tag{5.7.15}$$

Equations (5.7.11) and (5.7.12) then provide us with

$$r^{(1)} = -2r_0^2\left(1-2\frac{\sigma}{n_0}\cos i_0\right)[\theta-\theta_0-\sin(\theta-\theta_0)],$$

$$t^{(1)} = -\sqrt{r_0^5/\mu}\left(1-2\frac{\sigma}{n_0}\cos i_0\right)\left[\frac{3}{2}(\theta-\theta_0)^2 + 4\cos(\theta-\theta_0) - 4\right], \tag{5.7.16}$$

$$\beta^{(1)} = -\frac{1}{2} r_0 \frac{\sigma}{n_0} \sin i_0[(\theta-\theta_0)\sin\theta - \sin\theta_0 \sin(\theta-\theta_0)].$$

Of course, to first order

$$t = t^{(0)} + \kappa t^{(1)}$$
$$= \frac{\theta - \theta_0}{n_0} + \kappa t^{(1)}$$

or

$$\theta - \theta_0 = n_0 t - \kappa n_0 t^{(1)}. \tag{5.7.17}$$

Now the first of (5.7.16) leads to

$$r = r_0 - 2\kappa r_0^2 \left(1 - 2\frac{\sigma}{n_0}\cos i_0\right)[(\theta - \theta_0) - \sin(\theta - \theta_0)];$$

substituting (5.7.17) and retaining only first-order terms yields

$$r = r_0 - 2\kappa r_0^2 \left(1 - 2\frac{\sigma}{n_0}\cos i_0\right)[n_0 t - \sin n_0 t].$$

The first-order part of this agrees with (5.6.9); similarly, the equivalence of $\beta^{(1)}$ and (5.6.11) can be shown. Taking (5.7.17) and the second of (5.7.16) we get

$$\theta - \theta_0 = n_0 t + \kappa r_0 \left(1 - 2\frac{\sigma}{n_0}\cos i_0\right)\left[\frac{3}{2}(\theta - \theta_0)^2 + 4\cos(\theta - \theta_0) - 4\right]. \tag{5.7.18}$$

Now

$$\theta = \theta_0 + f^{(0)} + \kappa f^{(1)}, \qquad \text{and} \qquad f^{(0)} = n_0 t,$$

so that again substituting (5.7.17) on the right-hand side of (5.7.18) and retaining first-order terms,

$$f^{(1)} = r_0 \left(1 - 2\frac{\sigma}{n_0}\cos i_0\right)\left[\frac{3}{2} n_0^2 t^2 + 4\cos n_0 t - 4\right],$$

which agrees with (5.6.10).

We have belabored this point of equivalence, perhaps, but its significance cannot be overemphasized; it is fundamental to all perturbation methods.

8. SECULAR AND PERIODIC EFFECTS; RECTIFICATION

In the discussions of the examples given in this chapter, we noted several times that the perturbed solutions have terms of two types, those which contain the independent variable directly, and those which contain it only as an argument of a trigonometric function. The first grow without limit as time increases and are called *secular*. Members of the second class return to their original values after one revolution or a fraction thereof and are called *periodic*. We had already seen something of this in Chapter 3, where we distinguished between precession (of the equinoxes) which is a secular effect, and nutation which is a periodic effect. It is obvious that, over a long time, secular terms predominate and, since they limit the accuracy and the prediction range of a perturbation theory they often receive more attention than do the periodic effects. One may expect that higher-order secular terms are generally nonlinear and the whole sequence may tend toward the power series representation of a periodic term of very long period and, possibly, large amplitude [22].

It is worth distinguishing among three aspects of the secular terms: limiting applicability as discussed above, convergence of the series representation, and physical instability of the orbital system described by the theory. Of the last two, Sterne [22, pp. 112–113] makes the following remarks. "The convergence of the resulting series has been the subject of many studies, for some of which the reader is referred to Poincaré [23, 24]. Past concern ... is thought by the author possibly to have been the result of confusing the mathematical question of convergence with the dynamical question of what the long-time behavior of the ... system really would be. ... [The] presence of ... secular terms ... cannot possibly show whether the series converge or whether the ... system is destined to undergo drastic changes.... Thus each term in the infinite series of secular terms $t - t^3/3! + t^5/5! - \cdots$ increases without limit and approaches infinity as t approaches infinity. Yet the series converges for all values of t, and in fact represents merely the bounded and gently varying function sin t. ... [Some] writers have argued that purely secular terms, that increase without limit, and even mixed terms that involve oscillations of increasing 'violence', imply divergence or 'instability.' It seems clear to the author that the existence of secular or mixed terms implies nothing at all about either convergence or long-time 'stability'."

The confusion Sterne mentions may stem, in part, from the normal reverence accorded the founders of a discipline and the belief that they must have had rational, well-considered, reasons for everything they did. As Dziobek [25, p. 280] observes, "Every device was employed by Euler, Lagrange, and Laplace to get rid of these [secular] terms. Anyone who studies their works must feel that, aside from mathematical considerations, a sort of metaphysical idea directed these earliest explorations which bridged the gap between entire ignorance and complete clearness."

As a final item in this chapter we must mention *rectification*, a practical and effective device for enhancing the accuracy of any given analytical perturbation solution. As applied to a first-order scheme, calculations of the perturbations, based on the disturbing forces evaluated with the unperturbed coordinates, are stepped forward in time until the perturbations amount to a (relatively) substantial fraction of the coordinates. At this point, the first-order results are combined with the Keplerian coordinates, and a new set of zero-order starting values is found. The first-order calculation is then carried forward another step, etc., etc. Using any of the finite-order solutions discussed in this text, we can subdivide a long prediction interval into subintervals and, at the beginning of each, absorb the accumulated perturbations by a redefinition (or rectification) of the unperturbed orbit. This strategy applies whether secular terms appear explicitly in our finite-order solution or are made implicit by devices such as the Lindstedt parameters. Its application is equally straightforward for cases with more than one perturbative effect. The convergence of this procedure, as the step size goes to zero, follows from the same rationale as the convergence proof for equations of the form $dy/dx = F(x,y)$, by the method of Picard iterants [26], where we rely on the fact that a set of higher-order differential equations can be transformed to first-order ones.

In the theoretical limit, as we take smaller and smaller steps, rectification allows us to obtain any accuracy desired. In practice, however, we always have some residuals from the higher-order terms, and accumulated roundoff.

It is unfortunate that rectification has been virtually ignored in the past. However, this methodology lends itself so well to the application of electronic computers that such a state of affairs cannot persist in our day, particularly since the economics (considering man-hours spent on algebraic manipulations and their verification) favors the machine.

REFERENCES

1. F. R. Moulton, *An Introduction to Celestial Mechanics*, 2nd ed. rev., Macmillan, New York, 1914.
2. W. M. Kaula, "Determination of the Earth's Gravitational Field", *Reviews of Geophysics*, **1,** 507, 1963.
3. T. E. Sterne and G. F. Schilling, "Some Preliminary Values of Upper Atmosphere Density from Observations of USSR Satellites", *Smithsonian Contributions to Astrophysics*, **2,** 207, 1958.
4. G. E. Cook, "Satellite Drag Coefficients", *Planet. Space Sci.*, **13,** 929, 1965.
5. USAF ARDC, *Handbook of Geophysics*, Macmillan, New York, 1960.
6. D. G. King-Hele and E. Quinn, "Air Density at Heights of 150–300 KM in the Years 1962–1964", *Planet. Space Sci.*, **13,** 693, 1965.
7. G. P. Newton, R. Horowitz, and W. Priester, "Atmospheric Density and Temperature Variation from the Explorer XVII Satellite and a Further Comparison with Satellite Drag", *Planet. Space Sci.*, **13,** 599, 1965.
8. R. Jastrow and C. A. Pearse, "Atmospheric Drag on the Satellite", *J. Geophys. Res.* **62,** 413, 1957.
9. S. L. Valley (Ed.), *Handbook of Geophysics and Space Environments*, McGraw-Hill, New York, 1965, Chap. 11.
10. J. A. Stratton, *Electromagnetic Theory*, McGraw-Hill, New York, 1941, p. 237.
11. C. W. Allen, *Astrophysical Quantities*, Athlone Press, London, 2nd ed., 1963.
12. a) D. Brouwer, "Integration of the Equations of General Planetary Theory in Rectangular Coordinates", *Astron. Journal*, **51,** 37, 1944.

b) J. M. A. Danby, "Integration of the Equations of Planetary Motion in Rectangular Coordinates," *Astron. Journal*, **67,** 287, 1962.

13. J. F. Encke, "Über die allgemeinen Störungen der Planeten", *Berliner Astronomisches Jahresbuch,* **319,** 319, 1857.
14. F. T. Geyling, "Perturbation Methods for Satellite Orbits", *Bell System Technical Journal,* **43,** 847, 1964.
15. D. G. King-Hele, "The Descent of an Earth Satellite Through the Upper Atmosphere", *Jour. Brit. Interplan. Soc.*, **15,** 314, 1956.
16. H. R. Westerman, "Perturbation Approach to the Effect of the Geomagnetic Field on a Charged Satellite", *ARS Journal*, **30,** 204, 1960.
17. M. L. Anthony and G. E. Fosdick, "Satellite Motions about an Oblate Planet", *Journal of the Aerospace Sciences*, **28,** 789, 1961.
18. E. Levin, "Solar Radiation Pressure Perturbations of Earth Satellite Orbits", *AIAA Journal*, **6,** 120, 1968.
19. A. Lindstedt, "Beitrag zur Integration der Differentialgleichungen der Störungstheorie", *K. Akad. Wiss., St. Petersburg*, **31,** 4, 1882.
20. R. E. Roberson, "Orbital Behavior of Earth Satellites" (Parts I and II), *J. Franklin Inst.*, **264,** 181, 269, 1957.
21. C. L. Charlier, *Die Mechanik des Himmels*, Vol. 1, de Gruyter, Berlin, 1927, p. 322.
22. T. E. Sterne, *An Introduction to Celestial Mechanics*, Interscience, New York, 1960.
23. H. Poincaré, *Leçons de Mechanique Celeste*, Gauthier-Villars, Paris, 1905, Vol. I.
24. H. Poincaré, *Les Methodes Nouvelles de la Mecanique Celeste*, Gauthier-Villars, Paris, 1892, Vol. I.
25. O. Dziobek, *Mathematical Theories of Planetary Motions*, Dover (reissue), New York, 1962.
26. A. G. Lubowe, "Order of a Perturbation Method", *AIAA Journal*, **3,** 568, 1965.

Chapter six

PERTURBATION IN THE ELEMENTS

1. THE OSCULATING ELLIPSE AND LAGRANGE'S PLANETARY EQUATIONS

We have shown several ways in which we can calculate the position and the velocity of an orbiting body subject to perturbations. In so doing, we may find it convenient to adopt the true or the eccentric anomaly as independent variable but since these can be related to time we have, in essence, found the position and velocity as functions of time.

We recall from Chapter 4 that the position and the velocity of a moving body, at a specified instant, define a Keplerian orbit. Thus, if at a moment t we were to compute the orbit elements by the means outlined, they would define the path the body would follow if all perturbations were suddenly removed. This curve is tangent to the actual trajectory at time t and is called the *osculating orbit* for that instant. For the sake of argument, let us assume that this orbit is always elliptic. Now, in general, the orbit elements for this ellipse differ from those we would find at $t-\Delta t$ or $t+\Delta t$. We may think of the body as passing continuously from one osculating ellipse to another.

This concept is extremely useful for two reasons. First, the orbit elements do not exhibit the normal variability of anomalistic motion as do the coordinates; hence any variation can be ascribed directly to the perturbing forces. Secondly, the elements possess a geometric significance clearer than that which can be deduced from the coordinates; hence the effect of the perturbation on the orbit can be seen immediately.

Since there are six elements, it is desirable that we should write the three second-order differential equations of motion expressed in the coordinates as six first-order differential equations expressed in the elements. This provides us with direct means of obtaining the variations and yields, to first order in the perturbations, differential equations which reduce to quadratures.

Let us first restrict ourselves to perturbative forces which can be derived from a potential function, say $-\tilde{R}$, the negative of which is the *disturbing function.* Then the equations of motion can be written

$$\frac{d^2x}{dt^2} + \frac{\mu x}{r^3} = \frac{\partial \tilde{R}}{\partial x}; \qquad \frac{d^2y}{dt^2} + \frac{\mu y}{r^3} = \frac{\partial \tilde{R}}{\partial y}; \qquad \frac{d^2z}{dt^2} + \frac{\mu z}{r^3} = \frac{\partial \tilde{R}}{\partial z}. \tag{6.1.1}$$

If the right-hand sides of (6.1.1) were zero, we could write the solutions as $x = x(t, a, e, i, \omega, \Omega, \tau)$, etc., or more briefly

$$x = x(t,\alpha_i); \qquad y = y(t,\alpha_i); \qquad z = z(t,\alpha_i), \tag{6.1.2}$$

where $i = 1, \ldots, 6$ and α_i is any of the orbit elements. The equations of motion which (6.1.2) satisfy are

$$\frac{\partial^2 x}{\partial t^2} + \frac{\mu x}{r^3} = 0; \qquad \frac{\partial^2 y}{\partial t^2} + \frac{\mu y}{r^3} = 0; \qquad \frac{\partial^2 z}{\partial t^2} + \frac{\mu z}{r^3} = 0, \tag{6.1.3}$$

since, in Keplerian motion, only the coordinates contain t; i.e., the elements are constant.

It would be convenient if the coordinates were precisely the same functions of the elements in perturbed as in unperturbed motion, i.e., if (6.1.2) were valid at all times. To obtain this, we must allow the elements, α_i, to be variable in time so that (6.1.2) holds even when the perturbing force does not vanish. Likewise, it is desirable to find the perturbed velocities by the same technique as used in Keplerian motion, i.e., simply by differentiating the coordinates with respect to time explicitly, without regard to the dependence of the elements on time. Thus we desire

$$dx/dt = \partial x/\partial t. \tag{6.1.4}$$

But actually, from (6.1.2)

$$\frac{dx}{dt} = \frac{\partial x}{\partial t} + \sum_i \frac{\partial x}{\partial \alpha_i}\frac{d\alpha_i}{dt},$$

so that we must then demand that*

$$\sum_i \frac{\partial x}{\partial \alpha_i}\dot{\alpha}_i = \sum_i \frac{\partial y}{\partial \alpha_i}\dot{\alpha}_i = \sum_i \frac{\partial z}{\partial \alpha_i}\dot{\alpha}_i = 0. \tag{6.1.5}$$

The three conditions (6.1.2) and the three conditions (6.1.5) are just sufficient to allow a unique solution of (6.1.1) after introduction of the six new variables $\alpha_i(t)$.

Now from (6.1.4), we obtain

$$\frac{d^2x}{dt^2} = \frac{\partial^2 x}{\partial t^2} + \sum_i \frac{\partial^2 x}{\partial t\, \partial \alpha_i}\dot{\alpha}_i, \tag{6.1.6}$$

*This is known as the *condition of osculation.* It assures that the osculating ellipse is tangent to the actual orbit, since it assures that the velocity in the osculating ellipse, treated as a Keplerian orbit, is identical with the actual velocity (at the point for which the osculating ellipse is defined).

so that the first of (6.1.1) becomes

$$\frac{\partial^2 x}{\partial t^2} + \sum_i \frac{\partial^2 x}{\partial t\,\partial \alpha_i}\dot{\alpha}_i + \frac{\mu x}{r^3} = \frac{\partial \tilde{R}}{\partial x}. \tag{6.1.7}$$

But $\partial^2 x/\partial t^2$ is, at any instant, the same as that which would be obtained in unperturbed motion if we had chosen the values of the α_i at that instant and treated them as constants; similarly for the coordinates x, y, z as they appear in $\mu x/r^3$. Thus these are related by (6.1.3), so that (6.1.7) becomes

$$\sum_i \frac{\partial^2 x}{\partial t\,\partial \alpha_i}\dot{\alpha}_i = \frac{\partial \tilde{R}}{\partial x}. \tag{6.1.8}$$

and also

$$\sum_i \frac{\partial^2 y}{\partial t\,\partial \alpha_i}\dot{\alpha}_i = \frac{\partial \tilde{R}}{\partial y}, \qquad \sum_i \frac{\partial^2 z}{\partial t\,\partial \alpha_i}\dot{\alpha}_i = \frac{\partial \tilde{R}}{\partial z}. \tag{6.1.9}$$

Now if we multiply $\Sigma[(\partial x/\partial \alpha_i)\dot{\alpha}_i]$ of (6.1.5) by $\partial \dot{x}/\partial \alpha_j$, multiply (6.1.8) by $\partial x/\partial \alpha_j$, and subtract, we get, noting that $\partial^2 x/(\partial t\,\partial \alpha_j) = \partial \dot{x}/\partial \alpha_j$,

$$\sum_i \left(\frac{\partial \dot{x}}{\partial \alpha_i}\frac{\partial x}{\partial \alpha_j} - \frac{\partial x}{\partial \alpha_i}\frac{\partial \dot{x}}{\partial \alpha_j}\right)\dot{\alpha}_i = \frac{\partial \tilde{R}}{\partial x}\frac{\partial x}{\partial \alpha_j}. \tag{6.1.10}$$

Adding corresponding equations in y and z to (6.1.10) and remembering that

$$\frac{\partial \tilde{R}}{\partial x}\frac{\partial x}{\partial \alpha_j} + \frac{\partial \tilde{R}}{\partial y}\frac{\partial y}{\partial \alpha_j} + \frac{\partial \tilde{R}}{\partial z}\frac{\partial z}{\partial \alpha_j} \equiv \frac{\partial \tilde{R}}{\partial \alpha_j}, \tag{6.1.11}$$

we find

$$\sum_i \left[\left(\frac{\partial \dot{x}}{\partial \alpha_i}\frac{\partial x}{\partial \alpha_j} - \frac{\partial x}{\partial \alpha_i}\frac{\partial \dot{x}}{\partial \alpha_j}\right) + \left(\frac{\partial \dot{y}}{\partial \alpha_i}\frac{\partial y}{\partial \alpha_j} - \frac{\partial y}{\partial \alpha_i}\frac{\partial \dot{y}}{\partial \alpha_j}\right) + \left(\frac{\partial \dot{z}}{\partial \alpha_i}\frac{\partial z}{\partial \alpha_j} - \frac{\partial z}{\partial \alpha_i}\frac{\partial \dot{z}}{\partial \alpha_j}\right)\right]\dot{\alpha}_i = \frac{\partial \tilde{R}}{\partial \alpha_j}. \tag{6.1.12}$$

For brevity we write this equation as

$$\sum_i [\alpha_j, \alpha_i]\dot{\alpha}_i = \frac{\partial \tilde{R}}{\partial \alpha_j}, \tag{6.1.13}$$

where the quantity $[\alpha_j, \alpha_i]$ is called a *Lagrangian bracket*.

There are three important properties of Lagrangian brackets. Two can be derived by inspection of the left-hand side of (6.1.12), namely,

$$[\alpha_i, \alpha_i] = 0, \qquad [\alpha_j, \alpha_i] = -[\alpha_i, \alpha_j]. \tag{6.1.14}$$

The third requires a bit more investigation. We will abbreviate the first two terms of the summand on the left-hand side of (6.1.12) as $[x]$; then

$$\frac{\partial}{\partial t}[x] = \frac{\partial \dot{x}}{\partial \alpha_i}\frac{\partial^2 x}{\partial t\,\partial \alpha_j} + \frac{\partial^2 \dot{x}}{\partial t\,\partial \alpha_i}\frac{\partial x}{\partial \alpha_j} - \frac{\partial x}{\partial \alpha_i}\frac{\partial^2 \dot{x}}{\partial t\,\partial \alpha_j} - \frac{\partial^2 x}{\partial t\,\partial \alpha_i}\frac{\partial \dot{x}}{\partial \alpha_j}.$$

Now the first and fourth terms in this expression are identical, since $\partial\dot{x}/\partial\alpha_i \equiv \partial^2 x/\partial t\,\partial\alpha_i$ and $\partial^2 x/\partial t\,\partial\alpha_j \equiv \partial\dot{x}/\partial\alpha_j$, and they cancel each other. Then we may write

$$\frac{\partial}{\partial t}[x] = \frac{\partial^2 \dot{x}}{\partial t\,\partial \alpha_i}\frac{\partial x}{\partial \alpha_j} - \frac{\partial x}{\partial \alpha_i}\frac{\partial^2 \dot{x}}{\partial t\,\partial \alpha_j}.$$

Now from (6.1.3)

$$\frac{\partial^2 x}{\partial t^2} = -\mu\frac{x}{r^3} = \frac{\partial}{\partial x}\left(\frac{\mu}{r}\right) = \frac{\partial V}{\partial x}.$$

Thus

$$\frac{\partial}{\partial t}[x] = \frac{\partial}{\partial \alpha_i}\left(\frac{\partial V}{\partial x}\right)\frac{\partial x}{\partial \alpha_j} - \frac{\partial x}{\partial \alpha_i}\frac{\partial}{\partial \alpha_j}\left(\frac{\partial V}{\partial x}\right),$$

which may be cast into the form

$$\frac{\partial}{\partial t}[x] = \frac{\partial}{\partial \alpha_i}\left(\frac{\partial V}{\partial x}\frac{\partial x}{\partial \alpha_j}\right) - \frac{\partial}{\partial \alpha_j}\left(\frac{\partial V}{\partial x}\frac{\partial x}{\partial \alpha_i}\right).$$

If now, we add similar expressions for

$$\frac{\partial[y]}{\partial t}, \qquad \frac{\partial[z]}{\partial t},$$

we find

$$\frac{\partial}{\partial t}[\alpha_j,\alpha_i] = \frac{\partial}{\partial \alpha_i}\left(\frac{\partial V}{\partial \alpha_j}\right) - \frac{\partial}{\partial \alpha_j}\left(\frac{\partial V}{\partial \alpha_i}\right) = 0, \tag{6.1.15}$$

which is the desired property. This last considerably simplifies the work of evaluating the Lagrange brackets because, as will appear, the brackets can be written as explicit functions of the eccentric anomaly E. Since, by (6.1.15), they are independent of time, we may evaluate them particularly at $t = \tau$, i.e., at $E = 0$, which reduces them to quite tractable expressions.

The process of evaluation is straightforward. We have from (3.4.2) and (3.4.3)

$$\begin{aligned} x &= l_1\,a(\cos E - e) + l_2\,a\sqrt{1-e^2}\sin E,\\ y &= m_1\,a(\cos E - e) + m_2\,a\sqrt{1-e^2}\sin E,\\ z &= n_1\,a(\cos E - e) + n_2\,a\sqrt{1-e^2}\sin E, \end{aligned} \tag{6.1.16}$$

where $l_1, l_2, m_1, m_2, n_1, n_2$ are given by (3.4.4) and (3.4.5). We may then perform the required differentiations, etc., remembering that the dependence of E on the elements a, e, $\tau(\chi)$ is given by Kepler's equation (2.2.35) or (2.2.36):

$$E - e \sin E = \sqrt{\mu/a^3}\,(t-\tau) = \sqrt{\mu/a^3}\, t + \chi. \tag{6.1.17}$$

We find

$$[a,e] = 0, \qquad [a,\Omega] = -\frac{1}{2}\sqrt{\frac{\mu(1-e^2)}{a}}\cos i,$$

$$[a,\tau] = \frac{1}{2}\frac{\mu}{a^2}, \qquad [a,\omega] = -\frac{1}{2}\sqrt{\frac{\mu(1-e^2)}{a}},$$

$$[a,i] = 0, \qquad [e,\tau] = 0,$$

$$[e,i] = 0, \qquad [\tau,\Omega] = 0,$$

$$[e,\Omega] = \sqrt{\frac{\mu a}{1-e^2}}\, e \cos i, \qquad [\tau,\omega] = 0,$$

$$[e,\omega] = \sqrt{\frac{\mu a}{1-e^2}}\, e, \qquad [i,\Omega] = \sqrt{\mu a(1-e^2)}\sin i,$$

$$[\tau,i] = 0, \qquad [i,\omega] = 0,$$

$$[\Omega,\omega] = 0.$$

Of course we also have from (6.1.14) $[\alpha_i,\alpha_i] = 0$, where α_i is any element. If we wish to use χ in place of τ, we get

$$[a,\chi] = -\frac{1}{2}\sqrt{\frac{\mu}{a}}, \qquad [\chi,i] = 0,$$

$$[e,\chi] = 0, \qquad [\chi,\Omega] = 0,$$

$$[\chi,\omega] = 0.$$

If these values are inserted in Eq. (6.1.13), we get

$$\frac{1}{2}\frac{\mu}{a^2}\dot{\tau} - \frac{1}{2}\sqrt{\frac{\mu(1-e^2)}{a}}\cos i\cdot\dot{\Omega} - \frac{1}{2}\sqrt{\frac{\mu(1-e^2)}{a}}\,\dot{\omega} = \frac{\partial\tilde{R}}{\partial a},$$

$$\sqrt{\frac{\mu a}{1-e^2}}\, e\cos i\cdot\dot{\Omega} + \sqrt{\frac{\mu a}{1-e^2}}\, e\,\dot{\omega} = \frac{\partial R}{\partial e},$$

$$-\frac{1}{2}\frac{\mu}{a^2}\dot{a} = \frac{\partial\tilde{R}}{\partial\tau},$$

$$\sqrt{\mu a(1-e^2)}\sin i\cdot\dot{\Omega} = \frac{\partial\tilde{R}}{\partial i},$$

$$\frac{1}{2}\sqrt{\frac{\mu(1-e^2)}{a}}\cos i\cdot\dot{a} - \sqrt{\frac{\mu a}{1-e^2}}\,e\cos i\cdot\dot{e} - \sqrt{\mu a(1-e^2)}\sin i\cdot\frac{di}{dt} = \frac{\partial\tilde{R}}{\partial\Omega},$$

$$\frac{1}{2}\sqrt{\frac{\mu(1-e^2)}{a}}\,\dot{a} - \sqrt{\frac{\mu a}{1-e^2}}\,e\,\dot{e} = \frac{\partial\tilde{R}}{\partial\omega}.$$

The alternative expressions in terms of χ can also be obtained. These six equations can be solved simultaneously for $\dot{a}$, $\dot{e}$, etc., the results being

$$\dot{a} = -\frac{2a^2}{\mu}\frac{\partial\tilde{R}}{\partial\tau}, \tag{6.1.18}$$

$$\dot{e} = -\frac{a(1-e^2)}{\mu e}\frac{\partial\tilde{R}}{\partial\tau} - \frac{1}{e}\sqrt{\frac{1-e^2}{\mu a}}\frac{\partial\tilde{R}}{\partial\omega}, \tag{6.1.19}$$

$$\dot{\tau} = \frac{2a^2}{\mu}\frac{\partial\tilde{R}}{\partial a} + \frac{a(1-e^2)}{\mu e}\frac{\partial\tilde{R}}{\partial e}, \tag{6.1.20}$$

$$\frac{di}{dt} = \frac{1}{\sqrt{\mu a(1-e^2)}\sin i}\left[\cos i\frac{\partial\tilde{R}}{\partial\omega} - \frac{\partial\tilde{R}}{\partial\Omega}\right], \tag{6.1.21}$$

$$\dot{\Omega} = \frac{1}{\sqrt{\mu a(1-e^2)}\sin i}\frac{\partial\tilde{R}}{\partial i}, \tag{6.1.22}$$

$$\dot{\omega} = \sqrt{\frac{1-e^2}{\mu a}}\frac{1}{e}\left[\frac{\partial\tilde{R}}{\partial e} - \frac{e\cot i}{1-e^2}\frac{\partial\tilde{R}}{\partial i}\right]. \tag{6.1.23}$$

In terms of χ the first three equations should be replaced by

$$\dot{a} = 2\sqrt{\frac{a}{\mu}}\frac{\partial\tilde{R}}{\partial\chi}, \tag{6.1.24}$$

$$\dot{e} = \frac{(1-e^2)}{e\sqrt{\mu a}}\frac{\partial\tilde{R}}{\partial\chi} - \frac{1}{e}\sqrt{\frac{1-e^2}{\mu a}}\frac{\partial\tilde{R}}{\partial\omega}, \tag{6.1.25}$$

$$\dot{\chi} = -\frac{1-e^2}{e\sqrt{\mu a}}\frac{\partial\tilde{R}}{\partial e} - 2\sqrt{\frac{a}{\mu}}\frac{\partial\tilde{R}}{\partial a}. \tag{6.1.26}$$

We have thus completed the task we set for ourselves earlier: Eqs. (6.1.18) through (6.1.23) or (6.1.24) through (6.1.26) and (6.1.21) through (6.1.23) provide us with the relations which express the effect of a perturbation on the osculating elements. This set is known as Lagrange's planetary equations.

2. ON THE APPLICATION OF LAGRANGE'S PLANETARY EQUATIONS

The analytic solution of the six simultaneous first-order differential equations (6.1.18) through (6.1.23), or of the alternative set, presents formidable difficulties in most cases. The foremost of these are that, except under rather unusual circumstances, none of the equations allow us to separate variables, and the right-hand sides are nonlinear in the elements. Of course, numerical means may be used; while some investigators† have pursued this, we will not discuss it here.

2.1. The Perturbation Approach

If the perturbing force is small compared to μ/r^2, we again expect that its effect will also be small, i.e., we will not find large changes in the osculating elements over a reasonable period of time. Once more let us employ the perturbation parameter κ as a measure of the magnitude of the disturbing force; thus we write its components as

$$\frac{\partial \tilde{R}}{\partial x} = \kappa \frac{\partial \tilde{R}^*}{\partial x}, \quad \frac{\partial \tilde{R}}{\partial y} = \kappa \frac{\partial \tilde{R}^*}{\partial y}, \quad \frac{\partial \tilde{R}}{\partial z} = \kappa \frac{\partial \tilde{R}^*}{\partial z}.$$

Then (6.1.11) provides us with $\partial \tilde{R}/\partial \alpha_j = \kappa\, \partial \tilde{R}^*/\partial \alpha_j$, and (6.1.18), for example, becomes

$$\dot{a} = -\frac{2a^2}{\mu} \kappa \frac{\partial}{\partial \tau} \tilde{R}^*(t, a, e, i, \omega, \Omega, \tau). \tag{6.2.1}$$

Now suppose we expand each element as

$$\alpha_j = \alpha_j^{(0)} + \kappa \alpha_j^{(1)} + \kappa^2 \alpha_j^{(2)} + \cdots, \tag{6.2.2}$$

where the $\alpha_j^{(i)}$ are functions to be determined. Substituting (6.2.2) into (6.2.1) and equating coefficients of like powers of κ, we find, to zero order, $\dot{a}^{(0)} = 0$ or $a^{(0)} =$ constant $\equiv a_0$. The first-order equation is then

$$\dot{a}^{(1)} = -\frac{2a_0^2}{\mu} \frac{\partial \tilde{R}_0^*}{\partial \tau}, \tag{6.2.3}$$

where $\partial \tilde{R}_0^*/\partial \tau$ is the zero-order part of the disturbing force.

To be clear on this last point, let us specify how $\partial \tilde{R}_0^*/\partial \alpha_j$ may be formed. We have demanded that, even in perturbed motion, the coordinates be expressed in terms of the elements and time exactly as they would be if unperturbed. Thus $x = x(t, a, e, i, \omega, \Omega, \tau)$, where we use the osculating values of elements at each instant. Hence, it is a simple matter to find $\partial x/\partial \alpha_j$, where α_j is any osculating element, since the dependence of x on α_j is the same as in Keplerian motion. Similarly, since $\tilde{R} = \tilde{R}(x, y, z, \dot{x}, \dot{y}, \dot{z}, t)$, it is easy to find $\partial \tilde{R}^*/\partial x$, etc. Then, by (6.1.11),

†See, for example, reference 1 for numerical variation of parameters methods due to S. Herrick *et al.*

we can write $\partial\tilde{R}^*/\partial\alpha_j$ in terms of the osculating elements and time, and expanding each α_j by (6.2.2) we obtain, as the term independent of κ, what we have called $\partial\tilde{R}_0^*/\partial\alpha_j$.

It is not difficult to see how to extend this iterative process to any order. In fact, its basic rationale parallels that of classical convergence proofs by Picard iterants. If we stop at the first level of approximation we have, for example,

$$a = a_0 + \kappa a^{(1)} = a_0 - \int \frac{2a_0^2}{\mu} \kappa \frac{\partial \tilde{R}_0^*}{\partial \tau} \, dt,$$

or

$$a - a_0 \equiv \Delta a = -\frac{2a_0^2}{\mu} \int \frac{\partial \tilde{R}_0}{\partial \tau} \, dt, \tag{6.2.4}$$

where we absorb κ in $\partial\tilde{R}_0/\partial\tau$.

2.2. On the Form of Kepler's Equation

As we have noted, to find expressions for the partial derivatives of $\tilde{R}$ we must differentiate the coordinates with respect to the elements. For this we use Eqs. (3.4.1) to (3.4.5). Now the dependence of x, y, z on i, ω, Ω is explicit in (3.4.3) to (3.4.5); however, their dependence on a, e, and especially τ (or χ) is expressed partly through Kepler's equation, (2.2.34), (2.2.35) or (2.2.37). Because the first two forms are so much more compact, it is usually more convenient to find $\partial E/\partial a$, $\partial E/\partial e$, $\partial E/\partial \tau$ (or $\partial E/\partial \chi$); if $\tilde{R}$ is to be written in terms* of f, we may use

$$\partial f/\partial \alpha_i = (\partial E/\partial \alpha_i)(df/dE),$$

where df/dE is obtained from (2.2.27) through (2.2.29).

Now we have $E - e \sin E = n(t-\tau) \equiv nt + \chi$, where $n = \sqrt{\mu/a^3}$; either form gives us simple expressions for $\partial E/\partial e$, $\partial E/\partial \tau$, or $\partial E/\partial \chi$. However, from the form of Kepler's equation containing τ, we obtain

$$\partial E(\tau)/\partial a = \frac{3}{2r}(e \sin E - E), \tag{6.2.5}$$

while from the form containing χ, we find

$$\partial E(\chi)/\partial a = \frac{3}{2r}(\chi + e \sin E - E). \tag{6.2.6}$$

There are two points of interest in connection with these equations. First, they imply a relation between $\partial\tilde{R}(\tau)/\partial a$ and $\partial\tilde{R}(\chi)/\partial a$ which deserves clarification.

*We have seen in the preceding chapter that the use of f or E rather than time as the independent variable may prove convenient. Whether we choose one or the other depends largely on the form of $\tilde{R}$, as will be shown below.

Second, they both contain the factor E as well as trigonometric functions of E and this is worthy of some discussion. As regards the first item, we bring this up to point out the relation between (6.1.20) and (6.1.26), the only two equations containing $\partial\tilde{R}/\partial a$. If accepted at their face value, it would appear that

$$\dot{\chi} = -n\dot{\tau}\ (\equiv -\sqrt{\mu/a^3}\,\dot{\tau}),$$

rather than

$$\dot{\chi} = -n\dot{\tau} - \dot{n}\tau, \tag{6.2.7}$$

which is obtained from the definition

$$\chi = -n\tau \equiv -\sqrt{\mu/a^3}\,\tau. \tag{6.2.8}$$

However, the point is that in (6.1.20) we naturally mean to use $\tilde{R}(\tau)$, since we are computing $\dot{\tau}$, while in (6.1.26) we have $\tilde{R}(\chi)$. Now

$$\frac{\partial\tilde{R}(\tau)}{\partial a} = \frac{\partial\tilde{R}(\chi)}{\partial a} + \frac{\partial\tilde{R}(\chi)}{\partial\chi}\frac{\partial\chi}{\partial a},$$

and thus, using (6.2.8),

$$\frac{\partial\tilde{R}(\tau)}{\partial a} = \frac{\partial\tilde{R}(\chi)}{\partial a} - \frac{3\chi}{2a}\frac{\partial\tilde{R}(\chi)}{\partial\chi}.$$

Then (6.1.20) may be rewritten as

$$\dot{\tau} = \frac{a(1-e^2)}{\mu e}\frac{\partial\tilde{R}(\chi)}{\partial e} + \frac{2a^2}{\mu}\frac{\partial\tilde{R}(\chi)}{\partial a} - \frac{3a\chi}{\mu}\frac{\partial\tilde{R}(\chi)}{\partial\chi},$$

which, inserted into (6.2.7), yields

$$\dot{\chi} = -\frac{1-e^2}{e\sqrt{\mu a}}\frac{\partial\tilde{R}(\chi)}{\partial e} - 2\sqrt{\frac{a}{\mu}}\frac{\partial\tilde{R}(\chi)}{\partial a} + \frac{3\chi}{\sqrt{\mu a}}\frac{\partial\tilde{R}(\chi)}{\partial\chi} + \frac{3\tau}{a^2}\frac{\partial\tilde{R}(\chi)}{\partial\chi}, \tag{6.2.9}$$

where we have used $\dot{n} = -(3n/2a)\dot{a}$, and (6.1.24). By virtue of (6.2.8), (6.2.9) reduces to (6.1.26).

As regards our second point, we find, however we write out $\partial\tilde{R}/\partial a$, that the angle E, or its equivalent form (2.2.30), appears as we noted above. Ultimately, this will bring into $\partial\tilde{R}/\partial a$ forms of the type

$$\frac{E\sin^jE\cos^kE}{(1-e\cos E)^m}.$$

Such terms give rise to considerable labor in evaluation of the integrals resulting from Lagrange's planetary equations; in many cases no closed-form solution exists. Hence, direct integration of the equation for $\dot{\tau}$ or $\dot{\chi}$ presents a much more formidable problem than does that of the other elements. Let us examine the case for χ.

Appreciable simplification results if we make the substitution

$$M = nt + \chi, \tag{6.2.10}$$

that is, if we use the mean anomaly. In terms of the mean motion, n, we may rewrite (6.1.26) as

$$\dot{\chi} = \frac{1 - e^2}{na^2 e}\frac{\partial \tilde{R}}{\partial e} - \frac{2}{na}\left(\frac{\partial \tilde{R}}{\partial a}\right) - \frac{2}{na}\frac{\partial \tilde{R}}{\partial n}\frac{\partial n}{\partial a}, \tag{6.2.11}$$

where $(\partial \tilde{R}/\partial a)$ signifies that the derivative is to be taken with respect to the semi-major axis without considering the dependence of n on that variable. Now

$$\frac{\partial \tilde{R}}{\partial \chi} = \frac{\partial \tilde{R}}{\partial M}\frac{\partial M}{\partial \chi} = \frac{\partial \tilde{R}}{\partial M},$$

and

$$\frac{\partial \tilde{R}}{\partial n} = \frac{\partial \tilde{R}}{\partial M}\frac{\partial M}{\partial n} = t\frac{\partial \tilde{R}}{\partial M},$$

since n is independent of χ. Thus $\partial \tilde{R}/\partial n = t\, \partial \tilde{R}/\partial \chi$. But $\dot{M} = n + t\dot{n} + \dot{\chi}$, and

$$\dot{n} = -\frac{3}{2}\frac{n}{a}\dot{a}.$$

Thus (6.2.11) becomes

$$\dot{M} = n - t\frac{3n}{2a}\dot{a} - \frac{1-e^2}{na^2 e}\frac{\partial \tilde{R}}{\partial e} - \frac{2}{na}\left(\frac{\partial \tilde{R}}{\partial a}\right) - \frac{2}{na}t\frac{\partial \tilde{R}}{\partial \chi}\frac{\partial n}{\partial a}.$$

By (6.1.24)

$$\frac{2}{na}\frac{\partial \tilde{R}}{\partial \chi} = \dot{a},$$

but also $\partial n/\partial a = -3n/2a$, so that

$$\dot{M} = n - \frac{1-e^2}{na^2 e}\frac{\partial \tilde{R}}{\partial e} - \frac{2}{na}\left(\frac{\partial \tilde{R}}{\partial a}\right); \tag{6.2.12}$$

this avoids completion of the difficult integrals but ultimately requires an evaluation of

$$\int n\, dt = \int \sqrt{\frac{\mu}{a^3}}\, dt = \int \sqrt{\frac{\mu}{\left(a_0 + \int \dot{a}\, dt\right)^3}}\, dt,$$

where a_0 is the value at the epoch and $\dot{a}$ is given by (6.1.24). For first-order analysis, when $\left(\int \dot{a}\,dt\right)/a_0 \ll 1$,

$$\int_{t_0}^{t} n\,dt = n_0\int_{t_0}^{t}\left(1 - \frac{3}{2a_0}\int \dot{a}\,dt\right)dt$$

$$= n_0(t-t_0) - \frac{3n_0}{2a_0}\int_{t_0}^{t}\left(\int \dot{a}\,dt\right)dt. \tag{6.2.13}$$

Having found M by (6.2.12) with the help of (6.2.13), we then use (6.2.10) in the form

$$M - M_0 = nt + \chi - n_0 t_0 - \chi_0 \tag{6.2.14}$$

to obtain χ. The element τ may be treated similarly.

2.3. Choice of Independent Variable

In Chapter 5 we explained why, for noncircular orbits, it was convenient to utilize one of the angular anomalies as the independent variable of the equations of motion; we also introduced the notions of perturbed and unperturbed anomaly. These considerations are equally important for Lagrange's planetary equations.

Before becoming involved in details of the transformation, it is worthwhile to examine again the meaning of perturbed and unperturbed representations of the anomaly. For this purpose let us address ourselves first to the true anomaly. In Keplerian motion this angle is defined in relation to the elements and time by Eq. (2.2.37), namely,

$$2\tan^{-1}\left(\sqrt{\frac{1-e}{1+e}}\tan\frac{f}{2}\right) - \frac{e\sqrt{1-e^2}\sin f}{1+e\cos f} = \sqrt{\frac{\mu}{a^3}}(t-\tau). \tag{6.2.15}$$

We can take this as a definition of true anomaly in disturbed motion also, providing the elements a, e, τ are understood to have their time-dependent values. This specification of perturbed true anomaly is consistent with all the notions of osculating elements we have introduced in this chapter.

The magnitude of $f(t)$ obtained as above is not the same as would be found had each of the elements a constant value. Naturally, we may choose some epoch at which to specify these values; the true anomaly obtained by utilizing these constants, say a_0, e_0, τ_0 is identical to that defined in Keplerian motion. Because of this, we designate it by $f^{(0)}$ and refer to it as the unperturbed true anomaly. Its relation to time is

$$2\tan^{-1}\left(\sqrt{\frac{1-e_0}{1+e_0}}\tan\frac{f^{(0)}}{2}\right) - \frac{e_0\sqrt{1-e_0^2}\sin f^{(0)}}{1+e_0\cos f^{(0)}} = \sqrt{\frac{\mu}{a_0^3}}(t-\tau_0); \tag{6.2.16}$$

compare (6.2.15).

For reasons which will appear presently, it is generally more convenient to use $f^{(0)}$ rather than f as the independent variable in Lagrange's planetary equations. Consequently, it is important to understand its significance. Mathematically, it simply represents a connection among convenient expressions for the variations of the elements and the (ultimately) preferred independent variable, time. Physically, $f^{(0)}$ has no real counterpart; however, it may be useful to think of it in the following way. Assume we have two bodies in orbit: one subject to perturbations and the other not. Both start at the same point in space and time with identical elements $a_0, e_0, i_0, \omega_0, \Omega_0, \tau_0$. We find we can follow the progress of the disturbed body most easily by reference to the angular position of the unperturbed, i.e., by reference to $f^{(0)}$. The orbit of the latter body thus plays the role of a useful auxiliary, especially since its progress in time is marked by a relatively simple equation, namely (6.2.16) in which all elements are constant. This auxiliary orbit corresponds to the concept of the nominal orbit of Chapters 4 and 5.

Turning now to the means of performing the transformation of independent variable, this is accomplished by dividing (6.1.18) through (6.1.26) by the time derivative of the true anomaly since $\dot{\alpha}_j = (d\alpha_j/d\varphi)(d\varphi/dt)$, where α_j is any element and φ is either the unperturbed or perturbed representation of the true anomaly. Equation (6.2.16) yields

$$\frac{df^{(0)}}{dt} = \sqrt{\frac{\mu}{a_0^3(1-e_0^2)^3}}\,(1+e_0\cos f^{(0)})^2, \tag{6.2.17}$$

or

$$\frac{df^{(0)}}{dt} = \frac{\sqrt{\mu a_0(1-e_0^2)}}{r^{(0)2}}. \tag{6.2.18}$$

Needless to say, these are simply statements of the constancy of the unperturbed angular momentum. Applying (6.2.18) to, say, (6.1.18) we obtain

$$\frac{da}{df^{(0)}} = -\frac{2a^2 r^{(0)2}}{\sqrt{\mu^3 a_0(1-e_0^2)}}\frac{\partial \tilde{R}}{\partial \tau}. \tag{6.2.19}$$

The derivation of this equation has been completely rigorous. If, however, we now utilize the perturbation method and Eq. (6.2.2), then (6.2.19) becomes, to first order,

$$\frac{da}{df^{(0)}} = -2\sqrt{\frac{a_0^7(1-e_0^2)^3}{\mu^3}}\,\frac{1}{(1+e_0\cos f^{(0)})^2}\frac{\partial \tilde{R}_0}{\partial \tau}; \tag{6.2.20}$$

note that the right-hand side of (6.2.20) contains only zero-order elements and functions of $f^{(0)}$. We may treat Eqs. (6.1.19) through (6.1.26) similarly; each provides us with a simple quadrature in $f^{(0)}$.

If we wish to use the perturbed true anomaly, we differentiate (6.2.15) to find df/dt. We obtain

$$\frac{df}{dt} = \sqrt{\frac{\mu}{a^3(1-e^2)^3}}(1+e\cos f)^2$$

$$\cdot\left\{1 - \dot{\tau} + \sqrt{\frac{a^3(1-e^2)}{\mu}}\frac{\sin f(2+e\cos f)}{(1+e\cos f)^2}\dot{e} - \frac{3}{2}\sqrt{\frac{a}{\mu}}\left[2\tan^{-1}\left(\sqrt{\frac{1-e}{1+e}}\tan\frac{f}{2}\right) - \frac{e\sqrt{1-e^2}\sin f}{1+e\cos f}\right]\dot{a}\right\}, \tag{6.2.21}$$

where $\dot{\tau}$ is given by (6.1.20), $\dot{e}$ by (6.1.19) or (6.1.25), and $\dot{a}$ by (6.1.18) or (6.1.24). For convenience, let us rewrite (6.2.21) as

$$\frac{df}{dt} = \sqrt{\frac{\mu}{a^3(1-e^2)^3}}(1+e\cos f)^2(1+\Gamma); \tag{6.2.22}$$

note that since Γ contains the time derivatives of the elements it is a quantity of $O(\kappa)$. Equations (6.2.22) and (6.1.18) provide us with

$$\frac{da}{df} = -2\sqrt{\frac{a^7(1-e^2)^3}{\mu^3}}\frac{1}{(1+\Gamma)(1+e\cos f)^2}\frac{\partial\tilde{R}}{\partial\tau}; \tag{6.2.23}$$

compare (6.2.19). Equation (6.2.23) is exact; applying (6.2.2) and writing only the first-order term yields

$$\frac{da}{df} = -2\sqrt{\frac{a_0^7(1-e_0^2)^3}{\mu^3}}\frac{1}{(1+e_0\cos f)^2}\frac{\partial\tilde{R}_0}{\partial\tau}. \tag{6.2.24}$$

This result is formally the same as (6.2.20); the solution of it in terms of f is identical to that of (6.2.20) in terms of $f^{(0)}$. However, it is important to remember that f is related to time by (6.2.15) and $f^{(0)}$ is related to t by (6.2.16). Thus f and $f^{(0)}$ differ by first-order terms and this results in the solutions of (6.2.20) and of (6.2.24) differing by second-order terms if both are solved for the same instant of time. Since, by design, both (6.2.20) and (6.2.24) are valid only to first order, this difference cannot be treated as significant.* Only in the time equation (6.2.12) does the difference between the perturbed and unperturbed anomalies result in a first-order contribution. Keeping these considerations in mind, it is often found simpler, in practice, to use the undisturbed representation of the anomaly as the independent variable.

*However, in computing first-order perturbations of x, y, z from the orbit elements, a contribution from the perturbation in f must be accounted for, as discussed later. Of course, if a second-order analysis is intended, a contribution from $(1 + \Gamma)$ in (6.2.23) must be retained.

All that we have said about the true anomaly holds also for the eccentric anomaly. Here the governing equation is, of course,

$$E - e \sin E = \sqrt{\frac{\mu}{a^3}}(t-\tau),$$

which is the counterpart of (6.2.15). We obtain, for instance,

$$\frac{da}{dE^{(0)}} = -2\sqrt{\frac{a_0^7}{\mu^3}}\left(1-e_0 \cos E^{(0)}\right)\frac{\partial \tilde{R}_0}{\partial \tau}. \tag{6.2.25}$$

The choice of true or eccentric anomaly as independent variable depends ultimately on the form of the perturbation. Consider (6.2.20); if $\partial\tilde{R}_0/\partial\tau$ should be proportional to $1/r^{(0)m}$, with $m \geq 2$, completion of the integral is quite easy. On the other hand, under the same circumstances, (6.2.25) leads to a quadrature involving $(1-e_0 \cos E^{(0)})^{-(m-1)}$. Such a form usually can be integrated, but frequently requires great labor. In general, it is better to find a factor $(\alpha+\beta \cos \varphi)^m$ in the numerator than in the denominator, and having the choice of E or f allows us this latitude.

3. ILLUSTRATIVE EXAMPLE. EFFECT OF EARTH'S OBLATENESS ON AN ORBITING BODY

We illustrate the method outlined above in the following example. Let us approximate the earth's gravitational potential by the first two terms of (5.3.18). We find equations of motion of the form

$$\ddot{x} + \frac{\mu}{r^3}x = \frac{\partial}{\partial x}\left[\frac{3}{2}J_2\mu\frac{R^2}{r^3}\left(\frac{1}{3} - \frac{z^2}{r^2}\right)\right],$$

where we have set $z/r = \sin \varphi'$. The term in the square brackets is the disturbing force (to order J_2).

Now for, say, $\partial\tilde{R}/\partial\tau$ we obtain

$$\frac{\partial \tilde{R}}{\partial \tau} = \frac{3}{2}J_2\mu R^2\left[\frac{5z^2-r^2}{r^6}\frac{\partial r}{\partial \tau} - \frac{2z}{r^5}\frac{\partial z}{\partial \tau}\right]. \tag{6.3.1}$$

Since (6.3.1) contains terms proportional to $1/r^4$, we should select the true anomaly as our new independent variable; further we intend to use the unperturbed representation. For a first-order analysis let us write

$$r^{(0)} = r(a_0,e_0,\tau_0,t) = a_0(1-e_0^2)/(1+e_0 \cos f^{(0)}).$$

However, as we pointed out earlier, it is more convenient to obtain $\partial r^{(0)}/\partial\tau_0$ by way of $E^{(0)}$. Now $r^{(0)} = a_0(1-e_0 \cos E^{(0)})$, whence

$$\frac{\partial r^{(0)}}{\partial \tau_0} = a_0 e_0 \sin E^{(0)} \frac{\partial E^{(0)}}{\partial \tau_0},$$

where

$$e_0 \sin E^{(0)} = \frac{r^{(0)}\dot{r}^{(0)}}{\sqrt{\mu a_0}}$$

and

$$\frac{\partial E^{(0)}}{\partial \tau_0} = -\sqrt{\frac{\mu}{a_0}}\frac{1}{r^{(0)}}.$$

Thus

$$\frac{\partial r^{(0)}}{\partial \tau_0} = -\dot{r}^{(0)}.$$

We develop $z^{(0)}$ and $\partial z^{(0)}/\partial\tau_0$ with the help of (3.4.3) through (3.4.5), using

$$\sin E^{(0)} = \frac{r^{(0)} \sin f^{(0)}}{a_0\sqrt{1-e_0^2}}$$

and (6.3.2)

$$\cos E^{(0)} = \frac{1}{a_0}[r^{(0)} \cos f^{(0)} + a_0 e_0],$$

as necessary.

Integrating the explicit form of (6.2.20) we obtain

$$a - a_0 = \frac{3J_2R^2}{a_0(1-e_0^2)^3}\left\{\left[1+e_0 \cos f^{(0)}\right]^3 \left[\frac{1}{3} - \sin^2 i_0 \sin^2(\omega_0 + f^{(0)})\right]\right\}_{f_0^{(0)}}^{f^{(0)}}. \quad (6.3.3)$$

Here the expression is to be evaluated between the limits $f_0^{(0)}$ and $f^{(0)}$, where the former is the initial value (at t_0) and $f^{(0)}$ is some later value. The quantity a is the value of the semimajor axis, perturbed to first order, at $f^{(0)}$. If, for simplicity, *we drop the superscript zero*, we obtain, in a similar manner,

$$e = e_0 + \frac{1-e_0^2}{2e_0}\frac{a-a_0}{a_0} + \frac{3J_2R^2 \sin^2 i_0}{a_0^2 e_0(1-e^2)}$$

$$\cdot\left\{ \sin\omega_0 \cos\omega_0 \sin f\left[\cos f + \frac{e_0}{3}\sin f(\cos^2 f + 2 - \sin^2 f)\right]\right.$$

$$\left. -(\sin^2\omega_0 - \cos^2\omega_0)\left[\frac{1}{2}\sin^2 f - \frac{e_0}{3}\cos^3 f\right]\right\}_{f_0}^{f}. \quad (6.3.4)$$

Equation (6.1.21) yields*

$$i = i_0 + \frac{3J_2R^2}{a_0^2(1-e_0^2)^2} \sin i_0 \cos i_0$$

$$\cdot\left\{(\sin^2\omega_0 - \cos^2\omega_0)\frac{\cos^2 f}{6}(3+2e_0\cos f)\right.$$

$$\left. + \sin\omega_0 \cos\omega_0 \sin f\left[\cos f + \frac{e_0}{3} + \frac{2}{3}e_0\cos^2 f\right]\right\}_{f_0}^{f} \tag{6.3.5}$$

and (6.1.22) and (6.1.23) give

$$\Omega = \Omega_0 - \frac{3J_2R^2}{a_0^2(1-e_0^2)^2}\cos i_0$$

$$\left\{f/2 + \sin^2\omega_0 \sin f\left[\frac{1}{2}\cos f + \frac{e_0}{3}\cos^2 f + \frac{2}{3}e_0\right]\right.$$

$$-\sin\omega_0\cos\omega_0\cos^2 f\left(1+\frac{2}{3}e_0\cos f\right)$$

$$\left. + \cos^2\omega_0 \sin f\left[-\frac{1}{2}\cos f + \frac{e_0}{3}\cos^2 f\right]\right\}_{f_0}^{f} \tag{6.3.6}$$

$$\omega = \omega_0 - \cos i_0(\Omega - \Omega_0) + \frac{3J_2R^2}{2a_0^2e_0(1-e_0^2)^2}$$

$$\cdot\left\{e_0 f + \sin f\left(1 + e_0\cos f + \frac{e_0^2}{3}\cos^2 f + \frac{2}{3}e_0^2\right)\right.$$

$$-\sin^2 i_0\left[\frac{3}{2}e_0 f + \sin^2\omega_0 \sin f\left(\frac{7}{3}\cos^2 f + \frac{2}{3} + 3e_0\cos^3 f + \frac{3}{2}e_0\cos f\right.\right.$$

$$\left.+ e_0^2\cos^4 f + \frac{2}{3}e_0^2\cos^2 f + \frac{4}{3}e_0^2\right) +$$

---

*The contents of the braces in (6.3.4) and (6.3.5) are identical, as must be expected from (6.1.19) and (6.1.21), if we observe that the rotationally symmetric geopotential used here yields $\partial\tilde{R}/\partial\Omega \equiv 0$.

$$+\sin\omega_0\cos\omega_0\cos f\left(4+3e_0\cos f-\frac{14}{3}\cos^2 f\right.$$

$$\left.-6e_0\cos^3 f-2e_0^2\cos^4 f+\frac{2}{3}e_0^2\cos^2 f\right)$$

$$+\cos^2\omega_0\sin f\left(\frac{7}{3}-\frac{7}{3}\cos^2 f+\frac{3}{2}e_0\cos f-3e_0\cos^3 f\right.$$

$$\left.\left.\left.+\frac{1}{3}e_0^2\cos^2 f+\frac{2}{3}e_0^2-e_0^2\cos^4 f\right)\right]\right\}_{f_0}^{f}. \tag{6.3.7}$$

In solving for χ, we obtain from (6.2.13) and (6.3.3),

$$\int_{t_0}^{t} n\,dt = n_0(t-t_0)+\frac{9J_2R^2}{2a_0^2(1-e_0^2)^3}(1+e_0\cos f_0)^3\left[\frac{1}{3}-\sin^2 i_0\sin^2(\omega_0+f_0)\right]$$

$$\cdot\left\{2\tan^{-1}\left(\sqrt{\frac{1-e_0}{1+e_0}}\tan\frac{f}{2}\right)-\frac{e_0\sqrt{1-e_0^2}\sin f}{1+e_0\cos f}\right\}_{f_0}^{f}$$

$$-\frac{9J_2R^2}{2a_0^2(1-e_0^2)^{3/2}}\left\{\frac{f}{3}+\frac{e_0\sin f}{3}\right.$$

$$-\sin^2 i_0\left[\sin^2\omega_0\left(\frac{f}{2}+\frac{\sin f\cos f}{2}+\frac{e_0}{3}\sin f\cos^2 f\right)\right.$$

$$-\sin\omega_0\cos\omega_0\left(\cos^2 f+\frac{2e_0}{3}\cos^3 f\right)$$

$$\left.\left.+\cos^2\omega_0\left(\frac{f}{2}-\frac{\sin f\cos f}{2}+\frac{e_0}{3}\sin^3 f\right)\right]\right\}_{f_0}^{f}.$$

Now considering the second term on the right, we recognize the factor to be evaluated at f and f_0 as $n_0(t-t_0)$. Equation (6.2.12) then leads to

$$M-M_0 = n_0(t-t_0)\left\{1+\frac{9J_2R^2}{2a_0^2(1-e_0^2)^3}(1+e_0\cos f_0)^3\left[\frac{1}{3}-\sin^2 i_0\sin^2(\omega_0+f_0)\right]\right\}$$

$$-\sqrt{1-e_0^2}\left[(\omega-\omega_0)+\cos i_0(\Omega-\Omega_0)\right]+$$

$$+\frac{3J_2R^2}{2a_0^2(1-e_0^2)^{3/2}}\Bigg\{f+e_0\sin f+3\sin^2 i_0 \cdot\Bigg[-\frac{1}{2}f+\sin^2\omega_0\sin f\left(-\frac{1}{2}\cos f-\frac{e_0}{3}\cos^2 f-\frac{4}{3}e_0\right) +\sin\omega_0\cos\omega_0\cos^2 f\left(1+\frac{2e_0}{3}\cos f\right) +\cos^2\omega_0\sin f\left(\frac{\cos f}{2}-\frac{e_0}{3}\sin^2 f\right)\Bigg]\Bigg\}_{f_0}^{f}.$$

Now, from (6.2.14), $\chi-\chi_0 = M-M_0-nt+n_0t_0$. But here we can write, to first order, $n = n_0-(3n_0/2a_0)(a-a_0)$, so that finally,

$$\chi-\chi_0 = \frac{9J_2R^2}{2a_0^2(1-e_0^2)^3}\left\{n_0t(1+e_0\cos f)^3\left[\frac{1}{3}-\sin^2 i_0\sin^2(\omega_0+f)\right]\right\}_{f_0}^{f} -\sqrt{1-e_0^2}[(\omega-\omega_0)+\cos i_0(\Omega-\Omega_0)] +\frac{3J_2R^2}{2a_0^2(1-e_0^2)^{3/2}}\Bigg\{f+e_0\sin f -3\sin^2 i_0\Bigg[\frac{f}{2}+\sin^2\omega_0\sin f\left(\frac{\cos f}{2}+\frac{e_0\cos^2 f}{3}+\frac{4e_0}{3}\right) -\sin\omega_0\cos\omega_0\cos^2 f\left(1+\frac{2e_0\cos f}{3}\right) -\cos^2\omega_0\sin^2 f\left(\frac{\cos f}{2}+\frac{e_0}{3}\sin^2 f\right)\Bigg]\Bigg\}_{f_0}^{f}, \tag{6.3.8}$$

where, in evaluation of the first term on the right-hand side, t is to be taken as t at $f=f^{(0)}$ and as t_0 at $f=f_0$. Thus, the changes in the elements of a body in orbit over an oblate earth are given by equations (6.3.3) through (6.3.8), to first order. They apply equally well to satellites and to ballistic missiles and are related to the time through (6.2.16) since we are using the unperturbed true anomaly as the independent variable.

Of particular interest is the case when we substitute $f = f_0 + 2\pi$, i.e., when a satellite has completed one revolution. The results are

$$a = a_0, \tag{6.3.9}$$

$$e = e_0, \tag{6.3.10}$$

$$i = i_0, \tag{6.3.11}$$

$$\Omega = \Omega_0 - \frac{3J_2R^2}{2a_0^2(1-e_0^2)^2}\, 2\pi \cos i_0, \tag{6.3.12}$$

$$\omega = \omega_0 + \frac{3J_2R^2}{2a_0^2(1-e_0^2)^2}\, \pi(5\cos^2 i - 1), \tag{6.3.13}$$

$$\chi = \chi_0 + \frac{3J_2R^2}{a_0^2(1-e_0^2)^3}\, \pi(1 + e_0\cos f_0)^3[1 - 3\sin^2 i_0 \sin^2(\omega_0 + f_0)]. \tag{6.3.14}$$

Hence, to first order, the size, shape, and inclination of the orbit are not changed from cycle to cycle.

Equation (6.3.12) shows that the line of nodes precesses to the east if i_0 is in the second quadrant and that the motion of this line is retrograde if i_0 lies in the first quadrant. The plane of the orbit stays fixed (in inertial space) if its initial inclination is 90° (polar orbit).

The motion of the line of apsides is given by (6.3.13); it can be seen that the argument of perigee advances in the direction of motion if i_0 is less than 63° 26′ or greater than 116° 34′, and regresses when the inclination is between these values. The secular effects in these results are well-known phenomena and were mentioned in Chapter 5.

4. FURTHER COMMENTS ON LAGRANGE'S PLANETARY EQUATIONS

The application of Lagrange's planetary equations is quite widespread and has been treated in numerous texts [1–6]. The calculations required are generally direct, and the results, as expressed in terms of the elements, are simple to interpret. We present here some further discussion of this approach to perturbation theory.

The results of Section 3 were given mainly in terms of the unperturbed anomaly, with mixed expressions in t and f occurring in (6.3.8). These solutions containing both anomalies and/or time often allow for some compactness which, as the reader is by now aware, is to be greatly desired. Another formulation sometimes allowing simpler expressions utilizes functions of multiple arguments of the angular variable rather than powers of trigonometric functions. The reader may find it instructive to convert (6.3.3)–(6.3.8) accordingly, resulting in generally less lengthy expressions.

There is no way of shortening certain results to the point where we can have complete faith in the algebra required to obtain them. Independent calculations can be a great help here, and it is frequently useful to employ separate formulations in terms of E and of f and then check the results by means of the relations (2.2.27)–(2.2.29). We illustrate this in Appendix A which at the same time presents the application of Lagrange's planetary equations to perturbations from extra-terrestrial gravity.

Whatever the description of the perturbed orbit, it is possible to generate from it an ephemeris. Let us briefly consider this task. Suppose we wish to establish the satellite position in geocentric cartesian coordinates x, y, z at the time t_1. We do this by means of (3.4.1)–(3.4.5) where the elements to be used are $a_1, e_1, i_1, \omega_1, \Omega_1, \tau_1$ corresponding to that time. The computation involves an integration of Lagrange's equations between the limits f_0 and f_1 or E_0 and E_1 where these anomalies are defined for the osculating orbit of t_0. For the transformations (3.4.1)–(3.4.5) which are valid at t_1, we must use the anomalies, say, $\tilde{f}$ or $\tilde{E}$, valid for the osculating orbit at that time. These differ from f_1 and E_1 since the orbit elements have changed, i.e., the osculating orbit at t_1 is connected to the time scale in a slightly different way from that defined at t_0. $\tilde{E}$ follows readily from Kepler's equation $\tilde{E} - e_1 \sin \tilde{E} = n_1(t_1 - \tau_1)$ and $\tilde{f}$ may be obtained by (2.2.29). These manipulations are equivalent to the integration of (6.2.21), or the corresponding equation for dE/dt, in order to find the perturbed anomalies. Once the anomalies are known, the positions x, y, z and the velocity vector

$$\dot{x} = \frac{dx}{dE}\dot{E}, \ldots \qquad \text{or} \qquad \dot{x} = \frac{dx}{df}\dot{f}, \ldots$$

follow from the appropriate relations in Chapter 3.

A set of expressions such as those under discussion is useful not only for ephemeris computations but also for so-called orbit stability studies. In this case one allows for the progressive changes in the orbit elements by replacing $a_0, e_0, \ldots,$ in the right-hand sides with the new values for $a, e, \ldots,$ after the completion of each integration interval from f_0 to f. This technique is a form of rectification as discussed in Chapter 5 and seems intuitively obvious. Combining it with the multiperiod algorithm of Mace and Thomas, *et al.* [9] results in a very effective computing device for long-range prediction and stability studies of nearly periodic orbits. This multiperiod technique bears a conceptual relation to numerical integration procedures.

As a final point we mention the iterative procedure by which higher-order terms in the osculating parameters are sometimes obtained. [8]. Instead of using the perturbation series (6.2.2) for the orbit elements to develop a hierarchy of perturbation equations from (6.1.18)–(6.1.26) in analogy to Chapter 5, we substitute first-order results for the elements, as obtained in Section 3, into the right-hand sides of the planetary equations for another quadrature. The resulting expressions for $a, e, \ldots$ will now be good to second order. (If the perturbed anomaly f is used as independent variable, a contribution from Γ must be included, as observed in Section 2. This application of Picard iterants to Lagrange's planetary equations is referred to by astronomers as the Poisson technique.) Let us also note that those first-order steps producing secular terms which are linear functions of the independent variable will, upon resubstitution (and another quadrature of the planetary equations), lead to quadratic secular terms in the second-order solution, and so forth. As pointed out in Chapter 5, this sequence of secular terms may develop into a power series in (κf) or (κE) which ultimately represents a long-period, cyclic term. Its period is of $0(2\pi/\kappa n)$. As we shall see later, these long-period terms also arise in the canonical formulations of Chapter 8, though in a somewhat different way.

5. APPLICATION TO ORBITS WITH SMALL ECCENTRICITIES AND INCLINATIONS

If we examine (6.1.19), (6.1.20), (6.1.23), (6.1.25), (6.1.26), and (6.2.12), we see that for orbits with very low eccentricities these equations yield very large changes in the elements unless $\partial\tilde{R}/\partial\omega$, $\partial\tilde{R}/\partial e$, $\partial\tilde{R}/\partial\tau$, or $\partial\tilde{R}/\partial\chi$ should fortuitously contain a multiplicative factor e. For circular orbits, the changes in e, τ, (χ), and ω are ill defined unless this condition is fulfilled. However, we also noted (Chapter 2) that in such a case the time of pericenter passage and the argument of pericenter are meaningless. Consequently, any change in eccentricity is bound to cause difficulty in defining changes in τ and ω. Similarly, we observe that when the inclination angle is small, Eqs. (6.1.21) and (6.1.22) are badly behaved. Again this has a geometric reason: the node is undefinable if the inclination is zero.

Such difficulties lie with the elements used, and not with Lagrange's equations *per se*. One can form equations which avoid these difficulties only by altering the elements themselves. If this is done only with an eye to simplicity of presentation, one may avoid the combining of normal anomalistic motion and the effects of perturbations. In going to another set of elements, it is rarely possible to preserve the second desideratum of Lagrange's method: ease of geometric interpretation. Let us turn to some examples based on special elements introduced in Chapter 2.

For the near-circular case, we may take

$$\bar{\chi} = \omega + \chi, \tag{6.5.1}$$

and let

$$\bar{\mu} = e \sin \omega; \qquad \bar{\nu} = e \cos \omega. \tag{6.5.2}$$

If we now employ $\bar{\mu}$, $\bar{\nu}$, $\bar{\chi}$ in place of e, ω, χ in Lagrange's equations we will obtain right-hand sides which are well behaved. Writing

$$\tilde{R}(a, e, \chi, i, \omega, \Omega) = \tilde{R}'[a, \bar{\mu}(e, \omega), \bar{\chi}(\omega, \chi), i, \bar{\nu}(e, \omega), \Omega],$$

i.e., expressing the disturbing function in terms of the new elements, we find

$$\frac{\partial\tilde{R}}{\partial\chi} = \frac{\partial\tilde{R}'}{\partial\bar{\chi}}\frac{\partial\bar{\chi}}{\partial\chi} = \frac{\partial\tilde{R}'}{\partial\bar{\chi}},$$

using (6.5.1), and

$$\frac{\partial \tilde{R}}{\partial e} = \sin\omega \frac{\partial \tilde{R}'}{\partial \bar{\mu}} + \cos\omega \frac{\partial \tilde{R}'}{\partial \bar{\nu}},$$

$$\frac{\partial R}{\partial \omega} = \bar{\nu}\frac{\partial R'}{\partial \bar{\mu}} - \bar{\mu}\frac{\partial R'}{\partial \bar{\nu}} + \frac{\partial R'}{\partial \bar{\chi}},$$

using (6.5.2). Obviously $\dot{\bar{\mu}} = e\,\dot{\omega}\cos\omega + \dot{e}\sin\omega$, etc. Also

$$\bar{\nu}\cos\omega + \bar{\mu}\sin\omega = e,$$

$$\bar{\mu}^2 + \bar{\nu}^2 = e^2,$$

$$\tan\omega = \bar{\mu}/\bar{\nu}.$$

Substituting in the pertinent equations, and dropping the prime, we find

$$\dot{a} = 2\sqrt{\frac{a}{\mu}}\,\frac{\partial \tilde{R}}{\partial \bar{\chi}}, \tag{6.5.3}$$

$$\dot{\bar{\mu}} = \frac{\sqrt{1-\bar{\mu}^2-\bar{\nu}^2}}{\sqrt{\mu a}}\frac{\partial \tilde{R}}{\partial \bar{\nu}} - \frac{\bar{\nu}\cot i}{\sqrt{\mu a(1-\bar{\mu}^2-\bar{\nu}^2)}}\frac{\partial \tilde{R}}{\partial i} - \frac{\bar{\mu}\sqrt{1-\bar{\mu}^2-\bar{\nu}^2}}{\sqrt{\mu a}\,(1+\sqrt{1-\bar{\mu}^2-\bar{\nu}^2})}\frac{\partial \tilde{R}}{\partial \bar{\chi}}, \tag{6.5.4}$$

$$\dot{\bar{\nu}} = -\frac{\sqrt{1-\bar{\mu}^2-\bar{\nu}^2}}{\sqrt{\mu a}}\frac{\partial \tilde{R}}{\partial \bar{\mu}} + \frac{\bar{\mu}\cot i}{\sqrt{\mu a(1-\bar{\mu}^2-\bar{\nu}^2)}}\frac{\partial \tilde{R}}{\partial i} - \frac{\bar{\nu}\sqrt{1-\bar{\mu}^2-\bar{\nu}^2}}{\sqrt{\mu a}(1+\sqrt{1-\bar{\mu}^2-\bar{\nu}^2})}\frac{\partial \tilde{R}}{\partial \bar{\chi}}, \tag{6.5.5}$$

$$\dot{\bar{\chi}} = \frac{\sqrt{1-\bar{\mu}^2-\bar{\nu}^2}}{\sqrt{\mu a}(1+\sqrt{1-\bar{\mu}^2-\bar{\nu}^2})}\left(\bar{\mu}\frac{\partial \tilde{R}}{\partial \bar{\mu}} + \bar{\nu}\frac{\partial \tilde{R}}{\partial \bar{\nu}}\right) - 2\sqrt{\frac{a}{\mu}}\frac{\partial \tilde{R}}{\partial a} - \frac{\cot i}{\sqrt{\mu a(1-\bar{\mu}^2-\bar{\nu}^2)}}\frac{\partial \tilde{R}}{\partial i}, \tag{6.5.6}$$

$$\dot{\Omega} = \frac{1}{\sin i\sqrt{\mu a(1-\bar{\mu}^2-\bar{\nu}^2)}}\frac{\partial \tilde{R}}{\partial i}, \tag{6.5.7}$$

$$\frac{di}{dt} = \frac{1}{\sqrt{\mu a(1-\bar{\mu}^2-\bar{\nu}^2)}}\left\{\cot i\left(\bar{\nu}\frac{\partial \tilde{R}}{\partial \bar{\mu}} - \bar{\mu}\frac{\partial \tilde{R}}{\partial \bar{\nu}} + \frac{\partial \tilde{R}}{\partial \bar{\chi}}\right) - \operatorname{cosec} i\,\frac{\partial \tilde{R}}{\partial \Omega}\right\}. \tag{6.5.8}$$

The parameters $\bar{\mu}$, $\bar{\nu}$, $\bar{\chi}$ can now be evaluated without difficulty at low eccentricities. However, their interpretation is another matter (except for perfectly circular orbits). If we try to find e, ω, τ from them, we encounter the same difficulties as before.

Moreover, we note that some of these equations now exhibit singularities for $e^2 = \bar{\mu}^2 + \bar{\nu}^2 \to 1$. The main thing is that the variations of the parameters, to be computed in terms of such special elements, may be translated into a position ephemeris in a convenient way. This will be discussed later.

Applying (6.5.3)–(6.5.8) to the problem of oblateness, we get the following results, where we show only the changes during one complete revolution:

$$a = a_0, \tag{6.5.9}$$

$$\bar{\mu} = \bar{\mu}_0 + \frac{3J_2R^2}{2a_0^2(1 - \bar{\mu}_0^2 - \bar{\nu}_0^2)^2}(5\cos^2 i_0 - 1)\pi\,\bar{\nu}_0, \tag{6.5.10}$$

$$\bar{\nu} = \bar{\nu}_0 - \frac{3J_2R^2}{2a_0^2(1 - \bar{\mu}_0^2 - \bar{\nu}_0^2)^2}(5\cos^2 i_0 - 1)\pi\,\bar{\mu}_0, \tag{6.5.11}$$

$$\bar{\chi} = \bar{\chi}_0 + \frac{3J_2R^2}{2a_0^2(1 - \bar{\mu}_0^2 - \bar{\nu}_0^2)^2}\pi \cdot\left\{5\cos^2 i_0 - 1 + \frac{2(1 + \bar{\mu}_0\sin\theta_0 + \bar{\nu}_0\cos\theta_0)^3}{1 - \bar{\mu}_0^2 - \bar{\nu}_0^2}(1 - 3\sin^2 i_0 \sin^2\theta_0)\right\}, \tag{6.5.12}$$

$$\Omega = \Omega_0 - \frac{3J_2R^2}{2a_0^2(1 - \bar{\mu}_0^2 - \bar{\nu}_0^2)^2}2\pi\cos i_0, \tag{6.5.13}$$

$$i = i_0, \tag{6.5.14}$$

where θ_0 is the value of the geocentric angle between the node and the position of the satellite at the epoch. The results for equations (6.5.10), (6.5.11), and (6.5.12) are, as remarked, somewhat difficult to interpret. However, we note that they can be used to prove that oblateness does not alter eccentricity even for the circular case (to first order, at least). That is, for $e_0 = 0$ we must have

$$\bar{\mu}_0 = \bar{\nu}_0 = 0, \quad \text{and hence} \quad \bar{\mu} \equiv \bar{\nu} \equiv 0, \quad \text{or} \quad e \equiv 0.$$

Similar constructs, made of the more usual elements, can be formed for cases with small eccentricity and inclination angle. Traditionally, astronomers have been faced with this very problem: planets nearly all have orbits of low e and low i. A set which has proved of some use is

$$a, \qquad \upsilon = \sin i \sin\Omega,$$
$$\bar{\mu} = e\sin(\omega + \Omega), \qquad \vartheta = \sin i\cos\Omega,$$
$$\bar{\nu} = e\cos(\omega + \Omega), \qquad \varepsilon = \omega + \Omega + \chi$$

where $\omega + \Omega$ and $\omega + \Omega + \chi$ are known as the *longitude of pericenter* and the *longitude at epoch*, as mentioned in Chapter 2. Another alters υ and ϑ to $\upsilon' = \tan i \sin\Omega$, $\vartheta' = \tan i\cos\Omega$. The latter are useless for near-polar orbits: a case not normally considered by astronomers. In addition, either set leads to difficulty in choosing the independent variable. Time is always the most obnoxious in terms of compactness while true or eccentric anomaly, well defined for orbits with $e \neq 0$, are meaningless for the circular case (and reckoning the angle from node is impossible for $i = 0$). Further these sets do not admit to ease of transformation to (and from) the coordinates $(x, y, z, \dot{x}, \dot{y}, \dot{z})$.

These difficulties can be avoided by using the following set:

$$\begin{aligned} &a; && \bar{\upsilon} = \sin \tfrac{i}{2} \sin \Omega; \\ &\bar{\mu} = e \sin (\omega + \Omega); && \bar{\vartheta} = \sin \tfrac{i}{2} \cos \Omega; \\ &\bar{\nu} = e \cos (\omega + \Omega); && \varepsilon = \omega + \Omega + \chi, \end{aligned} \tag{6.5.15}$$

with the *true orbital longitude* $\theta = f + \omega + \Omega$ as the independent variable.* The latter always has meaning except for nearly retrograde orbits ($i \simeq 180°$). Needless to say, there are many other sets of elements that may be invented for various applications [10, 11, 12], introducing parameters valid for the entire family of conics, from circle to straight line, albeit at a further sacrifice of geometric transparency. Reference 13 employs the anomalistic period instead of the semi-major axis as an orbit element; this helps alleviate some of the nonlinearities in orbit-determination equations.

We have already seen that most of these special elements are not introduced as an aid to physical or geometric understanding of the perturbation effects. Nor is it simplicity of mathematics, except for elimination of singularities. We must conclude that the prime purpose is ease of handling, especially by computing machine. By the use of such quantities we can avoid exceeding "the range" of a calculator or the loss of significant digits. This is especially true if a general-purpose program is to handle all kinds of orbits including those that are, or become after some time, of low (or high) eccentricity, low (or high) inclination angle, or a combination of these.

6. THE GAUSS FORM OF LAGRANGE'S EQUATIONS

The derivation given in the first section of this chapter is restricted to use with perturbing forces which can be derived from a potential function. If we interpret the right-hand sides of (6.1.1) simply as components of a force per unit mass, whatever its origin, we can rewrite Lagrange's planetary equations so that they are applicable in all cases.

We start by reinterpreting the partial derivatives as

$$\partial\tilde{R}/\partial x = F_x/m; \qquad \partial\tilde{R}/\partial y = F_y/m; \qquad \partial\tilde{R}/\partial z = F_z/m, \tag{6.6.1}$$

where F_x, F_y, F_z are the x, y, z components of a force vector and m is the mass of the body. Now let us resolve this vector as follows (see Fig. 6.1):

---

*Paralleling the difficulty with χ that we faced in Section 2.2, we have the same situation with ε in this set. The substitution of a new variable, $L = nt + \varepsilon$, the *mean orbital longitude*, circumvents the problem, as did $M = nt + \chi$ earlier.

S: along the instantaneous radius vector

T: perpendicular to the instantaneous radius vector in the direction of motion

N: normal to the osculating plane of the orbit (positive in the right-hand sense, i.e., colinear with the angular momentum vector).

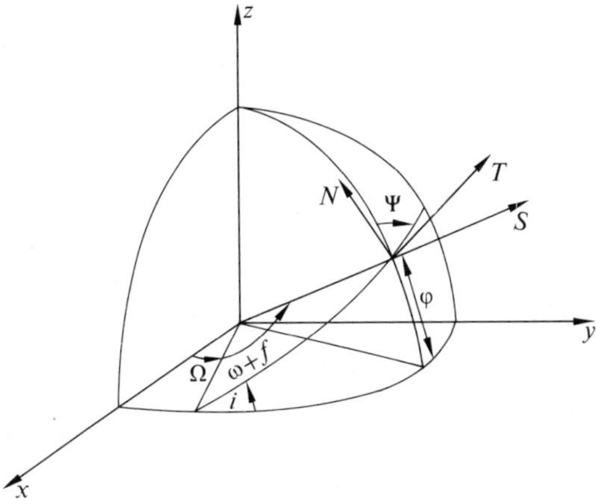

Figure 6.1

We can express the x, y, z components in terms of S, T, N by straightforward means. For example,

$$F_z/m = S\sin\varphi + T\cos\psi\cos\varphi + N\sin\psi\cos\varphi.$$

However, by spherical trigonometry,

$$\sin\varphi = \sin(\omega+f)\sin i, \qquad \cos\psi\cos\varphi = \cos(\omega+f)\sin i,$$
$$\sin\psi\cos\varphi = \cos i.$$

Thus we can express the components in terms of the orbit elements and the true anomaly. In final form we may write

$$F_x/m = S(l_1\cos f + l_2\sin f) - T(l_1\sin f - l_2\cos f) + Nl_3, \tag{6.6.2}$$

$$F_y/m = S(m_1\cos f + m_2\sin f) - T(m_1\sin f - m_2\cos f) + Nm_3, \tag{6.6.3}$$

$$F_z/m = S(n_1\cos f + n_2\sin f) - T(n_1\sin f - n_2\cos f) + Nn_3, \tag{6.6.4}$$

where l_1, l_2, m_1, m_2, n_1, n_2 have been defined in Eqs. (3.4.4) through (3.4.5) and l_3, m_3, n_3 in (5.6.2). We may note here that

$$l_1^2 + m_1^2 + n_1^2 = l_2^2 + m_2^2 + n_2^2 = l_3^2 + m_3^2 + n_3^2 = 1, \tag{6.6.5}$$

and

$$\begin{aligned} l_1l_2 + m_1m_2 + n_1n_2 &= l_1l_3 + m_1m_3 + n_1n_3 \\ &= l_2l_3 + m_2m_3 + n_2n_3 = 0. \end{aligned} \tag{6.6.6}$$

Now from (6.1.11) and (6.6.1) we have

$$\frac{\partial\tilde{R}}{\partial\alpha_j} = \frac{F_x}{m}\frac{\partial x}{\partial\alpha_j} + \frac{F_y}{m}\frac{\partial y}{\partial\alpha_j} + \frac{F_z}{m}\frac{\partial z}{\partial\alpha_j}. \tag{6.6.7}$$

Then we obtain, for example,

$$\left(\frac{\partial \tilde{R}}{\partial a}\right) = \frac{F_x}{m}\left(\frac{\partial x}{\partial a}\right) + \frac{F_y}{m}\left(\frac{\partial y}{\partial a}\right) + \frac{F_z}{m}\left(\frac{\partial z}{\partial a}\right), \tag{6.6.8}$$

where the parentheses indicate, as before, that the derivative is to be taken with respect to a only as it occurs explicitly in x, y, z and disregarding the fact that E and f are functions of a by virtue of Kepler's equation and (2.2.37). In the manner outlined earlier, we may find

$$(\partial x/\partial a) = l_1 \frac{r}{a} \cos f + l_2 \frac{r}{a} \sin f,$$

with similar expressions for $(\partial y/\partial a)$ and $(\partial z/\partial a)$. Substituting into (6.6.8) and using (6.6.2) through (6.6.6), we obtain

$$(\partial \tilde{R}/\partial a) = S\, r/a. \tag{6.6.9}$$

Similarly, one can obtain the equivalent expressions for other partial derivatives of $\tilde{R}$; then Eqs. (6.1.21) through (6.1.25) become

$$\dot{a} = 2\sqrt{\frac{a^3}{\mu(1-e^2)}}\left[S\, e \sin f + \frac{a(1-e^2)}{r} T\right], \tag{6.6.10}$$

$$\dot{e} = \sqrt{\frac{a(1-e^2)}{\mu}}\,[S \sin f + T(\cos E + \cos f)], \tag{6.6.11}$$

$$\frac{di}{dt} = \frac{1}{\sqrt{\mu a(1-e^2)}} N\, r \cos(\omega + f), \tag{6.6.12}$$

$$\dot{\Omega} = \frac{1}{\sin i \sqrt{\mu a(1-e^2)}} N\, r \sin(\omega + f), \tag{6.6.13}$$

$$\dot{\omega} = -\dot{\Omega} \cos i - \frac{1}{e}\sqrt{\frac{a(1-e^2)}{\mu}}\left\{S \cos f - T\left[1 + \frac{r}{a(1-e^2)}\right]\sin f\right\}. \tag{6.6.14}$$

Finally, Eq. (6.2.12) yields

$$\dot{M} = n - \frac{2}{\sqrt{\mu a}} S\, r - \dot{\omega}\sqrt{1-e^2} - \dot{\Omega}\sqrt{1-e^2} \cos i. \tag{6.6.15}$$

We will find it useful to write here the complete expression for $\partial\tilde{R}/\partial a$, i.e., the one obtained after taking account of the dependence of n on semi-major axis:

$$\frac{\partial\tilde{R}}{\partial a} = S\left\{\frac{2(1-e^2)+3e^2\sin^2 f}{2(1+e\cos f)} - \frac{3e\sin f}{2\sqrt{1-e^2}}E\right\}$$
$$- T\left\{\frac{3(1+e\cos f)}{2\sqrt{1-e^2}}E - \frac{3e\sin f}{2}\right\};$$

compare (6.6.9). Equation (6.1.20) then yields

$$\dot{\tau} = \frac{a^2}{\mu}\left\{S\left[\frac{2(1-e^2)+3e^2\sin^2 f}{1+e\cos f} - \frac{3e\sin f}{\sqrt{1-e^2}}E - \frac{1-e^2}{e}\cos f\right]\right.$$
$$\left. - T\left[\frac{3(1+e\cos f)}{\sqrt{1-e^2}}E - 3e\sin f - \frac{1-e^2}{e}\sin f\left(1+\frac{1}{1+e\cos f}\right)\right]\right\}. \tag{6.6.16}$$

As discussed in Section 2.3, we have a choice of independent variables. The arguments here are identical to those given earlier: for the first-order case, it is immaterial whether we choose the perturbed or unperturbed representation of anomaly since the transformation of independent variable uses (6.2.22) where the quantity Γ is $0(\kappa)$. In second- and higher-order analyses, where Γ must be retained in all planetary equations, we must rewrite Γ in terms of S, T, and N rather than, as implied earlier, in terms of the partial derivatives of $\tilde{R}$. We obtain

$$\Gamma = S\frac{r^2}{\mu e}\cos f - T\frac{r^2}{\mu e}\sin f\left[1+\frac{r}{a(1-e^2)}\right], \tag{6.6.17}$$

where we have used (6.6.16).

As an alternate derivation of Gauss' form of the planetary equations, it is interesting to note that the perturbation equations (6.6.10)–(6.6.14) and (6.6.16) can be written down from fundamental principles by considering the small changes $\Delta a \ldots \Delta\tau$ caused by small impulses $S\Delta t$, $T\Delta t$, $N\Delta t$ at any point of the orbit. First of all we have

$$\Delta v = (S\sin\gamma + T\cos\gamma)\Delta t, \qquad \Delta\gamma = (S\cos\gamma - T\sin\gamma)\frac{\Delta t}{v}, \qquad \Delta\psi = -\frac{N}{v\cos\gamma}\Delta t, \tag{6.6.18}$$

where v, γ, and ψ were defined in Chapter 4, Section 7. We take $\Delta r = \Delta\varphi = \Delta\lambda = \Delta t_0 = 0$, of course, since they are not influenced at $t = 0$ by an impulse. Equations (6.6.18) can now be used with the linear orbit sensitivities (4.7.1), (4.7.2), (4.7.5)–(4.7.9) and (4.2.12), (4.2.13), (4.2.19) to obtain expressions for $\Delta a(S, N, T, \Delta t, a, e, \ldots)$, $\Delta e(S, N, T, \Delta t, a, e, \ldots)$, etc., where (4.2.12), (4.2.13), and (4.2.19) serve to express all trigonometric functions in terms of orbit parameters. Summarizing the result, we have

$$\begin{bmatrix} \Delta a \\ \vdots \\ \Delta\tau \end{bmatrix} = \begin{bmatrix} \frac{\partial a}{\partial S} & \frac{\partial a}{\partial T} & \frac{\partial a}{\partial N} \\ \vdots & \vdots & \vdots \\ \frac{\partial \tau}{\partial S} & \frac{\partial \tau}{\partial T} & \frac{\partial \tau}{\partial N} \end{bmatrix} \times \begin{bmatrix} S \\ T \\ N \end{bmatrix} \Delta t. \tag{6.6.19}$$

Dividing by Δt and letting $\Delta t \to 0$ we arrive at Gauss' form of Lagrange's planetary equations for $\dot{a} \ldots \dot{\tau}$. Executing the quadratures for the elements we develop, in effect, the Duhamel (or convolution) integrals for the infinitesimal impulses $S\,dt$, $T\,dt$, $N\,dt$, yielding the perturbations of the path as a function of time.

This approach is not restricted to conservative perturbations, nor does it involve the laborious manipulation of Lagrange brackets. Derivations of the planetary equations along these lines have also been indicated in references 5 (p. 238) and 14.

7. ILLUSTRATIVE EXAMPLE. THE EFFECT OF SOLAR RADIATION PRESSURE ON AN EARTH SATELLITE

Let us take a satellite spherically symmetric in shape and reflectivity so that β and A of Eq. (5.3.29) are constants. Then the total force of radiation is also constant; we shall designate it by F_p.

If the sun's position is given by α, δ the components of the force are

$$F_x = -F_p \cos\delta \cos\alpha; \qquad F_y = -F_p \cos\delta \sin\alpha; \qquad F_z = -F_p \sin\delta, \tag{6.7.1}$$

assuming the rays are collimated. Now if we multiply (6.6.2) by l_1, (6.6.3) by m_1, (6.6.4) by n_1, add and utilize (6.6.5) and (6.6.6) we have

$$S\cos f - T\sin f = l_1\frac{F_x}{m} + m_1\frac{F_y}{m} + n_1\frac{F_z}{m}.$$

Similarly, we may obtain

$$S\sin f + T\cos f = l_2\frac{F_x}{m} + m_2\frac{F_y}{m} + n_2\frac{F_z}{m},$$

from which we have

$$\begin{aligned} S &= -\frac{F_p}{mr_p}(h_1\cos f + h_2\sin f), \\ T &= \frac{F_p}{mr_p}(h_1\sin f - h_2\cos f), \end{aligned} \tag{6.7.2}$$

where we have used

$$h_1 = l_1 x_p + m_1 y_p + n_1 z_p,$$
$$h_2 = l_2 x_p + m_2 y_p + n_2 z_p, \tag{6.7.3}$$

and r_p represents the earth-to-sun distance. Further,

$$N = -\frac{F_p}{mr_p} h_3, \tag{6.7.4}$$

where

$$h_3 = l_3 x_p + m_3 y_p + n_3 z_p. \tag{6.7.5}$$

If an orbit study is to be extended over considerable time, one must allow for the apparent annual motion of the sun in a geocentric frame. This may be accomplished by periodically updating the solar coordinates x_p, y_p, z_p as part of the rectifications of Lagrange's equations, discussed before. We have also considered (in Chapter 5) the means by which the earth's shadow may be introduced into the perturbation analysis. In each anomalistic period, the expressions for the perturbations of the orbital elements must be evaluated between the limits of the illuminated part of the orbit.

Transforming the independent variable to the unperturbed true anomaly (which we hereafter denote by f), (6.6.10) becomes, to first order,

$$\frac{da}{df} = 2\frac{a^3(1-e^2)}{\mu}\left[S\frac{e\sin f}{(1+e\cos f)^2} + T\frac{1}{1+e\cos f}\right],$$

where we have suppressed the subscript zero on the right-hand side. Then, with the aid of (6.7.2),

$$\frac{da}{df} = \frac{2a^3(1-e^2)F_p}{m\mu r_p}\left[\frac{h_1\sin f - h_2(e+\cos f)}{(1+e\cos f)^2}\right],$$

and

$$a - a_0 = \frac{2a(1-e^2)F_p}{m\mu r_p}\left\{\frac{h_1/e - h_2\sin f}{1+e\cos f}\right\}_{f_0}^{f}, \tag{6.7.6}$$

where all elements on the right are understood to have their initial magnitudes, those valid at f_0, and where the expression is to be evaluated between the limits shown.

Similarly, we obtain expressions for the other elements. Let $\Sigma = \sin f$, $\psi = \cos f$, $\varphi^2 = 1 - e^2$. Then

$$e - e_0 = \frac{a^3\varphi^4 F_p}{m\mu r_p e}\left\{\frac{h_1/e - h_2\Sigma}{1 + e\psi} - \frac{h_1\varphi^2}{2e(1 + e\psi)^2} + h_2\left[\Sigma\frac{2 + e^2 + (e + 2e^3)\psi}{2\varphi^2(1 + e\psi)^2} - \frac{3e}{2\varphi^3}E\right]\right\}_{f_0}^{f}, \tag{6.7.7}$$

$$i - i_0 = \frac{a^2\varphi^4 F_p}{m\mu r_p}\left\{\frac{dh_1}{di}\frac{1}{2e(1 + e\psi)^2} - \frac{dh_2}{di}\left[\Sigma\frac{2 + e^2 + (e + 2e^3)\psi}{2\varphi^4(1 + e\psi)^2} - \frac{3e}{2\varphi^5}E\right]\right\}_{f_0}^{f}, \tag{6.7.8}$$

$$\Omega - \Omega_0 = -\frac{a^2\varphi^4 F_p}{m\mu r_p \sin i}\left\{\frac{dh_1}{di}\left[\Sigma\frac{2 + e^2 + (e + 2e^3)\psi}{2\varphi^4(1 + e\psi)^2} - \frac{3e}{2\varphi^5}E\right] + \frac{dh_2}{di}\frac{1}{2e(1 + e\psi)^2}\right\}_{f_0}^{f}, \tag{6.7.9}$$

$$\omega - \omega_0 + \cos i_0(\Omega - \Omega_0) = -\frac{a^2\varphi^4 F_p}{m\mu r_p e}\left\{h_1\left[\Sigma\frac{3e + (1 + 2e^2)\psi}{2\varphi^2(1 + e\psi)^2} - \frac{3}{2\varphi^3}E\right] + h_2\frac{1 + 2e\psi}{2e^2(1 + e\psi)^2}\right\}_{f_0}^{f}, \tag{6.7.10}$$

$$\tau - \frac{n_0}{n}\tau_0 - \frac{\varphi}{n}[(\omega - \omega_0) + (\Omega - \Omega_0)\cos i] - \left(1 - \frac{n_0}{n}\right)t$$

$$= \frac{3a^2\varphi^2 F_p}{m\mu r_p}\frac{n_0(t - t_0)}{n}\frac{h_1\psi_0 + h_2\Sigma_0}{1 + e\psi_0} - \frac{5a^2\varphi^5 F_p}{m\mu r_p n}$$

$$\cdot\left\{h_1\left[\Sigma\frac{2 + e^2 + e(e + 2e^3)\psi}{2\varphi^4(1 + e\psi)^2} - \frac{3e}{2\varphi^5}E\right] + h_2\frac{1}{2e(1 + e\psi)^2}\right\}_{f_0}^{f}. \tag{6.7.11}$$

It is worthwhile to pause and examine these results briefly. We note, generally, that for fully illuminated orbits ($f' = f_0 + 2\pi$), there is no change expected in semi-major axis; the radiation energy imparted to the satellite during one half its orbit is just necessary to overcome the retarding solar pressure during the other half. When the earth's shadow is to be accounted for, however, changes in a will occur; total energy can be raised or lowered according to the geometry of the orbit and the earth-sun line. In the absence of other effects, the annual "motion" of the sun will then force a yearly cycle on the semimajor axis: first increasing and then decreasing, or *vice versa*, with a net change, to first order, of zero.

Eccentricity always has a secular term:

$$\Delta e_s = -\frac{3a^2\varphi F_p}{2m\mu r_p} h_2(E' - E_0).$$

However, this too may be a cyclic effect when examined over long-time intervals. Changes in inclination and Ω are similar: it is interesting to note their secular terms contain e as a multiplicative factor and consequently these terms are absent from our analysis given in Section 3.4, Chapter 5.

The argument of perigee has a secular term which varies inversely with e; rapid changes in the location of perigee are bound to occur for low-eccentricity orbits, except when perigee is located at one of two stable points on the orbit. For the special case where the sun lies in the orbit plane and other effects due to the earth's shadow, oblateness, etc., are neglected, these stable points form a line of apsides normal to the earth-sun line. This is also mentioned in Chapters 5 and 7 and the change of eccentricity given there agrees with the above formula. A more complete discussion of radiation effects as a function of orbit geometry and interaction with other perturbations is beyond the scope of this chapter. A very comprehensive study, and possibly the first of its kind, was made by Shapiro and Jones using the variation of parameters technique; it was partially documented in [15]. Another early contribution in this area is due to Musen [16].

8. CONCLUDING REMARKS

As mentioned in Chapter 5, there is no guarantee that solutions to the perturbation equations can be found conveniently even after the effects have been separated into their respective orders. Thus, extension of the satellite drag analysis of Section 5.5.2 to eccentric orbits by methods of this chapter encounters considerable formal difficulty. We could try a new form of the equations of motion, but the method of variation of the elements still has great appeal. This is so not only because of ease of interpretation but also because the quadratures required can often be approximated so much more simply than can other forms. We provide one example of this in Appendix B: an approximation to the first-order equations describing the effect of atmospheric drag on an earth satellite [see reference 17 for more detail].

Reviewing the rather extensive literature pertaining generally to perturbations in the elements, one should also note some approaches not identical to those we have given but which appear to be related to the classical Variation of Parameters.

Applications of the planetary equations to earth satellites began to appear before and during the early Sputnik era (see references 18–22). Eventually, some higher-order analyses were published [9, 13, 23, 24, 25] as a contribution toward stability studies of satellite orbits and refinement of the geopotential by means of satellite observations.*

For the purpose of carrying out long-range predictions and representing the secular perturbations as effectively as possible, some authors employed modified or "mean" elements. Merson [26] points out that the classical elements $a, e, \ldots, \chi$ appearing in an oblateness analysis may be redefined to minimize the amplitude of periodic terms. This may constitute an advantage for the computation of position ephemerides. However, the new elements do not satisfy the condition of osculation, and any requirement for velocity translates into an awkward evaluation of time derivatives. In a similar vein, Sterne and Garfinkel conducted studies of *intermediary orbits.* These are given in terms of modified elements which absorb some of the oblateness effects in closed form [27, 28]. The latter reference introduces some canonic notation and represents a transition to the subject of Chapter 7 of this work. Similarly, the work of Petty and Breakwell [29], in which mean elements are derived by applying an "averaging" process of the equations of motion, leads to a class of techniques deserving a separate discussion.

In closing this chapter, we should mention the analysis which was often referred to in the early Sputnik era [30, 31] and formed the basis for a series of ramifications elicited by King-Hele and his associates. This approach employed a "hybrid" method that is formulated neither strictly in terms of orbit parameters nor entirely in coordinates. To start with, the equations of motion are written for the position coordinates, but subsequently are rearranged, where convenient, in

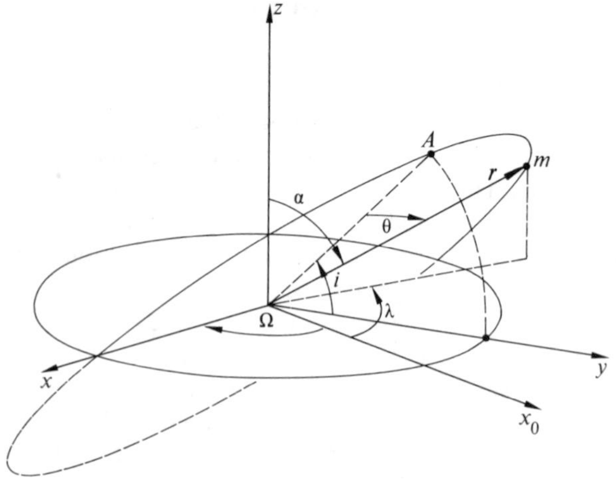

Figure 6.2

*Reference 19 distinguishes itself by giving perturbation formulae for a general term in the Legendre series for the geopotential. It is a contribution toward satellite theories involving rather elaborate representations of the earth's gravity field.

terms of specially chosen modifications of the classical orbit elements, all the while anticipating the well-known secular effects due to oblateness perturbations.

King-Hele introduced an orbit plane whose inclination is strictly constant and whose initial node defines an inertial cartesian system x_0, y_0, z. The orbit plane is allowed to rotate about the z axis, its instantaneous nodal angle Ω being measured from the x_0 axis. This angle defines the rotating axes x, y in the equatorial plane (Fig. 6.2); the y, z plane contains the point of maximum latitude, A, of the orbit plane. The instantaneous satellite position is given by the angle θ, measured in the orbit plane from A, which also serves as reference for the argument of perigee ω. One further introduces the longitude λ of the satellite m relative to the x_0 axis, and its co-latitude α. Note that, for convenience, we have used the symbols i, Ω, θ, ω, λ here, though they do not correspond strictly to the definitions employed earlier in this chapter. As the reader will observe, we use e in a slightly different way also.

The basic structure of the solution assumed by King-Hele is

$$1/r = L[1 + e\cos(\theta - \omega) + J_2 g(\theta) + J_2 e h(\theta) + 0(J_2^2)], \tag{6.8.1}$$

where

$$d\omega/d\theta = \kappa. \tag{6.8.2}$$

Also

$$d\Omega/d\theta = \nu + 0(J_2 e). \tag{6.8.3}$$

L and e can be considered strictly constant since the undetermined functions $g(\theta)$ and $h(\theta)$ will be used to represent the periodic perturbations expected in the semi-major axis and eccentricity due to oblateness. The quantities κ and ν are constants of $0(J_2)$ and thus anticipate the correct secular effects for ω and Ω. The most severe restriction of this theory is the constant angle i. This, in itself, suffices to destroy the condition of osculation (since the instantaneous velocity vector cannot lie in the orbit plane with this constraint) and it also limits the accuracy of predicted positions from this analysis. The constant maximum latitude of the satellite enforced by this device does not allow for the known periodic perturbations in the inclination of the osculating orbit. Finally, the detailed formulation employs power series expansions in terms of e and restricts itself to small eccentricities.

The equations of motion in terms of the spherical coordinates r, α, λ follow immediately from those of Chapter 5 for r, φ, λ since $\varphi = \pi/2 - \alpha$:

$$\ddot{r} - r\dot{\alpha}^2 - r\sin^2\alpha\dot{\lambda}^2 = -\frac{\mu}{r^2} - \frac{3J_2\mu R^2}{2r^4}(1 - 3\cos^2\alpha), \tag{6.8.4}$$

$$\frac{1}{r}\frac{d}{dt}(r^2\dot{\alpha}) - r\sin\alpha\cos\alpha\dot{\lambda}^2 = \frac{3J_2\mu R^2}{r^4}\sin\alpha\cos\alpha, \tag{6.8.5}$$

$$\frac{d}{dt}(r^2\sin^2\alpha\dot{\lambda}) = 0. \tag{6.8.6}$$

Here we have only retained terms of $0(J_2)$. (Note that the fundamental plane in this system is the equator, rather than the unperturbed orbit, as with most analyses in Chapter 5.) As usual, one takes advantage of the momentum equation

$$r^2\dot{\lambda}\sin^2\alpha = p = \text{const.}, \tag{6.8.7}$$

to adopt λ as independent variable. Then (6.8.5) becomes

$$(d^2/d\lambda^2)\cot\alpha + \cot\alpha = -3J_2\mu R^2/p^2 r \sin^3\alpha\cos\alpha. \tag{6.8.8}$$

Now the left-hand side of this equation may be rearranged by means of various trigonometric identities and with the help of (6.8.3) for $d\Omega/d\theta$. Then

$$\frac{d^2}{d\lambda^2}(\cot\alpha) + \cot\alpha = -2\nu\frac{\sin^3\alpha}{\sin^3 i}\cos\alpha. \tag{6.8.9}$$

As a by-product of this derivation one finds

$$\frac{d\theta}{d\lambda} = \frac{\sin^2\alpha}{\cos i}\left(1 + \nu\frac{\sin^2\alpha}{\cos i}\right) + 0(J_2 e). \tag{6.8.10}$$

Equating (6.8.8) and (6.8.9) yields

$$\nu = \tfrac{3}{2}J_2 L^2 R^2 \cos i, \tag{6.8.11}$$

where we note from (6.8.1) that $1/r = u \simeq L$ is a sufficient approximation in (6.8.8). Ultimately one finds that the identity $\cot\alpha = \tan i \sin(\lambda + \Omega)$ yields the solution of (6.8.8) if one takes

$$\Omega = \tfrac{3}{2}J_2 L^2 R^2 \cos i\cdot\theta + 0(J_2 e). \tag{6.8.12}$$

To solve (6.8.4) we find an expression for $\dot{\theta}$ from (6.8.10) and (6.8.6) and transform the equation of motion to θ as independent variable. In terms of $u = 1/r$ this yields

$$u'' + u = L + \tfrac{3}{2}J_2 L R^2 u^2(1 - 3\cos^2\alpha) - 2\nu u\frac{\sin^2 i}{\cos i}\sin^2\theta + 0(J_2 e), \tag{6.8.13}$$

where primes denote $d/d\theta$. Utilizing the form (6.8.1) and noting that perturbations in ω make a negligible contribution, of order $J_2 e$, we have

$$u'' = L[-e\cos(\theta - \omega) + \tfrac{3}{2}J_2 g'' + 0(J_2 e)]. \tag{6.8.14}$$

With the help of (6.8.1) and (6.8.14) we get from (6.8.13)

$$g'' + g = \tfrac{1}{2}L^2R^2(5\cos^2 i - 3 - \sin^2 i\cos 2\theta) + 0(e),$$

and the solution

$$g = L^2R^2\left[\frac{5\cos^2 i - 3}{2} + \frac{\sin^2 i}{6}\cos 2\theta + K_1\cos\theta + K_2\sin\theta\right], \tag{6.8.15}$$

where K_1 and K_2 are integration constants. Since the geometric significance of the complementary solution in (6.8.15) is simply to modify the e and ω of (6.8.1), we set $K_1 = K_2 = 0$ on the assumption that the nominal orbit parameters L, e, ω, i will be selected to satisfy the initial conditions for (6.8.4) and (6.8.5). As usual, it remains to develop the "time relation" $\theta(t)$ by way of (6.8.6). King-Hele does this in detail and also shows that an extension of the analysis to $0(J_2 e)$, thus admitting ω' into the perturbation equations, yields the well-known advance of pericenter. In fact, his work was subsequently developed to progressively higher orders, including a variety of physical effects.

The work of Brenner and Latta [31] improved King-Hele's original analysis by abandoning the condition of constant orbit inclination (as was also done in one of King-Hele's later papers) and by retaining e in closed-form expressions. This avoids some of the very elaborate series manipulations in King-Hele's original approach.

Several mixed formulations of this kind may be found in the literature, where coordinate perturbations or vector equations of motion are related to (mean) orbit elements. Sometimes this yields a concise analysis [32]; sometimes it is motivated by computational advantages. A classical method in this category is that due to Hansen. It has yielded some very effective computing procedures [33]. Since its general derivation requires a detailed explanation, we shall save it for Chapter 9.

In surveying the literature, one cannot fail to be impressed by the variety and number of contributions on satellite orbit prediction. Some are classical approaches; others proceed from what we may call an engineering point of view. Some manifest originality; many are redundant. Chapters 5 and 6 have introduced a fair number of formulations; more are to be discussed. There is then the inevitable question: What are the relative merits of these techniques? A complete answer would probably require a term-by-term comparison of the various methods, which lies well beyond our present capacity for patience, and numerous computer runs. Possibly the eventual automation of symbol manipulations by computers may remedy this. For the time being, one finds only partial comparisons, some analytic and some numerical. We shall return to this point at the end of this volume.

REFERENCES

1. R. M. L. Baker and M. W. Makemson, *An Introduction to Astrodynamics*, Academic Press, New York, 1960.
2. D. Brouwer and G. M. Clemence, *Methods of Celestial Mechanics*, Academic Press, New York, 1961.
3. F. R. Moulton, *An Introduction to Celestial Mechanics*, Macmillan, New York, 1914.
4. W. M. Smart, *Celestial Mechanics*, Longmans, New York, 1953.
5. J. M. A. Danby, *Fundamentals of Celestial Mechanics*, Macmillan, New York, 1962.
6. T. E. Sterne, *An Introduction to Celestial Mechanics*, Interscience Publishers, New York, 1960.

7. A. G. Lubowe, "Order of a Perturbation Method," *AIAA Journal*, **3,** 568, 1965.

8. A. G. Lubowe, "Efficient and Accurate Orbit Prediction for Very Long Periods of Time," *Progress in Astronautics*, Vol. 17, Academic Press, New York, 1966, p. 247.

9. D. Mace and L. H. Thomas, "An Extrapolation Formula for Stepping the Calculation of the Orbit of an Artificial Satellite Several Revolutions Ahead at a Time," *Astron. J.*, **65,** 300, 1960; C. J. Cohen and E. C. Hubbard, "An Algorithm Applicable to Numerical Integration of Orbits in Multirevolution Steps," *Astron. J.*, **65,** 454, 1960; G. P. Taratynova, "Numerical Solution of Equations of Finite Differences and Their Application to the Calculation of Orbits of Artificial Earth Satellites," *Artificial Earth Satellites*, 1960, No. 4 (English translation in *ARS Journal*, **31,** 976, 1961).

10. S. Herrick, "Universal Variables," *Astron. J.*, **70,** 309, 1965.

11. A. M. Garofalo, "A New Set of Variables for Astronomical Problems," *Astron. J.*, **65,** 177, 1960.

12. R. R. Newton, "Variables That Are Determinate for Any Orbit," *ARS Journal*, **31,** 364, 1961.

13. A. J. Claus and A. G. Lubowe, "A High-Accuracy Perturbation Method with Direct Application to Communication Satellite Orbit Prediction," *Astronautica Acta*, **9,** 275, 1963.

14. A. I. Luré, "The Equations of Disturbed Motion in the Kepler Problem," *Planet. Space Sci.*, **8,** 79, 1961.

15. a) R. W. Parkinson, H. M. Jones, and I. I. Shapiro, "Effects of Solar Radiation Pressure on Earth Satellite Orbits," *Science*, **131,** 920, 1960.
b) P. E. Zadunaisky, I. I. Shapiro, H. M. Jones, "Experimental and Theoretical Results on the Orbit of Echo I," *Smithsonian Inst. Ast. Obs. Spec. Rep.*, Special Report no. 61, 1961.

16. P. Musen, "The Influence of Solar Radiation Pressure on the Motion of an Artificial Satellite," *Jour. of Geophysical Res.*, **65,** 1391, 1960.

17. H. R. Westerman, "Secular Effects of Atmospheric Drag on Satellite Orbits," *Astron. J.*, **68,** 382, 1963.

18. H. G. L. Krause, "Die säkularen und periodischen Störungen eines künstlichen Satelliten," Proc. 7th Int. Astronaut. Cong., p. 523, Rome, 1956.

19. I. M. Jatsunskiy, "The Effect of Geophysical Factors on Satellite Motion," *Uspekhi Fizicheskikh Nauk*, **63,** 59, September 1957.

20. I. D. Zhongolovitch, "Formulae Relating to the Motion of a Particle in the Gravitational Field of a Level Ellipsoid of Revolution," (in Russian), *Bull. Inst. Theor. Astr.* (Leningrad), **7,** 521, 1960.

21. M. M. Moe, "Luni-Solar Perturbations of the Orbit of an Earth Satellite," *ARS J.*, **30,** 485, 1960.

22. T. E. Sterne, "Development of Some General Theories of the Orbits of Artificial Earth Satellites," *Astron. J.*, **63,** 424, 1958.

23. G. V. Groves, "Motion of a Satellite in the Earth's Gravitational Field," *Proc. Roy. Soc.*, **254(A),** 48, 1960.

24. Y. Kozai, "Second Order Solution of Artificial Satellite Theory without Air Drag," *Astron. J.*, **67,** 446, 1962.

25. M. L. Lidov, "Evolution of the Orbits of Artificial Satellites of Planets as Affected by the Gravitational Perturbations from External Bodies," *AIAA J.*, **1,** 1985, 1963.

26. R. H. Merson, "The Motion of a Satellite in an Axisymmetric Gravitational Field," *Geophysical J. Roy. Astron. Soc.*, **4,** 17, 1961.

27. T. E. Sterne, "The Gravitational Orbit of a Satellite of an Oblate Planet," *Astron. J.*, **63,** 28, 1958.

28. B. Garfinkel, "The Motion of a Satellite of an Oblate Planet," *Astron. J.*, **63,** 88, 1958.

29. C. M. Petty and J. V. Breakwell, "Satellite Orbits about a Planet with Rotational Symmetry," *J. Franklin Inst.,* **270,** 259, 1960.

30. D. G. King-Hele, "The Effect of the Earth's Oblateness on the Orbit of a Near Satellite," *Proc. Roy. Soc.,* **247(A),** 49, 1958.

31. J. L. Brenner and G. E. Latta, "The Theory of Satellite Orbits, Based on a New Coordinate System," *Proc. Roy. Soc.*, **258(A),** 470, 1960.

32. G. N. Ward, "On the Secular Variations of the Elements of Satellite Orbits," *Proc. Roy. Soc.*, **266(A),** 130, 1962.

33. P. Musen, "Application of Hansen's Theory to the Motion of an Artificial Satellite in the Gravitational Field of the Earth," *J. Geophys. Res.*, **64,** 2271, 1959.

Chapter seven

LAGRANGE'S AND HAMILTON'S EQUATIONS. APPLICATION TO MOVING COORDINATES

1. INTRODUCTION

In Chapter 5 we introduced the fundamental concepts of perturbation theory and illustrated some approaches in terms of geocentric Cartesian and spherical reference frames. We started from a statement of the satellite problem in a Newtonian formulation, for example,

$$m\ddot{x} = X(x,y,z,\dot{x},\dot{y},\dot{z},t); \qquad m\ddot{y} = Y(x,y,z,\dot{x},\dot{y},\dot{z},t); \qquad m\ddot{z} = Z(x,y,z,\dot{x},\dot{y},\dot{z},t), \quad (7.1.1)$$

where X, Y, Z denoted the force components in the corresponding directions and we transformed these equations on a more or less *ad hoc* basis. As was pointed out, some mathematical difficulties in orbit analysis are often alleviated by appropriate choice of a coordinate system. This raises the question as to how we might discover preferred sets of coordinates for a given problem. In Chapter 6 we furnished one answer to this question, a classical one due to Lagrange. The motion of the satellite was expressed in terms of the characteristic parameters of its osculating ellipse. These, in contrast to the space coordinates, x, y, z or r, β, θ of Chapter 5, are relatively slowly varying functions of time, well suited to describing the changes in orbit geometry.

In the following two chapters our search for more general ways of effecting such transformations leads us to Hamilton's canonical set of equations. Lagrangian theory is reviewed in the process. We illustrate the latter by describing the perturbed motion of a satellite, to first order, in terms of the ξ, η, ζ coordinates of Chapter 4, Section 8, thus providing a more complete treatment of these particular equations of motion. Much of the remainder of this chapter is devoted to various examples. Finally, we discuss some modifications of the ξ, η, ζ system, which returns us to the quest for appropriate coordinate transformations, leading to the canonical methods of Chapter 8.

2. LAGRANGE'S AND HAMILTON'S EQUATIONS

The reader is aware of the ease with which the equations of motion of a satellite can be written in terms of a variety of coordinate systems by means of the Lagrangian formulation. The procedure has the advantage of being purely formal and automatic in contrast to the Newtonian formulation which relies strictly on inspection. With unusual coordinate systems the latter process becomes laborious (though it has the advantage of forcing the analyst to appreciate the physical significance of each term in the equations). It may be helpful to review briefly the derivation of Lagrange's dynamical equations and the formal procedure involved in their application before proceeding to Hamilton's equations.

Let us assume that (7.1.1) describes the motion of a particle in a system consisting of s bodies where the coordinates of each particle are denoted: x_r, y_r, z_r. Now suppose that we wish to express the motion of this system in some other set of coordinates q_i, where $i = 1, \ldots, n$ and $n \leq 3s$, the equality sign being valid if each of the $3s$ Cartesian coordinates represent an independent degree of freedom. The Cartesian coordinates can be expressed in terms of the q_i according to

$$x_r = x_r(q_1, \ldots, q_n, t); \qquad y_r = y_r(q_1, \ldots, q_n, t); \qquad z_r = z_r(q_1, \ldots, q_n, t). \tag{7.2.1}$$

We may then write

$$\dot{x}_r = \frac{\partial x_r}{dt} + \frac{\partial x_r}{\partial q_1}\dot{q}_1 + \cdots + \frac{\partial x_r}{\partial q_n}\dot{q}_n, \text{ etc.} \tag{7.2.2}$$

from which we observe that

$$\frac{\partial \dot{x}_r}{\partial \dot{q}_i} = \frac{\partial x_r}{\partial q_i}, \quad \frac{\partial \dot{y}_r}{\partial \dot{q}_i} = \frac{\partial y_r}{\partial q_i}, \quad \frac{\partial \dot{z}_r}{\partial \dot{q}_i} = \frac{\partial z_r}{\partial q_i}. \tag{7.2.3}$$

With the help of (7.2.3) and (7.1.1) we find that

$$\begin{aligned} \frac{d}{dt}\left[\frac{1}{2}m_r\frac{\partial(\dot{x}_r^2)}{\partial \dot{q}_i}\right] &= m_r\frac{d}{dt}\left(\dot{x}_r\frac{\partial x_r}{\partial q_i}\right) \\ &= X_r\frac{\partial x_r}{\partial q_i} + m_r\dot{x}_r\frac{\partial \dot{x}_r}{\partial q_i}, \end{aligned} \tag{7.2.4}$$

(where we assume that the sequence of differentiations with respect to t and q_i is reversible). Summing (7.2.4) over all x_r, y_r, z_r in the system, we find

$$\begin{aligned} \frac{d}{dt}\frac{\partial}{\partial \dot{q}_i}\sum_r \frac{1}{2}m_r(\dot{x}_r^2 + \dot{y}_r^2 + \dot{z}_r^2) &= \sum_r\left(X_r\frac{\partial x_r}{\partial q_i} + Y_r\frac{\partial y_r}{\partial q_i} + Z_r\frac{\partial z_r}{\partial q_i}\right) \\ &\quad + \frac{\partial}{\partial q_i}\sum_r \frac{1}{2}m_r(\dot{x}_r^2 + \dot{y}_r^2 + \dot{z}_r^2). \end{aligned} \tag{7.2.5}$$

To interpret the first summation on the right-hand side, we observe that the work done by external forces over a small displacement of the rth particle is

$$X_r dx_r + Y_r dy_r + Z_r dz_r = (\overline{X}_r + \tilde{X}_r)dx_r + (\overline{Y}_r + \tilde{Y}_r)dy_r + (\overline{Z}_r + \tilde{Z}_r)dz_r$$
$$= -dV + \tilde{X}_r dx_r + \tilde{Y}_r dy_r + \tilde{Z}_r dz_r. \qquad (7.2.6)$$

The representation of $\overline{X}_r dx_r + \overline{Y}_r dy_r + \overline{Z}_r dz_r = -dV$ as an exact differential is true only if the forces $\overline{X}_r$, $\overline{Y}_r$, $\overline{Z}_r$ originate from a conservative field. This means that they can only be functions of particle position and not velocity. Hence $\partial\overline{X}_r/\partial\dot{x}_r = \partial\overline{X}_r/\partial\dot{y}_r = \ldots \partial\overline{Z}_r/\partial\dot{z}_r = 0$, for all values of r. From this it follows that V, the potential function of this field, does not depend on the velocities. It also follows that we may write

$$\sum_r \left(\overline{X}_r \frac{\partial x_r}{\partial q_i} + \overline{Y}_r \frac{\partial y_r}{\partial q_i} + \overline{Z}_r \frac{\partial z_r}{\partial q_i}\right) = -\frac{\partial V}{\partial q_i}. \qquad (7.2.7)$$

Now $\tilde{X}_r$, $\tilde{Y}_r$, $\tilde{Z}_r$ are the nonconservative forces (in the x, y, z system) acting on the rth particle and in analogy to (7.2.7) we may write

$$\sum_r \left(\tilde{X}_r \frac{\partial x_r}{\partial q_i} + \tilde{Y}_r \frac{\partial y_r}{\partial q_i} + \tilde{Z}_r \frac{\partial z_r}{\partial q_i}\right) = Q_i, \qquad (7.2.8)$$

which is recognized as the generalized nonconservative force corresponding to q_i.

The second summation on the right-hand side of (7.2.5)

$$\tfrac{1}{2}\sum_r m_r(\dot{x}_r^2 + \dot{y}_r^2 + \dot{z}_r^2) = T, \qquad (7.2.9)$$

is the kinetic energy of the system. It will be useful to note that, while this is a positive definite quadratic form* in $\dot{x}_r$, $\dot{y}_r$, $\dot{z}_r$, the same can (but need not necessarily) be the case in terms of the q_i's. It will be so if (7.2.1) does not involve the time explicitly (i.e., if, in (7.2.2), $\partial x_r/\partial t = \partial y_r/\partial t = \partial z_r/\partial t = 0$). This rules out such features as time-dependent constraints in the relations between the q_i's and x_r, y_r, z_r.

Using (7.2.7) and (7.2.9), we may write (7.2.5) as

$$\frac{d}{dt}\left[\frac{\partial T}{\partial \dot{q}_i}\right] = \frac{\partial}{\partial q_i}(T - V) + Q_i. \qquad (7.2.10)$$

On the grounds that $\partial V/\partial \dot{q}_i = 0$ we may now introduce the functional $L = T - V$ in (7.2.10), and obtain

$$\frac{d}{dt}\left[\frac{\partial L}{\partial \dot{q}_i}\right] - \frac{\partial L}{\partial q_i} = Q_i, \qquad i = 1, \ldots, n. \qquad (7.2.11)$$

---

*Any system of coordinates in which the kinetic energy can be written down by inspection (usually an inertial one) will result explicitly in a sum of squared velocity terms which make the positive definiteness of this quantity obvious. Such coordinate systems are sometimes referred to as "natural" ones.

This is a system of n equations corresponding to the n degrees of freedom that the q_i represent. L is referred to as the *kinetic potential* or the *Lagrangian* and (7.2.11) is known as Lagrange's equations of motion. The procedure involved in their use consists of the following steps:

a) Write down

$$T = \tfrac{1}{2}\sum_r m_r(\dot{x}_r^2 + \dot{y}_r^2 + \dot{z}_r^2),$$

$$V(x_r, y_r, z_r),$$

and $\tilde{X}_r$, $\tilde{Y}_r$, $\tilde{Z}_r$ by inspection (where one does not necessarily have to work in a Cartesian system).

b) Express these quantities in terms of any desired set of coordinates q_i by use of (7.2.1) and find the Lagrangian and the nonconservative forces Q_i.

c) Generate the equations of motion according to (7.2.11).

Thus, we see how the introduction of the functional L reduces the process of writing the equations of motion to a standard procedure. Much of advanced classical dynamics is a generalized pursuit of this aim and several techniques for reducing the equations of motion to as simple a form as possible have resulted from it. Various functionals were introduced in addition to L, the best-known among them being the Hamiltonian $\mathscr{H}$.

Many of these additional techniques share the common feature that they convert the equations of motion from a system of n second-order differential equations to $2n$ first-order equations. For this purpose one introduces the n additional dependent variables

$$p_i = \partial L/\partial \dot{q}_i, \qquad i = 1, \ldots, n, \tag{7.2.12}$$

which are known as the generalized momenta. Recalling that L is quadratic in $\dot{q}_i$, we see that the expressions (7.2.12) are linear in $\dot{q}_i$ and hence may be easily inverted (assuming a nonvanishing Jacobian) to yield

$$\dot{q}_i = \dot{q}_i(q_1, \ldots, q_n, p_1, \ldots, p_n, t), \qquad i = 1, \ldots, n. \tag{7.2.13}$$

Such expressions could be used to eliminate $\dot{q}_i$ wherever it occurs; thus a functional such as L, which involves q_i, $\dot{q}_i$, and t, may be expressed as $L(q_i, p_i, t)$. In such a case, the p_i are descriptors of the motion on a level equal with the q_i.

Hamilton's functional, the *Hamiltonian*, may now be introduced according to the definition,

$$\mathscr{H} = \sum_i \dot{q}_i \frac{\partial L}{\partial \dot{q}_i} - L, \tag{7.2.14}$$

where it is understood that we may employ (7.2.13) to write $\mathscr{H}(q_i, p_i, t)$. Sometimes the mixed representation

$$\mathscr{H} = \sum_i \dot{q}_i p_i - L(q_i, \dot{q}_i, t) \tag{7.2.15}$$

proves useful. In fact, we use it to establish the differential equations for q_i and p_i in terms of $\mathscr{H}$. On the basis of (7.2.15) we may write

$$d\mathscr{H} = \sum_i \dot{q}_i dp_i + \sum_i p_i d\dot{q}_i - \sum_i \frac{\partial L}{\partial \dot{q}_i} d\dot{q}_i - \sum_i \frac{\partial L}{\partial q_i} dq_i - \frac{\partial L}{\partial t} dt, \tag{7.2.16}$$

where a relation between $d\dot{q}_i$ and dp_i, dq_i, dt is implicit by virtue of (7.2.13). If we now remember the definition (7.2.12) for p_i, the terms in $d\dot{q}_i$ drop out of (7.2.16).

Observing further from Lagrange's equations (7.2.11) that $\partial L/\partial q_i = \dot{p}_i - Q_i$, we finally have

$$d\mathscr{H} = \sum_i \dot{q}_i dp_i - \sum_i \dot{p}_i dq_i + \sum_i Q_i dq_i - \frac{\partial L}{\partial t} dt. \tag{7.2.17}$$

From this it follows that

$$\dot{q}_i = \frac{\partial \mathscr{H}}{\partial p_i}, \qquad \dot{p}_i = -\frac{\partial \mathscr{H}}{\partial q_i} + Q_i, \ (i = 1, \ldots, n,) \qquad \frac{\partial L}{\partial t} = -\frac{\partial \mathscr{H}}{\partial t}. \tag{7.2.18}$$

These represent Hamilton's form of the equations of motion, also known as the canonical equations.

Let us note from the third equation in (7.2.18) that if L does not contain t explicitly, neither does $\mathscr{H}$. Further, if the nonconservative forces Q_i vanish, $\mathscr{H}$ is an invariant of the motion, as can be shown by the following argument.

Since under these circumstances $L = L(q_1, \ldots, q_n, \dot{q}_1, \ldots, \dot{q}_n)$, we have

$$\frac{dL}{dt} = \sum_i \left(\frac{\partial L}{\partial q_i} \dot{q}_i + \frac{\partial L}{\partial \dot{q}_i} \ddot{q}_i \right). \tag{7.2.19}$$

By virtue of Lagrange's equations (7.2.11) this becomes, with the $Q_i = 0$,

$$\sum_i \left[\frac{d}{dt} \left(\frac{\partial L}{\partial \dot{q}_i} \right) \dot{q}_i + \frac{\partial L}{\partial \dot{q}_i} \ddot{q}_i \right] = \frac{d}{dt} \sum_i \dot{q}_i \frac{\partial L}{\partial \dot{q}_i}. \tag{7.2.20}$$

From the left-hand side of (7.2.19) and the right-hand side of (7.2.20) we find that

$$\frac{d}{dt} \left(\sum_i \dot{q}_i \frac{\partial L}{\partial \dot{q}_i} - L \right) = 0. \tag{7.2.21}$$

But by virtue of the definition (7.2.14) of the Hamiltonian this last is $d\mathscr{H}/dt = 0$, which establishes the invariance of $\mathscr{H}$.

Now a little consideration of the definition of L and the transformations (7.2.1) shows that $\partial L/\partial t = 0$ does not necessarily imply $\partial x_r/\partial t = \partial y_r/\partial t = \partial z_r/\partial t = 0$; i.e., the transformation (7.2.1) need not necessarily avoid an explicit appearance of t. But if it does, and if $Q_i = 0$, then $\mathscr{H}$, in addition to being an invariant of the motion, represents the total energy of the system. This can be shown as follows.

We recall from our earlier remarks about the kinetic energy T that we may write in this case

$$L = T - V = \frac{1}{2}\sum_u\sum_v C_{uv}\dot{q}_u\dot{q}_v - V(q_1,\ldots,q_n), \tag{7.2.22}$$

where $u = 1,\ldots,n$, $v = 1,\ldots,n$ and

$$\begin{aligned} C_{uv} &= \sum_r m_r\left(\frac{\partial x_r}{\partial q_u}\frac{\partial x_r}{\partial q_v} + \frac{\partial y_r}{\partial q_u}\frac{\partial y_r}{\partial q_v} + \frac{\partial z_r}{\partial q_u}\frac{\partial z_r}{\partial q_v}\right) \\ &= C_{uv}(q_1,\ldots,q_n). \end{aligned}$$

Obviously $C_{uv} = C_{vu}$. Applying (7.2.22) to (7.2.14), we thus find that

$$\mathscr{H} = 2T - (T - V) = T + V. \tag{7.2.23}$$

3. RELATIONS BETWEEN LAGRANGE'S AND HAMILTON'S EQUATIONS OF MOTION AND HAMILTON'S PRINCIPLE

Before illustrating the use of (7.2.18) in the solution of specific orbital problems it is illuminating, as well as useful for later reference, to examine the equations of Section 2 as they derive from Hamilton's principle. The latter may be regarded as a fundamental premise underlying classical mechanics, on a par with Newton's laws. The two are equivalent bases for all formulations of analytical dynamics and are reducible to each other. Both originated from abstractions of physical observations, though Hamilton's principle suggested itself from somewhat less commonplace phenomena as, for example, certain features of geometric optics.

The Hamilton principle states that if a dynamic system passes from one configuration $(q_1,q_2,\ldots,q_n)_{t_1}$ at t_1 to another $(q_1,q_2,\ldots,q_n)_{t_2}$ at t_2 the motion must be such that the integral

$$\int_{t_1}^{t_2} L\,dt, \tag{7.3.1}$$

is an extremum. This means that if we were to change the actual path or the time history of the natural motion between fixed t_1 and t_2 the value of the integral would not change to first order; in other words, the *first variation* of the integral vanishes. In vector notation

$$\delta\int_{t_1}^{t_2} L(\boldsymbol{q},\dot{\boldsymbol{q}},t)dt = 0, \tag{7.3.2}$$

where $\boldsymbol{q} = [q_1(t),q_2(t),\ldots,q_n(t)]$ and $\dot{\boldsymbol{q}} = [\dot{q}_1(t),\dot{q}_2(t),\ldots,\dot{q}_n(t)]$ are the dynamic state vectors. At the trajectory endpoints

$$\delta\boldsymbol{q}(t_1) = \delta\boldsymbol{q}(t_2) = 0. \tag{7.3.3}$$

Since the Lagrangian L involves the variables q_i and $\dot{q}_i$, it is plausible that the properties (7.3.2) and (7.3.3) of the motion impose local conditions on these variables everywhere along the trajectory. These are just the Euler-Lagrange equations, and yield the equations of motion in the form (7.2.11) or (7.2.18).*

Now, in the foregoing, we stated the Hamilton principle for conservative dynamic systems, i.e., where all external forces are expressible as the gradient of a potential which is a function only of the configuration $\boldsymbol{q}$ of the system. However, the variational principle expressed by (7.3.2) can be generalized to include other forces as well. In order to see this we retrace the connection between Hamilton's principle and Newton's equations and arrive at the canonical equations in their most general form [1, Chapter 9].

Assume that we have written the Newtonian equations of motion for the dynamical system in terms of some natural set of coordinates $\mathbf{x}_r$ (i.e., a set in terms of which the kinetic energy can be written down by inspection). Here $r = 0,1,\ldots,s$ identifies a particle in the system. Then, in vector notation,

$$m_r\ddot{\mathbf{x}}_r = \mathbf{f}_r, \tag{7.3.4}$$

where $\mathbf{f}_r$ contains, in general, conservative and dissipative forces. Now we may write

$$\sum_r \int_{t_1}^{t_2} \left(m_r\ddot{\mathbf{x}}_r - \mathbf{f}_r\right) \cdot \overrightarrow{\delta \mathbf{x}}_r dt = 0, \tag{7.3.5}$$

where the $\overrightarrow{\delta \mathbf{x}}_r$ represent a variation of the trajectory. This means that instead of finding itself at $\mathbf{x}_r(t_k)$, at any instant t_k of the motion, the system is forced to take the slightly different configuration $\mathbf{x}_r(t_k)+\delta\mathbf{x}_r(t_k)$. The integral in (7.3.5) vanishes because its integrand, expressing the dynamic equilibrium (7.3.4) at every point of the trajectory, vanishes throughout the motion. For convenience in the later discussion we also stipulate that the terminal configurations shall not be varied, that is,

$$\delta\mathbf{x}_r(t_1) = \delta\mathbf{x}_r(t_2) = 0. \tag{7.3.6}$$

Now let us consider the different parts of (7.3.5) separately. We integrate the first term on the left-hand side by parts

$$\sum_r \int_{t_1}^{t_2} m_r\ddot{\mathbf{x}}_r \cdot \delta\mathbf{x}_r dt = \sum_r m_r \left\{ \left[\dot{\mathbf{x}}_r \cdot \delta\mathbf{x}_r \right]_{t_1}^{t_2} - \int_{t_1}^{t_2} \dot{\mathbf{x}}_r \cdot \delta\dot{\mathbf{x}}_r dt \right\}.$$

---

*Due to (7.2.12) and (7.2.14) we can also write (7.3.2) as $\delta \int_{t_1}^{t_2} [\boldsymbol{p}\cdot\dot{\boldsymbol{q}} - \mathscr{H}(\boldsymbol{q},\boldsymbol{p},t)]dt = 0.$
We noted in the preceding section and we shall also see in the next chapter that such hybrid forms, instead of a representation in terms of solely $(\boldsymbol{q},\dot{\boldsymbol{q}})$ or $(\boldsymbol{q},\boldsymbol{p})$, can often prove quite useful.

Then with the help of (7.3.6), we find

$$\sum_r \int_{t_1}^{t_2} m_r \ddot{\mathbf{x}}_r \cdot \delta \mathbf{x}_r dt = -\sum_r \frac{m_r}{2} \int_{t_1}^{t_2} \delta\left(\dot{x}_r^2\right) dt = -\delta \int_{t_1}^{t_2} T\, dt, \tag{7.3.7}$$

that is, the first part of (7.3.5) is reduced to the variation of the integral of the kinetic energy between the limits t_1 and t_2. (Note that the final form of (7.3.7) is not restricted to any particular set of coordinates.) Next we imagine that the second part of (7.3.5) is subjected to a coordinate transformation from $\mathbf{x}_r$ to q_i, where $i = 1,2,\ldots,n$. Then the virtual work done by the forces $\mathbf{f}_r$ can be written

$$\sum_r \mathbf{f}_r \cdot \delta \mathbf{x}_r = \sum_i \sum_r \left(\mathbf{g}_r \cdot \frac{\partial \mathbf{x}_r}{\partial q_i} \delta q_i - \nabla_r V \cdot \frac{\partial \mathbf{x}_r}{\partial q_i} \delta q_i \right), \tag{7.3.8}$$

where $\mathbf{g}_r$ represents the nonconservative part of $\mathbf{f}_r$ and $\nabla_r V$ the gradient of a potential function representing the conservative force field. Now we let

$$\sum_r \mathbf{g}_r \cdot \frac{\partial \mathbf{x}_r}{\partial q_i} = Q_i \tag{7.3.9}$$

denote the dissipative forces resulting from the covariant transformation. (Note that the subscript i is reserved for scalar quantities.) Similarly the conservative forces become

$$\sum_r \nabla_r V \cdot \frac{\partial \mathbf{x}_r}{\partial q_i} = \frac{\partial V}{\partial q_i}. \tag{7.3.10}$$

Substitution of (7.3.9) and (7.3.10) into (7.3.5) yields

$$\delta \int_{t_1}^{t_2} (T - V) dt + \int_{t_1}^{t_2} \sum_i Q_i \delta q_i dt = 0, \tag{7.3.11}$$

which we recognize as an extension of Hamilton's principle to include nonconservative forces. Again the integral which makes up the first part of (7.3.11) is not restricted to any particular coordinate system. If we use the q_i coordinates, implying that $L = L(q_i, \dot{q}_i, t)$, we may interpret the geometric variations of the first integrand in (7.3.11) as

$$\delta L = \sum_i \left(\frac{\partial L}{\partial q_i} \delta q_i + \frac{\partial L}{\partial \dot{q}_i} \delta \dot{q}_i \right). \tag{7.3.12}$$

Realizing that $$\int_{t_1}^{t_2} \frac{\partial L}{\partial \dot{q}_i} \delta \dot{q}_i dt = \left[\frac{\partial L}{\partial \dot{q}_i} \delta q_i \right]_{t_1}^{t_2} - \int_{t_1}^{t_2} \frac{d}{dt}\left(\frac{\partial L}{\partial \dot{q}_i} \right) \delta q_i dt,$$

where the first term vanishes because $\delta q_i = 0$ at t_1 and t_2, we have

$$\int_{t_1}^{t_2} \sum_i \left[\frac{\partial L}{\partial q_i} - \frac{d}{dt}\left(\frac{\partial L}{\partial \dot{q}_i}\right) + Q_i\right] \delta q_i dt = 0. \tag{7.3.13}$$

In view of the arbitrariness of the δq_i, each bracket in the integrand has to vanish independently. This leads to Lagrange's equations of motion (7.2.11).*

As in the preceding section we reduce these second-order equations to first-order ones by Eq. (7.2.12). The latter are linear in $\dot{q}_i$ since T is at most of second degree in $\dot{q}_i$. With their help we could obtain from Lagrange's equations

$$\dot{p}_i - \partial L/\partial q_i = Q_i, \qquad i = 1,2,\ldots,n. \tag{7.3.14}$$

Now (7.3.14) and (7.2.12) provide a system of $2n$ first-order equations, due to the change from Lagrangian to Hamiltonian variables, but this system does not possess the degree of symmetry to be found in Hamilton's equations.

To acquire complete generality in the canonical formulation, we start back at the transformation introduced in (7.3.8). Instead of assuming $\mathbf{x}_r = \mathbf{x}_r(q_i,t)$, which restricts us to the *point transformations* that come naturally in a Lagrangian formulation, we write

$$\mathbf{x}_r = \mathbf{x}_r(q_i, p_i, t). \tag{7.3.15}$$

Using this in (7.3.8) we have, in addition to (7.3.9) and (7.3.10),

$$\sum_r \mathbf{g}_r \cdot \frac{\partial \mathbf{x}_r}{\partial p_i} = P_i,$$

and (7.3.16)

$$\sum_r \nabla_r V \cdot \frac{\partial \mathbf{x}_r}{\partial p_i} = \frac{\partial V}{\partial p_i}.$$

Thus (7.3.11) becomes

$$\delta \int_{t_1}^{t_2} L\, dt + \int_{t_1}^{t_2} \sum_i (Q_i \delta q_i + P_i \delta p_i) dt = 0. \tag{7.3.17}$$

Now we may again introduce the Hamiltonian through its definition

$$L = \sum_i p_i \dot{q}_i - \mathcal{H}; \tag{7.3.18}$$

*See references 2, p. 115, 3, p. 155, and 4 for standard derivations of this kind, originally due to Euler and Lagrange.

by manipulations similar to those leading from (7.3.12) to (7.3.13) we reduce (7.3.17) to

$$\int_{t_1}^{t_2}\left[\sum_i\left(\dot{q}_i-\frac{\partial\mathscr{H}}{\partial p_i}+P_i\right)\delta p_i+\sum_i\left(-\dot{p}_i-\frac{\partial\mathscr{H}}{\partial q_i}+Q_i\right)\delta q_i\right]dt=0. \qquad (7.3.19)$$

Individual vanishing of the coefficients for each* δq_i and δp_i then leads to the canonic system in its general form, involving nonconservative forces in each equation:

$$\begin{aligned}\dot{q}_i &= \partial\mathscr{H}/\partial p_i - P_i\\ \dot{p}_i &= -\partial\mathscr{H}/\partial q_i + Q_i\end{aligned} \qquad i=1,2,\ldots,n. \qquad (7.3.20)$$

Equation (7.3.17), written as

$$\delta\int_{t_1}^{t_2}\left[\sum_i p_i\dot{q}_i-\mathscr{H}(q,p,t)\right]dt+\int_{t_1}^{t_2}\sum_i[Q_i\delta q_i+P_i\delta p_i]dt=0, \qquad (7.3.21)$$

represents the Hamilton principle in its most general form. It may be considered the mathematical equivalent of the canonical equations (7.3.20).†

As one might expect, the first-order system (7.3.20) may be derived in many forms for any specific problem, depending on the transformation (7.3.15) or the sequence of such transformations. Systematic procedures exist for taking advantage of the opportunities afforded and these we shall examine in the next chapter. In the rest of this chapter we adopt the ξ, η, ζ system introduced in Chapter 4, derive its generalized momenta p_ξ, p_η, p_ζ and the corresponding canonical equations. These are treated for both near-circular and general orbits and explicit results for some perturbation effects are discussed.

4. THE EQUATIONS OF MOTION IN MOVING COORDINATES, ξ, η, ζ

The reader will recall the ξ, η, ζ coordinate system, shown in Fig. 7.1. It uses a Keplerian orbit as a reference, the path which would be followed in the absence of perturbations. We refer to this as the nominal, or reference, orbit; its elements will be designated $a_o, e_o, \ldots$. We further denote the instantaneous position of the unperturbed body on it by O'; this is the nominal position of the orbiting body and is located by the argument of latitude θ from the nominal ascending node. This angle may be written as $\theta=\omega_o+f$ where ω_o is the argument of the nominal perigee and f represents the nominal true anomaly. If the reference orbit is circular, ω_o

---

*Note that the equal treatment given to δq_i and δp_i is justified at this point by the structure of 7.3.20, where they appear as dependent variables on a par with each other. (Discussions related to this aspect can be found, for instance, in references 2, p. 168, 4, p. 109, and 5, p. 217.)

†Another derivation of this nonconservative principle can be found in reference 1 (p. 248); a more thorough discussion of its mathematical interpretations is given in reference 6.

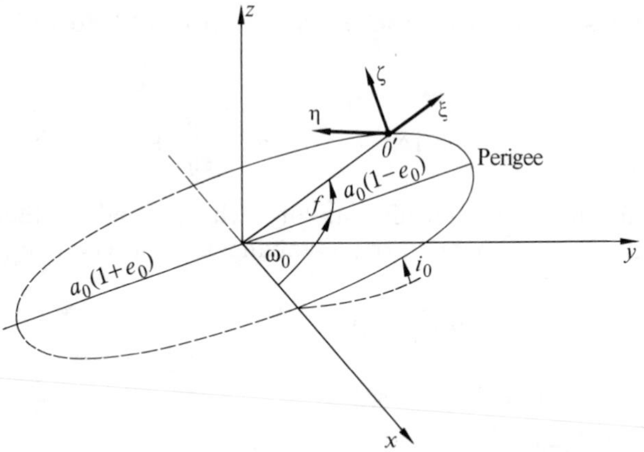

Figure 7.1

does not mark any point of geometric significance but will be retained to preserve the notation.

Using O' as the origin of coordinates, we erect the orthogonal triad ξ,η,ζ on it. The ξ axis points in the direction of the nominal radius vector $r^{(0)}$, η in the direction of anomalistic motion, and ζ normal to the nominal orbit plane. The ξ,η,ζ components of displacement are due solely to the perturbations on the path and determine the actual satellite position relative to O'. Thus, since $r^{(0)}$ is the radial distance to O', the actual geocentric distance of the satellite is

$$r = [(r^{(0)}+\xi)^2+\eta^2+\zeta^2]^{1/2}.$$

As Fig. 7.1 indicates, we choose to place the node on the positive x axis. This is merely a convenience and does not constitute a loss of generality in any subsequent examples. We follow the standard procedure of Section 2 in writing the equations of motion.

The Cartesian coordinates of the satellite are

$$\begin{aligned} x &= (r^{(0)}+\xi)\cos\theta - \eta\sin\theta, \\ y &= (r^{(0)}+\xi)\sin\theta\cos i_o + \eta\cos\theta\cos i_o - \zeta\sin i_o, \\ z &= (r^{(0)}+\xi)\sin\theta\sin i_o + \eta\cos\theta\sin i_o + \zeta\cos i_o. \end{aligned} \tag{7.4.1}$$

The Lagrangian

$$L = \frac{m}{2}(\dot{x}^2+\dot{y}^2+\dot{z}^2) - \frac{\mu m}{r} - \tilde{V}, \tag{7.4.2}$$

where $\tilde{V}$ is the perturbing potential, together with (7.2.12), provides us with the momenta. That is, taking the q_i as ξ, η, ζ, we have

$$p_\xi = \frac{\partial L}{\partial \dot{\xi}} = m\left[\dot{x}\frac{\partial \dot{x}}{\partial \dot{\xi}} + \dot{y}\frac{\partial \dot{y}}{\partial \dot{\xi}} + \dot{z}\frac{\partial \dot{z}}{\partial \dot{\xi}}\right], \text{ etc.}$$

or

$$p_\xi = m(\dot{r}^{(0)}+\dot{\xi}-\eta\dot{\theta}), \qquad p_\eta = m(\dot{\eta}+r^{(0)}\dot{\theta}+\xi\dot{\theta}), \qquad p_\zeta = m\dot{\zeta}. \tag{7.4.3}$$

Using (7.2.14), the Hamiltonian becomes

$$\mathscr{H} = \frac{1}{2m}\left(p_\xi^2+p_\eta^2+p_\zeta^2\right)+p_\xi\left(\eta\dot{\theta}-\dot{r}^{(0)}\right)-p_\eta\left(\xi\dot{\theta}+r^{(0)}\dot{\theta}\right)-\frac{\mu m}{r}+\tilde{V}. \tag{7.4.4}$$

Substituting this into (7.2.18), the canonical equations take the form

$$\dot{p}_\xi = p_\eta\dot{\theta}-\frac{\mu m(r^{(0)}+\xi)}{[(r^{(0)}+\xi)^2+\eta^2+\zeta^2]^{3/2}}-\frac{\partial\tilde{V}}{\partial\xi}+Q_\xi, \tag{7.4.5}$$

$$\dot{p}_\eta = -p_\xi\dot{\theta}-\frac{\mu m\eta}{[(r^{(0)}+\xi)^2+\eta^2+\zeta^2]^{3/2}}-\frac{\partial\tilde{V}}{\partial\eta}+Q_\eta, \tag{7.4.6}$$

$$\dot{p}_\zeta = -\frac{\mu m\zeta}{[(r^{(0)}+\xi)^2+\eta^2+\zeta^2]^{3/2}}-\frac{\partial\tilde{V}}{\partial\zeta}+Q_\zeta, \tag{7.4.7}$$

$$\dot{\xi} = \frac{1}{m}p_\xi+\eta\dot{\theta}-\dot{r}^{(0)}, \tag{7.4.8}$$

$$\dot{\eta} = \frac{1}{m}p_\eta-\xi\dot{\theta}-r^{(0)}\dot{\theta}, \tag{7.4.9}$$

$$\dot{\zeta} = \frac{1}{m}p_\zeta. \tag{7.4.10}$$

Since we expect the departures ξ, η, ζ from undisturbed motion to be small compared to $r^{(0)}$, we may employ the approximation

$$[(r^{(0)}+\xi)^2+\eta^2+\zeta^2]^{-3/2} \simeq r^{(0)-3}[1-3\xi/r^{(0)}].$$

Now, retaining only terms linear in $\xi/r^{(0)}$, etc., (7.4.5)–(7.4.7) become

$$\dot{p}_\xi = p_\eta\dot{\theta}-\frac{\mu m}{r^{(0)2}}\left[1-2\frac{\xi}{r^{(0)}}\right]-\tilde{V}_\xi+Q_\xi, \tag{7.4.11}$$

$$\dot{p}_\eta = -p_\xi\dot{\theta}-\frac{\mu m}{r^{(0)3}}\eta-\tilde{V}_\eta+Q_\eta, \tag{7.4.12}$$

$$\dot{p}_\zeta = -\frac{\mu m}{r^{(0)3}}\zeta-\tilde{V}_\zeta+Q_\zeta, \tag{7.4.13}$$

where we have used $\tilde{V}_\xi = \partial\tilde{V}/\partial\xi$, etc. For an unperturbed system ($\tilde{V} = Q_\xi = Q_\eta = Q_\zeta = 0$ and $\xi = \eta = \zeta = 0$), we see that (7.4.13) and (7.4.10) are trivially satisfied while (7.4.11), (7.4.12) and (7.4.8), (7.4.9) may be combined into

$$\ddot{r}^{(0)} = r^{(0)}\dot{\theta}^2-\mu/r^{(0)2} \quad\text{and}\quad 2\dot{r}^{(0)}\dot{\theta}+r^{(0)}\ddot{\theta} = 0. \tag{7.4.14}$$

These we recognize as the equations of a conic section orbit: the nominal orbit, of course. Thus, $r^{(0)}$ represents the zero-order solution, as defined in Chapter 5, while

(7.4.8)–(7.4.13), linearized in ξ, η, ζ, describe these quantities as first-order perturbations. Unfortunately, these last equations are badly coupled and, in general, cannot be solved in their present form. We shall see, in Chapter 8, that the Hamiltonian representation often lends itself to the selection of coordinates which permit uncoupling of the equations of motion. However, at this point, we content ourselves with merely one advantage of Hamilton's method: the ease of finding the explicit form of such equations when employing unfamiliar coordinates. To proceed further, we eliminate p_ξ, p_η, and p_ζ from (7.4.8)–(7.4.13).

Taking cognizance of (7.4.14), we can obtain equations only in ξ, η, ζ and their derivatives. Transforming to f as the independent variable, using

$$\dot{f} = \sqrt{\mu a_0(1-e_0^2)}/r^{(0)^2},$$

we have

$$\xi'' - 2\eta' - \xi - 2[\xi + e_o(\xi' - \eta)\sin f]/[1 + e_o \cos f]$$
$$= -\frac{a_o^3(1-e_o^2)^3}{\mu m}\tilde{V}_\xi/[1+e_o \cos f]^4, \tag{7.4.15}$$

$$\eta'' + 2\xi' - \eta + [\eta - 2e_o(\eta' + \xi)\sin f]/[1 + e_o \cos f]$$
$$= -\frac{a_o^3(1-e_o^2)^3}{\mu m}\tilde{V}_\eta/[1+e_o \cos f]^4, \tag{7.4.16}$$

$$\zeta'' + [\zeta - 2\zeta' e_o \sin f]/[1 + e_o \cos f] = -\frac{a_o^3(1-e_o^2)^3}{\mu m}\tilde{V}_\zeta/[1+e_o \cos f]^4, \tag{7.4.17}$$

where primes designate derivatives with respect to θ (or f) and terms involving Q_i on the right-hand side, not shown in (7.4.15)–(7.4.17), would have quite an analogous form to the ones in $\tilde{V}_\xi$, $\tilde{V}_\eta$, $\tilde{V}_\zeta$. We note that the only possible nonlinearities for ξ, η, ζ remaining in these equations would be due to the perturbing function, though many of the coefficients are rather awkward functions of f. As they stand, these relations are very close to the classical Hill equations for "variational orbits."

5. SOLUTIONS FOR NEAR-CIRCULAR ORBITS

In order to simplify the system (7.4.15)–(7.4.17), let us consider only small eccentricities and reduce the coefficients to $0(e_o)$. Then the system becomes

$$\xi'' - 2\eta' - 3\xi + 2e_0\xi \cos f - 2e_0(\xi' - \eta)\sin f = -\frac{a_0^3}{\mu m}(1 - 4e_0 \cos f)\tilde{V}_\xi, \tag{7.5.1}$$

$$\eta'' + 2\xi' - e_0\eta \cos f - 2e_0(\eta' + \xi)\sin f = -\frac{a_0^3}{\mu m}(1 - 4e_0 \cos f)\tilde{V}_\eta, \tag{7.5.2}$$

$$\zeta'' + \zeta - e_0\zeta \cos f - 2e_0\zeta' \sin f = -\frac{a_0^3}{\mu m}(1 - 4e_0 \cos f)\tilde{V}_\zeta. \tag{7.5.3}$$

Now ξ, η, ζ are due entirely to the perturbations and are of order κ due to the linearizations we carried out in the process of simplifying the original (exact) equations of motion.* In the same way, we can consider the terms which contain e_0 in (7.5.1)–(7.5.3) as "corrections" to a circular orbit, corrections of order e_0, which we also assume to be small. It is therefore conceivable to treat these terms as we do perturbations, invoking separability as discussed in Chapter 5.

In following this procedure, we write the solutions of (7.5.1) to (7.5.3) as†

$$\xi = \bar{\xi} + e_0 \xi_e, \quad \eta = \bar{\eta} + e_0 \eta_e, \quad \zeta = \bar{\zeta} + e_0 \zeta_e, \tag{7.5.4}$$

where the $\bar{\xi}$, etc., are of order κ. Extracting these terms from Eqs. (7.5.1) to (7.5.3), we obtain

$$\bar{\xi}'' - 2\bar{\eta}' - 3\bar{\xi} = -\frac{a_0^3}{\mu m} \tilde{V}_\xi, \tag{7.5.5}$$

$$\bar{\eta}'' + 2\bar{\xi}' = -\frac{a_0^3}{\mu m} \tilde{V}_\eta, \tag{7.5.6}$$

$$\bar{\zeta}'' + \bar{\zeta} = -\frac{a_0^3}{\mu m} \tilde{V}_\zeta, \tag{7.5.7}$$

where, to be consistent to $O(\kappa)$, $\tilde{V}$ is evaluated using positions in the nominal circular orbit. If we denote the complementary and particular solutions of (7.5.5)–(7.5.7) by $\bar{\xi}_c$, $\bar{\eta}_c$, $\bar{\zeta}_c$ and $\bar{\xi}_p$, $\bar{\eta}_p$, $\bar{\zeta}_p$ respectively, we find

$$\bar{\xi}_c = 2\bar{\eta}'_0 + 4\bar{\xi}_0 - (2\bar{\eta}'_0 + 3\bar{\xi}_0)\cos f + \bar{\xi}_0 \sin f, \tag{7.5.8}$$

$$\bar{\eta}_c = \bar{\eta}_0 - 2\bar{\xi}'_0 - 3(\bar{\eta}'_0 + 2\bar{\xi}_0) f + 2(2\bar{\eta}'_0 + 3\bar{\xi}_0)\sin f + 2\bar{\xi}'_0 \cos f, \tag{7.5.9}$$

$$\bar{\zeta}_c = \bar{\zeta}'_0 \sin f + \bar{\zeta}_0 \cos f. \tag{7.5.10}$$

Here $\bar{\xi}_0, \bar{\eta}_0, \bar{\zeta}_0$ and $\bar{\xi}'_0, \bar{\eta}'_0, \bar{\zeta}'_0$ are constants of integration. By setting $f = 0$, we observe that they are the values of $\bar{\xi}_c, \ldots, \bar{\zeta}'_c$ at nominal perigee.

Next, we find (by the method of variation of constants)

$$\bar{\xi}_p = \frac{a_0^3}{\mu m}\left[-2\int \tilde{V}_\eta df + 2\cos f \int \tilde{V}_\eta \cos f\, df + 2\sin f \int \tilde{V}_\eta \sin f\, df + \cos f \int \tilde{V}_\xi \sin f\, df - \sin f \int \tilde{V}_\xi \cos f\, df\right], \tag{7.5.11}$$

---

*Had we carried the expansion of $1/r$ to terms in ξ^2, etc., we would have provided the basis for a second-order theory. For a discussion of the nonlinear problem see, for instance, references 7 and 8.

†Strictly speaking, (7.5.4) requires that $e_0 > O(\kappa)$; otherwise ξ_e, η_e, ζ_e would be $O(\kappa^2)$ and the entire analysis would have to be extended to second order. An analysis somewhat akin to this formulation, and valid for small e, is given in reference 9 (p. 94).

$$\bar{\eta}_p = \frac{a_0^3}{\mu m}\left[3\iint \tilde{V}_\eta df\,df + 2\int \tilde{V}_\xi df - 4\sin f\int \tilde{V}_\eta \cos f\,df\right.$$
$$\left. + 4\cos f\int \tilde{V}_\eta \sin f\,df - 2\sin f\int \tilde{V}_\xi \sin f\,df - 2\cos f\int \tilde{V}_\xi \cos f\,df\right], \quad (7.5.12)$$

$$\bar{\zeta}_p = \frac{a^3}{\mu m}\left[\cos f\int \tilde{V}_\zeta \sin f\,df - \sin f\int \tilde{V}_\zeta \cos f\,df\right], \quad (7.5.13)$$

where the lower limit of the integrals is taken at the epoch ($f = f_0$) and the upper limit is taken at the instant for which the actual satellite position is to be calculated.

The terms of $0(e_0)$ from (7.5.1)–(7.5.3) yield the following differential equations for ξ_e, η_e, ζ_e:

$$\xi_e'' - 2\eta_e' - 3\xi_e = 2(2\bar{\xi}_0' - \bar{\eta}_0)\sin f - 4(\bar{\eta}_0' + 2\bar{\xi}_0)\cos f$$
$$+ 6(\bar{\eta}_0' + 2\bar{\xi}_0) f\sin f + 2(2\bar{\eta}_0' + 3\bar{\xi}_0)\cos 2f$$
$$- 2\bar{\xi}_0' \sin 2f + 2(\bar{\xi}_p' - \bar{\eta}_p)\sin f - 2\bar{\xi}_p \cos f + \frac{4a_0^3}{\mu m}\tilde{V}_\xi \cos f, \quad (7.5.14)$$

$$\eta_e'' + 2\xi_e' = -2(\bar{\eta}_0' + 2\bar{\xi}_0)\sin f + (\bar{\eta}_0 - 2\bar{\xi}_0')\cos f - 3(\bar{\eta}_0' + 2\bar{\xi}_0) f\cos f$$
$$+ 2(2\bar{\eta}_0' + 3\bar{\xi}_0)\sin 2f + 2\bar{\xi}_0' \cos 2f + 2(\bar{\eta}_p' + \bar{\xi}_p)\sin f$$
$$+ \bar{\eta}_p \cos f + \frac{4a_0^3}{\mu m}\tilde{V}_\eta \cos f, \quad (7.5.15)$$

$$\zeta_e'' + \zeta_e = -\frac{\bar{\zeta}_0}{2} + \frac{3\bar{\zeta}_0'}{2}\sin 2f + \frac{3\bar{\zeta}_0}{2}\cos 2f + 2\zeta_p' \sin f$$
$$+ \zeta_p \cos f + \frac{4a_0^3}{\mu m}\tilde{V}_\zeta \cos f. \quad (7.5.16)$$

Since the differential operators in these equations are the same as in (7.5.5)–(7.5.7), their complementary solution may be absorbed in (7.5.8)–(7.5.10) without explicit distinction. A particular solution of (7.5.14)–(7.5.16) will be written as $\xi_{e0}, \xi_{ep}, \xi_{eV}$, etc., corresponding to the components of the right-hand sides involving $\bar{\xi}_0, \ldots, \zeta_0', \xi_p, \ldots, \zeta_p'$, or $\tilde{V}_\xi, \tilde{V}_\eta, \tilde{V}_\zeta$, respectively. Thus,

$$\xi_{e0} = (\bar{\eta}_0 - 2\bar{\xi}_0')\sin f - \tfrac{5}{2}(\bar{\eta}_0' + 2\bar{\xi}_0)\cos f - 3(\bar{\eta}_0' + 2\bar{\xi}_0) f\sin f, \quad (7.5.17)$$

$$\eta_{e0} = 7(\bar{\eta}_0' + 2\bar{\xi}_0)\sin f + (\bar{\eta}_0 - 2\bar{\xi}_0')\cos f - 3(\bar{\eta}_0' + 2\bar{\xi}_0) f\cos f$$
$$- \frac{\bar{\xi}_0}{2}\cos 2f - (\bar{\eta}_0' + \tfrac{3}{2}\bar{\xi}_0)\sin 2f, \quad (7.5.18)$$

$$\zeta_{e0} = -\frac{\bar{\zeta}_0}{2} - \frac{\bar{\zeta}_0'}{2}\sin 2f - \frac{\bar{\zeta}_0}{2}\cos 2f. \quad (7.5.19)$$

For $\xi_{ep}, \eta_{ep}, \zeta_{ep}$ we replace $-(a_0^3/\mu m)\,\tilde{V}_\xi$, etc., in (7.5.11) to (7.5.13) by

$$2(\bar{\xi}'_p - \bar{\eta}'_p)\sin f - 2\bar{\xi}_p \cos f; \qquad 2(\bar{\eta}'_p + \bar{\xi}'_p)\sin f + \bar{\eta}_p \cos f; \qquad 2\bar{\zeta}'_p \sin f + \bar{\zeta}_p \cos f,$$

and for $\xi_{eV}, \eta_{eV}, \zeta_{eV}$ by

$$\frac{4a_0^3}{\mu m}\tilde{V}_\xi \cos f; \qquad \frac{4a_0^3}{\mu m}\tilde{V}_\eta \cos f; \qquad \frac{4a_0^3}{\mu m}\tilde{V}_\zeta \cos f.$$

In examining this formulation we note that the complementary solution $\bar{\xi}_c, \bar{\eta}_c, \bar{\zeta}_c$ was already obtained in Chapter 4 (and, by a different approach, in Chapter 5). We recall that these expressions could be used to describe departures from a desired orbit due to injection errors or the relative motion of two neighboring orbital bodies if their separation vector and its time derivative were known at some instant. More general expressions for these "orbit sensitivities," valid on any kind of conic-section orbit, are given in Section 6. In the remainder of this section we will illustrate the particular solutions obtained using various physical perturbations.

5.1. Perturbations from the Geopotential

Although we have devoted considerable attention to the problem of oblateness effects, some additional information can be obtained with the formulation under consideration. In order to point out these features of the perturbed motion, it suffices to assume that the nominal orbit be circular with radius a_0.

We consider the perturbing potential due only to the first oblateness term, i.e., from (5.3.18),

$$\tilde{V} = -\frac{3J_2R^2\mu m}{2[(a_0+\xi)^2+\eta^2+\zeta^2]^{3/2}}\left\{\frac{1}{3} - \frac{z^2}{[(a_0+\xi)^2+\eta^2+\zeta^2]}\right\}. \tag{7.5.20}$$

When writing the derivatives of this potential with respect to ξ, η, ζ we use the necessary linearizations and observe that $z/r = \sin\varphi' \simeq \sin\theta \sin i_0$. Then

$$\begin{aligned}
\tilde{V}_\xi &= \frac{3J_2R^2\mu m}{2a_0^4}(1 - 3\sin^2\theta \sin^2 i_0);\\
\tilde{V}_\eta &= \frac{3J_2R^2\mu m}{2a_0^4}\sin^2\theta \sin^2 i_0;\\
\tilde{V}_\zeta &= \frac{3J_2R^2\mu m}{2a_0^4}\sin 2i_0 \sin\theta.
\end{aligned} \tag{7.5.21}$$

Substitution of (7.5.21) into (7.5.11)–(7.5.13) yields

$$\bar{\xi}_p = \frac{3J_2R^2}{2a_0}\left[-1 + \sin^2 i_0\left(\frac{3}{2} + \frac{1}{6}\cos 2\theta\right)\right],$$
$$\bar{\eta}_p = \frac{3J_2R^2}{2a_0}\left[(2-3\sin^2 i_0)f + \frac{1}{12}\sin^2 i_0 \sin 2\theta\right], \qquad (7.5.22)$$
$$\bar{\zeta}_p = \frac{3J_2R^2}{2a_0}\sin 2i_0\left[f\cos\theta - \frac{1}{2}\sin\theta\right],$$

where these expressions are to be evaluated between f_0 and f. The nonperiodic terms in $\bar{\xi}_p$ and $\bar{\eta}_p$ reflect the difference in attractive force due to the equatorial bulge, while the periodic terms, containing the double argument 2θ, represent an elliptic distortion of the orbit due to the asphericity of the perturbing potential. We further note that conservation of angular momentum would require that the radial decrement

$$\frac{3J_2R^2}{2a_0}\left(-1 + \frac{3}{2}\sin^2 i_0\right)$$

contained in $\bar{\xi}_p$ be accompanied by an increase of

$$\frac{3J_2R^2 n}{2a_0}\left(1 - \frac{3}{2}\sin^2 i_0\right)$$

in the average circumferential velocity, where n is the angular rate in the nominal circular orbit. Actually, the secular term in η_p amounts to twice that effect; thus, the periodic excursions described by the satellite during two successive revolutions exhibit an angular offset

$$\frac{3\pi J_2R^2}{a_0^2}\left(1 - \frac{3}{2}\sin^2 i_0\right).$$

This is precisely the "inertial" advance of perigee, $\Delta\omega + \cos i_0\, \Delta\Omega$, as can be obtained from the results of Chapter 6. In a similar way the single argument θ in $\bar{\zeta}_p$ gives rise to changes in the orientation of the orbit plane. Thus, the term $\sin\theta$ signifies a constant perturbation of the inclination whereas the term $f\cos\theta$ may be interpreted as a precession. Indeed, one can observe from the geometry of the node that

$$\left[\Omega\right]_{\theta=2\pi j}^{\theta=2\pi(j+1)} = -\frac{1}{\sin i_0}\left[\bar{\zeta}_0\right]_{\theta=2\pi j}^{\theta=2\pi(j+1)}, \qquad (7.5.23)$$

where j is the *revolution number*. Evaluating (7.5.23) for the secular term of $\bar{\zeta}_p$ and dividing by the anomalistic period, we find

$$\dot{\Omega} = -\frac{3}{2}\left(\frac{\mu}{a_0^7}\right)^{1/2} J_2R^2\cos i_0,$$

which agrees with the results found earlier.

The equations (7.5.22) naturally do not give a full description of the perturbed motion but must be accompanied by terms of the form (7.5.8)–(7.5.10) resulting from initial conditions. Thus,

$$\begin{aligned}\bar{\xi} &= \bar{\xi}_c + \bar{\xi}_p \\ &= \frac{2}{n}\dot{\bar{\eta}}_0 + 4\bar{\xi}_0 - \left(\frac{2}{n}\dot{\bar{\eta}}_0 + 3\bar{\xi}_0\right)\cos f + \frac{1}{n}\dot{\bar{\xi}}_0 \sin f \\ &\quad + \frac{3J_2R^2}{2a_0}\left[-1 + \sin^2 i_0\left(\frac{3}{2} + \frac{1}{6}\cos 2\theta\right)\right],\end{aligned} \tag{7.5.24}$$

where $n = \sqrt{\mu/a_0^3}$. This representation allows us to select initial conditions so as to minimize perturbation effects, e.g., to preserve circularity on the average by suppressing all but periodic terms in ξ or by keeping v as near as possible to $\sqrt{\mu/a_0}$. For this last we need the time derivative of

$$\bar{\eta} = \bar{\eta}_c + \bar{\eta}_p,$$

namely

$$\begin{aligned}\dot{\bar{\eta}} &= -3(\dot{\bar{\eta}}_0 + 2n\bar{\xi}_0) + 2(2\dot{\bar{\eta}}_0 + 3n\bar{\xi}_0)\cos f - 2\dot{\bar{\xi}}_0 \sin f \\ &\quad + \frac{3J_2R^2}{2a_0}n\left[(2 - 3\sin^2 i_0) + \frac{1}{6}\sin^2 i_0 \cos 2\theta\right].\end{aligned} \tag{7.5.25}$$

Since ω_0 has no special significance for a nominally circular orbit, let us assume that at $t = t_0$, $\theta_0 = \omega_0$ and hence $f_0 = 0$. Then the total initial values are

$$\bar{\xi}(t = t_0) = \bar{\xi}_0 + \frac{3J_2R^2}{2a_0}\left[-1 + \sin^2 i_0\left(\frac{3}{2} + \frac{1}{6}\cos 2\theta_0\right)\right], \tag{7.5.26}$$

$$\bar{\eta}(t = t_0) = \bar{\eta}_0 + \frac{J_2R^2}{8a_0}\sin^2 i_0 \sin 2\theta_0, \tag{7.5.27}$$

$$\dot{\bar{\xi}}(t = t_0) = \dot{\bar{\xi}}_0 - \frac{J_2R^2}{2a_0}n \sin^2 i_0 \sin 2\theta_0, \tag{7.5.28}$$

$$\dot{\bar{\eta}}(t = t_0) = \dot{\bar{\eta}}_0 + \frac{3J_2R^2}{2a_0}n\left[2 + \sin^2 i_0\left(-3 + \frac{1}{6}\cos 2\theta_0\right)\right]. \tag{7.5.29}$$

Now let us denote the constant terms in $\bar{\xi}$ and $\dot{\bar{\eta}}$ as

$$\overline{\Delta a} = \frac{3J_2R^2}{2a_0}\left[-1 + \frac{3}{2}\sin^2 i_0\right] + \frac{2}{n}\dot{\bar{\eta}}_0 + 4\bar{\xi}_0, \tag{7.5.30}$$

and

$$\overline{\Delta v} = \frac{3J_2R^2}{2a_0}n\left[2 - 3\sin^2 i_0\right] - 3(\dot{\bar{\eta}}_0 + 2n\bar{\xi}_0). \tag{7.5.31}$$

Since neither $\bar{\eta}_0$ nor $\bar{\xi}_0$ occur in these last, we could set them equal to zero in (7.5.27) and (7.5.28), leaving us free to manipulate $\bar{\xi}_0$ and $\dot{\bar{\eta}}_0$. Unfortunately, (7.5.30) and (7.5.31) are not linearly independent in these two quantities; let us impose the conditions that for $\overline{\Delta a} = 0$ we inject at the nominal radius, i.e., with $\bar{\xi}(t = t_0) = 0$, or for $\overline{\Delta v} = 0$, we inject with the nominal velocity, i.e., $\dot{\bar{\eta}}_0(t = t_0) = 0$.

Thus, in the first case, the vanishing of (7.5.26) and (7.5.30) represents the governing conditions. Solving these for $\bar{\xi}_0$ and $\dot{\bar{\eta}}_0$ and substituting into (7.5.25) and (7.5.31) yields what may be called the anomalistic residuals

$$\overline{\Delta v} = \frac{3J_2R^2}{2a_0} n \left[\frac{1}{2} - \frac{3}{4}\sin^2 i_0\right], \tag{7.5.32}$$

$$\dot{\bar{\eta}}(t = t_0) = \frac{3J_2R^2}{2a_0} n \left[\sin^2 i_0 \left(\frac{3}{2} + \frac{5}{6}\cos 2\theta_0\right) - 1\right]. \tag{7.5.33}$$

The last is the value of the additional velocity to be provided at injection so as to fix $\overline{\Delta a}$ at zero. We note that $\overline{\Delta v}$ vanishes here if $i_0 = \sin^{-1}\sqrt{2/3}$. The vanishing of (7.5.33) results in a transcendental condition between i_0 and the argument of latitude at the point of insertion θ_0.

In the second case, where $\overline{\Delta v} = \dot{\bar{\eta}}(t = t_0) = 0$, the vanishing of (7.5.29) and (7.5.31) furnish the relevant conditions. By virtue of (7.5.26) and (7.5.30) this results in the following radial residuals:

$$\overline{\Delta a} = \frac{3J_2R^2}{2a_0}\left[\frac{1}{3} - \frac{1}{2}\sin^2 i_0\right], \tag{7.5.34}$$

$$\bar{\xi}(t = t_0) = \frac{3J_2R^2}{2a_0}\left[\frac{2}{3} + \sin^2 i_0\left(\frac{1}{2}\cos 2\theta_0 - 1\right)\right], \tag{7.5.35}$$

where (7.5.35) provides the insertion condition on the radial component. Again, (7.5.34) vanishes at $i_0 = \sin^{-1}\sqrt{2/3}$ and a transcendental condition between i_0 and θ_0 arises if we demand that $\bar{\xi}(t = t_0) = 0$.

In a fashion similar to the above, one may derive values for $\bar{\zeta}_0$ and $\bar{\zeta}'_0$ such that the average inclination of the actual orbit has a specified value.

5.2. Perturbations Due to Atmospheric Drag

We now employ the formulation of Section 4 to study the case of drag perturbations. We have from Section 3, Chapter 5, that

$$F_x = -C_D\frac{A\rho}{2m}v_a\dot{x}_a, \qquad F_y = -C_D\frac{A\rho}{2m}v_a\dot{y}_a, \qquad F_z = -C_D\frac{A\rho}{2m}v_a\dot{z}_a,$$

and using (7.2.8),

$$Q_\xi = -\frac{C_DA\rho}{2m}v_a\left[\dot{x}_a\frac{\partial x}{\partial \xi} + \dot{y}_a\frac{\partial y}{\partial \xi} + \dot{z}_a\frac{\partial z}{\partial \xi}\right].$$

Using (7.4.1) to zero order (after differentiation), we find

$$Q_\xi = -\frac{C_D A\rho}{2m} v_a \dot{r}^{(0)},$$

and, if we were to take a nominally circular orbit, we would have $Q_\xi = 0$. Similarly, we obtain

$$Q_\eta = -\frac{C_D A\rho}{2m} v_a [r^{(0)}\dot{\theta} - \sigma r^{(0)} \cos i_0],$$

and

$$Q_\zeta = -\frac{C_D A\rho}{2m} v_a \sigma r^{(0)} \sin i_0 \cos \theta.$$

Without loss of generality, let us take $v_a = v$ (the absolute geocentric velocity) for convenience. For perfectly circular orbits, then

$$Q_\eta = -\frac{C_D A\rho}{2m} (\mu/a_0)^{1/2} [(\mu/\alpha_0)^{1/2} - \sigma a_0 \cos i_0] \equiv \text{F}, \tag{7.5.36}$$

$$Q_\zeta = -\frac{C_D A\rho}{2m} (\mu\, a_0)^{1/2} \sigma \sin i_0 \cos \theta \equiv G \cos \theta, \tag{7.5.37}$$

where F and G are contractions for the constant factors. We may now formally use Q_η and Q_ζ in place of $-\tilde{V}_\eta$ and $-\tilde{V}_\zeta$ with (7.5.11)–(7.5.13), while $\tilde{V}_\xi = 0$.

The results of this calculation are

$$\bar{\xi}_p = \frac{2a_0^3}{\mu m} Ff, \tag{7.5.38}$$

$$\bar{\eta}_p = \frac{a_0^3 F}{\mu m}\left[4 - \frac{3}{2} f^2\right], \tag{7.5.39}$$

$$\bar{\zeta}_p = \frac{a_0^3 G}{4\mu m}[2f \sin \theta - \cos \theta], \tag{7.5.40}$$

the lower limit in these expressions again being f_0 or θ_0. They manifest the by now recognized behavior of near-circular orbits in the presence of drag, namely, a spiral decay given by the linear dependence of ξ on f (remembering that F is negative) and the attendant anomalistic perturbation given by the quadratic term in η. We note that with the inclusion of $\bar{\xi}_c$ and $\bar{\eta}_c$ from initial conditions, the radial and circumferential perturbations may exhibit periodic behavior. In ζ_p, finally, the secular term is again of interest since it describes a linear decrease of orbit inclination with time. We note that $\left[\frac{1}{a_0}\bar{\zeta}_2'\right]_{\theta=0}^{\theta=2\pi j}$ gives the change in orbit inclination at the completion of the jth revolution. Division by $2\pi j$ yields the rate of change of inclination of the mean orbit. This is found from (7.5.40) to be

$$di/df = a_0^2 G/2\mu m, \tag{7.5.41}$$

where we recall that $G<0$. The physical interpretation of this result as a precession caused by the perturbing torque from the rotating atmosphere was given in Chapter 5.

We now turn to a rather straightforward extension of these results incorporating the time-dependence of drag forces. In Chapter 5 we observed that such conditions might arise from diurnal solar effects, atmospheric heating connected with phenomena of other than daily periods, and from satellite tumbling. Many of these effects might be represented as trigonometric series in f, at least for an *a posteriori* analysis. If such a series is written for each of the three types of time-dependent effects mentioned, the perturbations due to all of them may be obtained from a termwise triple product.

Suppose that we multiply the factor F of (7.5.36) by the "time function"

$$[1 + H_1 \sin(\alpha_1+\lambda_1 f)][1 + H_2 \sin(\alpha_2+\lambda_2 f)][1 + H_3 \sin(\alpha_3+\lambda_3 f)], \tag{7.5.42}$$

where

H_1, H_2, H_3 are the amplitude parameters,
$\alpha_1, \alpha_2, \alpha_3$ are the phase angles,
$\lambda_1, \lambda_2, \lambda_3$ are the frequency ratios of the periodic perturbations relative to the anomalistic motion.

When we simplify this notation to $\theta_1 = \alpha_1+\lambda_1 f$, etc., and insert this time function into (7.5.36), (7.5.11), and (7.5.12), we obtain

$$\xi_p = \frac{2a_0^3F}{\mu m}\left\{ f - A_1 - A_2 - A_3 + \tfrac{1}{2}(B_{12}+B_{23}+B_{13}) \right.$$
$$\left. + \frac{H_1H_2H_3}{4}\left[\frac{\cos(\theta_1+\theta_2+\theta_3)}{(\lambda_1+\lambda_2+\lambda_3)[1-(\lambda_1+\lambda_2+\lambda_3)^2]} - \Gamma_1 - \Gamma_2 - \Gamma_3\right]\right\}, \tag{7.5.43}$$

where for $(i, j, k) = (1, 2, 3)$,

$$A_i = \frac{H_i \cos\theta_i}{\lambda_i(1-\lambda_i^2)},$$
$$B_{ij} = H_iH_j\left[\frac{\sin(\theta_i-\theta_j)}{(\lambda_i-\lambda_j)[1-(\lambda_i-\lambda_j)^2]} - \frac{\sin(\theta_i+\theta_j)}{(\lambda_i+\lambda_j)[1-(\lambda_i+\lambda_j)^2]}\right],$$
$$\Gamma_i = \frac{\cos(-\theta_i+\theta_j+\theta_k)}{(-\lambda_i+\lambda_j+\lambda_k)[1-(-\lambda_i+\lambda_j+\lambda_k)^2]}, \quad (i \neq j \neq k),$$

and

$$\bar{\eta}_p = \frac{a_0^3F}{\mu m}\left\{4 - \tfrac{3}{2}f^2 + C_1 + C_2 + C_3 + \tfrac{1}{2}(D_{12}+D_{23}+D_{13})\right.$$
$$\left. + \frac{H_1H_2H_3}{4}\left[\Sigma_1 + \Sigma_2 + \Sigma_3 - \frac{3 + (\lambda_1+\lambda_2+\lambda_3)^2}{(\lambda_1+\lambda_2+\lambda_3)^2}\,\frac{\sin(\theta_1+\theta_2+\theta_3)}{1 - (\lambda_1+\lambda_2+\lambda_3)^2}\right]\right\}, \tag{7.5.44}$$

with

$$C_i = \frac{H_i(3+\lambda_i^2)\sin\theta_i}{\lambda_i^2(1-\lambda_i^2)},$$

$$D_{ij} = H_i H_j \left[\frac{3+(\lambda_i-\lambda_j)^2}{(\lambda_i-\lambda_j)^2}\frac{\cos(\theta_i-\theta_j)}{1-(\lambda_i-\lambda_j)^2} - \frac{3+(\lambda_i+\lambda_3)^2}{(\lambda_i+\lambda_j)^2}\frac{\cos(\theta_i+\theta_j)}{1-(\lambda_i+\lambda_j)^2}\right],$$

$$\Sigma_i = \frac{3+(-\lambda_i+\lambda_j+\lambda_k)^2}{(-\lambda_i+\lambda_j+\lambda_k)^2}\frac{\sin(-\theta_i+\theta_j+\theta_k)}{1-(-\lambda_i+\lambda_j+\lambda_k)^2}, \quad i \neq j \neq k.$$

The relation for $\bar{\zeta}_p$ may be found in an analogous manner through the proper modification of (7.5.37).

Rather than pursue this further, let us return to the case of the "static" atmosphere and investigate the refinements to be added to (7.5.38)–(7.5.40) for an extension of our calculations to $0(e_0\kappa)$; such a solution would then be applicable to slightly eccentric nominal orbits. (The nominal eccentricity impresses periodic perturbations on the relative velocity components in the ξ, η, and ζ directions and since these effects can be allowed for in the form of (7.5.43) and (7.5.44)—with appropriate modifications for the fact that $Q_\xi \neq 0$—we do not stop to exhibit the results.) Following the procedure outlined previously for the calculation of

$$\xi_{ep}, \ldots, \zeta_{eV}$$

we obtain

$$\xi_{ep} = \frac{a_0^3 F}{2\mu m}[-3f^2\sin f - 9f\cos f + \tfrac{29}{2}\sin f], \tag{7.5.45}$$

$$\eta_{ep} = \frac{a_0^3 F}{2\mu m}[-3f^2\cos f + 22f\sin f + 41\cos f], \tag{7.5.46}$$

$$\zeta_{ep} = \frac{a_0^3 F}{4\mu m}[\tfrac{5}{2}\cos\omega_0 - \tfrac{1}{6}\cos(\omega_0+2f) - f\sin\omega_0 - f\sin(\omega_0+2f)], \tag{7.5.47}$$

and

$$\xi_{eV} = \frac{4a_0^3 F}{\mu m}[f\cos f - \tfrac{3}{2}\sin f], \tag{7.5.48}$$

$$\eta_{eV} = -\frac{8a_0^3 F}{\mu m}[2\cos f + f\sin f], \tag{7.5.49}$$

$$\zeta_{eV} = \frac{2a_0^3 G}{\mu m}[-\cos\omega_0 + \tfrac{1}{3}\cos(\omega_0+2f)]. \tag{7.5.50}$$

5.3. Perturbations Due to Luni-Solar Gravitation

In Chapters 5 and 6 some of our examples have considered the effects of a stationary extraterrestrial mass on a satellite orbit. We now re-examine this problem to $0(\kappa)$ when the mean motion of the extraterrestrial center of gravitation is nonzero.

Let the perturbing body P be situated in the x,y plane, where the latter does not, in general, have to contain the equator. The central angle $\bar{\theta} = \bar{\theta}_0 + \lambda f$ locates P in this plane on a circular orbit analogous to the way in which O' was located in the satellite orbit plane (Fig. 7.2). $\bar{\theta}$ is measured from the node, which lies on the positive x axis in our case, and the initial position of P is given by $\bar{\theta}_0 + \lambda f_0$. λ is the ratio between the angular rate of P and that of the satellite and is less than unity in all practical cases. Note that in this example the independent variable f appears in the disturbing function $\tilde{V}$.*

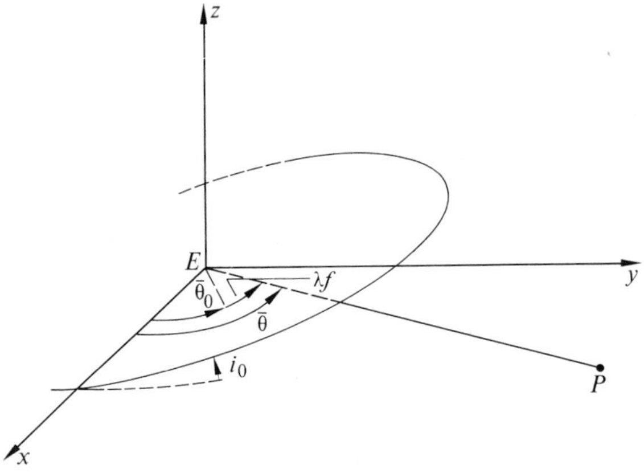

Figure 7.2

The perturbing potential is

$$\tilde{V} = -\tilde{R} = -Gm_P m\left[\frac{1}{r_{Pm}} - \frac{xx_P + yy_P}{r_P^2}\right], \tag{7.5.51}$$

where x_P and y_P are the coordinates of P, $r_P^2 = x_P^2 + y_P^2$, and

$$r_{Pm}^2 = (x_P - x)^2 + (y_P - y)^2 + z^2.$$

With the appropriate linearizations this yields

$$\frac{1}{m}\frac{\partial \tilde{V}}{\partial x} \simeq -\frac{Gm_P}{r_P^3}\left[\frac{3x_P}{r_P^2}(xx_P + yy_P) - x\right]. \tag{7.5.52}$$

Then, taking $x \simeq a_0 \cos\theta$, $y \simeq a_0 \sin\theta \cos i_0$, and $z \simeq a_0 \sin\theta \sin i_0$, we obtain

*The parlance of analytical dynamics refers to systems where the independent variable appears in the disturbing function as *rheonomic* in contrast to systems where it does not, which are called *scleronomic*.

$$\tilde{V}_\xi = \frac{\partial \tilde{V}}{\partial x}\frac{\partial x}{\partial \xi} + \frac{\partial \tilde{V}}{\partial y}\frac{\partial y}{\partial \xi} + \frac{\partial \tilde{V}}{\partial z}\frac{\partial z}{\partial \xi}$$

$$= -\frac{3a_0 G m_p m}{8r_p^3}\left[\frac{4}{3}\cos^2 i_0 - \frac{2}{3}\sin^2 i_0 + 2\sin^2 i_0 \cos 2\theta + 2\sin^2 i_0 \cos 2\bar{\theta}\right.$$

$$\left. + (1-\cos i_0)^2 \cos 2(\bar{\theta}+\theta) + (1+\cos i_0)^2 \cos^2(\bar{\theta}+\theta)\right],$$

$$\tilde{V}_\eta = -\frac{3a_0 G m_p m}{8r_p^3}\left[-2\sin^2 i_0 \sin 2\theta + (1+\cos i_0)^2 \sin 2(\bar{\theta}-\theta)\right.$$

$$\left. -(1-\cos i_0)^2 \sin 2(\bar{\theta}+\theta)\right],$$

$$\tilde{V}_\zeta = \frac{3a_0 G m_p m}{4r_p^3}\left[\sin 2i_0 \sin\theta + (1-\cos i_0)\sin i_0 \sin(2\bar{\theta}+\theta)\right.$$

$$\left. +(1+\cos i_0)\sin i_0 \sin(2\bar{\theta}-\theta)\right]. \tag{7.5.53}$$

If we substitute these expressions into (7.5.11)–(7.5.13) we find the particular solutions

$$\bar{\xi}_p = \bar{g}\left[\frac{2}{3}\left(2\cos^2 i_0 - \sin^2 i_0\right) - \frac{4}{3}\sin^2 i_0 \cos 2\theta\right.$$

$$- \frac{2}{4\lambda^2-1}\sin^2 i_0 \cos 2\bar{\theta} - \frac{(\lambda+2)(1-\cos i_0)^2}{(\lambda+1)(2\lambda+1)(2\lambda+3)}\cos 2(\bar{\theta}+\theta)$$

$$\left. - \frac{(\lambda-2)(1+\cos i_0)^2}{(\lambda-1)(2\lambda-1)(2\lambda-3)}\cos 2(\bar{\theta}-\theta)\right], \tag{7.5.54}$$

$$\bar{\eta}_p = \bar{g}\left[-\frac{4}{3}\left(2\cos^2 i_0 - \sin^2 i_0\right) f + \frac{11}{6}\sin^2 i\ \sin 2\theta\right.$$

$$+ \frac{2\sin^2 i_0}{\lambda(4\lambda^2-1)}\sin 2\bar{\theta} + \frac{(4\lambda^2+12\lambda+11)(1-\cos i_0)^2}{4(\lambda+1)^2(2\lambda+1)(2\lambda+3)}\sin 2(\bar{\theta}+\theta)$$

$$\left. - \frac{(4\lambda^2-12\lambda+11)(1+\cos i_0)^2}{4(\lambda-1)^2(2\lambda-1)(2\lambda-3)}\sin 2(\bar{\theta}-\theta)\right], \tag{7.5.55}$$

$$\bar{\zeta}_p = \bar{g}\left[-\frac{1}{2}\sin 2i_0 \sin\theta + f\sin 2i_0 \cos\theta + \frac{(1-\cos i_0)\sin i_0}{2\lambda(\lambda+1)}\sin(2\bar{\theta}+\theta)\right.$$

$$\left. + \frac{(1+\cos i_0)\sin i_0}{2\lambda(\lambda-1)}\sin(2\bar{\theta}-\theta)\right], \tag{7.5.56}$$

where $\bar{g} = 3Gm_p a_0^4/8\mu r_p^3$.

The solution given by (7.5.54)–(7.5.56) obviously ceases to be valid for $\lambda = 0$, ± 1, $\pm 1/2$, $\pm 3/2$. These are the commensurability conditions so often encountered in such problems. As the reader may know, there exists considerable literature on the asymptotic solutions of differential equations, especially designed to deal with resonance problems. We can do no more than acknowledge that fact here.

Clearly, we could execute the calculations for each of the special values of λ. However, for all but $\lambda = 0$ the results would be meaningless since these particular nonzero values for λ imply that a_0 and r_p must be of the same order of magnitude; hence, the approximations used in obtaining (7.5.52) would no longer hold. Treating the case $\lambda = 0$, we now find

$$\begin{aligned}\bar{\xi}_p &= \bar{g}[\tfrac{2}{3}(2\cos^2 i_0 - \sin^2 i_0) - \tfrac{4}{3}\sin^2 i_0 \cos 2\theta + 2\sin^2 i_0 \cos 2\bar{\theta}_0 \\ &\quad - \tfrac{2}{3}(1-\cos i_0)^2 \cos 2(\theta+\bar{\theta}_0) - \tfrac{2}{3}(1+\cos i_0)^2 \cos 2(\theta-\bar{\theta}_0)], \qquad (7.5.57)\\ \bar{\eta}_p &= \bar{g}[-\tfrac{4}{3}(2\cos^2 i_0 - \sin^2 i_0 + 3\sin^2 i_0 \cos 2\theta_0) f + \tfrac{11}{6}\sin^2 i_0 \sin 2\theta \\ &\quad + \tfrac{11}{12}(1-\cos i_0)^2 \sin 2(\theta+\bar{\theta}_0) + \tfrac{11}{12}(1+\cos i_0)^2 \sin 2(\theta-\bar{\theta}_0)], \qquad (7.5.58)\\ \bar{\zeta}_p &= \bar{g}\{[-(1+\cos i_0)\sin i_0 \cos(\theta-2\bar{\theta}_0) + (1-\cos i_0)\sin i_0 \cos(\theta+2\bar{\theta}_0) \\ &\quad + \sin 2i_0 \cos\theta] f - \tfrac{1}{2}\sin 2i_0 \sin\theta - \tfrac{1}{2}(1-\cos i_0)\sin i_0 \sin(\theta+2\bar{\theta}_0) \\ &\quad + \tfrac{1}{2}(1+\cos i_0)\sin i_0 \sin(\theta-2\bar{\theta}_0)\}. \qquad (7.5.59)\end{aligned}$$

This example, with a stationary perturbing body P, lends itself especially well to the simple interpretations we demonstrated in Chapter 5. Note that if we take $x_p = z_p = 0$, $y_p = r_p$, and $i_0 = 0$, we find

$$\bar{\xi}_p = \bar{g}[\tfrac{4}{3} + \tfrac{8}{3}\cos 2\theta]; \qquad \bar{\eta}_p = \bar{g}[-\tfrac{8}{3}\theta - \tfrac{11}{3}\sin 2\theta]; \qquad \bar{\zeta}_p = 0, \quad (7.5.60)$$

which agrees with the results of Chapter 5*. Now we recall that the periodic terms in this result from Chapter 5 represent an elongation of the orbit at right angles to the line *EP*. To see what comes of this perturbation when we consider P to be a moving body, let us take the same geometric model, but with $\lambda \neq 0$. Expression (7.5.54) yields

$$\bar{\xi}_p = \bar{g}\left\{\frac{4}{3} + \left(\frac{(2-\lambda)4}{(1-\lambda)(1-2\lambda)(3-2\lambda)}\right)\cos[2(1-\lambda)f + 2\omega_0]\right\}. \qquad (7.5.61)$$

From this we observe that successive minima or maxima of $\bar{\xi}_p$ are separated by the angle $\pi/(1-\lambda)$, which means that the line of apsides of this orbit moves in phase with P, as might have been suspected. At the same time, the periodic term in $\bar{\eta}_p$,

*The nonperiodic differences relative to the expressions following from Eqs. (5.3.15) to (5.3.17), namely, $\xi = 4\bar{g}$ and $\eta = -6\bar{g}\theta$, simply represent a change in the radius of the circular reference orbit with an attendant change of the mean angular rate. They can be compensated for by the complementary solution in the present formulation.

namely,

$$-\bar{g}\frac{(4\lambda^2-12\lambda+11)}{(1-\lambda)^2(1-2\lambda)(3-2\lambda)}\sin[2(1-\lambda)f+2\omega_0],$$

shows us that the points of maximum tangential perturbations remain 45° out of phase with respect to the orbit axes. For the lunar perturbations on a 24 hour satellite, where $\lambda \simeq 1/28$, we find that $\bar{\eta}_p$ is in the order of one mile.

Returning now to the case where $\lambda = 0$, keeping $\bar{\theta}_0 = \pi/2$, but taking $i_0 \neq 0$, we investigate the precessional motion of the orbit. From (7.5.59) we find

$$\bar{\zeta}_p = \bar{g}\sin 2i_0[-\sin\theta + 2\theta\cos\theta], \tag{7.5.62}$$

where we can interpret the secular term as a rotation of the orbit plane about the y axis, which was demonstrated in Chapter 5 for this model. To complete the comparison, let $\Delta\bar{\zeta}_p$ be the change in $\bar{\zeta}_p$ at the node over one anomalistic period. Then $\dot{\Omega} = -\Delta\bar{\zeta}_p n/2\pi a_0 \sin i_0 = -3\cos i_0\, Gm_P a_0^{3/2}/2r_P^3\mu^{1/2}$. Finally, let $\Delta\bar{\zeta}'_p$ denote the change of $d\bar{\zeta}_p/df$ at the node over one period; this is zero in the present case. It follows from $di_0/dt = \Delta\bar{\zeta}'_p n/2\pi$ that there is no change of inclination, as should be expected for small angles of rotation of the orbit plane about the y axis.

5.4. Perturbations from Radiation Pressure

As the final example of this formulation for near-circular orbits we examine in some detail the effects of radiation pressure. When the satellite is fully illuminated by the sun, the total radiation force on the satellite, F_p, is computed according to (5.3.29). As opposed to the way this force was resolved into components in Chapter 5, we take here a slightly more accurate form: $X = -F_p(x_P - x)/r_{Pm}$, etc., where r_{Pm} is the distance from the sun to the satellite. We then enter (7.2.8) with these expressions to calculate Q_ξ, etc.

As we have stated, the illumination of a low-altitude satellite orbit will in general be nonuniform due to the earth's shadow, albedo, and atmospheric absorption. In Chapter 5 we briefly discussed the determination of the shadow

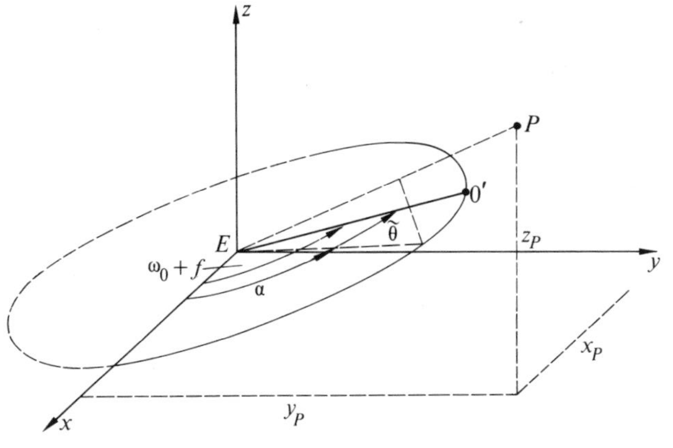

Figure 7.3

limits, which would entail an abrupt change in the radiation force every time the satellite crossed one of these boundaries. For the present discussion we use a continuous approximation to the shadow effect as follows. Assume that the orthogonal projection of the line EP on the nominal orbit plane marks the angle α from the node (Fig. 7.3); the angle from this projected line to the nominal satellite position is $\tilde{\theta} = f+\omega_0-\alpha = f+\tilde{\alpha}$. We will use the first two terms of a Fourier cosine series in this angle as an elementary approximation for the light-intensity distribution around the orbit. Thus

$$F = \frac{F_p}{1+\psi}(1+\psi \cos \tilde{\theta}), \tag{7.5.63}$$

where ψ is the amplitude parameter attached to the first harmonic in the series, and F_p is the projection of the pressure force on the orbit plane. With the usual simplifications we get:

$$Q_\xi = \frac{F_p a_0}{r_P(1+\psi)}\Big[1+\psi \cos \tilde{\theta} - \bar{x} \cos \theta - (\bar{y} \cos i_0 + \bar{z} \sin i_0)\sin \theta - \tfrac{1}{2}\psi(\bar{y} \cos i_0 + \bar{z} \sin i_0)[\sin(\theta+\tilde{\theta}) + \sin \alpha] - \tfrac{1}{2}\psi\bar{x}[\cos(\theta+\tilde{\theta}) + \cos \alpha]\Big], \tag{7.5.64}$$

$$Q_\eta = \frac{F_p a_0}{r_P(1+\psi)}\Big[\bar{x} \sin \theta - (\bar{y} \cos i_0 + \bar{z} \sin i_0)\cos \theta + \tfrac{1}{2}\psi\bar{x}[\sin(\theta+\tilde{\theta}) + \sin \alpha] - \tfrac{1}{2}\psi(\bar{y} \cos i_0 + \sin i_0)[\cos(\theta+\tilde{\theta}) + \cos \alpha]\Big], \tag{7.5.65}$$

$$Q_\zeta = -\frac{F_p a_0}{r_P(1+\psi)}(\bar{z} \cos i_0 - \bar{y} \sin i_0)(1+\psi \cos \tilde{\theta}), \tag{7.5.66}$$

where $\bar{x} = x_P/a_0$, $\bar{y} = y_P/a_0$, $\bar{z} = z_P/a_0$, and, as usual θ marks the position of the satellite itself. Substitution of these expressions into (7.5.11)–(7.5.13) yields

$$\begin{aligned}\bar{\xi}_p = \tilde{g}\Big[&1-\tfrac{1}{2}\bar{x}\psi \cos \alpha - \tfrac{1}{2}(\bar{y} \cos i_0 + \bar{z} \sin i_0)\psi \sin \alpha \\ &+f[\psi\bar{x} \sin \alpha - \psi(\bar{y} \cos i_0 + \bar{z} \sin i_0)\cos \alpha + \tfrac{1}{2}\psi \sin \tilde{\theta} \\ &\quad -\tfrac{3}{2}\bar{x} \sin \theta + \tfrac{3}{2}(\bar{y} \cos i_0 + \bar{z} \sin i_0)\cos \theta] \\ &+\tfrac{1}{4}\psi \cos \tilde{\theta} - \tfrac{7}{4}\bar{x} \cos \theta - \tfrac{7}{4}(\bar{y} \cos i_0 + \bar{z} \sin i_0)\sin \theta \\ &\quad +\tfrac{1}{3}\psi\bar{x} \cos(\theta+\tilde{\theta}) + \tfrac{1}{3}\psi(\bar{y} \cos i_0 + \bar{z} \sin i_0)\sin(\theta+\tilde{\theta})\Big],\end{aligned} \tag{7.5.67}$$

$$\begin{aligned}\bar{\eta}_p = \tilde{g}\Big[&2\psi\bar{x} \sin \alpha + \psi(\bar{y} \cos i_0 + \bar{z} \sin i_0)\cos \alpha \\ &+f[\bar{x}(\psi \cos \alpha - 3 \cos \theta) + (\bar{y} \cos i_0 + \bar{z} \sin i_0)(\psi \sin \alpha - 3 \sin \theta) - 2 + \psi \cos \theta] \\ &+f^2\,\tfrac{3}{4}\psi[(\bar{y} \cos i_0 + \bar{z} \sin i_0)\cos \alpha - \bar{x} \sin \alpha] \\ &-\tfrac{3}{2}\psi \sin \tilde{\theta} + \tfrac{11}{2}\bar{x} \sin \theta - \tfrac{11}{2}(\bar{y} \cos i_0 + \bar{z} \sin i_0)\cos \theta \\ &-\tfrac{11}{24}\psi\bar{x} \sin(\theta+\tilde{\theta}) + \tfrac{11}{24}\psi(\bar{y} \cos i_0 + \bar{z} \sin i_0)\cos(\theta+\tilde{\theta})\Big],\end{aligned} \tag{7.5.68}$$

$$\bar{\zeta}_p = \tilde{g}(\bar{y}\sin i_0 - \bar{z}\cos i_0)(1+\tfrac{1}{4}\psi\cos\tilde{\theta}+\tfrac{1}{2}f\psi\sin\tilde{\theta}), \tag{7.5.69}$$

where $\tilde{g} = F_p a_0^4/\mu r_P(1+\psi)$.

In order to extract some simple interpretations from these results, let us first set $x_P = y_P = 0$, $i_0 = 0$, $\psi = 0$, and $z_P = r_P$ so that the orbit lies in the x,y plane and is fully illuminated from the positive z axis. Then $\bar{\xi}_p = \tilde{g}$, $\bar{\eta}_p = -2f\tilde{g}$, and $\bar{\zeta}_p = -\bar{z}\tilde{g}$. The meaning of these results is obvious. $\bar{\zeta}_p$ represents a uniform downward translation of the orbit plane due to the radiation pressure from above. The divergence of this radiation from point P generates a radial outward component of thrust on the satellite giving a constant value for $\bar{\xi}_p$ and the negative secular term in $\bar{\eta}_p$, as necessitated by the conservation of angular momentum. These results must be combined with (7.5.8)–(7.5.10) to obtain the actual motion.

Another simple case illustrates the precession of the orbit plane when it is not normal to the line $\overline{EP}$. Take $x_P = z_P = 0$, $y_P = r_P$, $i_0 \neq 0$, and $\psi \neq 0$. Then the secular term in $\bar{\zeta}_p$, according to (7.5.69), causes the value of this perturbation at the node to increase during each anomalistic period by the amount

$$\Big[\bar{\zeta}_p\Big]_{\theta=2\pi j}^{2\pi(j+1)} = -\frac{\pi F_p a_0^3 \psi \sin i_0}{\mu(1+\psi)}.$$

This leads to

$$\dot{\Omega} = -\Big[\bar{\zeta}_p\Big]_{\theta=2\pi j}^{\theta=2\pi(j+1)} \frac{n}{2\pi \sin i_0} = \frac{F_p\psi}{2(1+\psi)}\left(\frac{a_0}{\mu}\right)^{1/2}. \tag{7.5.70}$$

As in the preceding example, one can show that $di_0/dt = 0$.

We turn to the hypothetical case of an orbit uniformly illuminated by a source in its own plane, i.e., $x_P = z_P = 0$, $y_P = r_P$, $i_0 = 0$, and $\psi = 0$. Admittedly, a close earth satellite orbit will always be subjected to non-negligible shadow effects but our simplified model is a useful stepping stone to a more realistic model involving earth shadow. With the above simplifications we get

$$\bar{\xi}_p = \tilde{g}\theta[\tfrac{3}{2}\bar{y}\cos\theta - \tfrac{7}{4}\bar{y}\sin\theta + 1], \tag{7.5.71}$$

$$\bar{\eta}_p = \tilde{g}\left[-\theta[3\bar{y}\sin\theta + 2] - \tfrac{11}{2}\bar{y}\cos\theta\right]. \tag{7.5.72}$$

This result is somewhat different from that obtained by elementary means in Chapter 5 for the case of perfectly collimated sunlight. Due to our assumption of a point source of radiation at a finite distance the additional terms $\tilde{g}$ and $-2\theta\tilde{g}$ appear in $\bar{\xi}_p$ and $\bar{\eta}_p$. The results (7.5.71) and (7.5.72) are discussed in more detail in Appendix C. Summarizing the observations made there, we find from $d\bar{\xi}_p/df = 0$ that the points of maximum departure from the nominal orbit are located by the transcendental equation $\theta = -(1/6)\text{ctn}\theta$. Perigee and apogee during each anomalistic period tend to occur near $\theta_q = (2j+1)\pi$ and $\theta_Q = 2\pi j$ respectively. The size of the orbit remains unchanged (to order κ) but departure from circularity grows monotonically with time. This secular behavior of ξ_{min} and ξ_{max} can be understood by interpreting the satellite motion as analogous to that of a linear oscillator which happens to resonate with the excitation from the radiation force. As we relax the linearizations leading to (7.4.12)–(7.4.14), the nonlinear gravitational restoring forces come into play; these (and other physical effects) might be expected to bound the perturbations of the orbit. We also discuss this in Appendix C.

6. ORBITS WITH ARBITRARY ECCENTRICITY

Considerable attention has been devoted recently to equations similar to (7.5.1)–(7.5.3) (particularly their homogeneous form). Their extension to arbitrary nominal orbits is of obvious value for many practical applications, in particular orbit determination and guidance studies. We now consider solutions of the linearized perturbation equations (7.4.15)–(7.4.17) for any value of e_0. Even for the homogeneous case a direct approach is discouraged by the awkward variable coefficients in these equations. However, the motion which (7.4.15)–(7.4.17) represent is also one which follows a conic trajectory, but one whose parameters differ somewhat from $a_0, e_0, \omega_0, \tau_0, i_0, \Omega_0$ by virtue of the initial conditions encountered at f_0. Consequently our problem reduces to a geometric one, namely, to express ξ_c, η_c, ζ_c as the first-order differences between neighboring conics.

Let a coordinate system be defined by the nominal orbit: the x axis passes through pericenter and the positive y axis is given by $f = \pi/2$. Now we need to formulate δx and δy in terms of the variations δa, δe, $\delta\omega$, and $\delta\tau$. The variation in ω implies that the axes of the perturbed orbit have a slightly different orientation from those of the nominal orbit, which define the x,y system.

Omitting the zero subscript from a and e for simplicity, we write

$$r = a(1-e\cos E), \qquad x = a(\cos E - e), \qquad y = a(1-e^2)^{1/2}\sin E, \tag{7.6.1}$$

and from Kepler's equation

$$\frac{\partial E}{\partial a} = \frac{3}{2a}\,\frac{E - e\sin E}{1-e\cos E}; \qquad \frac{\partial E}{\partial e} = \frac{\sin E}{1-e\cos E}; \qquad \frac{\partial E}{\partial \tau} = \frac{(\mu/a^3)^{1/2}}{1-e\cos E}. \tag{7.6.2}$$

With the help of these expressions one finds

$$\begin{aligned} \delta x &= \frac{\partial x}{\partial a}\delta a + \frac{\partial x}{\partial e}\delta e + \frac{\partial x}{\partial \tau}\delta\tau - (\delta\omega + \delta\Omega\cos i) r\sin f, \\ \delta y &= \frac{\partial y}{\partial a}\delta a + \frac{\partial y}{\partial e}\delta e + \frac{\partial y}{\partial \tau}\delta\tau + (\delta\omega + \delta\Omega\cos i) r\cos f, \end{aligned} \tag{7.6.3}$$

which are transformed to the ξ, η system according to

$$\xi = \delta x\cos f + \delta y\sin f; \qquad \eta = -\delta x\sin f + \delta y\cos f. \tag{7.6.4}$$

In executing (7.6.4) we denote $E - e\sin E$ (or its counterpart in terms of f; see

(2.2.37)) as M, the mean anomaly. The result is

$$\xi = \delta a\left[\frac{1-e^2}{1+e\cos f} - \frac{3e\sin f}{2(1-e^2)^{1/2}}M\right] - \delta e\, a\cos f - \delta\tau\, e\left(\frac{\mu}{a(1-e^2)}\right)^{1/2}\sin f, \qquad (7.6.5)$$

$$\eta = -\,\delta a\frac{3(1+e\cos f)}{2(1-e^2)^{1/2}}M + \delta e\, a\frac{2+e\cos f}{1+e\cos f}\sin f$$

$$-\,\delta\tau\left(\frac{\mu}{a(1-e^2)}\right)^{1/2}(1+e\cos f) + (\delta\omega+\delta\Omega\cos i)\frac{a(1-e^2)}{1+e\cos f}, \qquad (7.6.6)$$

where we have retained the form $(\delta\omega+\delta\Omega\cos i)$ of the last coefficient to exhibit its kinematic origin. One may verify in a straightforward manner that these expressions satisfy (7.4.15) and (7.4.16). The constants of integration δa, δe, $(\delta\omega+\delta\Omega\cos i)$, and $\delta\tau$ follow from the initial conditions $\xi = \xi_0$, $\eta = \eta_0$, $d\xi/df = \xi'_0$, $d\eta/df = \eta'_0$ at $f = f_0$, $M = M_0$. If we denote

$$\begin{pmatrix}\xi_0\\ \eta_0\\ \xi'_0\\ \eta'_0\end{pmatrix} = \rho_0, \qquad \begin{pmatrix}\xi\\ \eta\\ \xi'\\ \eta'\end{pmatrix} = \rho, \qquad \begin{pmatrix}\delta a\\ \delta e\\ \delta\omega\\ \delta\tau\end{pmatrix} = \delta\alpha,$$

the determining equations read

$$\rho_0 = A_0\delta\alpha, \qquad (7.6.7)$$

where the matrix A_0 is derivable from (7.6.5) and (7.6.6). The perturbed motion is represented by

$$\rho = AA_0^{-1}\,\rho_0. \qquad (7.6.8)$$

For the special case $f_0 = M_0 = 0$ one finds, for instance,

$$\xi = \frac{2}{(1-e)^2}[\xi_0(2+e)+\eta'_0(1+e)]\left\{\frac{1-e^2}{1+e\cos f} - \frac{3e\sin f}{2(1-e^2)^{1/2}}M\right\}$$

$$-\frac{1+e}{1-e}\left[3\xi_0+2\eta'_0\right]\cos f + \xi'_0\sin f, \qquad (7.6.9)$$

$$\eta = \frac{-3}{(1-e)^2}[\xi_0(2+e)+\eta'_0(1+e)]\frac{1+e\cos f}{(1-e^2)^{1/2}}M + \frac{1+e}{1-e}\left[3\xi_0+2\eta'_0\right]\frac{2+e\cos f}{1+e\cos f}\sin f$$

$$+\,\eta_0\frac{(1+e)}{1+e\cos f} + \frac{\xi'_0}{e}\left[1+e\cos f - \frac{(1+e)^2}{1+e\cos f}\right]. \qquad (7.6.10)$$

For the general case $f_0 \neq 0$ one may find $A_0^{-1}\rho_0 = \delta\alpha$ either by direct inversion of A_0 or by developing $\delta\alpha$ in terms of $\xi_0, \ldots, \eta'_0$ from the orbit sensitivities given in Chapter 4. The rationale of this approach was described in Chapter 6, Section 6, as an alternative derivation of Gauss' form of the planetary equations. The reader may find the development of this generalization of (7.6.9) and (7.6.10) a useful exercise.

The solution of (7.4.17) is found in a corresponding fashion by considering variations δi and $\delta\Omega$, or directly in terms of ζ_0 and ζ_0', from the following kinematic considerations. If r_0 is the initial radius at f_0, a displacement ζ_0 normal to the orbit plane implies a rotation of the actual plane of motion by an angle ζ_0/r_0 about the line $f_0-\pi/2$. If the total velocity vector v_0 at f_0 is to remain parallel to itself, as the condition $\zeta_0 \neq 0$, $(d\zeta/dt)_{f_0} = \dot{\zeta}_0 = 0$ implies, it can be shown that a simultaneous rotation $-[e\zeta_0 \sin f_0/(1+e\cos f_0)]$ must be applied about r_0. Finally, an initial value of $\dot{\zeta}_0$, different from zero, implies a rotation $\dot{\zeta}_0/\dot{f}_0 r_0 = \zeta_0'/r_0$ of the orbit plane about r_0. Developing $\zeta(f)$ from a superposition of these small-angle rotations one finds

$$\zeta = \frac{1}{1+e\cos f}\left\{\zeta_0[\cos(f-f_0)+e\cos f]+\zeta_0'\sin(f-f_0)(1+e\cos f_0)\right\}, \qquad (7.6.11)$$

which can be shown to satisfy (7.4.17). This result is valid for any conic trajectory since the nature of the orbit did not enter its derivation. The corresponding expression in terms of orbit elements turns out to be

$$\zeta = \frac{2p}{1+e\cos f}[\delta i \sin\theta - \delta\Omega \sin i \cos\theta], \qquad (7.6.12)$$

where p is the *semi-latus rectum* of the particular conic involved. Equations (7.6.5), (7.6.6), and (7.6.11) reduce to (7.5.8)–(7.5.10), as they should, if e approaches zero.

The counterparts of (7.6.5) and (7.6.6) for hyperbolic orbits may be found in a perfectly analogous way

$$\xi = \delta a\left[\frac{e^2-1}{1+e\cos f} - \frac{3e\sin f}{2(e^2-1)^{1/2}}M\right] + \delta e\, a\cos f - \delta\tau\, e\left(\frac{\mu}{a(e^2-1)}\right)^{1/2}\sin f, \qquad (7.6.13)$$

$$\eta = -\delta a\frac{3(1+e\cos f)}{2(e^2-1)^{1/2}}M - \delta e\, a\frac{(2+e\cos f)}{1+e\cos f}\sin f$$

$$-\delta\tau\left(\frac{\mu}{a(e^2-1)}\right)^{1/2}(1+e\cos f) + (\delta\omega+\delta\Omega\cos i)\frac{a(e^2-1)}{1+e\cos f}. \qquad (7.6.14)$$

When dealing with parabolic or near-parabolic orbits the preceding formulas break down due to the small divisors $1-e^2$ or e^2-1; moreover, in these cases, $a\to\infty$. However, as before, the *latus rectum* $2p = a(1-e^2)$ or $a(e^2-1)$ remains bounded and is a useful parameter. Thus, if we approach the neighborhood $e\simeq 1$ from an elliptic orbit, $\delta a(1-e^2) = 2\delta p + 2ae\delta e$. Letting $e = 1+\delta e = 1+\varepsilon$ we have

$$\delta a(1-e^2) = 2\delta p - 2p(1+\varepsilon). \qquad (7.6.15)$$

By means of this expression we may rewrite the terms of $0(\delta a)$ and $0(\delta e)$ in (7.6.5) and (7.6.6) as terms of $0(\delta p)$ and $0(\varepsilon)$:

$$\xi = \delta p\left\{\frac{2-\frac{3}{2}\sin^2 f}{1+\cos f} - \frac{1}{2}\sin^2 f\frac{(1-\cos f)}{(1+\cos f)^2}\right\}$$
$$+ \varepsilon p\left\{-\tfrac{3}{2}(1-\cos f) + \frac{2(1+2\cos f)}{(1+\cos f)^2} + \frac{3(1-\cos f)^3}{10(1+\cos f)^2}\right\}$$
$$- \delta\tau\left(\frac{\mu}{2p}\right)^{1/2}\sin f, \qquad (7.6.16)$$

$$\eta = -\delta p\tfrac{3}{2}\sin f\left\{1 + \frac{1-\cos f}{3(1+\cos f)}\right\}$$
$$+ \varepsilon p\tfrac{3}{2}\sin f\left\{\frac{\cos f-\frac{1}{3}}{(1+\cos f)^2} - \frac{2+\cos f}{1+\cos f} + \frac{1}{5}\left(\frac{1-\cos f}{1+\cos f}\right)^2\right\}$$
$$- \delta\tau\left(\frac{\mu}{2p}\right)^{1/2}(1+\cos f) + \frac{(\delta\omega+\delta\Omega\cos i)2p}{1+\cos f}. \qquad (7.6.17)$$

It is clear that $\varepsilon > 0$ represents a perturbation toward hyperbolic orbits and $\varepsilon < 0$ toward elliptic ones.

The expressions given here represent a generalization of the orbit sensitivities discussed in Chapter 4 and Section 5. This type of first-order analysis has been quite popular in guidance work, since expressions like (7.6.5)–(7.6.17) estimate the departures of the actual motion from a reference trajectory due to errors in the dynamic state at f_0. These errors could be introduced at injection, or by a correction maneuver, or may be considered as the residuals from an orbit-determination procedure. Thus, the various expressions given in this chapter may be used to exhibit the error propagation through different phases of aerospace missions, such as near-circular parking orbits, near-parabolic transfer trajectories, hyperbolic flyby and re-entry trajectories. The literature abounds with similar formulations in terms of various coordinate systems [11 to 20]. Some of these are not restricted by the linearizations contained in Eqs. (7.4.15) to (7.4.17) and are therefore valid also for large departures from the nominal orbit [7, 8]. This extends the range of applicability for the resulting expressions and decreases the frequency with which the nominal orbit has to be rectified in a study of error propagation.

REFERENCES

1. E. T. Whittaker, *Analytical Dynamics*, Cambridge Univ. Press, 1959.
2. C. Lanczos, *The Variational Principles of Mechanics*, Univ. of Toronto Press, 1962.
3. F. B. Hildebrand, *Methods of Applied Mathematics*, Prentice-Hall, Englewood Cliffs, N.J., 1952.

4. P. Funk, *Variationsrechnung und ihre Anwendung in Physik und Technik*, Springer, Berlin, 1962.
5. A. Sommerfeld, *Mechanics*, Academic Press, New York, 1952.
6. G. Leitmann, "Some Remarks on Hamilton's Principle," *J. Appl. Mech.* **30,** 623, 1963.
7. M. L. Anthony and F. T. Sasaki, "The Rendezvous Problem for Nearly Circular Orbits," *AIAA Journal*, **3,** 1666, 1965.
8. H. S. London, "Second Approximation to the Solution of the Rendezvous Equations," *AIAA Journal*, **1,** 1691, 1963.
9. D. Brouwer and G. M. Clemence, *Methods of Celestial Mechanics*, Academic Press, New York, 1961.
10. E. Levin, "Solar Radiation Pressure Perturbations of Earth Satellite Orbits," *AIAA Journal*, **6,** 120, 1968.
11. M. L. Wisneski, "Error Matrix for Flight on a Circular Orbit," *ARS Journal*, **32,** 1416, 1962.
12. K. C. Kochi, "Exact Two-Body Error Sensitivity Coefficients," *AIAA Journal*, **2,** 1502, 1964.
13. R. G. Stern, "Analytic Solution of the Equations of Motion of an Interplanetary Space Vehicle in the Midcourse Phase of Its Flight," Fourteenth Congress of the International Astronautical Federation, Paris, Sept. 1963.
14. J. M. A. Danby, "The Matrizant of Keplerian Motion," *AIAA Journal*, **2,** 16, 1964.
15. W. H. Clohessy and R. S. Wiltshire, "Terminal Guidance System for Satellite Rendezvous," *Journal of Aerospace Science*, **27,** No. 9, Sept. 1960.
16. W. H. Tempelman, "New Investigations in the Field of Error Propagation," in *Guidance and Control*, Vol. II, R. C. Langford and C. J. Mundo (eds.), p. 727, (Progress in Astronautics and Aeronautics, Vol. 13), Academic Press, 1964.
17. F. T. Geyling, "Coordinate Perturbations from Kepler Orbits," *AIAA Journal*, **1,** 1899, 1963.
18. W. H. Goodyear, "Completely General Closed-Form Solution for Coordinates and Partial Derivatives of the Two-Body Problem," *Astron. Journal*, **70,** 189, 1965.
19. V. V. Beletskiy and V. A. Yegorov, "Interplanetary Flights with Constant Output Engines," *Cosmic Research*, **2,** 34, 1964 (Translated from the Russian by the Foreign Technology Division of the USAF as Astia Document AD 603012).
20. J. Tschauner, "The Elliptic Orbit Rendezvous," *AIAA Journal*, **5,** 1110, 1967.

Chapter eight

THE METHOD OF CANONICAL TRANSFORMATIONS

1. INTRODUCTION

The analyses of Chapter 7 in terms of the coordinates ξ, η, ζ, had rather immediate geometric significance. However, writing the general equations of motion *ab initio* in these coordinates is hardly possible by inspection. The formalistic dynamics outlined in Chapter 7 (Sections 2 and 3) reduces this to a recipe. Its usefulness becomes apparent in many cases where we wish to try new coordinates that appeal to intuition as being appropriate for the problem at hand; i.e., when we are faced with differential equations insoluble in one coordinate system and we seek to transform them to more tractable expressions.

As a particular feature of this approach, we may capitalize on transformations that eliminate some variables from the Hamiltonian. Such variables are referred to as *ignorable coordinates.* They do not participate in the solution of the transformed equations of motion but can be recovered once the solution has been found. This often turns out to simplify the actual process of solution.

Pursuing the notion of ignorable coordinates, most working procedures based on Hamiltonian dynamics endeavor to eliminate entire classes of variables from the original system of differential equations. Here the formal procedure of writing the original equations and generating suitable transformations in an organized fashion would have the greatest value. The form of Hamilton's equations must be preserved at all stages, and this imposes constraints on the selection of variables. For this reason, the transformations are called *canonical.*

If several stages must be gone through, the successive transformations will tend to produce an increasing amount of symmetrization, i.e., the coordinates and the momenta will become less and less distinguishable on physical grounds and more difficult to relate to the set of natural coordinates, which was used to write down the original set of differential equations. Even the time may lose its privileged role and be absorbed in an augmented system of coordinates.*

While the ultimate form of the governing equations may thus be trivially simple to solve, there remains the labor of obtaining explicit results in terms of some physically meaningful coordinates. In general this requires the inversion of several canonic transformations and becomes a tedious undertaking. Consequently, the merits of Hamiltonian procedures in celestial mechanics have been subject to some debate. Certain schools of thought in dynamic astronomy and theoretical physics support the loyal, if not dogmatic, use of Hamiltonian mechanics, while others take a more independent point of view [3]. On the one hand, there is the appealing simplicity of general, symbolic developments by the Hamiltonian formalism. On the other hand, this formal elegance is not necessarily commensurate with easy execution, physical insight, or efficient computing algorithms. All aspects must enter a total evaluation of the Hamiltonian method and its meaningful comparison with others. Such an exhaustive comparison is beyond the scope of this chapter. We observe that much of the present value of canonic formulations derives from their utility as a basis for convergence studies, stability criteria, and asymptotic representations in general perturbation theories.

In the following pages we approach the canonic transformation theory from Hamilton's principle (7.3.21). While our derivations are formal in character, we attempt to motivate each crucial step. Where a more careful discussion of mathematical points seems advisable we refer to the literature. Along these lines, [1 and 2] are comprehensive treatises on analytical dynamics in various phase spaces and reference 4 provides good coverage of variational arguments. As implied, applications of Hamiltonian techniques to orbital mechanics are extensive and will be noted in the appropriate places.

2. CANONICAL TRANSFORMATIONS AND THE HAMILTON-JACOBI EQUATION

A canonical transformation has been defined as one which preserves the form of Hamilton's equations, namely, (7.3.20)

$$\begin{aligned} \dot{q}_i &= \partial\mathscr{H}/\partial p_i - P_i, \\ & \qquad\qquad\qquad\qquad i = 1, 2, \ldots, n, \\ \dot{p}_i &= -\,\partial\mathscr{H}/\partial q_i + Q_i, \end{aligned} \tag{8.2.1}$$

where q_i and p_i are the coordinates and momenta, respectively, which deal with the dynamical problem in n dimensions. $\mathscr{H}(q_i, p_i, t)$ is the Hamiltonian given by (7.2.14) or (7.2.15) and $P_i(q_i, p_i)$, $Q_i(q_i, p_i)$ are the generalized nonconservative forces defined in (7.3.9) and (7.3.16).

*The description of dynamical systems in various phase spaces brings us to the field of *geometric dynamics*. Though the Lagrangian and Hamiltonian play an important role in this subject, other functionals can be introduced and give rise to additional representations. [1, 2].

In this section, we discuss the conditions necessary for a transformation to new variables, say q'_i, p'_i, to be canonic. These variables might provide a simplified Hamiltonian, i.e., one not explicitly dependent on some of the coordinates and thus making solution of the equations of motion simpler. Indeed, we may wish to prescribe the form of the new Hamiltonian beforehand and find the q'_i, p'_i which, with it, satisfy a system of canonical equations.

2.1. Canonical Transformations

The governing conditions for canonical transformations may be derived from Hamilton's principle, as we do in this section. We have already pointed out that this principle may be considered a basic premise of analytic dynamics; it represents a necessary and sufficient condition for the validity of canonic equations in the chosen coordinate system [1, p.110]. Thus, if a transformation preserves the form of (7.3.21), it also preserves (7.3.20) and we have in terms of the new coordinates q'_i and p'_i,

$$\dot{q}'_i = \partial \mathscr{H}^*/\partial p'_i - P'_i, \qquad \dot{p}'_i = -\partial \mathscr{H}^*/\partial q'_i + Q'_i. \tag{8.2.2}$$

Here $\mathscr{H}^* = \mathscr{H}^*(q', p', t)$, the new Hamiltonian, is a function of the new variables; its relation to $\mathscr{H}(q, p, t)$ needs to be determined.

Let the canonic transformation be written as

$$q_i = q_i(q', p', t); \qquad p_i = p_i(q', p', t), \qquad i = 1, 2, \ldots n. \tag{8.2.3}$$

Now, as shown in Appendix D, the Jacobian $\left|\dfrac{\partial(q, p)}{\partial(q', p')}\right|$ of a canonical transformation does not vanish, so that we may also use the inverse form

$$q'_i = q'_i(q, p, t); \qquad p'_i = p'_i(q, p, t), \tag{8.2.4}$$

and the mixed forms

$$p_i = p_i(q, q', t); \qquad p'_i = p'_i(q, q', t), \tag{8.2.5}$$

or

$$q_i = q_i(p, p', t); \qquad q'_i = q'_i(p, p', t), \qquad \text{etc.}$$

Hamilton's principle (7.3.21), in terms of the new variables and the new Hamiltonian, takes the form

$$\delta \int_{t_1}^{t_2} \left[\sum_i p'_i \dot{q}'_i - \mathscr{H}^*(q', p', t)\right] dt + \int_{t_1}^{t_2} \sum_i \left[Q'_i \delta q'_i + P'_i \delta p'_i\right] dt = 0. \tag{8.2.6}$$

Substituting (8.2.3) into the second integral of (7.3.21) and comparing with (8.2.6) we find

$$Q'_i = \sum_i \left[Q_j \frac{\partial p_j}{\partial q'_i} + P_j \frac{\partial p_j}{\partial q'_i}\right] \qquad \text{and} \qquad P'_i = \sum_j \left[Q_j \frac{\partial q_j}{\partial p'_i} + P_j \frac{\partial p_j}{\partial p'_i}\right]. \tag{8.2.7}$$

Thus the second integral in (8.2.6) develops in a straightforward fashion without imposing any conditions on the transformation. In so doing, the nonconservative forces transform according to (8.2.7).

The first integral in (8.2.6) places the restrictions on (8.2.3) that are peculiar to canonic transformations. Imagine that we use (8.2.3) in the first part of (7.3.21) to obtain

$$\delta \int_{t_1}^{t_2} \left\{ \sum_i \sum_j p_i(q', p', t) \left(\frac{\partial q_i}{\partial q'_j} \dot{q}'_j + \frac{\partial q_i}{\partial p'_j} \dot{p}'_j + \frac{\partial q_i}{\partial t} \right) \right.$$

$$\left. - \mathscr{H}[q(q', p', t); p(q', p', t); t] \right\} dt = 0. \qquad (8.2.8)$$

Now suppose that we rearrange the double summation in this integrand to read

$$\sum_i p'_i \dot{q}'_i + f(q', p', \dot{q}', \dot{p}', t),$$

where f would involve a variety of forms depending on (8.2.3) to (8.2.5). If (8.2.8) is to achieve the structure of the first integral in (8.2.6) it is necessary that f reduce to an exact differential of some function $S(q, p, q', p', t)$ in terms of the dynamic variables and time. The quantity $\delta[S]_{t_1}^{t_2}$ can be shown to vanish since we do not allow terminal variations in the coordinates or the time; so S makes no contribution to (8.2.6). This concept plays a crucial role in the Hamilton-Jacobi theory and we shall return to it presently.

In general, the f we get from (8.2.8) will not represent an exact differential but must be augmented by adding some function, say, $g(q', p', \dot{q}', \dot{p}', t)$. Thus (8.2.8) becomes

$$\delta \int_{t_1}^{t_2} \left\{ \sum_i p'_i \dot{q}'_i + f + g - \mathscr{H} - g \right\} dt = 0. \qquad (8.2.9)$$

Now, we said that $\mathscr{H}^*$ takes the place of the old Hamiltonian $\mathscr{H}$, but we have yet to say what $\mathscr{H}^*$ turns out to be. Note first that a Hamiltonian does not in general represent a physical entity, in contrast to the Lagrangian; nor does the Hamiltonian always represent an integral of the motion, which would be expected to remain invariant under a transformation. Since $(f + g)$ has been arranged to become an ignorable term in (8.2.9), we are obliged to define the new Hamiltonian as,

$$\mathscr{H}^* = \mathscr{H} + g, \qquad (8.2.10)$$

to achieve the form of (8.2.6). This includes the rather obvious choice $g = -f$, where no exact differential occurs explicitly in the transformed variational integral and we let the Hamiltonian be augmented by $-f$. Whether the choice of g is unique for particular cases must remain open at this point.

A simple example may be illustrative here. Consider the case of planar motion about a single center of attraction. In terms of cartesian coordinates we have the Lagrangian

$$L = \tfrac{1}{2}m(\dot{x}^2 + \dot{y}^2) - V(x, y), \tag{8.2.11}$$

where the potential V need not be specified for our present purpose. By (7.2.12)

$$p_x = m\dot{x} \qquad \text{and} \qquad p_y = m\dot{y}. \tag{8.2.12}$$

Now suppose we transform to polar coordinates r, θ where the line $\theta = 0$ rotates at a uniform rate σ. Then

$$x = r\cos(\theta + \sigma t) \qquad \text{and} \qquad y = r\sin(\theta + \sigma t). \tag{8.2.13}$$

The relation between the old and new momenta has yet to be found to complete the transformation. This may be done by deriving the new momenta from their definitions in terms of the Lagrangian. Since the Lagrangian is a physical invariant we need express it only in terms of the new variables. Substituting expressions for $\dot{x}$ and $\dot{y}$ from (8.2.13) into (8.2.11), we obtain

$$L = \tfrac{1}{2}m[\dot{r}^2 + r^2(\dot{\theta} + \sigma)^2] - V'(r, \theta). \tag{8.2.14}$$

Again by (7.2.12)

$$p_r = m\dot{r} \qquad \text{and} \qquad p_\theta = mr^2(\dot{\theta} + \sigma). \tag{8.2.15}$$

Referring to (8.2.12) we see the geometrically evident relations

$$\begin{aligned} p_x &= p_r\cos(\theta + \sigma t) - \frac{p_\theta}{r}\sin(\theta + \sigma t); \\ p_y &= p_r\sin(\theta + \sigma t) + \frac{p_\theta}{r}\cos(\theta + \sigma t). \end{aligned} \tag{8.2.16}$$

Since (8.2.15) was derived from (8.2.14) we know that (8.2.16) completes a canonic transformation. Writing the old Hamiltonian we have

$$\mathscr{H}(x, y, p_x, p_y) = p_x\dot{x} + p_y\dot{y} - L = \frac{1}{2m}\left(p_x^2 + p_y^2\right) + V(x, y);$$

in terms of the new coordinates, using (8.2.16)

$$\mathscr{H}(r, \theta, p_r, p_\theta) = \frac{1}{2m}\left(p_r^2 + \frac{p_\theta^2}{r^2}\right) + V(r, \theta).$$

However, the new Hamiltonian is

$$\mathscr{H}^*(r, \theta, p_r, p_\theta) = p_r\dot{r} + p_\theta\dot{\theta} - L = \left[\frac{p_r^2}{2m} + \frac{p_\theta^2}{2mr^2} - \sigma p_\theta\right] + V(r, \theta),$$

so that

$$\mathscr{H}^* = \mathscr{H} - \sigma p_\theta. \tag{8.2.17}$$

The reader can easily verify that the canonic equations for r, θ, p_r, p_θ in terms of $\mathscr{H}^*$ correspond to the original equations of the problem (in terms of x, y, and $\mathscr{H}$).

In this elementary example we did not require recourse to the variational integral to construct the canonic transformation but let us see now what happened to this integral. Using (8.2.13) and (8.2.16) to write $\sum_i p_i\dot{q}_i$ in terms of the new variables we obtain, following our treatment of (8.2.8),

$$f = \sum_i (p_i\dot{q}_i - p_i'\dot{q}_i') = \sigma p_\theta, \tag{8.2.18}$$

which is not an exact differential. If we take $g = -f$ in (8.2.10) we find

$$\mathscr{H}(r, \theta, p_r, p_\theta, t) - \sigma p_\theta = \mathscr{H}^*(r, \theta, p_r, p_\theta, t),$$

which confirms (8.2.17). While the variational integral was used in this example only to corroborate the direct calculation of $\mathscr{H}^*$, it leads to a rather more "automatic" procedure for sufficiently complicated problems. This approach involves the function S which we now consider.

Suppose that the extra terms denoted by f had been augmented by g (as in 8.2.9) to form the exact differential of S, that is,

$$(f + g)dt = dS(q', p', \dot{q}', \dot{p}', t). \tag{8.2.19}$$

Since S serves to connect the new form of Hamilton's principle, (8.2.6), with the old one (7.3.21), it is appropriately represented by a combination of the old and new variables. Furthermore, it turns out to be useful to write dS not as a function of all four kinds of canonic variables and their derivatives but only two, say q_i and q_i'. This implies a canonic transformation (as yet unknown) of the form (8.2.5) and we may imagine that the explicit occurrences of p_i, p_i', $\dot{p}_i$, and $\dot{p}_i'$ in dS have been eliminated with the help of it. Thus $S = S(q, q', t)$ and

$$dS = \left[\sum_i \left(\frac{\partial S}{\partial q_i}\dot{q}_i + \frac{\partial S}{\partial q_i'}\dot{q}_i'\right) + \frac{\partial S}{\partial t}\right] dt. \tag{8.2.20}$$

Integrating dS as part of (8.2.6) we find

$$\delta[S(q, q', t)]_{t_1}^{t_2} = \left[\sum_i \left(\frac{\partial S}{\partial q_i}\delta q_i + \frac{\partial S}{\partial q_i'}\delta q_i'\right) + \frac{\partial S}{\partial t}\delta t\right]_{t_1}^{t_2}.$$

This expression vanishes since we are permitting no variations in the terminal values of new or old coordinates or the time. Since $p = p(q, q', t)$ and $p' = p'(q, q', t)$ this means that also the terminal variations of the momenta vanish. (A discussion of the permissible variations, especially at the boundaries, is relevant to all these arguments, and the reader is referred to reference 4 for an adequate treatment). Suppose now we examine S to see if it permits useful observations to be made relating the old and new forms of the variational integral. Equating the integrands of (7.3.21) and (8.2.9), with the help of (8.2.10) and (8.2.19), we have

$$\sum_i p_i\dot{q}_i - \mathscr{H} = \sum_i p'_i\dot{q}'_i + \sum_i \left(\frac{\partial S}{\partial q_i}\dot{q}_i + \frac{\partial S}{\partial q'_i}\dot{q}'_i\right) + \frac{\partial S}{\partial t} - \mathscr{H}^*. \tag{8.2.21}$$

By virtue of the form $S = S(q, q', t)$ the only time derivatives in (8.2.21) are $\dot{q}_i$ and $\dot{q}'_i$. Since q_i and q'_i are the independent variables of the transformation (8.2.5) and capable of independent arbitrary variations, the coefficients of $\dot{q}_i$ and $\dot{q}'_i$ must vanish individually, namely,

$$p_i = \partial S/\partial q_i, \tag{8.2.22}$$

and

$$p'_i = -\,\partial S/\partial q'_i; \qquad i = 1, 2, \ldots, n. \tag{8.2.23}$$

The remaining terms of (8.2.21) yield

$$\mathscr{H}^* = \mathscr{H} + \partial S/\partial t, \tag{8.2.24}$$

which indicates the way the Hamiltonian has to be augmented in terms of S.

Assuming the function S can be found for any particular case (though, in general, its existence and uniqueness may require a rigorous examination), Eqs. (8.2.22) to (8.2.24) are necessary conditions for the transformation to be canonic (their sufficiency must as yet be proven). In fact, they describe a transformation of the type (8.2.5) by giving relations between the q_i, q'_i, which are contained in S, and p_i, p'_i, which are not. S is called the *generating function* of the transformation.

The conditions (8.2.22) to (8.2.24) may be considered from several different points of view. First, we could choose any function of q_i, q'_i, and t which is at least once differentiable with respect to each variable and employ (8.2.22) and (8.2.23) to yield information equivalent to (8.2.5). With the transformed Hamiltonian being given by (8.2.24), we could find the equations of motion in the new representation to see if the q'_i can be solved for. Such an intuitive approach can be treated adaptively and may be of use in some cases.

Alternatively, we could assume a specific transformation law (8.2.5) and calculate S from (8.2.22) to (8.2.24). If a solution for S exists, the transformation is shown to be canonic. Sometimes a combination of these two points of view is useful. There are problems where an existing form of the equations of motion suggests improvements if some of the coordinates or momenta were redefined in a certain way. Assuming a suitable form for S, one can then determine the changes in the conjugate variables and the Hamiltonian by means of (8.2.22) to (8.2.24). We shall return to this notion in Section 4.

As one more approach to (8.2.22) to (8.2.24), we may start from a preconceived form of the new Hamiltonian $\mathscr{H}^*$. Now the transformation is to be calculated so that it yields this Hamiltonian. Then (8.2.24) becomes the governing equation for S, which in turn determines the transformation through (8.2.22) and (8.2.23). Here the name *generating function* for S is particularly appropriate.

In connection with this last viewpoint, we discuss below the Hamilton-Jacobi equation, separation of variables, and iterative perturbation techniques that lead to progressively simpler Hamiltonians. However, let us first describe S in somewhat greater generality. Up to this point we considered generating functions of the form $S(q, q', t)$ because $\dot{q}_i$ and $\dot{q}'_i$ appeared in the old and new forms (7.3.21) and (8.2.6) of the variational integral. Clearly, other types of generating functions, containing different combinations of old and new variables, may also be suitable. Thus, for example, the generating function needed to represent a transformation of the form

$$q = q(q', t); \qquad p = p(p', t), \tag{8.2.25}$$

would have to be of the type $S(q, p', t)$ or $S(q', p, t)$ but not $S(q, q', t)$ or $S(p, p', t)$. Transformations of this kind are known as *point transformations.*

To obtain the counterparts of (8.2.22) to (8.2.24) for other generating functions we consider other forms of the variational integral. In (7.3.21) we can replace any term $p_i\dot{q}_i$ by $d(p_iq_i)/dt - q_i\dot{p}_i$. Integrating the derivative of the product term as part of the variational integral yields

$$\delta[p_iq_i]_{t_1}^{t_2} = 0. \tag{8.2.26}$$

(The vanishing of this variation prescribes $\delta q_i = 0$ and $\delta p_i = 0$ at t_1 and t_2. As in all variational arguments [4] a clear and consistent distinction must be made between "independent" and "dependent" variables in describing variations of the path.)

Accepting (8.2.26), Eq. (7.3.21) can assume any of the forms

$$\delta \int_{t_1}^{t_2} \left[\sum_{i=1}^{k} p_i\dot{q}_i - \sum_{j=k+1}^{n} q_j\dot{p}_j - \mathscr{H}(q, p, t) \right] dt = 0. \tag{8.2.27}$$

An analogous expression to (8.2.27) may be written for (8.2.6). One can see that a juxtaposition of these hybrid forms of the Hamilton principle, analogous to (8.2.21), leads to transformation conditions in terms of the most general function

$$S = S(q_r, p_s, q'_u, p'_v, t), \tag{8.2.28}$$

where

$$\begin{aligned} r &= 1, \dots k, \\ s &= k+1, \dots n, \end{aligned} \quad 0 \le k \le n$$
$$\begin{aligned} u &= 1, \dots l, \\ v &= l+1, \dots n, \end{aligned} \quad 0 \le l \le n,$$

and we observe for later use that $\sum_{n+1}^{n} x_i = 0$ for any n and x. Thus

$$p_r = \frac{\partial S}{\partial q_r}; \qquad q_s = -\frac{\partial S}{\partial p_s}; \qquad p'_u = -\frac{\partial S}{\partial q'_u}; \qquad q'_v = \frac{\partial S}{\partial p'_v}; \tag{8.2.29}$$

and

$$\mathscr{H}^* = \mathscr{H} + \partial S/\partial t.$$

In many problems several choices are open among the different possible kinds of generating functions: $S(q, q', t)$, $S(q, p', t)$, $S(p, q', t)$, $S(p, p', t)$. They merely imply different forms of the transformation being undertaken, i.e., Eqs. (8.2.3) to (8.2.5). As long as it is the same transformation, the augmented Hamiltonian must be the same. Hence

$$\frac{\partial S(q, q', t)}{\partial t} = \frac{\partial S(q, p', t)}{\partial t} = \frac{\partial S(p, q', t)}{\partial t} = \frac{\partial S(p, p', t)}{\partial t}. \tag{8.2.30}$$

Let us see how our earlier example, involving a transformation to rotating coordinates, can be handled in terms of a generating function; say

$$S(p, q', t) = -rp_x \cos(\theta + \sigma t) - rp_y \sin(\theta + \sigma t). \tag{8.2.31}$$

Now (8.2.13) follows from

$$x = -\partial S/\partial p_x, \qquad y = -\partial S/\partial p_y.$$

Furthermore

$$p_r = -\partial S/\partial r, \qquad p_\theta = -\partial S/\partial \theta.$$

Inversion of the latter pair of equations yields (8.2.16). Finally

$$\partial S/\partial t = \sigma r[p_x \sin(\theta + \sigma t) - p_y \cos(\theta + \sigma t)] = -\sigma p_\theta, \tag{8.2.32}$$

which confirms the augmentation of the Hamiltonian calculated in (8.2.17).

In this example the generating function served as a convenient means for finding the new Hamiltonian. We now deal with the inverse situation.

2.2. The Hamilton-Jacobi Equation

Let us establish a technique for finding generating functions that lead to a specified new Hamiltonian for an especially simple form of the canonic equations. Obviously the most desirable set of equations would be

$$\partial \mathscr{H}^*/\partial p'_i = \dot{q}'_i = 0, \tag{8.2.33}$$

$$\partial \mathscr{H}^*/\partial q'_i = -\dot{p}'_i = 0, \tag{8.2.34}$$

implying that q_i' and p_i' are constants and that $\mathscr{H}^*$ vanishes identically, or is a constant, or is a function of the time alone. Since these alternatives do not give rise to significant differences in what follows we take, for simplicity,

$$\mathscr{H}^* \equiv 0 = \mathscr{H} + \partial S/\partial t. \tag{8.2.35}$$

Let us consider a generating function of the form $S = S(q, p', t)$. With the help of (8.2.29) ($k = n$, $l = 0$), Eq. (8.2.35) becomes

$$\mathscr{H}\left(q_1, \cdots, q_n, \frac{\partial S}{\partial q_1}, \cdots, \frac{\partial S}{\partial q_n}, t\right) + \frac{\partial S}{\partial t} = 0. \tag{8.2.36}$$

This partial differential equation for S is known as the Hamilton-Jacobi equation. Alternative forms involving $S(q, q', t)$, etc. can be written down immediately but do not give rise to essentially different procedures of solution. The form (8.2.36) seems to have gained wide acceptance in astronomical practice.

Now, on the one hand we know from (8.2.34) that the p_i' are constants; on the other hand we know from the theory of partial differential equations that a complete integral of (8.2.36) must contain $(n + 1)$ constants.* One of these must be purely additive since, if S is a solution of (8.2.36), $S + \alpha$ is one too. But this additive constant does not affect (8.2.29) and we cease to consider it. Thus we let $S = S(q_i, \alpha_i, t)$ where the n non-additive constants α_i may be taken as the new momenta† p_i'. Assuming that $p_i' \equiv \alpha_i$, we obtain from (8.2.29) (with $k = n$, $l = 0$)

$$p_i = \frac{\partial S(q, \alpha, t)}{\partial q_i}, \tag{8.2.37}$$

and

$$q_i' = \beta_i = \frac{\partial S(q, \alpha, t)}{\partial \alpha_i}, \tag{8.2.38}$$

where the q_i' are constants because $\dot{q}_i' = \partial \mathscr{H}^*/\partial \alpha_i \equiv 0$. From the initial conditions we find $q_i(t = t_0)$, $p_i(t = t_0)$ and then (8.2.37), evaluated at t_0, leads to the α_i (i.e., the p_i'). Similarly, (8.2.38) with $t = t_0$ may then be solved for β_i. Finally, we again use (8.2.38), with general t, and invert it to obtain $q_i = q_i(\alpha, \beta, t)$, which constitutes the solution of our problem.‡

From a conceptual point of view (8.2.36) to (8.2.38) provide a rather straight-

---

*Reference 5, §§ 42 and 50.

†In a completely general approach one might represent the new momenta as linearly independent functions of these constants, i.e., $p_i' = \gamma_i(\alpha)$; in practice this generality has scarcely any significance.

‡As with (8.2.22)–(8.2.24), one notes that (8.2.37) and (8.2.38) are the ultimate outcome of the premise that q_i, p_i, and α_i, β_i satisfy Hamilton's principle in each coordinate system and hence the canonic equations (albeit with $\mathscr{H}^* \equiv 0$). They therefore constitute a set of necessary conditions for canonic transformations; but their sufficiency remains to be demonstrated. We do this in Appendix E by the Jacobi theorem.

forward representation for the solutions of dynamic problems.* However, it must be emphasized that most of the manipulations required for nontrivial problems arise from the operations described in the last few sentences of the preceding paragraph. Several facts should be recognized in working with these equations. As stated, it is immaterial whether the constants α_i themselves or some functions $\gamma_j(\alpha)$ thereof are recognized as the new momenta. In fact, there is no fundamental need for associating the α_i with the transformed momenta (especially since the distinction between momenta and coordinates is frequently lost in the transformation). Since the α_i and β_i are merely constants of integration, the working procedure associated with (8.2.37) and (8.2.38) is unaffected if we interpret these equations in terms of $S(q, q', t)$ rather than $S(q, p', t)$.

We close this section with some remarks about special cases when the time or any one of the variables q_i do not appear explicitly in the Hamiltonian. For conservative systems $\mathscr{H}$ is independent of time; then $\partial\mathscr{H}/\partial t = 0$ and $\mathscr{H} =$ constant. Thus (8.2.36) reduces to

$$\partial S/\partial t = -\text{const.} \tag{8.2.39}$$

In this case the total number of integration constants in S is still n and we can express the right-hand side of (8.2.39) in terms of one of them, say α_1, which is, according to (8.2.36), also the Hamiltonian. Then the generating function must have the form

$$S = -\alpha_1 t + \hat{S}(q_i, \alpha_i, t). \tag{8.2.40}$$

Equations (8.2.37) and (8.2.38) remain unaffected for $i \neq 1$; but for $i = 1$, (8.2.38) reads

$$t + \beta_1 = \frac{\partial \hat{S}(q_i, \alpha_i, t)}{\partial \alpha_1}. \tag{8.2.41}$$

Next, consider another special situation where any one of the q_i, say q_2, does not appear in the Hamiltonian, i.e., it happens to be an "ignorable" coordinate. From Hamilton's equations

$$\partial\mathscr{H}/\partial q_2 = \dot{p}_2 = 0,$$

and hence $p_2 = \text{const.} = \alpha_2$. Therefore

$$\partial S/\partial q_2 = \alpha_2, \tag{8.2.42}$$

and hence

$$S = \alpha_2 q_2 + \hat{\hat{S}}(q_1, q_3, \ldots, q_n, \alpha_i, t). \tag{8.2.43}$$

*In fact, being a special case of (8.2.29) where the new coordinates and momenta are all constants of integration, Eqs. (8.2.36) through (8.2.38) supply a complete integral of the problem.

Equations (8.2.37) and (8.2.38) remain unaffected for $i \neq 2$, but for $i = 2$ the latter becomes

$$\beta_2 - q_2 = \frac{\partial \hat{\hat{S}}(q_1, q_3, \ldots, q_n, \alpha_i, t)}{\partial \alpha_2}. \tag{8.2.44}$$

Obviously (8.2.41) and (8.2.44) could occur simultaneously in the same problem and, in general, any combination of $\partial \mathscr{H}/\partial t = 0$, $\partial \mathscr{H}/\partial q_i = 0$, $i = 1 \cdots n$ can be accommodated in this fashion. In practice these special forms develop anyway from a standard application of (8.2.37) and (8.2.38), as can be easily demonstrated. Sometimes, however, the recognition of ignorable coordinates will ease the chore of developing explicit expressions for the solution $q_j(\alpha_i, \beta_i, t)$ of a specific problem.

3. SEPARATION OF VARIABLES

As shown in the preceding section, one may reduce the solution of a dynamic problem to that of the Hamilton-Jacobi equation. In general this partial differential equation is tractable only if the variables q_i and t are separable within the generating function and the Hamiltonian. In the simplest case, involving explicit separability, (8.2.36) admits a solution consisting of additive terms, each of which is a function of only one coordinate or the time. The basic rationale for the separation of variables is well known. In all applications success in separating the variables depends largely on the choice of a suitable system of coordinates, q_i, to begin with. Existing theory includes several general tests for separability of the Hamilton-Jacobi equation but, in practice, the trial substitution of a separable form of S into (8.2.36) turns out to be the usual expedient.* If we let

$$S = \sum_i^n S_i(q_i, \alpha_i, \ldots, \alpha_n) + S_{n+1}(t, \alpha_1, \ldots, \alpha_n), \tag{8.3.1}$$

then (8.2.36) becomes

$$\sum_i^n \mathscr{H}_i\,(q_i, \partial S_i/\partial q_i, \alpha_1, \ldots, \alpha_n) + \mathscr{H}_{n+1}(t, \alpha_1, \ldots, \alpha_n) + \partial S_{n+1}/\partial t = 0. \tag{8.3.2}$$

Recognizing the functional independence of various parts of this equation we can stipulate that

$$\mathscr{H}_{n+1}(t) + \partial S_{n+1}/\partial t = c_{n+1}, \tag{8.3.3}$$

and

$$\mathscr{H}_i(q_i) = c_i, \qquad i = 1, \ldots, n. \tag{8.3.4}$$

---

*Much more can be said about separability in general, for which we refer the reader to the literature, e.g., references 1, p. 128; 5, 7; 8, p. 240; 9, and notably 10, which contains a good review of work by Liouville, Staeckel, Burgatti, Denim *et al.*

The c_i are the *constants of separation*. In order to satisfy (8.3.2) one requires that

$$\sum_{i}^{n+1} c_i = 0. \tag{8.3.5}$$

On account of the last condition we have, in effect, introduced n arbitrary constants and, since the explicit appearance of the α_i and S_i and $\mathscr{H}_i$ is as yet undetermined, we are free to identify the c_i with the α_i in some convenient fashion. For example

$$\begin{aligned} c_i &= \alpha_i, \qquad i = 1, \ldots, n, \\ c_{n+1} &= -\sum_{i}^{n} \alpha_i. \end{aligned} \tag{8.3.6}$$

A special case of separability arises if $\partial\mathscr{H}/\partial t = 0$ and $\partial\mathscr{H}/\partial q_i = 0$ for $i \neq 1$; i.e., all coordinates are ignorable except one. Then

$$\mathscr{H}\left(q_1, \frac{\partial S_1}{\partial q_1}\right) + \frac{\partial S_{n+1}}{\partial t} = 0, \tag{8.3.7}$$

which leads to

$$\partial S_{n+1}/\partial t = -\alpha_1, \qquad \text{and} \qquad \mathscr{H}\left(q_1, \frac{\partial S_1}{\partial q_1}\right) = \alpha_1. \tag{8.3.8}$$

Since we know from (8.2.42) that for the ignorable coordinates

$$\partial S_i/\partial q_i = \alpha_i, \qquad i \neq 1, \tag{8.3.9}$$

the solution (8.3.1) then takes the form

$$S = S_1 + \sum_{i=2}^{n} \alpha_i q_i - \alpha_i t. \tag{8.3.10}$$

In the following subsections we demonstrate (1) the separation of variables approach for the Kepler problem in spherical coordinates and (2) the separability for certain nonspherical potential functions in spheroidal coordinates. In the latter case, as with many nontrivial problems, separability does not imply closed form solutions.

3.1. Illustrative Example. The Hamilton-Jacobi Equation and the Two-Body Problem

We select the Keplerian problem not because it affords any new insight into conic motion but rather just the opposite. Its familiarity is such that the physics of the solution will not be masked by the methodology in question; in particular, the task of relating the new "variables" to the original coordinates is more easily assessed in this simple case. This selection also serves to introduce the reader to those coordinates and momenta which have found rather widespread use in classical celestial mechanics, namely, the Delaunay variables.

It is easily seen that a statement of the Kepler problem in cartesian coordinates leads to an inseparable Hamiltonian. Spherical coordinates are a more appropriate choice, and an obvious one because of the spherical symmetry of the potential function. We note that they are not the only ones yielding a separable Hamiltonian in this case. The parabolic coordinates

$$x = \sqrt{uv}\cos\lambda, \qquad y = \sqrt{uv}\sin\lambda, \qquad z = \tfrac{1}{2}(u-v),$$

may serve the same purpose [8, p. 242]; however, here we shall remain with the spherical system.

Consider two masses m and M, and suppose we describe their motion in the spherical coordinate system (r, φ, λ) centered on M, where

$$x = r\cos\varphi\cos\lambda; \qquad y = r\cos\varphi\sin\lambda; \qquad z = r\sin\varphi.$$

The Lagrangian (per unit mass of the smaller body m) is

$$L = \frac{1}{2}[\dot{r}^2 + r^2\dot{\varphi}^2 + r^2\dot{\lambda}^2\cos^2\varphi] + \frac{\mu}{r}. \tag{8.3.11}$$

Taking

$$q_1 = r, \qquad q_2 = \varphi, \qquad q_3 = \lambda, \tag{8.3.12}$$

we obtain

$$p_1 = \dot{q}_1, \qquad p_2 = q_1^2\dot{q}_2, \qquad p_3 = q_1^2\dot{q}_3\cos^2 q_2, \tag{8.3.13}$$

and

$$\mathscr{H} = \tfrac{1}{2}\left[p_1^2 + \frac{p_2^2}{q_1^2} + \frac{p_3^2}{q_1^2\cos^2 q_2}\right] - \frac{\mu}{q_1}, \tag{8.3.14}$$

where the latter represents the total energy and is time-invariant. Hamilton's equations of motion are then

$$\dot{q}_1 = p_1, \qquad \dot{p}_1 = \frac{p_2^2}{q_1^3} + \frac{p_3^2}{q_1^3\cos^2 q_2} - \frac{\mu}{q_2},$$

$$\dot{q}_2 = \frac{p_2}{q_2}, \qquad \dot{p}_2 = -\frac{p_3^2\tan q_2}{q_1^2\cos^2 q_2},$$

$$\dot{q}_3 = \frac{p_3}{q_1^2\cos^2 q_2}, \qquad \dot{p}_3 = 0.$$

Of course these can be solved and the equation $\dot{p}_3 = 0$ suggests an obvious place to start. However, let us show how to accomplish this by using the Hamilton-Jacobi equation (8.2.36).

We obtain

$$\frac{1}{2}\left[\left(\frac{\partial S}{\partial q_1}\right)^2 + \frac{1}{q_1^2}\left(\frac{\partial S}{\partial q_2}\right)^2 + \frac{1}{q_1^2\cos^2 q_2}\left(\frac{\partial S}{\partial q_3}\right)^2\right] - \frac{\mu}{q_1} + \frac{\partial S}{\partial t} = 0, \tag{8.3.15}$$

and then proceed as in (8.3.1):

$$S = S_1(q_1) + S_2(q_2) + S_3(q_3) + S_4(t).$$

The function $S_4(t)$ is by (8.3.8) equal to $-\alpha_1 t$, and thus (8.3.15) can be written

$$q_1^2\cos^2 q_2\left[\left(\frac{\partial S_1}{\partial q_1}\right)^2 + \frac{1}{q_1^2}\left(\frac{\partial S_2}{\partial q_2}\right)^2 - \frac{2\mu}{q_1} - 2\alpha_1\right] = -\left(\frac{\partial S_3}{\partial q_3}\right)^2.$$

The left-hand side being, by supposition, independent of q_3 and the right-hand side independent of q_1 and q_2, either can only be a constant, say $-\alpha_3^2$, so that $S_3 = \alpha_3 q_3$. The final separation constant we call α_2^2 and then find

$$q_1^2(dS_1/dq_1)^2 - 2\alpha_1 q_1^2 - 2\mu q_1 = -\alpha_2^2, \qquad (dS_2/dq_2)^2 + \alpha_3^2\sec^2 q_2 = \alpha_2^2. \tag{8.3.16}$$

The generating function of the transformation can thus be written (neglecting the arbitrary additive constant)

$$S = -\alpha_1 t + \int\frac{\sqrt{2\alpha_1 q_1^2 + 2\mu q_1 - \alpha_2^2}}{q_1}\,dq_1 + \int\sqrt{\alpha_2^2 - \alpha_3^2\sec^2 q_2}\,dq_2 + \alpha_3 q_3. \tag{8.3.17}$$

Now we employ (8.2.37), set the old momenta p_i equal to the appropriate initial conditions in terms of r, $\dot r$, etc., and invert the equations to find the values for the α_i in these terms. We find

$$\alpha_1 = \tfrac{1}{2}[\dot r_0^2 + r_0^2(\dot\varphi_0^2 + \dot\lambda_0^2\cos^2\varphi_0)] - \frac{\mu}{r_0}, \tag{8.3.18}$$

$$\alpha_2 = r_0^2\sqrt{\dot\varphi_0^2 + \dot\lambda_0^2\cos^2\varphi_0}, \tag{8.3.19}$$

$$\alpha_3 = r_0^2\dot\lambda\cos^2\varphi_0. \tag{8.3.20}$$

Before proceeding further in identifying these quantities geometrically, let us also obtain the new coordinates, $q_i'(=\beta_i)$.

To do this, we do not have first to complete the integrals of (8.3.17), since according to (8.2.38) the new coordinates are given by the partial derivatives of S with respect to the α_i. Thus

$$\beta_1 = \frac{\partial S}{\partial\alpha_1} = -t + \int\frac{q_1\,dq_1}{\sqrt{2\alpha_1 q_1^2 + 2\mu q_1 - \alpha_2^2}},$$

or

$$t + \beta_1 = \frac{\sqrt{2\alpha_1 q_1^2 + 2\mu q_1 - \alpha_2^2}}{2\alpha_1} - \frac{\mu}{2\alpha_1\sqrt{-2\alpha_1}} \cos^{-1}\left(\frac{2\alpha_1 q_1 + \mu}{\sqrt{2\alpha_1\alpha_2^2 \pm \mu^2}}\right). \tag{8.3.21}$$

Also

$$\beta_2 = \frac{\partial S}{\partial \alpha_2} = \cos^{-1}\left(\frac{\mu q_1 - \alpha_2^2}{q_1\sqrt{2\alpha_1\alpha_2^2 + \mu^2}}\right) + \sin^{-1}\left(\sqrt{\frac{\alpha_2^2}{\alpha_2^2 - \alpha_3^2}} \sin q_2\right), \tag{8.3.22}$$

and

$$\beta_3 = \frac{\partial S}{\partial \alpha_3} = q_3 - \sin^{-1}\left(\sqrt{\frac{\alpha_3^2}{\alpha_2^2 - \alpha_3^2}} \tan q_2\right). \tag{8.3.23}$$

It remains to relate the α_i, β_i to quantities we recognize and thus provide a meaningful solution. (As is always the case, knowing the answer in advance is rather helpful even to the intellectually honest.)

We first identify the α_i as physical quantities which are invariants in a conservative system. Thus α_1 is recognized from (8.3.18) as the total energy (per unit mass) and hence

$$\alpha_1 = \mathscr{H}(q_i, p_i) = \tfrac{1}{2}v^2 - \mu/r = -\mu/2a, \tag{8.3.24}$$

where the last follows from (2.2.18). Similarly, (8.3.19) makes it obvious that α_2 represents the total angular momentum; thus, utilizing (2.2.9), we have

$$\alpha_2 = r^2\dot{f} = \sqrt{\mu a(1 - e^2)}. \tag{8.3.25}$$

Finally, (8.3.20) represents the polar angular momentum. Since $r\dot{\lambda}\cos\varphi = r\dot{f}\sin\psi$, where ψ is the course angle defined in Chapter 4, we find

$$\alpha_3 = r^2\dot{\lambda}\cos^2\varphi = r^2\dot{f}\sin\psi\cos\varphi = r^2\dot{f}\cos i = \sqrt{\mu a(1 - e^2)}\cos i, \tag{8.3.26}$$

using (4.2.10)

Now (8.3.21) has the structure of well-known conic-section time equations and we let the factor in parentheses be expressed in terms of a new variable E, that is,

$$\frac{2\alpha_1 q_1 + \mu}{\sqrt{2\alpha_1\alpha_2^2 + \mu^2}} = \cos E.$$

This then provides $q_1(= r) = a(1 - e\cos E)$, using (8.3.24) and (8.3.25). The equation (8.3.21) can be rewritten $E - e\sin E = \sqrt{\mu/a^3}\,(t + \beta_1)$, which serves to relate β_1 to a more familiar element,

$$\beta_1 = -\tau. \tag{8.3.27}$$

If we take (8.3.22), and here let

$$\frac{\mu q_1 - \alpha_2^2}{q_1\sqrt{2\alpha_1\alpha_2^2 + \mu^2}} = -\cos f,$$

we obtain from this

$$q_1 = r = \frac{a(1 - e^2)}{1 + e\cos f}.$$

Then (8.3.22) with $q_2 = \varphi$ yields

$$\frac{\sin\varphi}{\sin i} = \sin(f + \beta_2).$$

This we recognize as the relation (4.2.13) between angles describing the motion in an inclined plane through the origin; which leads to

$$\beta_2 = \omega. \tag{8.3.28}$$

Finally, we can rewrite (8.3.23) with $q_3 = \lambda$ as $\cot i \tan\varphi = \sin(\lambda - \beta_3)$, which, employing (4.2.12), allows us to identify β_3 as

$$\beta_3 = \Omega. \tag{8.3.29}$$

We have thus established the new coordinates, β_i and the new momenta, α_i, by (8.2.37) and (8.2.38). Note that a good portion of the labor lay in relating the new to the old variables and that, indeed, much of this was short-circuited because of our familiarity with Keplerian motion. Now let us see how things work out in a nontrivial problem.

3.2. Illustrative Example. The Hamilton-Jacobi Equation and Motion about an Oblate Planet

In the preceding example, we were led by separability arguments to try a spherical coordinate system. This idea grew out of a consideration of the symmetry of the potential. In this section, the analogous reasoning is applied to a class of spheroidal potentials and we find ourselves welcoming the capability of Hamiltonian formulations to cope with unusual or complex coordinate systems.

Since, to a first approximation, the earth acts as an oblate spheroid, it occurred to Vinti [11] that the Hamiltonian might be separable when expressed in oblate spheroidal coordinates. This Hamiltonian would contain terms which express the gravitational potential due to an equatorial bulge. (This approach has also been taken more recently [10, 12, 13] by several other authors.)

Let us first provide a short description of oblate spheroidal coordinates. The simplest way of relating them to more familiar ones is given by (8.3.30) below. We have

$$x = c[(q_1^2 + 1)(1 - q_2^2)]^{\frac{1}{2}} \cos q_3; \qquad y = c[(q_1^2 + 1)(1 - q_2^2)]^{\frac{1}{2}} \sin q_3; \qquad z = cq_1q_2. \tag{8.3.30}$$

Here q_3 is the right ascension and c is a constant to be chosen subsequently. For a given value of q_1, we obtain a surface in the shape of an oblate spheroid, i.e., a figure whose meridians (formed by planes passing through the z axis) are ellipses; e.g., for $q_3 = 0$,

$$\frac{x^2}{c^2(q_1^2 + 1)} + \frac{z^2}{c^2q_1^2} = 1. \tag{8.3.31}$$

Planes perpendicular to the z axis cut the figure in circles. For a given value of q_2, we obtain a hyperboloid of revolution; thus for $q_3 = 0$,

$$\frac{x^2}{c^2(1 - q_2^2)} - \frac{z^2}{c^2q_2^2} = 1. \tag{8.3.32}$$

Note that q_1 can take on any (real) value but that $|q_2| \leq 1$ if the coordinates are not to become imaginary.

This brief discussion indicates that the approach taken here departs from the methods presented in earlier chapters. We are not going to solve the Kepler problem first and then, retaining spherical coordinates, append additional terms to the potential to amend our initial results. Rather, we are going to look at the total problem in specially chosen spheroidal coordinates, hoping to include as many nonspherical effects as possible in a separable Hamiltonian before resorting to higher-order perturbations.

The Hamiltonian statement of the problem can be set up simply enough. The relations (8.3.30) allow us to find the Lagrangian (7.2.22), whereupon (7.2.12) provides

$$p_1 = mc^2\left(\frac{q_1^2 + q_2^2}{q_1^2 + 1}\right)\dot{q}_1; \qquad p_2 = mc^2\left(\frac{q_1^2 + q_2^2}{1 - q_2^2}\right)\dot{q}_2; \qquad p_3 = mc^2(q_1^2 + 1)(1 - q_2^2)\dot{q}_3. \tag{8.3.33}$$

If we absorb the factor $1/m$ in each component of the momentum and also in the Hamiltonian, then (7.2.15) gives

$$\mathscr{H} = \frac{1}{2c^2}\left\{\frac{q_1^2 + 1}{q_1^2 + q_2^2}p_1^2 + \frac{1 - q_2^2}{q_1^2 + q_2^2}p_2^2 + \frac{p_3^2}{(q_1^2 + 1)(1 - q_2^2)}\right\} + V(q_1, q_2, q_3). \tag{8.3.34}$$

As in the Kepler problem, we have a time-invariant Hamiltonian representing the total energy. The Hamilton-Jacobi equation we hope to solve is

$$\frac{(q_1^2+1)^2(1-q_2^2)}{q_1^2+q_2^2}\left(\frac{\partial S}{\partial q_1}\right)^2+\frac{(q_1^2+1)(1-q_2^2)^2}{q_1^2+q_2^2}\left(\frac{\partial S}{\partial q_2}\right)^2+\left(\frac{\partial S}{\partial q_3}\right)^2$$
$$+\,2c^2V(q_1,q_2,q_3)(q_1^2+1)(1-q_2^2)=2c^2\alpha_1(q_1^2+1)(1-q_2^2), \qquad (8.3.35)$$

where α_1 is the energy constant. We now postulate a generating function of the form

$$S=S_1(q_1)+S_2(q_2)+S_3(q_3)-\alpha_1 t. \qquad (8.3.36)$$

Substitution of this expression into (8.3.35) shows that the equation becomes separable if the potential takes the form

$$V=\frac{1}{q_1^2+q_2^2}[f(q_1)+g(q_2)]+\frac{h(q_3)}{2c^2(q_1^2+1)(1-q_2^2)}. \qquad (8.3.37)$$

We would require $h(q_3)=-(dS_3/dq_3)^2$ if $h(q_3)$ does not vanish. Restricting ourselves to the rotationally symmetric potentials requires $h(q_3)$ to be constant; thus

$$dS_3/dq_3=\text{const.}=\alpha_3. \qquad (8.3.38)$$

Since the rotational symmetry ensures an invariant component of angular momentum about the polar axis, we may interpret α_3 as that quantity.

We must now choose $f(q_1)$ and $g(q_2)$ in the first part of (8.3.37) to satisfy Laplace's equation in spheroidal coordinates. Such a solution is developed in reference 11, and after selecting some of its coefficients to avoid singularities on the polar axis and at infinity, one finds*

$$V=\frac{b_1q_1-b_2q_2}{(q_1^2+q_2^2)}, \qquad (8.3.39)$$

where b_1 and b_2 are not yet determined. Comparison of this with series expansions for the geopotential in terms of Legendre functions shows that

$$b_1=-\frac{\mu}{R}\sqrt{\frac{2}{3J_2}},$$
$$b_2=-\frac{\mu}{R}\frac{2J_1}{3J_2},$$

*At this point it is interesting to note the connection with another mathematical model for spheroidal potentials. While gravity from a prolate spheroid is representable by a pair of supplementary point masses at $\pm\varepsilon$ on the polar axis, an oblate spheroid can be represented formally by placing these mass points at $\pm j\varepsilon$, where $j=\sqrt{-1}$. This fact was utilized in [12], resulting in the potential function $V=b_1q_1/(q_1^2+q_2^2)$, which is slightly less general than (8.3.39).

and thus

$$V = \frac{\mu}{R(q_1^2 + q_2^2)}\left[q_2 \frac{2J_1}{3J_2} - q_1\sqrt{\frac{2}{3J_2}}\right]. \tag{8.3.40}$$

J_2, the coefficient of P_2, represents the governing oblateness term. J_1 is the coefficient of P_1, representing an asymmetry about the equatorial plane. It does not usually appear in expressions for the geopotential but was retained by Vinti as a partial (empirical) compensation for the absence of P_3, the "pear shape," from (8.3.39). Further details on his selection of numerical values for the coefficients of V are given in [11].

We may now proceed to separate the Hamilton-Jacobi equation. Using (8.3.38) and (8.3.40) in (8.3.35), we may reduce the latter to

$$(q_1^2 + 1)\left(\frac{dS_1}{dq_1}\right)^2 - \frac{\alpha_3^2}{(q_1^2 + 1)} - \mu R\sqrt{6J_2}\, q_1 - 3\alpha_1 R^2 J_2 q_1^2$$

$$= (q_2^2 - 1)\left(\frac{dS_2}{dq_2}\right)^2 + \frac{\alpha_3^2}{(q_2^2 - 1)} - 2\mu R J_1 q_2 + 3\alpha_1 R^2 J_2 q_2^2 = -\alpha_2^2, \tag{8.3.41}$$

where α_2 is the constant of separation. Developing the quadratures for S_1 and S_2 and substituting into (8.3.36) we ultimately get

$$S = \pm \int\left[\alpha_3^2 + (q_1^2 + 1)\left(-\alpha_2^2 + \mu R\sqrt{6J_2}\, q_1 + 3\alpha_1 R^2 J_2 q_1^2\right)\right]^{1/2} \frac{dq_1}{q_1^2 + 1}$$

$$\pm \int\left[-\alpha_3^2 + (1 - q_2^2)\left(\alpha_2^2 - 2\mu R J_1 q_2 + 3\alpha_1 R^2 J_2 q_2^2\right)\right]^{1/2} \frac{dq_2}{1 - q_2^2}$$

$$+ \alpha_3 q_3 - \alpha_1 t. \tag{8.3.42}$$

By virtue of (8.2.37) and (8.3.33) the algebraic signs in front of the quadratures in (8.3.42) must follow from the signs of $\dot{q}_1$ and $\dot{q}_2$ encountered in the interval of integration. Limits have been omitted from the integral signs for simplicity, though it is implied in each case that the lower and upper limits in terms of q_1 and q_2 would correspond to the initial and terminal points of the trajectory under consideration.

As in Section 3.1 we obtain the new coordinates through $\tilde{q}_i = \beta_i = \partial S/\partial\alpha_i$, or

$$\beta_1 = -t \pm \tfrac{3}{2}R^2 J_2 \int \frac{q_1^2 dq_1}{Q_1} \pm \tfrac{3}{2}R^2 J_2 \int \frac{q_2^2 dq_2}{Q_2}, \tag{8.3.43}$$

$$\beta_2 = \mp \alpha_2 \int \frac{dq_1}{Q_1} \pm \alpha_2 \int \frac{dq_2}{Q_2}, \tag{8.3.44}$$

$$\beta_3 = \pm \alpha_3 \int \frac{dq_1}{(q_1^2 + 1)Q_1} \mp \alpha_3 \int \frac{dq_2}{(1 - q_2^2)Q_2} + q_3, \tag{8.3.45}$$

where, for convenience, we have written

$$Q_1 = \left[\alpha_3^2 + (q_1^2 + 1)(-\alpha_2^2 + \mu R\sqrt{6J_2}\, q_1 + 3\alpha_1 R^2 J_2 q_1^2)\right]^{1/2},$$

$$Q_2 = \left[-\alpha_3^2 + (1 - q_2^2)(\alpha_2^2 - 2\mu R\, J_1\, q_2 + 3\alpha_1 R^2 J_2 q_2^2)\right]^{1/2}, \qquad (8.3.46)$$

and the limits of integration are implied as before.

To evaluate the constants of motion, we can proceed as in Section 3.1. In this case, the α_i can be related to initial conditions through (8.2.37), (8.3.33), and (8.3.42); we would most likely have first to find the connection between q_i, $\dot{q}_i$ and the more familiar variables using (8.3.30). The constants β_i would follow from (8.3.43) to (8.3.45) with q_i set to their initial values. Then the inversion of these equations to obtain, in terms of α_i, β_i, and t, the coordinates q_i, and hence x, y, z would complete the solution.

Recalling that α_1 and α_3 represent the constant energy and polar angular momentum respectively, as in the Kepler problem, we must expect that α_2 would have no such simple interpretation since the total angular momentum undergoes periodic variations for inclined orbits in the oblate potential field. However, the invariant α_2 does bear a relation to the momentum vector—one which is appropriate to the spheroidal coordinate system. Its exact nature and connection with the Kepler problem (if J_1 and J_2 are allowed to approach zero) becomes evident from a detailed treatment of the initial conditions. The same is true for the β_i. The interpretation of these constants of motion hinges on the fact that Q_1 and Q_2 must permit factorization for (8.3.43) to (8.3.45) to admit closed-form solutions, by elliptic integrals. For actual ephemeris calculations this approach may be preferable to the *ad hoc* series expansions and changes of variables employed in reference [11].

When it comes to examining the merits of Vinti's method, one should keep in mind that it provides a solution incorporating somewhat more than first-order effects and may serve as basis for higher-order perturbations. Thus, its overall effectiveness should really be judged in the context of a second- or third-order analysis. Of course, there are other approaches to the satellite problem which aim for higher-order separable Hamiltonians. Sterne and Garfinkel have sought geopotentials leading to modifications of the Kepler problem that allow for the governing secular effects of the earth's asphericity [14, 15]. While proceeding in a way that preserves separability of the Hamiltonian, they seek closed-form solutions that may serve as "intermediary" orbits for further analysis. These solutions represent elliptic motion in a slowly-moving coordinate frame and are equivalent to the Lindstedt approach mentioned in Chapter 5. Since the resulting orbits are described by *mean elements* rather than osculating elements they do not yield instantaneous satellite position and velocity as conveniently as the variation-of-parameters solutions of Chapter 6. But, if used as the basis for a more complete theory, they lead to periodic terms of smaller amplitudes than does a set of osculating elements. Another analysis in this category is that by Mersman [16]; it is written in terms of the radius, argument of latitude, nodal angle, radial velocity, total angular momentum, and polar angular momentum, which can be shown to constitute a canonic set of variables.

4. THE PERTURBATION APPROACH AND THE HAMILTON-JACOBI METHOD

In Section 3 we gave examples of cases where all variables could be made cyclic. This does not happen often; in most cases, the forces acting do not allow us to choose a coordinate system in which the Hamilton-Jacobi equation is separable. However, it may be possible to proceed by a succession of canonical transformations, each taking a progressively higher-order effect into account. Suppose one has a Hamiltonian divisible as follows,

$$\mathscr{H}(q_i, p_i, t) = \mathscr{H}_0(q_i, p_i, t) + \tilde{\mathscr{H}}_i(q_i, p_i, t), \tag{8.4.1}$$

where $\mathscr{H}_0$ is that part whose coordinates can be made ignorable by a suitable transformation. In such a case, Eq. (8.2.24) may be written

$$\mathscr{H}^* = \mathscr{H}_0 + \tilde{\mathscr{H}}_1 + \frac{\partial S}{\partial t}. \tag{8.4.2}$$

Let this be divided into

$$\mathscr{H}_0\left(q_i, \frac{\partial S}{\partial q_i}, t\right) + \frac{\partial}{\partial t} S(q_i, p_i', t) = 0, \tag{8.4.3}$$

which is of the Hamilton-Jacobi type for the desired transformation, and

$$\mathscr{H}^*(q_i', p_i', t) = \tilde{\mathscr{H}}_1.$$

Thus, the new Hamiltonian is now not zero but $\tilde{\mathscr{H}}_1$ expressed in the new variables. Of course, Hamilton's equations still apply, so that here

$$\dot{q}_i' = \partial\tilde{\mathscr{H}}_1/\partial p_i', \qquad \dot{p}_i' = -\,\partial\tilde{\mathscr{H}}_1/\partial q_i'; \tag{8.4.4}$$

where, in general, we shall not find q_i' and p_i' to be constants. In practice, it is, however, convenient to solve (8.4.3), treating q_i' and p_i' as if they were constants β_i, α_i, which they would be if $\tilde{\mathscr{H}}_1$ vanished. Then, turning to (8.4.4), one considers the q_i', p_i' as time dependent functions $\beta_i(t)$ and $\alpha_i(t)$ that must satisfy these perturbation equations. This rationale is somewhat analogous to the variation-of-parameters method of Chapter 6 and is explained more fully in Appendix F. As far as solving (8.4.4) is concerned, the idea is that $\tilde{\mathscr{H}}_1$ can lead to still another transformation, perhaps by dividing it: $\tilde{\mathscr{H}}_1 = \mathscr{H}_1 + \tilde{\mathscr{H}}_2$, etc., until an adequate solution is obtained.

The applicability of this approach to perturbation problems should now be obvious: $\mathscr{H}_1$, $\mathscr{H}_2$, $\mathscr{H}_3 \ldots$ can be considered to represent non-Keplerian effects (of progressively longer periods) to successively higher orders of accuracy. In orbital mechanics, $\mathscr{H}_0$ may be represented by (8.3.14), or (8.3.34) with (8.3.40), and $\tilde{\mathscr{H}}_1$ by some perturbing potential. If $\mathscr{H}_0$ is the Hamiltonian of the Kepler problem, one would be tempted to use

$$q_1' = -\tau, \quad p_1' = -\mu/2a, \qquad q_2' = \omega, \quad p_2' = \sqrt{\mu a(1-e^2)},$$
$$q_3' = \Omega, \quad p_3' = \sqrt{\mu a(1-e^2)}\cos i, \tag{8.4.5}$$

as in Section 3.1. These coordinates have seen some use in celestial mechanics; we shall consider them and a few related ones in the following section.

4.1. The Delaunay Variables

In the first place, the coordinate-momentum set given by (8.4.5) is not without drawbacks. The situation here for q_1' is similar to that found with τ in Lagrange's planetary equations (cf. Chapter 6) and the remedy is the same, to change variables to the mean anomaly. (In regard to this quantity, it has been traditional to designate it by the letter l when dealing with canonic transformations; since little confusion can result from this shift of notation, let us do so). Thus we seek to modify one of the variables in a specified way and need to find the complementary changes in the others, as well as in the Hamiltonian itself. This is indeed typical employment for generating functions, as discussed with (8.2.22) to (8.2.24). A reasonable form to assume for S is

$$S = -\sum_{i=1}^{3} p_i' q_i', \tag{8.4.6}$$

with q_i' and p_i' as given in (8.4.5), but where we let the q_i' be expressed in terms of the new coordinates $\tilde{q}_i$ to achieve a mixed form. Let us denote the latter by l, g, h and define them by suitable relations with the old set. Thus,

$$l = n(t-\tau) = n(t+q_1') = \left(\frac{\mu}{a^3}\right)^{1/2}(t+q_1'). \tag{8.4.7}$$

Utilizing the expression for p_1' from (8.4.5), this yields

$$q_1' = \mu l(-2p_1')^{-3/2} - t. \tag{8.4.8}$$

Since there is no compelling reason to change the other two coordinates, we let

$$q_2' = g = \omega \qquad \text{and} \qquad q_3' = h = \Omega. \tag{8.4.9}$$

We are now in a position to write (8.4.6) in the desired mixed form, but we observe that the relations (8.2.29) must apply (note that the primed quantities are here the "old" variables). Consequently, we obtain

$$S = -\mu(-2p_1')^{-1/2}l + p_1't - p_2'g - p_3'h, \tag{8.4.10}$$

where a factor of -2 was applied to the first term in order to satisfy $q'_1 = -\partial S/\partial p'_1$. The existence of this generating function indicates that we have found a canonic transformation incorporating (8.4.7). We can use it now to find the new momenta, which we designate L, G, H, and the new Hamiltonian. Thus,

$$L = -\partial S/\partial l = \mu(-2p'_1)^{-1/2} = \sqrt{\mu a}, \quad G = -\partial S/\partial g = p'_2, \quad H = -\partial S/\partial h = p'_3, \tag{8.4.11}$$

and

$$\mathscr{H}^* = \mathscr{H} + \partial S/\partial t = \mathscr{H} + p'_1 = \mathscr{H} - \mu^2/2L^2. \tag{8.4.12}$$

The new set defined by (8.4.7), (8.4.9), and (8.4.11), where only l, L differ from q'_i, p'_i, is known as the *Delaunay variables*. To summarize:

$$\begin{aligned} l &= \sqrt{\frac{\mu}{a}}(t - \tau), & L &= \sqrt{\mu a}, \\ g &= \omega, & G &= \sqrt{\mu a(1 - e^2)} \\ h &= \Omega, & H &= \sqrt{\mu a(1 - e^2)} \cos i, \end{aligned} \tag{8.4.13}$$

where the equations of motion are

$$\dot{z} = \partial \mathscr{H}^*/\partial Z, \qquad \dot{Z} = -\partial \mathscr{H}^*/\partial z; \tag{8.4.14}$$

z being any of the coordinates (l, g, h) and Z the conjugate momentum.

Several combinations and variations of the Delaunay set have also been used. The more popular ones are: the modified Delaunay set

$$\begin{aligned} l_1 &= l + g + h, & L_1 &= L, \\ g_1 &= g + h, & G_1 &= G - L, \\ h_1 &= h, & H_1 &= H - G; \end{aligned} \tag{8.4.15}$$

the Poincaré variables

$$\begin{aligned} l_2 &= l + g + h, & L_2 &= L, \\ g_2 &= \sqrt{2(L - G)} \cos(g + h), & G_2 &= \sqrt{2(L - G)} \sin(g + h), \\ h_2 &= \sqrt{2(G - H)} \cos h, & H_2 &= \sqrt{2(G - H)} \sin h; \end{aligned} \tag{8.4.16}$$

and what we may call the Brouwer set

$$\begin{aligned} l_3 &= l, & L_3 &= L - G, \\ g_3 &= g + l, & G_3 &= G - H, \\ h_3 &= h + l + g, & H_3 &= H. \end{aligned} \tag{8.4.17}$$

They are obtained by manipulations similar to that shown above.

The various sets of canonic variables we have listed are those most frequently employed in astronomical perturbation methods. They can be used to express the zero-order Hamiltonian in a simple form and the higher-order effects in an iterative fashion. One fact stands out: every one of the systems (8.4.13) to (8.4.17) contains the mean anomaly, and hence the time, in one of its variables. Any connection between these systems and various angular arguments appearing in a typical disturbing function involves Kepler's equation. The formal difficulties raised by this transcendental relation were circumvented in Chapters 5 and 6 by shifting to one of the anomalies as independent variable. To a limited extent this can also be done in canonic perturbation methods, but by and large, if the time is retained as independent variable, one is forced to introduce, for $\mathscr{H}$ and S, series expansions over and above those already necessary to accommodate various higher-order perturbation effects. This raises serious questions regarding the interpretation and the computing efficiency of such schemes, particularly in comparison with those of Chapters 5 and 6. More will be said about this later.

Besides the complications caused by appearance of the mean anomaly in the coordinates, we must take account of the fact that the time may appear explicitly in the Hamiltonian, through the perturbing potential. This can be due, for example, to motion of a perturbing body or to seasonal changes in solar and atmospheric conditions. It means that the Hamiltonian is $\mathscr{H} = \mathscr{H}(q_i, p_i, \nu t)$, where ν represents some scale factor or frequency assigned to the time by the physical model. A simple way to recover the autonomous form of a canonic system under these circumstances is to count the quantity νt as if it were another canonic variable, say k. We thus augment the original set of variables—for example, the three pairs (l, L), (g, G), (h, H), by a fourth pair (k, K), and we wish all to satisfy equations like (8.4.14). Obviously, we must also augment the Hamiltonian $\mathscr{H}$ in some way so that, for the new Hamiltonian $\hat{\mathscr{H}}$,

$$\dot{k} = \partial \hat{\mathscr{H}}/\partial K, \qquad \dot{K} = -\partial \hat{\mathscr{H}}/\partial k. \tag{8.4.18}$$

Now if

$$k \equiv \nu t, \tag{8.4.19}$$

then $\dot{k} = \nu$. Thus, we desire $\partial \hat{\mathscr{H}}/\partial K = \nu$; this can be obtained if

$$\hat{\mathscr{H}} = \mathscr{H} + \nu K, \tag{8.4.20}$$

since $\mathscr{H}$ does not, by assumption, depend on K. Hence

$$\dot{k} = \partial \hat{\mathscr{H}}/\partial K = \nu, \tag{8.4.21}$$

as stipulated. It remains to identify K, and we can use the second of (8.4.18) for this purpose. From it we can find K and then $\hat{\mathscr{H}}$. Thus, a small amount of additional work allows us to treat Hamiltonians containing the time without further distinction.

4.2. The Method of Delaunay

We have stated that, because of the appearance of the mean anomaly in every one of the classical sets of canonic variables, we are forced to expansions, not only to accommodate powers of the perturbation parameter, but also to allow for the transcendental nature of the coordinate-time relation. As we have seen in Chapter 2, the classical way to accomplish this is to expand about the eccentricity, or, in Delaunay variable terms, the quantity $1 - G^2/L^2$. The ability to divide the Hamiltonian as discussed earlier in this section, treating each term, one at a time, by a succession of canonic transformations, is thus an asset in handling the resulting series.

A systematic procedure for isolating the parts of $\mathscr{H}$ and generating the suitable transformation at each step was introduced by Delaunay. Since this technique is adequately covered in the literature [16, 17, 18], involves unwieldy expansions, and can be thought of as a special case of the von Zeipel method explained in the next section, we will not treat it here in detail. Suffice it to say that the starting point is a Hamiltonian expressed in the variables (8.4.13), or a corresponding set, and expanded into a trigonometric series whose arguments are linear combinations of the angle variables and whose coefficients may be classified by some order $0(\kappa_1^n, \kappa_2^m \ldots e^s)$ where $\kappa_1, \kappa_2 \ldots$ are perturbation parameters and e is some other small quantity, such as the eccentricity. The method then involves a sequence of canonic transformations such that each new Hamiltonian lacks one of the terms (presumably the most significant one) in its predecessor. After any one of these transformations we could choose to accept the degree of approximation that has been accomplished and neglect the remaining higher-order periodic terms in the Hamiltonian. The latter would be a function only of the latest set of action variables and these would be constants with their conjugate angle variables linear functions of time. This procedure follows the general rationale outlined in the previous section and the ultimate goal is to produce a Hamiltonian which contains no terms to a specified order of approximation. As must be expected, the real difficulty arises in finding the formal relation between the last set of variables and the first one. We will see something of this in Section 5.

5. THE METHOD OF VON ZEIPEL

While Delaunay used a procedure that eliminated one term at a time from the Hamiltonian, the technique devised by von Zeipel [19] can cope with several terms in one transformation. In some cases, it will eliminate all relevant terms in one operation; in others, it is more appropriate to distinguish between terms whose periods are of different lengths and to treat them separately. This will be discussed here in some detail (even though the method involves the lengthy periodic expansions we have so far avoided). We do this not only for the sake of the method itself, but also because its thorough appreciation is necessary for understanding the formal genesis of "small divisors" connected with various resonance conditions and what has come to be known as the "critical inclination" [20].

5.1. The Basic von Zeipel Technique

We consider first the fundamental rationale of the von Zeipel method; later some special situations will be examined in detail. We shall use the notation L_i, l_i ($i = 1, \ldots, 4$) for the action and angle variables, presuming their augmentation by the time and its conjugate. The method proceeds from the expanded Hamiltonian

$$\mathscr{H} = \sum_j \left\{ \kappa^j \left[\sum_k C_{kj}(L_i) \cos\left(\sum_i p_{kji} l_i \right) \right] \right\}, \tag{8.5.1}$$

where the $C_k(L_i)$ are the coefficients of the elliptic expansion, usually equivalent to powers of the eccentricity, and the p_{ki} are integers introduced by the appropriate trigonometric identities relating f, ω, Ω, and vt to l_1, l_2, l_3, l_4 and also arising in the conversion of powers of trigonometric functions to multiple arguments in the derivation of $\mathscr{H}$. For the sake of compactness we shall write (8.5.1) as

$$\mathscr{H} = \mathscr{H}_0 + \mathscr{H}_1 + \mathscr{H}_2 + \cdots, \tag{8.5.2}$$

where the subscript indicates the order j of each term.

The Hamilton-Jacobi equation in the present circumstance is

$$\mathscr{H}(l_i, \partial S/\partial l_i) = \mathscr{H}^*, \tag{8.5.3}$$

since any additional term of the form $\partial S/\partial t$ is absorbed in $\mathscr{H}$ when using the augmented system of variables. As regards the form of $\mathscr{H}^*$ in (8.5.3), clearly setting $\mathscr{H}^* = 0$ is too ambitious; von Zeipel settles for

$$\mathscr{H}^* = \mathscr{H}^*(L'_i), \tag{8.5.4}$$

where the L'_i are the new action variables, to be determined by the transformation. Equation (8.5.4) leads immediately to $L'_i = \text{const}$ ($\dot{L}'_i = -\partial\mathscr{H}^*/\partial l'_i = 0$) and thus to $\mathscr{H}^*$ also being constant. Then, from

$$l'_i = \partial\mathscr{H}^*/\partial L'_i = \text{const}, \tag{8.5.5}$$

we have the l'_i as simple linear functions of time.

Equation (8.5.3) implies that

$$S = S(L'_i, l_i), \tag{8.5.6}$$

and

$$L_i = \partial S/\partial l_i, \qquad l'_i = \partial S/\partial L'_i. \tag{8.5.7}$$

Now we assume that the generating function can be written as a trigonometric series arranged according to $0(\kappa^j)$ corresponding to (8.5.2):

$$S = S_0 + S_1 + S_2 + \cdots + S_n. \tag{8.5.8}$$

This assumption is plausible from an inspection of (8.5.3) where S must have the facility to compensate at each $0(\kappa^j)$ for the periodic terms introduced into the equation by $\mathscr{H}$ but which are not to propagate into the new Hamiltonian $\mathscr{H}^*$. (This equation also shows that we would have to provide for time dependence in S only if $\partial\mathscr{H}/\partial t \neq 0$.) It must be emphasized that the series form of S is being assumed pragmatically; its justification usually derives from the perturbation procedure that it makes possible. However, the existence and uniqueness of S, and its convergence properties for various classes of problems, are by no means beyond doubt [21].

In order to put (8.5.3) into a useful form, we note that (8.5.8) and the first of (8.5.7) yield

$$L_i = \frac{\partial S}{\partial l_i}\left(L'_i, l_i\right) = \frac{\partial S_0}{\partial l_i} + \frac{\partial S_1}{\partial l_i} + \frac{\partial S_2}{\partial l_i} + \cdots + \frac{\partial S_n}{\partial l_i}. \tag{8.5.9}$$

If we take

$$S_0(L'_i, l_i) = \sum_i L'_i l_i, \tag{8.5.10}$$

this becomes

$$L_i = L'_i + \frac{\partial S_1}{\partial l_i} + \frac{\partial S_2}{\partial l_i} + \cdots + \frac{\partial S_n}{\partial l_i};$$

similarly, (8.5.11)

$$l'_i = l_i + \frac{\partial S_1}{\partial L'_i} + \frac{\partial S_2}{\partial L'_i} + \cdots + \frac{\partial S_n}{\partial L'_i}.$$

In view of these, the proposed transformation reduces to the identity transformation for $\kappa = 0$, as it should, and then $\mathscr{H}^* = \mathscr{H}_0$. For $\kappa \neq 0$, we must have

$$\mathscr{H}^*(L'_i) = \mathscr{H}^*_0(L'_i) + \mathscr{H}^*_1(L'_i) + \mathscr{H}^*_2(L'_i) + \cdots \tag{8.5.12}$$

The basic concept of the von Zeipel method can now be explained. The Hamilton-Jacobi equation (8.5.3) is to be expanded in powers of κ which arise not only from the perturbing potential itself but also from the series (8.5.9), which represents the $\partial S/\partial l_i$. Utilizing (8.5.12), the Hamilton-Jacobi equation can be separated by $0(\kappa^j)$ and the choice of the $\mathscr{H}^*_j$ becomes obvious when L'_i is substituted for $\partial S_0/\partial l_i$ since $\mathscr{H}^*$ can, by hypothesis, contain only the L'_i. Then, if the S_j can be found, the exact forms of the l_i and the L_i follow from (8.5.11). Finally the values of the L'_i and the integration constants arising in l'_i according to (8.5.5) are determined by applying initial conditions to (8.5.11) in a fashion similar to the procedure connected with (8.2.37) and (8.2.38).

To carry this out in detail, we utilize a Taylor expansion about $\partial S_0/\partial l_i$, of $\mathscr{H}(l_i, \partial S/\partial l_i)$ in (8.5.3). Selecting a term of order j to begin with, we obtain

$$\mathscr{H}_j = \mathscr{H}_j(l_i, L'_i) + \sum_i \left[\left(\frac{\partial \mathscr{H}_j}{\partial L'_i}\right)\left(\frac{\partial S_1}{\partial l_i} + \frac{\partial S_2}{\partial l_i} + \cdots\right)\right]$$

$$+ \tfrac{1}{2}\sum_{i,j}\left[\left(\frac{\partial^2 \mathscr{H}_j}{\partial L'_i \partial L'_j}\right)\left(\frac{\partial S_1}{\partial l_i} + \cdots\right)\left(\frac{\partial S_1}{\partial l_j} + \cdots\right)\right] + \cdots, \qquad (8.5.13)$$

where we have used $\partial S_0/\partial l_i = L_i$ and the partial derivatives of $\mathscr{H}_j$ are understood to mean $(\partial \mathscr{H}_j/\partial L_i)_{L_i = L'_i}$. Note that the first term on the right-hand side of (8.5.13) is $0(\kappa^j)$, but that the leading product in the first sum is $0(\kappa^{j+1})$ since S_1 is of order κ. Likewise, succeeding terms of higher orders can be recognized. Thus, to second order, (8.5.3) becomes

$$\mathscr{H}_0(L'_i) + \sum_i \left(\frac{\partial \mathscr{H}_0}{\partial L'_i}\right)\cdot\left(\frac{\partial S_1}{\partial l_i} + \frac{\partial S_2}{\partial l_i}\right) + \tfrac{1}{2}\sum_{i,j}\left(\frac{\partial^2 \mathscr{H}_0}{\partial L'_i \partial L'_j}\right)\left(\frac{\partial S_1}{\partial l_i}\,\frac{\partial S_1}{\partial l_j}\right)$$

$$+ \mathscr{H}_1(l_i, L'_i) + \sum_i \left(\frac{\partial \mathscr{H}_1}{\partial L'_i}\right)\left(\frac{\partial S_1}{\partial l_i}\right) + \mathscr{H}_2(l_i, L'_i)$$

$$= \mathscr{H}_0^*(L'_i) + \mathscr{H}_1^*(L'_i) + \mathscr{H}_2^*(L'_i), \qquad (8.5.14)$$

where we have assumed $\mathscr{H}_0$ does not contain the l_i, as is the case with Keplerian motion.

Equating terms, as usual, of equal orders, we have immediately

$$\mathscr{H}_0(L'_i) = \mathscr{H}_0^*(L'_i), \qquad (8.5.15)$$

which serves to define the zero-order term of the new Hamiltonian. The first order parts of (8.5.14) yield

$$\sum_i \left(\frac{\partial \mathscr{H}_0}{\partial L'_i}\right)\left(\frac{\partial S_1}{\partial l_i}\right) + \mathscr{H}_1(l_i, L'_i) = \mathscr{H}_1^*(L'_i), \qquad (8.5.16)$$

and, finally, the remaining terms lead to

$$\sum_i \left(\frac{\partial \mathscr{H}_0}{\partial L'_i}\right)\left(\frac{\partial S_2}{\partial l_i}\right) + \tfrac{1}{2}\sum_{i,j}\left(\frac{\partial^2 \mathscr{H}_0}{\partial L'_i \partial L'_j}\right)\left(\frac{\partial S_1}{\partial l_i}\,\frac{\partial S_1}{\partial l_j}\right)$$

$$+ \sum_i \left(\frac{\partial \mathscr{H}_1}{\partial L'_i}\right)\left(\frac{\partial S_1}{\partial l_i}\right) + \mathscr{H}_2(l_i, L'_i) = \mathscr{H}_2^*(L'_i). \qquad (8.5.17)$$

To obtain the solution of (8.5.16) let us assume that we write the secular part of $\mathscr{H}_1$ (which is independent of the l_1) as $\bar{\mathscr{H}}_1(L_i')$; the periodic part will be given as

$$\hat{\mathscr{H}}_1(l_i, L_i = L_i') = \kappa \sum_k C_k(L_i') \cos\left(\sum_i p_{ki} l_i\right); \tag{8.5.18}$$

according to (8.5.1), where we have omitted the subscript $j = 1$ for simplicity. Since $\mathscr{H}_1^*$ contains only the L_i', we can take

$$\mathscr{H}_1^*(L_i') = \bar{\mathscr{H}}_1(L_i'), \tag{8.5.19}$$

and thus S_1 must satisfy

$$\sum_i \left(\frac{\partial \mathscr{H}_0}{\partial L_i'}\right)\left(\frac{\partial S_1}{\partial l_i}\right) = -\hat{\mathscr{H}}_1(l_i, L_i'). \tag{8.5.20}$$

Using (8.5.18), we see that this has a solution of the form,

$$S_1 = -\kappa \sum_k \frac{C_k(L_i') \sin\left(\sum_i p_{ki} l_i\right)}{\sum_i p_{ki}(\partial \mathscr{H}_0/\partial L_i')} + s_1; \tag{8.5.21}$$

where s_1 is an undetermined function which arises if partial derivatives of S_1 with respect to some of the l_i do not appear in (8.5.20). Such a condition usually arises in orbital mechanics because $\mathscr{H}_0$ is only a function of $L(=\sqrt{\mu a}$, see Eq. (8.4.13)), or L and K, and hence the terms on the left-hand side of (8.5.20) do not involve $\partial S_1/\partial g$ and $\partial S_1/\partial h$. The appearance of s_1 as an arbitrary quantity offers a degree of freedom to the solution, since we could have, e.g., in $G = G' + \partial S/\partial g$, a term $\partial s_1/\partial g$. This is utilized in several more recent extensions of the method but is avoided in the standard von Zeipel application by arbitrarily setting s_1 equal to zero. We notice in passing that representing the right-hand side of (8.5.20) entirely by trigonometric terms makes it very simple to accommodate more than one partial derivative of S_1 on the left. Thus, the series expansion of the Hamiltonian offers a practicable approach to the solution of partial differential equations such as (8.5.20), which could otherwise be rather difficult.

Turning now to (8.5.17), we observe that the last three terms on the left-hand side are known and, in general, contain both secular and periodic components. Let us define two functions, $\bar{\varphi}$ and $\hat{\varphi}$, by

$$\bar{\varphi}(L_i') + \hat{\varphi}(l_i, L_i') \equiv \frac{1}{2}\sum_{i,j}\left(\frac{\partial^2 \mathscr{H}_0}{\partial L_i' \partial L_j'}\right)\left(\frac{\partial S_1}{\partial l_i}\frac{\partial S_1}{\partial l_j}\right) + \sum_i \left(\frac{\partial \mathscr{H}_1}{\partial L_i'}\right)\left(\frac{\partial S_1}{\partial l_i}\right) + \mathscr{H}_2(l_i, L_i'), \tag{8.5.22}$$

where $\bar{\varphi}$ is independent of the angle variables l_i, and $\hat{\varphi}$ consists of terms of the form given on the right-hand side of (8.5.18), but of $0(\kappa^2)$. With (8.5.22), (8.5.17) becomes

$$\sum_i \left(\frac{\partial \mathscr{H}_0}{\partial L'_i}\right)\left(\frac{\partial S_2}{\partial l_i}\right) + \bar{\varphi}(L'_i) + \hat{\varphi}(l_i, L'_i) = \mathscr{H}_2^*(L'_i); \tag{8.5.23}$$

obviously, we select

$$\mathscr{H}_2^*(L'_i) = \bar{\varphi}(L'_i), \tag{8.5.24}$$

and then S_2 has the form of (8.5.21), except being of $0(\kappa^2)$:

$$S_2 = -\kappa^2 \sum_m \frac{\Phi_m(L'_i)\sin\left(\sum_i p_{mi} l_i\right)}{\sum_i p_{mi}(\partial \mathscr{H}_0/\partial L'_i)} + s_2. \tag{8.5.25}$$

Again s_2 is taken as zero in this application of the method.

This constitutes the basic set of operations with a second-order von Zeipel technique. Reiterating the means of extracting the solution: the first of (8.5.11) used with (8.5.21) and (8.5.25) provides the $L_i = L_i(l_i, L'_i)$ from which the values for L'_i may be obtained by substituting the proper initial conditions for l_i and L_i. Next we combine (8.5.15), (8.5.19), and (8.5.24) to form $\mathscr{H}^*(L'_i)$ and obtain $\dot{l}'_i$ from (8.5.5). Integrating this and equating it to the second of (8.5.11) we have

$$l'_i = \rho'_i + \frac{\partial \mathscr{H}^*}{\partial L'_i} t = l_i + \frac{\partial S_1}{\partial L'_i} + \frac{\partial S_2}{\partial L'_i}, \tag{8.5.26}$$

where the L'_i are now known and the integration constants ρ'_i follow, once more, from the initial values of l_i. In principle, the first of (8.5.11) and (8.5.26) may be solved for $l_i = l_i(l'_i, L'_i)$ and $L_i = L_i(l'_i, L'_i)$ as an explicit solution in the original canonic variables and these, in turn, can be related to the common orbit elements or $x, y, z, \dot{x}, \dot{y}, \dot{z}, t$. In practice, such manipulations usually require numerical and iterative procedures [22].

5.2. Further Considerations of the von Zeipel Method

The technique outlined above constitutes a working procedure for some problems [cf. e.g. 19]. However, certain observations are in order here, and one in particular leads us to a frequently-employed extension of the method.

First, we note that higher-order contributions to $\mathscr{H}^*$ will occur even though no such terms are present in the original Hamiltonian as, for example, with a geopotential truncated beyond J_2. This is not a drawback but a fact to be kept in mind in selecting the order of the analysis and matching it to that of the perturbing force to be considered.

Secondly, we observe that the denominators in (8.5.21) and (8.5.25) may approach zero for certain combinations of p_{ki} and $\partial \mathscr{H}_0/\partial L'_i$. These are the so-called small divisors that result from resonance conditions arising out of (nearly) commensurate periods of the perturbed and perturbing bodies. The so-called *critical inclination* for the oblateness problem, though related to this phenomenon, involves a small divisor arising in a somewhat different manner.

Our third point requires a distinction to be made between the different l_i which appear in $\mathscr{H}(l_i, L_i)$. For preciseness, let us again specify these (together with their conjugates), essentially repeating (8.4.13):

$$\begin{aligned} l_1 &\equiv l = \sqrt{\frac{\mu}{a}}(t - \tau), \qquad & L_1 &\equiv L = \sqrt{\mu a}, \\ l_2 &\equiv g = \omega, & L_2 &\equiv G = \sqrt{\mu a(1 - e^2)}, \\ l_3 &\equiv h = \Omega, & L_3 &\equiv H = \sqrt{\mu a(1 - e^2)} \cos i, \end{aligned}$$

where, for the moment, we deal with a nonaugmented set of variables. Now l_2 and l_3 are to be considered as slowly varying quantities compared to l_1; for this reason a trigonometric term whose argument contains l_1 with or without the other angular variables is known as a short-period term; if the argument does not contain l_1 the name long-period term is applied. The reason we discriminate here is that frequently conditions develop, in the approach under discussion, that give rise to solutions in which l_1 is a multiplicative factor; these are, of course, simply secular terms, and they should no longer trouble us. However, as we have seen, there are means to avoid their explicit appearance, and the classicists have always taken advantage of such approaches. Since a full appreciation of the von Zeipel technique is impossible without discussing such an extension, we will treat it.

The conditions mentioned could arise first in dealing with (8.5.20). Suppose we divide the periodic part of $\mathscr{H}_1$, namely $\tilde{\mathscr{H}}_1(l_i, L'_i)$ of the equation referred to, into two series, one containing all short-period terms and denoted by

$$\tilde{\tilde{\mathscr{H}}}_1 = \tilde{\tilde{\mathscr{H}}}(l_1, \ldots, L'_i),$$

and the other containing only the long-period terms and denoted by $\tilde{\mathscr{H}}_1 = \tilde{\mathscr{H}}_1(l_2, \ldots, L'_i)$. Now recalling that $\mathscr{H}_0$ is a function of L_1 only (for the case being considered), (8.5.20) takes the form

$$S_1 = -\frac{1}{(\partial \mathscr{H}_0/\partial L'_1)} \int \left[\tilde{\tilde{\mathscr{H}}}_1(l_1, \ldots, L'_i) + \tilde{\mathscr{H}}_1(l_2, \ldots, L'_i) \right] dl_1.$$

This equation shows two things: If $\tilde{\mathscr{H}}_1 = 0$ we may use the original closed-form expression for $\tilde{\tilde{\mathscr{H}}}_1$ instead of its series expansion. Assuming the quadrature for S_1 is tractable in that form, it leads to a more compact result. If, on the other hand $\tilde{\mathscr{H}}_1 \neq 0$ a secular term in S_1 seems unavoidable. This gives terms of similar character in $L_2(= \partial S/\partial l_2)$ and $L_3(= \partial S/\partial l_3)$, and in relating these to a, e, and i.

Furthermore, if S_1 contains explicit secular terms, we may expect (8.5.23) to become much more difficult to handle. Even without this, we would encounter the same sort of difficulty with secular terms if the periodic function $\hat{\varphi}$ manifests short and long-period components and if, in addition, $\partial\mathscr{H}_0/\partial L'_i = 0$ for $i > 1$. To avoid this predicament, a new approach is needed.

Let us assume that indeed $\tilde{\mathscr{H}}_1(l_2, \ldots, L_i)$ vanishes but that $\tilde{\varphi}(l_2, \ldots, L_i)$ does not. Then the option usually taken is to forego the elimination of the long-period terms in the transformation of $\mathscr{H}$ to $\mathscr{H}^*$ and seek a second transformation which treats only those variables left over, i.e., we first use S to go from

$$\mathscr{H} = \overline{\mathscr{H}}_0(L_1) + \overline{\mathscr{H}}_1(L_i) + \tilde{\tilde{\mathscr{H}}}_1(l_1, \ldots, L_i) + \overline{\mathscr{H}}_2(L_i) + \tilde{\tilde{\mathscr{H}}}_2(l_1, \ldots, L_i) + \tilde{\mathscr{H}}_2(l_2, \ldots, L_i)$$

to

$$\mathscr{H}^* = \overline{\mathscr{H}}{}^*_0(L'_i) + \overline{\mathscr{H}}{}^*_1(L'_i) + \overline{\mathscr{H}}{}^*_2(L'_i) + \tilde{\mathscr{H}}{}^*_2(l_2, \ldots, L'_i),$$

where $\overline{\mathscr{H}}{}^*_0(L'_1) = \overline{\mathscr{H}}_0(L_1 = L'_1)$ as in (8.5.15), $\overline{\mathscr{H}}{}^*_1(L'_i)$ is given by (8.5.19), and $\overline{\mathscr{H}}{}^*_2 + \tilde{\mathscr{H}}{}^*_2 = \bar{\varphi} + \tilde{\varphi}$; $\tilde{\tilde{\varphi}}$ would be absorbed in S_2 according to (8.5.25). Then, another generating function, say S^*, would lead us from $\mathscr{H}^*$ to

$$\mathscr{H}^{**} = \overline{\mathscr{H}}{}^{**}_0(L''_i) + \overline{\mathscr{H}}{}^{**}_1(L''_i) + \overline{\mathscr{H}}{}^{**}_2(L''_i).$$

Note that since neither $\mathscr{H}^*$ nor $\mathscr{H}^{**}$ involve l'_1, S^* should not either. However, otherwise all proceeds as before: we take

$$S^* = \sum_{i=2} L''_i l'_i + S^*_1 + S^*_2 + \cdots, \tag{8.5.27}$$

and

$$L'_i = \frac{\partial S^*}{\partial l'_i} = L''_i + \frac{\partial S^*_1}{\partial l'_i} + \frac{\partial S^*_2}{\partial l'_i} + \cdots. \tag{8.5.28}$$

Then, the expansion of $\mathscr{H}^*$ about L''_i provides the Hamilton-Jacobi equation (to second order):

$$\begin{aligned} &\overline{\mathscr{H}}{}^*_0(L''_i) + \sum_i \left(\frac{\partial \overline{\mathscr{H}}{}^*_0}{\partial L''_i}\right)\left(\frac{\partial S^*_1}{\partial l'_i} + \frac{\partial S^*_2}{\partial l'_i}\right) + \tfrac{1}{2}\sum_{i,j}\left(\frac{\partial^2 \overline{\mathscr{H}}{}^*_0}{\partial L''_i \partial L''_j}\right)\left(\frac{\partial S^*_1}{\partial l'_i}\frac{\partial S^*_1}{\partial l'_j}\right) \\ &+ \overline{\mathscr{H}}{}^*_1(L''_i) + \sum_i \left(\frac{\partial \overline{\mathscr{H}}{}^*_1}{\partial L''_i}\right)\frac{\partial S^*_1}{\partial l'_i} + \overline{\mathscr{H}}{}^*_2(L''_i) + \tilde{\mathscr{H}}{}^*_2(l'_2, \ldots, L''_i) \\ &= \overline{\mathscr{H}}{}^{**}_0(L''_i) + \overline{\mathscr{H}}{}^{**}_1(L''_i) + \overline{\mathscr{H}}{}^{**}_2(L''_i), \end{aligned} \tag{8.5.29}$$

where again the partial derivatives of $\mathscr{H}^*$ are understood to mean

$$(\partial \overline{\mathscr{H}}{}^*_j/\partial L'_i)_{L'_i = L''_i}$$

Now the zeroth order part of (8.5.29) yields

$$\overline{\mathscr{H}}_0^*(L_i'') = \overline{\mathscr{H}}_0^{**}(L_i''). \tag{8.5.30}$$

The first-order equation is

$$\sum_i \left(\frac{\partial \overline{\mathscr{H}}_0^*}{\partial L_i''}\right)\frac{\partial S_1^*}{\partial l_i'} + \overline{\mathscr{H}}_1^*(L_i'') = \overline{\mathscr{H}}_1^{**}(L_i''). \tag{8.5.31}$$

But (8.5.15) indicates that $\partial\overline{\mathscr{H}}_0^*/\partial L_i' = (\partial\mathscr{H}_0/\partial L_i)_{L_i = L_i'}$ while one of the circumstances which led to this approach is that $\mathscr{H}_0$ be a function of L_1 only; hence $(\partial\overline{\mathscr{H}}_0^*/\partial L_i'') = 0, i > 1$. However, as noted, S^* does not contain l_1', i.e., $\partial S_1^*/\partial l_1 = 0$. Thus, (8.5.31) leads to

$$\overline{\mathscr{H}}_1^*(L_i'') = \overline{\mathscr{H}}_1^{**}(L_i''), \tag{8.5.32}$$

which defines the first-order part of $\mathscr{H}^{**}$. Finally, the second-order part of (8.5.29) is

$$\sum_{i=2}\left(\frac{\partial \overline{\mathscr{H}}_1^*}{\partial L_i''}\right)\frac{\partial S_1^*}{\partial l_1'} + \overline{\mathscr{H}}_2^*(L_i'') + \tilde{\mathscr{H}}_2^*(l_2', \ldots, L_i'') = \overline{\mathscr{H}}_2^{**}(L_i''), \tag{8.5.33}$$

where all other terms vanish for the reasons given immediately above; note that S_2^* is not involved in (8.5.33). As might be expected, we take

$$\overline{\mathscr{H}}_2^{**}(L_i'') = \overline{\mathscr{H}}_2^*(L_i''), \tag{8.5.34}$$

and obtain a solution for S_1^* similar to (8.5.21) from

$$\sum_{i=2}\left(\frac{\partial \overline{\mathscr{H}}_1^*}{\partial L_i''}\right)\frac{\partial S_1^*}{\partial l_i'} = -\tilde{\mathscr{H}}_2^*(l_2', \ldots, L_i''). \tag{8.5.35}$$

Here again small divisors may arise.

This technique may be developed to higher-order terms, though the algebraic labor soon becomes formidable. In principle one can execute manipulations analogous to those described at the end of Section 5.1 and arrive at $l_i' = l_i'(L_i'', l_i'', t)$ and $L_i' = L_i'(L_i'', l_i'', t)$. Substitution of these results into $l_i = l_i(L_i', l_i', t)$ and $L_i = L_i(L_i', l_i', t)$ finally leads to $l_i = l_i(L_i'', l_i'', t)$ and $L_i = L_i(L_i'', l_i'', t)$, etc. To summarize this approach: we employ two consecutive transformations. In the first, the short-period terms are eliminated by calculating each component S_j of the generating function from the jth order perturbation equation. In the second transformation, the long-period terms are eliminated by calculating each S_j^* from the $(j + 1)$th order perturbation equation. This approach will be useful in the analysis of oblateness effects [23, 24, 25] and has been extended to situations involving more than one perturbation parameter. As a reminder of its restrictive conditions: it applies in cases where $\overline{\mathscr{H}}_1 \equiv 0$ and $\partial\mathscr{H}_0/\partial L_i \equiv 0$ for $i > 1$ ($\partial\mathscr{H}_0/\partial l_i = 0$ always being taken for granted). These conditions may be avoided in some cases by using a separable Hamiltonian, other than the Keplerian one, as a zero-order solution, yielding a more convenient intermediary orbit [11, 20, 25]. In cases where $\tilde{\mathscr{H}}_1 \not\equiv 0$ but $\partial\mathscr{H}_0/\partial L_i' \equiv 0$ for $i > 1$ secular terms in S_1 become unavoidable by any of the techniques discussed so far and a totally different approach seems necessary. We also note that no remedies have been suggested here for the small divisors that may arise in (8.5.21), (8.5.25), etc.

In the remainder of this chapter we illustrate the techniques discussed in this section with two examples. One is the two-dimensional analysis of radiation pressure effects from a moving source; it demonstrates the case $\tilde{\mathscr{H}}_1 \neq 0$, $\partial\mathscr{H}_0/\partial L_i' \neq 0$ for $i > 1$. The other examines oblateness effects and exhibits the case $\tilde{\mathscr{H}}_1 = 0$, $\partial\mathscr{H}_0/\partial L_i' = 0$ for $i > 1$.

5.3. Illustrative Example. Radiation Pressure Effects on a Satellite Orbit*

Our intent here is to demonstrate some of the manipulations involved in applying the von Zeipel method. As stated, this treatment requires rather lengthy algebraic expressions which tend to obscure the rationale of the technique. To limit this as much as possible we shall take certain liberties with the problem statement and with the harmonic series involved; it is hoped, however, that these will not destroy the utility of the example.

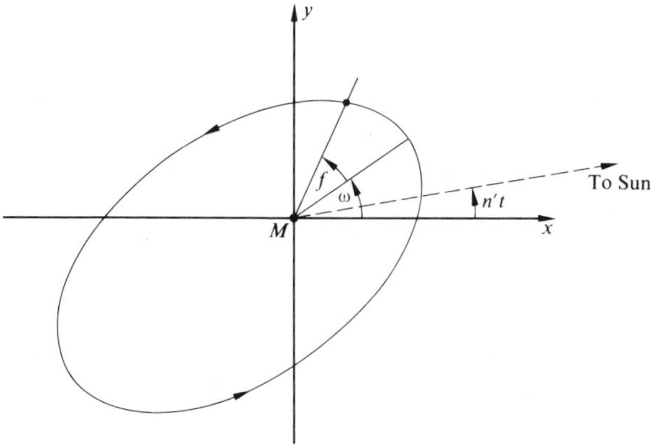

Figure 8.1

We consider a two-dimensional space with the satellite moving around a mass point, in the x, y coordinate system (see Fig. 8.1). The sun is at an angular position given by $n't$ where n' is the solar mean motion. Now the Hamiltonian for the unperturbed satellite in x, y, $p_x(= m\dot{x})$, $p_y(= m\dot{y})$ coordinates is easily seen to be

$$\mathscr{H}_0 = \frac{1}{2m}(p_x^2 + p_y^2) - \frac{\mu m}{\sqrt{x^2 + y^2}};$$

*By way of historical interest, this problem is equivalent to an analysis of the Stark effect, which served as the first occasion for an application of Hamiltonian methods in mathematical physics. The present development is somewhat related to [26].

from Section 4, this becomes

$$\mathscr{H}_0 = -\mu^2/2L_1^2, \tag{8.5.36}$$

where we use the canonic set defined in Section 5.2. Note that for the planar case under consideration $l_3(=\Omega)$ and $L_3(=\sqrt{\mu a(1-e^2)}\cos i)$ need be of no further concern.

Taking the sun at virtually infinite distance, the forces due to radiation pressure are

$$F_x = -F_p \cos n't; \qquad F_y = -F_p \sin n't, \tag{8.5.37}$$

where F_p is a constant defined in Section 3.4 of Chapter 5. According to (7.3.9) and (7.3.16), the generalized forms of (8.5.37) are

$$Q_i = F_x \frac{\partial x}{\partial l_i} + F_y \frac{\partial y}{\partial l_i}; \qquad P_i = F_x \frac{\partial x}{\partial L_i} + F_y \frac{\partial y}{\partial L_i}, \tag{8.5.38}$$

which then give rise to Hamilton's equations as expressed in (7.3.20) with the q_i there being our present l_i and the p_i being our L_i. The immediate problem is that of finding the perturbed Hamiltonian. A little consideration suggests

$$\mathscr{H} = -\mu^2/2L_1^2 + F_p(x \cos n't + y \sin n't), \tag{8.5.39}$$

where the last term has the formal appearance of a *disturbing potential* $\tilde{V}$, such that $F_x = -\partial\tilde{V}/\partial x$ and $F_y = -\partial\tilde{V}/\partial y$. Since this contains time explicitly we adopt the approach of Section 4.1 by letting $l_4 = n't$ and obtain finally*

$$\mathscr{H} = -\mu^2/2L_1^2 + n'L_4 + F_p(x \cos l_4 + y \sin l_4). \tag{8.5.40}$$

We recall that the pertinent equation for L_4 is derived from the unperturbed, augmented Hamiltonian, i.e., the first two terms on the right of (8.5.40): $\dot{L}_4 = -\partial\mathscr{H}/\partial l_4 = 0$. L_4 is an arbitrary constant and for our present discussion we assume the value of $n'L_4$ to be such that this product is of order unity rather than $0(F_p)$; this assumption is crucial to the subsequent treatment of long-period terms.

Note that we have yet to express x and y in terms of l_i, L_i. We take $x = r\cos(f+\omega)$; $y = r\sin(f+\omega)$; the third term in (8.5.40) can then be written as

$$\tilde{R} = F_p a(r/a)[\cos f \cos(l_4 - l_2) + \sin f \sin(l_4 - l_2)]. \tag{8.5.41}$$

It remains to express $(r/a)\cos f$ and $(r/a)\sin f$ in terms of l_i, L_i; this is done with the aid of Cayley's tables [27] designed for applications such as this. The tables employ various techniques for series expansions (Chapter 2 or [18]) providing, as

*In most texts on dynamical astronomy a sign change is applied to $\mathscr{H}$ before entering the series manipulations of von Zeipel's technique. Presumably, this is done to avoid carrying a minus sign in front of the Keplerian term through all that follows. We do not adopt that convention since it may cause confusion when reference is made to formulas in earlier sections.

coefficients of each harmonic term, a polynomial in e, reflecting the classic preoccupation with near-circular orbits. Cayley gives the coefficients up to e^7; we will content ourselves with carrying results to the second power of the eccentricity, sufficient to provide the reader with an inkling of the pattern and of the operosity of the method. Since certain required operations are tantamount to differentiation by e, we will start by retaining terms in e^3 where appropriate. Thus

$$\frac{r}{a}\cos f = -\tfrac{3}{2}e + (1 - \tfrac{3}{8}e^2)\cos l_1 + (\tfrac{1}{2}e - \tfrac{1}{3}e^3)\cos 2l_1 + \tfrac{3}{8}e^2\cos 3l_1 + \tfrac{1}{3}e^3\cos 4l_1,$$

and

$$\frac{r}{a}\sin f = (1 - \tfrac{5}{8}e^2)\sin l_1 + (\tfrac{1}{2}e - \tfrac{5}{12}e^3)\sin 2l_1 + \tfrac{3}{8}e^2\sin 3l_1 + \tfrac{1}{3}e^3\sin 4l_1.$$

The application of some simple trigonometric identities then allows us to write (8.5.41) as

$$\tilde{R} = F_p a \sum_{k=-2}^{4} C_k \cos\theta_k, \tag{8.5.42}$$

where

$$\theta_k = kl_1 + l_2 - l_4, \tag{8.5.43}$$

and

$$C_{-2} = e^3/24, \quad C_{-1} = e^2/8, \quad C_0 = -3e/2, \quad C_1 = 1 - e^2/2,$$
$$C_2 = e/2 - 3e^3/8, \quad C_3 = 3e^2/8, \quad C_4 = e^3/3. \tag{8.5.44}$$

The reader will observe we have retained the custom of writing a and e in (8.5.42) and (8.5.44); in the present context they are merely symbols representing

$$a = L_1^2/\mu, \qquad e^2 = 1 - L_2^2/L_1^2. \tag{8.5.45}$$

We also note that all terms in (8.5.42) fall into the short-period class except for that with the coefficient C_0.

The operations described in Section 5.1 can now be executed. We have

$$\mathscr{H}_0 = -\mu^2/2L_1^2 + n'L_4, \tag{8.5.46}$$

$$\mathscr{H}_1 = F_p\frac{L_1^2}{\mu}\left\{\frac{e^3}{24}\cos\theta_{-2} + \frac{e^2}{8}\cos\theta_{-1} - \frac{3e}{2}\cos\theta_0 + \left(1 - \frac{e^2}{2}\right)\cos\theta_1 + \left(\frac{e}{2} - \frac{3}{8}e^3\right)\cos\theta_2 + \frac{3}{8}e^2\cos\theta_3 + \frac{e^3}{3}\cos\theta_4\right\}, \tag{8.5.47}$$

with $\mathscr{H}_2 = 0$. The partial derivatives of (8.5.14) are

$$\frac{\partial\mathscr{H}_0}{\partial L_1'} = \frac{\mu^2}{L_1'^3}, \qquad \frac{\partial\mathscr{H}_0}{\partial L_4'} = n', \qquad \frac{\partial^2\mathscr{H}_0}{\partial L_1'^2} = -\frac{3\mu^2}{L_1'^4},$$

with all other partials of $\mathscr{H}_0$ vanishing, and

$$\left(\frac{\partial \mathscr{H}_1}{\partial L_1'}\right) = F_p\left\{\frac{2L_1'}{\mu}\left[\frac{e'^3}{24}\cos\theta_{-2} + \frac{e'^2}{8}\cos\theta_{-1} - \frac{3e'}{2}\cos\theta_0 + \left(1 - \frac{e'^2}{2}\right)\cos\theta_1 \right.\right.$$

$$\left. + \left(\frac{e'}{2} - \frac{3e'^3}{8}\right)\cos\theta_2 + \frac{3}{8}e'^2\cos\theta_3 + \frac{e'^3}{3}\cos\theta_4\right]$$

$$+ \frac{L_1'^2}{\mu}\frac{\partial e'}{\partial L_1'}\left[\frac{e'^2}{8}\cos\theta_{-2} + \frac{e'}{4}\cos\theta_{-1} - \frac{3}{2}\cos\theta_0 - e'\cos\theta_1\right.$$

$$\left.\left. + \left(\frac{1}{2} - \frac{9e'^2}{8}\right)\cos\theta_2 + \frac{3}{4}e'\cos\theta_3 + e'^2\cos\theta_4\right]\right\}, \tag{8.5.48}$$

$$\left(\frac{\partial \mathscr{H}_1}{\partial L_2'}\right) = F_p\frac{L_1'^2}{\mu}\frac{\partial e'}{\partial L_2'}\left[\frac{e'^2}{8}\cos\theta_{-2} + \frac{e'}{4}\cos\theta_{-1} - \frac{3}{2}\cos\theta_0 - e'\cos\theta_1\right.$$

$$\left. + \left(\frac{1}{2} - \frac{9e'^2}{8}\right)\cos\theta_2 + \frac{3}{4}e'\cos\theta_3 + e'^2\cos\theta_4\right], \tag{8.5.49}$$

where we must use the second of (8.5.45) to obtain

$$\frac{\partial e'}{\partial L_1'} = \frac{1 - e'^2}{e'L_1'}; \qquad \frac{\partial e'}{\partial L_2'} = -\frac{\sqrt{1 - e'^2}}{e'L_1'};$$

it is because of the form of these that we retained terms in e^3 in (8.5.47).

Now, *if we drop the primes* on L_i and e, (8.5.14) gives

$$-\frac{\mu^2}{2L_1^2} + n'L_4 + \left[\frac{\mu^2}{L_1^3}\left(\frac{\partial S_1}{\partial l_1} + \frac{\partial S_2}{\partial l_1}\right) + n'\left(\frac{\partial S_1}{\partial l_4} + \frac{\partial S_2}{\partial l_4}\right)\right]$$

$$-\frac{3\mu^2}{2L_1^4}\left(\frac{\partial S_1}{\partial l_1}\right)^2 + \mathscr{H}_1 + \left(\frac{\partial \mathscr{H}_1}{\partial L_1}\right)\frac{\partial S_1}{\partial l_1} + \left(\frac{\partial \mathscr{H}_1}{\partial L_2}\right)\frac{\partial S_1}{\partial l_2}$$

$$= \mathscr{H}_0^*(L_i) + \mathscr{H}_1^*(L_i) + \mathscr{H}_2^*(L_i), \tag{8.5.50}$$

where (8.5.47) to (8.5.49) are to be substituted, as appropriate.

Obviously, we choose

$$\mathscr{H}_0^*(L_i') = -\mu^2/2L_1^2 + n'L_4. \tag{8.5.51}$$

The first-order part of (8.5.50) is

$$\frac{\mu^2}{L_1^3}\frac{\partial S_1}{\partial l_1} + n'\frac{\partial S_1}{\partial l_4} + F_p\frac{L_1^2}{\mu}\left[\frac{e^3}{24}\cos\theta_{-2} + \frac{e^2}{8}\cos\theta_{-1} - \frac{3e}{2}\cos\theta_0\right.$$

$$\left. + \left(1 - \frac{e^2}{2}\right)\cos\theta_1 + \left(\frac{e}{2} - \frac{3}{8}e^3\right)\cos\theta_2 + \frac{3}{8}e^2\cos\theta_3 + \frac{e^3}{3}\cos\theta_4\right] = \mathscr{H}_1^*(L_i). \tag{8.5.52}$$

The secular part of $\mathscr{H}_1$ is nonexistent; hence

$$\mathscr{H}_1^*(L_i) = 0, \tag{8.5.53}$$

and then by (8.5.20) and (8.5.21),

$$S_1 = -F_p\frac{L_1^2}{\mu}\left\{\frac{(e^3/24)\sin\theta_{-2}}{-2\mu^2/L_1^3 - n'} + \frac{(e^2/8)\sin\theta_{-1}}{-\mu^2/L_1^3 - n'} - \frac{(3e/2)\sin\theta_0}{-n'} + \frac{(1 - e^2/2)\sin\theta_1}{\mu^2/L_1^3 - n'}\right.$$

$$\left. + \frac{(e/2 - 3e^3/8)\sin\theta_2}{2\mu^2/L_1^3 - n'} + \frac{(3e^2/8)\sin\theta_3}{3\mu^2/L_1^3 - n'} + \frac{(e^3/3)\sin\theta_4}{4\mu^2/L_1^3 - n'}\right\}, \tag{8.5.54}$$

where, as stated, we set s_1 to zero.

Proceeding now to the second-order part of (8.5.50), we obtain, with some patience and after repeated application of the trigonometric identity $\cos\alpha\cos\beta = \frac{1}{2}\cos(\alpha + \beta) + \frac{1}{2}\cos(\alpha - \beta)$, the form given in (8.5.23), namely,

$$\frac{\mu^2}{L_1^3}\frac{\partial S_2}{\partial l_1} + n'\frac{\partial S_2}{\partial l_4} + \bar{\varphi}(L_i') + \hat{\varphi}(l_i, L_i') = \mathscr{H}_2^*(L_i'). \tag{8.5.55}$$

In the present case

$$\bar{\varphi} = -F_p^2\left\{\frac{3}{2}\left[\frac{1/2 - e^2/4}{\nu_1^2} + \frac{e^2/2}{\nu_2^2}\right] - \frac{L_1^3}{\mu}\left[\frac{e^2/32}{\nu_{-1}} + \frac{9/8 - 9e^2/16}{\nu_0} - \frac{1 - e^2/4}{\nu_1}\right.\right.$$

$$\left.\left. - \frac{1/8 - e^2/32}{\nu_2} - \frac{9e^2/32}{\nu_3}\right]\right\}, \tag{8.5.56}$$

where we have set

$$\nu_k = k\frac{\mu^2}{L_1^3} - n', \tag{8.5.57}$$

and

$$\hat{\varphi} = -F_p^2\left\{\sum_{j=1}^{3} A_j(L_i')\cos jl_1 + \sum_{k=-2}^{6} B_k(L_i')\cos\alpha_k\right\}. \tag{8.5.58}$$

Here we have taken

$$\alpha_k = kl_1 + 2l_2 - 2l_4. \tag{8.5.59}$$

The coefficients of (8.5.58) are

$$A_1 = \frac{3e/2}{\nu_1\nu_2} - \frac{L_1^3}{\mu^2}\left(\frac{3e/32}{\nu_{-1}} - \frac{9e/16}{\nu_0} + \frac{29e/32}{\nu_1} + \frac{1-e^2-\sqrt{1-e^2}}{e\nu_1} - \frac{15e/16}{\nu_2} - \frac{3e/16}{\nu_3}\right),$$

$$A_2 = \frac{27e^2/16}{\nu_1\nu_3} - \frac{3e^2/16}{\nu_{-1}\nu_1} + \frac{L_1^3}{\mu^2}\left(\frac{3e^2/192}{\nu_{-2}} + \frac{3/8 - 15e^2/16}{\nu_0} + \frac{1/4}{\nu_1} + \frac{3e^2/4}{\nu_3} + \frac{e^2/4}{\nu_4}\right),$$

$$A_3 = \frac{L_1^3}{\mu^2}\left(-\frac{e/16}{\nu_{-1}} + \frac{9e/16}{\nu_0} + \frac{e/16}{\nu_2} + \frac{9e/16}{\nu_3}\right),$$

$$A_4 = \frac{L_1^3}{\mu^2}\left(-\frac{e^2/576}{\nu_{-2}} - \frac{3e^2/32}{\nu_{-1}} + \frac{3e^2/4}{\nu_0} + \frac{e^2/16}{\nu_2} + \frac{3e^2/32}{\nu_3} + \frac{3e^2/4}{\nu_4}\right),$$

$$B_{-2} = \frac{L_1^3}{\mu^2}\left(\frac{3e^2/192}{\nu_{-2}} - \frac{e^2/32}{\nu_{-1}} + \frac{3e^2/32}{\nu_0}\right),$$

$$B_{-1} = \frac{L_1^3}{\mu^2}\left(-\frac{3e/32}{\nu_{-1}} - \frac{3e/16}{\nu_0} + \frac{3e/32}{\nu_1}\right),$$

$$B_0 = -\frac{3e^2/16}{\nu_{-1}\nu_1} - \frac{L_1^3}{\mu^2}\left(\frac{7e^2/576}{\nu_{-2}} + \frac{9/8 - 5e^2/16}{\nu_0} - \frac{e^2/16}{\nu_1} + \frac{e^2/32}{\nu_2}\right),$$

$$B_1 = \frac{L_1^3}{\mu^2}\left(-\frac{e/16}{\nu_{-1}} + \frac{3e/4}{\nu_0} - \frac{15e/8}{\nu_1} + 3\,\frac{1-e^2-\sqrt{1-e^2}}{4e\nu_1} + \frac{e/16}{\nu_2}\right),$$

$$B_2 = \frac{3/4 - 3e^2/8}{\nu_1^2} - \frac{L_1^3}{\mu^2}\left(\frac{3e^2/64}{\nu_{-1}} - \frac{3/8 - 33e^2/32}{\nu_0} - \frac{1 - 19e^2/64}{\nu_1} - \frac{3/8 - 33e^2/16}{\nu_2} - \frac{3e^2/32}{\nu_3}\right),$$

$$B_3 = \frac{3e/2}{\nu_1\nu_2} + \frac{L_1^3}{\mu^2}\left(\frac{9e/16}{\nu_0} + \frac{e/2}{\nu_1} + \frac{1-e^2-\sqrt{1-e^2}}{4e\nu_1} + \frac{3e/4}{\nu_2} + \frac{9e/16}{\nu_3}\right),$$

$$B_4 = \frac{3e^2/4}{\nu_2^2} + \frac{27e^2/16}{\nu_1\nu_3} + \frac{L_1'^3}{\mu^2}\left(\frac{3e^2/4}{\nu_0} + \frac{3e^2/16}{\nu_1} + \frac{1/8 + e^2/32}{\nu_2} + \frac{3e^2/4}{\nu_3} + \frac{3e^2/4}{\nu_4}\right),$$

$$B_5 = \frac{L_1'^3}{\mu^2}\left(\frac{3e/16}{\nu_2} - \frac{3e/16}{\nu_3}\right)$$

$$B_6 = \frac{L_1'^3}{\mu^2}\left(\frac{e^2/4}{\nu_2} + \frac{9e^2/32}{\nu_3} + \frac{e^2/4}{\nu_4}\right).$$

We display these only to demonstrate their form.

From (8.5.55), we obviously choose

$$\mathscr{H}_2^*(L_i') = \bar{\varphi}, \tag{8.5.60}$$

which leaves us with

$$\frac{\mu^2}{L_1'^3}\frac{\partial S_2}{\partial l_1} + n'\frac{\partial S_2}{\partial l_4} = F_p^2\left\{\sum_j A_j \cos jl_1 + \sum_k B_k \cos(kl_1 + 2l_2 - 2l_4)\right\}.$$

Note that we have one long-period term ($k = 0$) on the right-hand side of this expression; nonetheless, it integrates in a straightforward manner because of the presence of $\partial S_2/\partial l_4$ on the left-hand side. Thus,

$$S_2 = F_p^2\left\{\sum_{j=1}^{3} \frac{A_j \sin jl_1}{j\mu^2/L_1'^3} + \sum_{k=-2}^{6} \frac{B_k \sin(kl_1 + 2l_2 - 2l_4)}{k\mu^2/L_1'^3 - 2n'}\right\}. \tag{8.5.61}$$

At this point, we remind the reader that the coefficients A_j and B_k are functions of the *primed* coordinates.

In principle, the problem we set out to solve has been completed; it remains only to clear away the details. Equations (8.5.51), (8.5.53), and (8.5.60) (suitably primed) provide us with the transformed Hamiltonian, $\mathscr{H}^*$; and the combination of (8.5.10), (8.5.54), and (8.5.61) yields the complete generating function. Using these expressions, we must now execute the process described in connection with (8.5.26). However, since a first-order rendition of this is trivial, while the second-order version involves a disproportionate amount of labor for its illustrative value, we forego the exercise here. When this aspect of the method is projected toward higher-order terms in e and F_p, the reader will agree that physical insight becomes marginal at best. In viewing this approach as a routine procedure for developing general perturbation theories of radiation-pressure effects, we stress again that the series inversions required to obtain $l_i(L_i', t)$ and $L_i(L_i', l_i', t)$ explicitly constitute a prime issue. Here is where symbolic manipulations by computer could have a decisive effect.

In closing, we make a few remarks on small divisors. First, the augmentation of the variables by l_4, L_4 so as to include n' explicitly has a marked effect on the solution. From (8.5.54) it becomes obvious that the case described by $n' = 0$ can no longer be considered as part of the results derivable from that formula but must be handled by executing the analysis without augmentation of the variables. Secondly, terms with higher powers of e introduce large multiples of l_1 in the cosine terms of (8.5.42), (8.5.54), (8.5.56), and (8.5.58) which admit denominators of the form $k\mu^2/L_1^3 - n'$, where k is an integer. Since the mean motion of an earth satellite is bound to be significantly larger than that of the sun, this combination of quantities causes no trouble. Small divisors, however, may arise in this problem with higher-order iterations of the von Zeipel procedure, where multiples of n' arise in the trigonometric terms. Then, in principle, the combination $\mu^2/L_1^3 - mn'$, with m an integer, could produce a resonance condition.

5.4. Illustrative Example. Oblateness Effects on a Satellite Orbit

We complete our discussion of the von Zeipel technique by examining the other case mentioned at the end of Section 5.2, namely, the one in which both the first-order, long period part of the disturbed Hamiltonian, $\tilde{\mathscr{H}}_1$, and the partial derivatives of $\mathscr{H}_0$ with respect to $L_i (i > 1)$ vanish. As the reader will remember, these conditions lead to the desire for a second transformation if secular terms in the solution are to be avoided, and the following illustration should contribute toward an understanding of this technique. As in the previous example, we will avoid some of the algebraic manipulations and sketch only the highlights.

The disturbing potential derived from the oblate earth is familiar to us by now

$$\tilde{V} = -(\mu J_2 R^2/2r^3)(1 - 3\sin^2\varphi'). \tag{8.5.62}$$

Using $\sin\varphi' = \sin i \sin(\omega + f)$ and the specific canonic variables adopted in Section 5.2, we have

$$\tilde{V} = -\frac{\mu^4 J_2 R^2}{4L_1^6}\left[\left(-1 + 3\frac{L_3^2}{L_2^2}\right)\frac{a^3}{r^3} + 3\left(1 - \frac{L_3^2}{L_2^2}\right)\frac{a^3}{r^3}\cos(2l_2 + 2f)\right]. \tag{8.5.63}$$

The Hamiltonian is

$$\mathscr{H} = -\mu^2/2L_1^2 + \tilde{V}, \tag{8.5.64}$$

which we need not augment with L_4 since time is not explicitly involved. If we proceed now with the usual series expansions in terms of l_1, [27] allows us to write

$$\frac{a^3}{r^3} = \frac{L_1^3}{L_2^3} + \sum_{j=1} 2P_j \cos jl_1, \tag{8.5.65}$$

and

$$\frac{a^3}{r^3}\cos(2l_2 + 2f) = \sum_{k=1} 2Q_k \cos(kl_1 + 2l_2), \tag{8.5.66}$$

where, to $0(e^3)$,

$$P_1 = \tfrac{3}{2}e + \tfrac{27}{16}e^3, \quad P_2 = \tfrac{9}{4}e^2, \quad P_3 = \tfrac{53}{16}e^3, \quad Q_1 = -\tfrac{1}{2}e + \tfrac{1}{16}e^3, \quad Q_2 = 1 - \tfrac{5}{2}e^2,$$

$$Q_3 = \tfrac{7}{2}e - \tfrac{123}{16}e^3, \quad Q_4 = \tfrac{17}{2}e^2, \quad Q_5 = \tfrac{845}{48}e^3.$$

This yields

$$\mathscr{H}_0 = -\mu^2/2L_1^2, \tag{8.5.67}$$

and

$$\mathscr{H}_1 = -\frac{\mu^4 J_2 R^2}{4L_1^6}\left[\left(-1 + 3\frac{L_3^2}{L_2^2}\right)\left(\frac{L_1^3}{L_2^3} + \sum_{j=1} 2P_j \cos jl_1\right)\right.$$

$$\left. + 3\left(1 - \frac{L_3^2}{L_2^2}\right)\sum_{k=1} 2Q_k \cos(kl_1 + 2l_2)\right]. \tag{8.5.68}$$

On the basis of these expansions we could execute the first-order transformation according to (8.5.20) and (8.5.21); but, as pointed out in Section 5.2, a case with $\tilde{\mathscr{H}}_1 = 0$ and $\partial\mathscr{H}_0/\partial l_i = 0$ for $i > 1$, such as this example, may permit a closed-form quadrature for S_1. This warrants a slight digression.

To retain $\mathscr{H}_1$ in closed form, we simply take (8.5.63) with

$$\frac{a}{r} = \frac{L_1^2}{L_3^2}\left[1 + \left(1 - \frac{L_2^2}{L_1^2}\right)^{1/2} \cos f\right].$$

Next, the Hamilton-Jacobi equation (8.5.14) yields

$$-\frac{\mu^2}{2L_1'^2} + \frac{\mu^2}{L_1'^3}\left(\frac{\partial S_1}{\partial l_1} + \frac{\partial S_2}{\partial l_1}\right) - \frac{3\mu^2}{2L_1'^4}\left(\frac{\partial S_1}{\partial l_1}\right)^2 + \mathscr{H}_1(l_i, L_i') + \sum_{i=1}^{3}\left(\frac{\partial \mathscr{H}_1}{\partial L_i'}\right)\frac{\partial S_1}{\partial l_i}$$

$$= \mathscr{H}_0^*(L_i') + \mathscr{H}_1^*(L_i') + \mathscr{H}_2^*. \tag{8.5.69}$$

Since a closed expression for $\mathscr{H}_1$ is possible only in terms of f, we anticipate that the result for S_1 will also contain this angle variable. Thus f replaces l_1 as short-period variable in this particular transformation. We must therefore represent $\partial S_1/\partial l_1$ as

$$\frac{\partial S_1}{\partial f}\frac{\partial f}{\partial l_1} = \frac{a^2 L_2'}{r^2 L_1'}\frac{\partial S_1}{\partial f}.$$

Now the zeroth order part of (8.5.69) is

$$\mathscr{H}_0^*(L_i') = -\mu^2/2L_1'^2, \tag{8.5.70}$$

which serves to define $\overline{\mathscr{H}}_0^*$; the first-order part yields

$$\mathscr{H}_1^*(L_i') = \frac{\mu^4 J_2 R^2}{4L_1^6}\left(1 - 3\frac{L_3^2}{L_2^2}\right)\frac{L_1^3}{L_2^3}, \tag{8.5.71}$$

and

$$\frac{-\mu^2 a^2 L_2'}{r^2 L_1'^4}\frac{\partial S_1}{\partial f} = \tilde{\tilde{\mathscr{H}}}_1(l_i, L_i') = \frac{\mu^4 J_2 R^2}{4L_1^6}\left(1 - 3\frac{L_3^2}{L_2^2}\right)\left(\frac{a^3}{r^3} - \frac{L_1^3}{L_2^3}\right)$$
$$- \frac{3\mu^4 J_2 R^2}{6L_1^6}\left(1 - \frac{L_3^2}{L_2^2}\right)\frac{a^3}{r^3}\cos 2(l_2 + f), \tag{8.5.72}$$

where we have dropped the primes on the right-hand sides. From (8.5.72) we obtain

$$S_1 = \frac{\mu^2 J_2 R^2}{4L_2^3}\left(1 - 3\frac{L_3^2}{L_2^2}\right)(f - l_1 + e\sin f)$$
$$- \frac{3}{2}\left(1 - \frac{L_3^2}{L_2^2}\right)\left[\sin 2(f + l_2) + e\sin(f + 2l_2) + \frac{e}{3}\sin(3f + 2l_2)\right]. \tag{8.5.73}$$

We are now in a position to write out the second-order part of (8.5.69)

$$\mathscr{H}_2^* = \frac{\mu^2}{L_1^3}\frac{\partial S_2}{\partial l_1} - \frac{3\mu^2}{2L_1^4}\left(\frac{\partial S_1}{\partial l_1}\right)^2 + \sum_{i=1}^{3}\left(\frac{\partial \mathscr{H}_1}{\partial L_i}\right)\frac{\partial S_1}{\partial l_i}$$
$$= \frac{\mu^2}{L_1^3}\frac{\partial S_2}{\partial l_1} + \bar{\varphi}(L_i) + \tilde{\tilde{\varphi}}(l_1, l_2, L_i) + \tilde{\varphi}(l_2, L_i). \tag{8.5.74}$$

Here we must realize that the partial derivatives $\partial\mathscr{H}_1/\partial L_i$ are to be formed with l_1 appearing as conjugate variable of L_1, rather than f. Thus we are forced to use the expansion (8.5.68) for this part of the Hamiltonian, which means that the entire treatment of (8.5.74) must now resort to a series development. At the end of all manipulations, we shall see that the relevant first-order terms still provide a relatively compact solution for this case, though all higher-order results emerge in greatly expanded form.

Substituting (8.5.73) in (8.5.74), executing the rather laborious manipulations, and distinguishing between the various parts of φ, we arrive at

$$\bar{\varphi}(L_i') = -\frac{\mu^6 J_2^2 R^4}{16L_1^9}\left\{A^2\sum_j\left(2P_j\frac{\partial P_j}{\partial L_1} - \frac{9}{L_1}P_j^2\right)\right.$$
$$+ B^2\sum_k\left(2Q_k\frac{\partial Q_k}{\partial L_1} + \frac{4}{k}Q_k\frac{\partial Q_k}{\partial L_2} - \frac{9}{L_1}Q_k^2\right)$$
$$\left. + B\cdot 24\frac{L_3^2}{L_2^3}\sum_k\frac{Q_k^2}{k}\right\}, \tag{8.5.75}$$

and

$$\widetilde{\varphi}(l_2, L_i') = -\frac{\mu^6 J_2^2 R^4}{16L_1'^9}\left\{2AB\sum_j\left(Q_j\frac{\partial P_j}{\partial L_1} + P_j\frac{\partial Q_j}{\partial L_1} - \frac{3}{L_1}P_jQ_j + \frac{2}{j}Q_j\frac{\partial P_j}{\partial L_2}\right)\right.$$
$$\left. - B\cdot 24\frac{L_3'^2}{L_2'^2}\sum_j\frac{1}{j}P_jQ_j\right\}\cos 2l_2, \qquad (8.5.76)$$

where the definitions to $0(e^3)$ of P_j and Q_j were given earlier. The quantities A and B are

$$A = -1 + 3\,L_3'^2/L_2'^2, \qquad B = 3(1 - L_3'^2/L_2'^2). \qquad (8.5.77)$$

The short-period part of (8.5.74) has the form

$$\tilde{\tilde{\varphi}} = -\frac{\mu^6 J_2^2 R^4}{16L_1'^9}\left\{\sum_{j=1}\Big[C_j\cos jl_1 + C_{2j}\cos 2jl_1 + C_{j2}\cos(jl_1 + 2l_2)\right.$$
$$+ C_{2j2}\cos(2jl_1 + 2l_2) + C_{2j4}\cos(2jl_1 + 4l_2)\Big]$$
$$+ \sum_{j=1}\sum_{k\neq j}\Big[C_{j+k}\cos(j+k)l_1 + C_{j-k}\cos(j-k)l_1$$
$$+ C_{j+k+2}\cos\left\langle(j+k)l_1 + 2l_2\right\rangle$$
$$+ C_{j-k-2}\cos\left\langle(j-k)l_1 - 2l_2\right\rangle$$
$$\left. + C_{j+k+4}\cos\left\langle(j+k)l_1 + 4l_2\right\rangle\Big]\right\}, \qquad (8.5.78)$$

where

$$C_j = -6\frac{L_1'^2}{L_2'^3}A^2P_j,$$

$$C_{2j} = A^2\left[2P_j\frac{\partial P_j}{\partial L_1} - \frac{9}{L_1}P_j^2\right],$$

$$C_{j2} = AB\left[4\frac{Q_j}{j} - 6\frac{L_1'^2}{L_2'^2}Q_j\right] - B\cdot 24\frac{L_1'^3L_3'^2}{L_2'^6}\frac{Q_j}{j},$$

$$C_{2j2} = AB\left[2P_j\frac{\partial Q_j}{\partial L_1} + 2Q_j\frac{\partial P_j}{\partial L_1} - \frac{6}{L_1}P_jQ_j + 4\frac{Q_j}{j}\frac{\partial P_j}{\partial L_2}\right]$$
$$+ B\cdot 24\frac{L_3'^2}{L_2'^2}Q_j\left(Q_j - \frac{P_j^2}{j}\right),$$

$$C_{2j4} = B^2\left[2Q_j\frac{\partial Q_j}{\partial L_1} - \frac{9}{L_1}Q_j^2 + 4\frac{Q_j}{j}\frac{\partial Q_j}{\partial L_2}\right],$$

$$C_{j+k} = A^2\left[2P_j\frac{\partial P_k}{\partial L_1} - \frac{9}{L_1}P_jP_k\right],$$

$$C_{j-k} = A^2\left[2P_j\frac{\partial P_k}{\partial L_1} - \frac{9}{L_1}P_jP_k\right] + B{\cdot}4\,Q_j\frac{Q_k}{k}$$

$$+ B^2\left[2Q_j\frac{\partial Q_k}{\partial L_1} - \frac{9}{L_1}Q_jQ_k + 4\frac{Q_j}{j}\frac{\partial Q_k}{\partial L_2}\right],$$

$$C_{j+k+2} = AB\left[2Q_j\frac{\partial P_k}{\partial L_1} + 2P_j\frac{\partial Q_k}{\partial L_1} - \frac{9}{L_1}P_jQ_k + 4\frac{Q_k}{k}\frac{\partial P_j}{\partial L_2}\right] - B{\cdot}4\,P_j\frac{Q_k}{k},$$

$$C_{j-k-2} = C_{j+k+2},$$

$$C_{j+k+4} = B^2\left[2Q_j\frac{\partial Q_k}{\partial L_1} - \frac{9}{L_1}Q_jQ_k + 4\frac{Q_j}{j}\frac{\partial Q_k}{\partial L_2}\right] + B{\cdot}4\,Q_j\frac{Q_k}{k}.$$

We now come to the decisive step that distinguishes this example from the previous one. Suppose, in developing the second-order transformation, we were to split (8.5.74) into

$$\mathscr{H}_2^* = \bar{\varphi}(L_i'),$$

and

$$\frac{\mu^2}{L_1'^3}\frac{\partial S_2}{\partial l_1} = -\tilde{\tilde{\varphi}}(l_1, l_2, L_1') - \tilde{\varphi}(l_2, L_i'). \tag{8.5.79}$$

It is clear that we obtain a new Hamiltonian which is a function of L_i' only; however, the second of (8.5.79) provides us with an S_2 which is a direct linear function of l_1, because of the form of $\tilde{\varphi}$. Since $L_i = L_i' + \partial S_1/\partial l_i + \partial S_2/\partial l_i + \cdots$, the second-order terms of L_2 and L_3 obtained by this option are secular in nature and, eventually, will dominate.

To avoid these explicit terms, we adopt the alternative described in Section 5.2, which completes the transformation by splitting (8.5.74) differently. Since the long-period terms are the source of trouble, let us select

$$\mathscr{H}_2^* = \bar{\varphi}(L_i') + \tilde{\varphi}(l_2, L_i'), \tag{8.5.80}$$

and

$$\frac{\mu^2}{L_1'^3}\frac{\partial S_2}{\partial l_1} = -\tilde{\tilde{\varphi}}(l_1, l_2, L_i').$$

This last leads to an S which is purely periodic so that the $L_i(=\partial S/\partial l_i)$ are also. The resulting manipulation may therefore be termed a short-period transformation in that it absorbs only (8.5.78). The details may be found in [20, 24]. The new Hamiltonian is now not a function of the L_i' only, but rather $\mathscr{H}^* = \mathscr{H}_0^*(L_i') + \mathscr{H}_1^*(L_i') + \mathscr{H}_2^*(l_2, L_i')$, where $\mathscr{H}_0^*$ is given by (8.5.70) and $\mathscr{H}_1^*$ by (8.5.71).

To eliminate the l_2-dependence in $\mathscr{H}_2^*$ we must go through another cycle, i.e., a so-called long-period transformation. So we try a new generating function,

$$S^* = \Sigma\, L_i' l_i' + S_1^* + S_2^* + \cdots$$

to take us to the desired form of the Hamiltonian, $\mathscr{H}^{**}\,(L_i')$. The procedure is that given in Section 5.2 following (8.5.28) and it serves no purpose to develop it again.

However, for the case at hand, some details are worthy of notice. While we retain $\mathscr{H}_2^{**}(L_i') = \bar{\varphi}(L_i')$, Eq. (8.5.35) becomes

$$\frac{3\mu^4 J_2 R^2}{4L_1'^3 L_2'^4}\left(-1 + 5\frac{L_3'^2}{L_2'^2}\right)\frac{dS_1^*}{dl_2} = -\,\tilde{\varphi}(l_2, L_i'). \tag{8.5.81}$$

A term involving $\partial S_1^*/\partial l_3$ plays no role in the solution. Equation (8.5.81) yields

$$S_1^* = \frac{\mu^2 J_2 R^2 (L_1''^2 - L_2''^2)\left(1 - 16\dfrac{L_3''^2}{L_2''^2} + 15\dfrac{L_3''^4}{L_2''^4}\right)\sin 2l_2'}{32 L_1''^2 L_2''^3\left(1 - 5\dfrac{L_3''^2}{L_2''^2}\right)}. \tag{8.5.82}$$

We note that this represents a first-order contribution to the solution of the oblateness problem, though it was extracted from the second-order perturbation equation. It is fortuitous with this particular disturbing function that the long-period contribution consists of a single term, which, together with the closed-form expression for short-period effects, makes for a relatively compact first-order solution. As noted, this lucky circumstance ceases to prevail with higher-order effects and the reader may get an idea of the ensuing series expansions from the literature [28].

A fundamental concern with (8.5.82) is the denominator, which becomes a "small divisor" when $5L_3''^3/L_2''^2$ approaches unity or $\cos^2 i \to 1/5$ (see also (6.3.13)). This is the well-known "critical inclination". The reader will note the different ways by which the vanishing denominators arise in (8.5.82) and (8.5.54), though mathematicians would recognize the critical inclination as well as the *bona-fide* resonance conditions of the earlier example as typical of situations where uniform convergence is lost. More powerful, asymptotic techniques must be applied to cope with these cases. Being more general, such representations can yield some insight as to which features of the formal result represent physical phenomena near the critical conditions and which are due merely to a degeneracy of the mathematical formulation.

6. CONCLUSION

In this rather summary treatment of canonical transformations, much has been left out. A variety of interesting issues, including applications of and connections between Lagrange and Poisson brackets, the structure of Jacobi's reciprocal relations, and notions of infinitesimal transformations, have been omitted.

Insofar as orbital equations are concerned, we have seen that the bulk of activity in this line has consisted of iterative perturbation procedures, outside of the relatively limited applications of Hamilton-Jacobi techniques to problems with separable Hamiltonians. The canonical perturbation procedures require a series expansion of the disturbing function before it is usable in the Delaunay or von Zeipel techniques. But that does not discriminate solely against these methods since no other approach can handle such problems in closed form either. A point in their favor is that once the Hamiltonian has been expanded, they reduce essentially to series manipulations (multiplications, inversions, and contractions) as encountered in writing out the integrands for higher-order generating functions and inverting the results of successive transformations toward the ultimate, explicit solution. The quadratures leading to $S_1, S_2, \ldots S_n$ are trivial since they involve only sums of trigonometric functions, which is often the only form in which the governing partial differential equations can be solved. This state of affairs does not change if the original Hamiltonian consists of terms representing several interacting physical perturbations, e.g., a sum of the disturbing functions for oblateness and radiation pressure. The algebraic manipulations are straightforward (in fact extremely monotonous) and offer a natural opportunity for symbol manipulation on computers.* Thus, given a problem that requires series expansion, these procedures may be good contenders for highly mechanized "production" methods. When it comes to generating ephemerides by canonical procedures, one should bear in mind that the prevailing sets of canonic variables, such as (8.4.13) through (8.4.17) do not represent osculating parameters. Thus, the calculation of velocities from $l_i(l'_i, L'_i, t)$ and $L_i(l'_i, L'_i, t)$, as obtained by Hamilton-Jacobi techniques, cannot take advantage of the condition of osculation (unless the canonical variables are first transformed back to an osculating set). In addition, there are two more aspects deserving comment. One is treatment of secular effects, and the other is the question of physical insight derivable from the structure of Hamiltonian solutions.

It is frequently argued that the confinement of secular terms to expressions for the coordinate transformations, such as (8.5.26) or the Lindstedt parameters of Chapter 5, is preferable to their explicit appearance as in some results of Chapter 6. To be sure, the purely periodic nature of S in the canonic formulation has some esthetic appeal, but from a computational point of view the need for rectification seems to be essentially the same in the different formulations, whether or not secular terms appear explicitly. This notion is based on the fact that all formulations have the ultimate purpose of producing position ephemerides in inertial coordinates which approach the unique exact solution of the dynamical problem to the same $0(\kappa^n)$.

With regard to physical insight, there seems to be little debate over such well-known secular trends as the precession of the nodes and the apsides for oblateness perturbations and similar effects. The governing short- and long-period terms

*Note the recent work of A. Deprit in this area [29].

require more interpretive effort (and corroboration from observational data). Whether such features of orbital motion are rendered more translucent by the necessarily lengthy canonical representations seems hardly resolvable in general terms. What is true, however, is that canonic formulations have often proved especially effective in dealing with fundamental matters, such as convergence of the perturbation series, asymptotic behavior, resonance, and stability problems of orbital motion, rather than as computing algorithms in competition with other ways of generating ephemerides.

REFERENCES

1. J. L. Synge, "Classical Dynamics," *Encyclopedia of Physics*, Vol. III, Part 1, S. Flügge (ed.), Springer, Berlin, 1960.
2. L. A. Pars, *Analytical Dynamics*, Heinemann, London, 1965.
3. R. Kurth, *Introduction to Mechanics of the Solar System*, Pergamon Press, New York, 1959, p. 146.
4. P. Funk, *Variationsrechnung und ihre Anwendung in Physik und Technik*, Springer, Berlin, 1962.
5. C. Caratheodory, *Variationsrechnung und Partielle Differential-Gleichungen erster Ordnung*, Vol. I, Teubner, Leipzig, 1956.
6. W. M. Smart, *Celestial Mechanics*, Longmans, Green and Co., New York, 1953.
7. P. Appell, *Traité de Mechanique Rationnelle*, Gauthier-Villars, Paris, 1911.
8. C. Lanczos, *The Variational Principles of Mechanics*, U. of Toronto Press, 1962.
9. P. Frank and R. v. Mises, *Differential- und Integralgleichungen der Mechanik und Physik*, Dover, New York, 1961.
10. M. S. Iarov-Iarovoi, "Integration of the Hamilton-Jacobi Equation by the Method of Separation of Variables," *J. Appl. Math and Mech.*, **27,** 1499, 1963 (Translation published May 1964).
11. J. P. Vinti, "New Method of Solution for Unretarded Satellite Orbits," *J. Res. Nat'l Bur Stds.*, **63B,** 105, 1959; J. P. Vinti, "Theory of an Accurate Intermediary Orbit for Satellite Astronomy," *J. Res. Nat'l Bur Stds.*, **65B,** 169, 1961.
12. Y. P. Aksenov, Y. A. Grebenikov, and V. G. Denim, "General Solution of the Problem of the Motion of an Artificial Satellite in the Normal Field of the Earth's Attraction," *J. Planet. Space Sci.*, **9,** 491, 1962.
13. O. R. Spiess, "Two Notes in Orbit Theory," in Proceedings XII International Astronautical Congress, Academic Press, New York, 1963.
14. T. E. Sterne, "The Gravitational Orbit of a Satellite of an Oblate Planet," *Astron. J.*, **63,** 28, 1958.
15. B. Garfinkel, "The Motion of a Satellite of an Oblate Planet," *Astron. J.*, **63,** 88, 1958.
16. W. A. Mersman, *Theory of the Secular Variations in the Orbit of a Satellite of an Oblate Planet*, NASA TR R-99, 1961, p. 34.

17. H. C. Plummer, *An Introductory Treatise on Dynamical Astronomy*, Dover (Reprint), New York, 1960.

18. E. W. Brown and C. A. Shook, *Planetary Theory*, Cambridge Univ. Press, 1933.

19. H. v. Zeipel, "Recherches sur les mouvements des petite planetes," *Arkiv fur Matematik, Astronomi och Fysik*, **11,** Nos. 1 and 7, 1916.

20. D. Brouwer, "Solution of the Problem of Artificial Satellite Theory Without Drag," *Astron. J.*, **64,** 378, 1959.

21. L. Brillouin, "Poincaré and the Shortcomings of the Hamilton-Jacobi Method for Classical or Quantized Mechanics," *Arch. Rat. Mech. Anal.*, **5,** 76, 1960.

22. B. J. Cain, "Determination of Mean Elements for Brouwer's Satellite Theory," *Astron. J.*, **67,** 39, 1962.

23. D. Brouwer and G. M. Clemence, *Methods of Celestial Mechanics*, Academic Press, New York, 1961.

24. Y. Kozai, "Second Order Theory of Artificial Satellite Theory Without Air Drag," *Astron. J.*, **67,** 446, 1962.

25. B. Garfinkel, "The Orbit of a Satellite of an Oblate Planet," *Astron. J.*, **64,** 353, 1959.

26. D. Brouwer, "Analytical Study of Resonance Caused by Radiation Pressure," in *Dynamics of Satellites*, M. Roy (ed.) (International Union of Theoretical and Applied Mechanics), Academic Press, New York, 1963, p. 34.

27. A. Cayley, "Tables of the Development of Functions in the Theory of Elliptic Motion," *Mem. Roy. Astron. Soc.*, **29,** 191, 1861.

28. G. E. O. Giacaglia, "The Influence of Higher-Order Zonal Harmonics on the Motion of an Artificial Satellite Without Drag," *Astron. J.*, **69,** 303, 1964.

29. A. Deprit, "Canonical Transformations Depending on a Small Parameter," *Celestial Mech. (Int. J. Space Dynamics)*, **1,** 1, 1969.

Chapter nine

HANSEN'S METHOD

1. INTRODUCTION

Although the method of Hansen possesses features reminiscent of techniques discussed in earlier chapters, it deserves a separate treatment. At first glance it abounds in changes of variables and transformations involving position coordinates and orbit elements, though none is canonic. The method is unique in that the motive behind some of its manipulations has baffled many, while its reputation as one of the most effective computing algorithms for (planetary) ephemerides [1] has remained virtually unchallenged. Our interest is to pursue the reasons behind this seeming contradiction and to expose the pertinent background so that others may be helped in their evaluation of the method.

In addition to several discussions of Hansen's method in the literature [2–9], the present authors have found it helpful to pursue Hansen's rationale in his original publications [10]. He deliberately sought representations which minimize the magnitudes of the perturbations relative to a reference orbit. In succeeding, he introduced transformations which allow some second-order terms to be included in the nominal first-order calculation if desired, but which lead to a rather involved solution. Unfortunately he makes no attempt to impress the reader with conciseness. The first article of reference 10 runs to 175 pages, the second to 145, and the third to 252 pages. A superficial observer might suspect that some of this material contains *ad hoc* manipulations in the guise of an erudite development; but Hansen's work is based on 30 years of insight which he uses to minimize the computational labor and maximize the convergence of his ultimate series expansions. The substance of his approach can be found in forty pages (64–103) of reference 10. The rest of his treatise contains discussions of the disturbing function, examples, praises of Gauss, and general polemics, with Encke singled out for somewhat special treatment.

2. TRANSFORMATION OF COORDINATES

In order to understand Hansen's *ideal coordinates* which play a key role in his development, we review some standard reference frames used in earlier chapters and the relations between them. Let us write the equations of motion for the perturbed central force problem in cartesian coordinates as

$$\ddot{x}_1 + \mu x_1/r^3 = \mu\,\partial\tilde{R}/\partial x_1; \quad \ddot{x}_2 + \mu x_2/r^3 = \mu\,\partial\tilde{R}/\partial x_2; \quad \ddot{x}_3 + \mu x_3/r^3 = \mu\,\partial\tilde{R}/\partial x_3. \tag{9.2.1}$$

We recall that these equations can be transformed to the six first-order ones, (6.1.21) through (6.1.26), by utilizing the osculating elements $a, e, \chi, \omega, \Omega, i$ of which the latter three yield the position of the osculating plane. Figure 9.1 serves to remind the reader of the geometry relating these Euler angles to the $x_1x_2x_3$ frame. Of course, the inertial cartesian system is connected with a spherical one by the elementary relations

$$x_1 = r\cos\varphi\cos\lambda; \qquad x_2 = r\cos\varphi\sin\lambda; \qquad x_3 = r\sin\varphi \tag{9.2.2}$$

where φ and λ are latitude and longitude of the moving body.

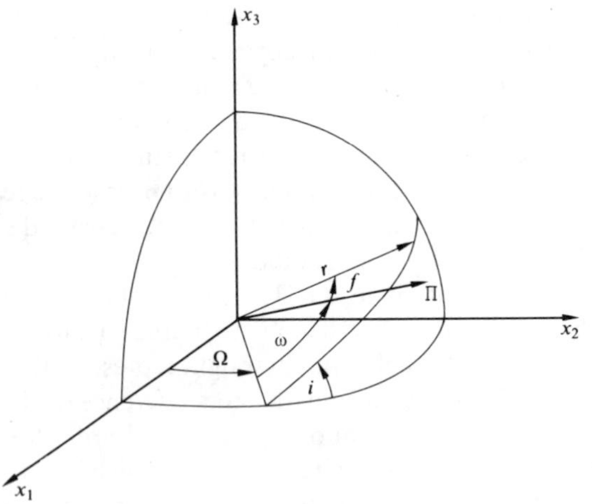

Figure 9.1

Now consider a moving rectangular system $X_1X_2X_3$ whose origin coincides with that of the inertial frame $x_1x_2x_3$, but which rotates with respect to the latter. The moving frame is characterized by the instantaneous axis of rotation, $\boldsymbol{\omega}$, and its orientation about this axis (tantamount to a specification of three Euler angles). The vector $\boldsymbol{\omega}$ will generally change its magnitude and direction with time and may trace out any path in inertial space, subject only to continuity conditions typical of most physical problems. The actual motion of the perturbed body m can be described relative to the moving frame, and the simplicity of that description will depend on the time history of rotations chosen for $X_1X_2X_3$. This idea was already encountered in our discussion of the Lindstedt parameters in Chapter 5 where the coordinate rotations were selected to eliminate secular terms from the explicit solution.

Hansen demands that the X_1 X_2 plane always contains the position vector **r** of m, and that this be the instantaneous axis of rotation for $X_1X_2X_3$. Clearly the instantaneous velocity vector **v** cannot have a component orthogonal to X_1X_2, since the axis of rotation for this plane is defined to pass through the point of application of **v**. This corresponds to the "out-of-plane" part of the classical conditions of osculation. It simplifies numerous algebraic developments, especially the expressions for velocity components, thus prompting Hansen to refer to his system as "ideal" coordinates.*

Since X_1X_2 has been defined to coincide with the osculating plane it follows that $X_3 \equiv 0$ for all time in Hansen's formulation (though the converse is not necessarily true). The orientation of this plane is given in the usual way by the osculating elements Ω and i (Fig. 9.2). The X_1 axis lies at an angle σ back from the node, so that the osculating value of the argument of latitude is denoted by $\theta - \sigma$. Hansen chooses the initial value of σ at $t = 0$ to be Ω, thus bringing the X_1 and x_1 axes close to each other, a natural arrangement for the planetary problems inspiring his original efforts. Eventually, as we shall see, he also relates σ to ω and χ, utilizing the "inplane" condition of osculation.

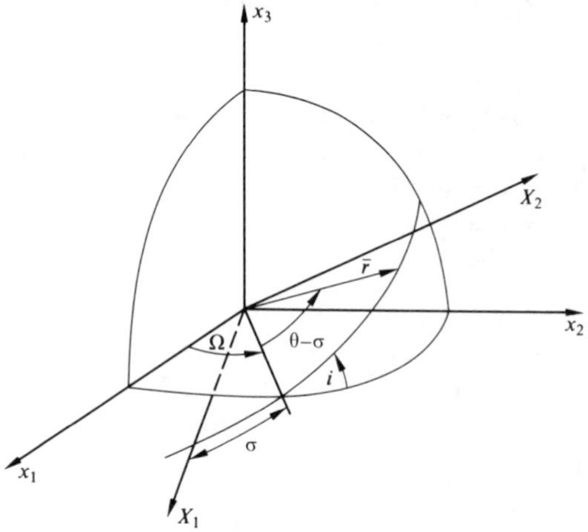

Figure 9.2

The fact that **r** is the instantaneous axis of rotation, i.e., is colinear with the rotation vector ω, may be stated succinctly in terms of the components of this vector

$$\omega_{X_1} = |\omega| \cos\theta, \qquad \omega_{X_2} = |\omega| \sin\theta, \qquad \omega_{X_3} = 0, \tag{9.2.3}$$

*The simple kinematic interpretation of r as instantaneous axis of rotation for the osculating orbit has been used to advantage also by some modern authors [11].

where θ is the angle from the X_1 axis to **r**. But since these components may also be expressed in terms of the time derivatives of the Euler angles Ω, i, σ

$$\omega_{X_1} = -\dot{\Omega} \sin i \sin \sigma + (di/dt) \cos \sigma; \qquad \omega_{X_2} = \dot{\Omega} \sin i \cos \sigma + (di/dt) \sin \sigma;$$

$$\omega_{X_3} = \dot{\Omega} \cos i - \dot{\sigma}. \tag{9.2.4}$$

The equations (9.2.3) impose a kinematic relation on Ω, i, σ. Thus,

$$\dot{\sigma} = \dot{\Omega} \cos i, \tag{9.2.5}$$

and

$$di/dt = \dot{\Omega} \cot (\theta - \sigma) \sin i, \tag{9.2.6}$$

which merely expresses the out-of-plane part of the condition of osculation.

Now the conversion from the x_1, x_2, x_3 frame to the X_1, X_2, X_3 system is obtained by a matrix α

$$\begin{pmatrix} X_1 \\ X_2 \\ X_3 \end{pmatrix} = \begin{pmatrix} \alpha_{11} & \alpha_{12} & \alpha_{13} \\ \alpha_{21} & \alpha_{22} & \alpha_{23} \\ \alpha_{31} & \alpha_{32} & \alpha_{33} \end{pmatrix} \begin{pmatrix} x_1 \\ x_2 \\ x_3 \end{pmatrix}, \tag{9.2.7}$$

where

$$\left.\begin{aligned} \alpha_{11} &= \cos \sigma \cos \Omega + \sin \sigma \sin \Omega \cos i, \\ \alpha_{12} &= \cos \sigma \sin \Omega - \sin \sigma \cos \Omega \cos i, \\ \alpha_{13} &= -\sin \sigma \sin i, \\ \alpha_{21} &= \sin \sigma \cos \Omega - \cos \sigma \sin \Omega \cos i, \\ \alpha_{22} &= \sin \sigma \sin \Omega + \cos \sigma \cos \Omega \cos i, \\ \alpha_{23} &= \cos \sigma \sin i, \\ \alpha_{31} &= \sin \Omega \sin i, \\ \alpha_{32} &= -\cos \Omega \sin i, \\ \alpha_{33} &= \cos i. \end{aligned}\right\}. \tag{9.2.8}$$

Here α_{ij} is the instantaneous value of the cosine of the angle between X_i and x_j. Equation (9.2.7) represents an orthonormal transformation, i.e., it preserves unit vectors, as becomes obvious from the fact that $\Sigma_j \alpha_{ij}^2 = 1$. If we write the unit vectors along the x_1, x_2, x_3 axes as $\mathbf{a}_1$, $\mathbf{a}_2$, $\mathbf{a}_3$, and those along the X_1, X_2, X_3 axes as $\mathbf{A}_1$, $\mathbf{A}_2$, $\mathbf{A}_3$ we have

$$\begin{pmatrix} \mathbf{A}_1 \\ \mathbf{A}_2 \\ \mathbf{A}_3 \end{pmatrix} = \begin{pmatrix} \alpha_{11} & \alpha_{12} & \alpha_{13} \\ \alpha_{21} & \alpha_{22} & \alpha_{23} \\ \alpha_{31} & \alpha_{32} & \alpha_{33} \end{pmatrix} \begin{pmatrix} \mathbf{a}_1 \\ \mathbf{a}_2 \\ \mathbf{a}_3 \end{pmatrix}. \tag{9.2.9}$$

In subsequent manipulations the standard features of this transformation, expressed in terms of Ω, σ, i, will be of frequent use:

$$\mathbf{A}_i \cdot \mathbf{A}_j = \mathbf{a}_i \cdot \mathbf{a}_j = \delta_{ij}, \tag{9.2.10}$$

where δ_{ij} is the Kronecker delta, and

$$\begin{aligned} \mathbf{A}_1 \times \mathbf{A}_2 &= \mathbf{A}_3, & \mathbf{A}_3 \times \mathbf{A}_1 &= \mathbf{A}_2, & \mathbf{A}_2 \times \mathbf{A}_3 &= \mathbf{A}_1, \\ \mathbf{a}_1 \times \mathbf{a}_2 &= \mathbf{a}_3, & \mathbf{a}_3 \times \mathbf{a}_1 &= \mathbf{a}_2, & \mathbf{a}_2 \times \mathbf{a}_3 &= \mathbf{a}_1. \end{aligned} \tag{9.2.11}$$

We also note the fundamental property of orthonormal transformations

$$\alpha^T = \alpha^{-1}, \tag{9.2.12}$$

where α stands for the 3×3 matrix in (9.2.7) or (9.2.9), and the superscripts T and -1 signify the transposed and inverse matrix. Let us abbreviate the 3×1 vector on the left-hand side of (9.2.7) as $\mathbf{X}$ and that on the right by $\mathbf{x}$. Then (9.2.7) reads

$$\mathbf{X} = \alpha \mathbf{x} \tag{9.2.13}$$

and, as a consequence of (9.2.12),

$$\mathbf{x} = \alpha^T \mathbf{X}. \tag{9.2.14}$$

The (X_1, X_2, X_3) system constitutes for Hansen *ideal coordinates* since due to its osculating properties,* it yields a simplified form of the perturbed equations of motion; these relations will be developed in the next two sections.

3. MOTION IN THE OSCULATING PLANE (RECTANGULAR FRAME)

If we differentiate (9.2.14) with respect to the time, we have

$$\dot{\mathbf{x}} = \alpha^T \dot{\mathbf{X}} + \dot{\alpha}^T \mathbf{X}, \tag{9.3.1}$$

where the matrix $\dot{\alpha}^T$ is composed of the time derivatives of α^T. If we use the relations (9.2.8) and write

$$\mathbf{X} = \begin{pmatrix} r \cos \theta \\ r \sin \theta \\ 0 \end{pmatrix}, \tag{9.3.2}$$

we find, with the aid of (9.2.5) and (9.2.6) that

$$\dot{\alpha}^T \mathbf{X} = 0, \tag{9.3.3}$$

or, in other words,

$$\dot{\mathbf{x}} = \alpha^T \dot{\mathbf{X}}. \tag{9.3.4}$$

This result is immediately obvious from the fact that $\boldsymbol{\omega}$ and $\mathbf{r}$ are always colinear, i.e., the rotation of the orbit plane produces no linear velocity over and above $\dot{\mathbf{X}}$ at the instantaneous satellite position. Thus we merely transform the vector $\dot{\mathbf{X}}$ like any position vector in the X_1, X_2 system according to (9.2.14).

Multiplying (9.3.4) by α from the left, we obtain

$$\dot{\mathbf{X}} = \alpha \dot{\mathbf{x}}, \tag{9.3.5}$$

**Ideal coordinates* differ from the ordinary osculating ones largely by the fact that with the former set the quantity θ also has the same form in perturbed and unperturbed motion (by the introduction of σ).

which implies, of course, that

$$\dot{\alpha}\mathbf{x} = 0. \tag{9.3.6}$$

The consequences of (9.3.3) and (9.3.6), in terms of the simplicity they provide in handling perturbations, pervade all of Hansen's method.

One of the relations that can be obtained from (9.2.9) and (9.2.10) is

$$\alpha_{11}\alpha_{21} + \alpha_{12}\alpha_{22} + \alpha_{13}\alpha_{23} = 0.$$

Differentiating this with respect to time, we set

$$A = \alpha_{11}\dot{\alpha}_{21} + \alpha_{12}\dot{\alpha}_{22} + \alpha_{13}\dot{\alpha}_{23} = -(\alpha_{21}\dot{\alpha}_{11} + \alpha_{22}\dot{\alpha}_{12} + \alpha_{23}\dot{\alpha}_{13}). \tag{9.3.7}$$

Similarly, we define

$$\begin{aligned} B &= \alpha_{11}\dot{\alpha}_{31} + \alpha_{12}\dot{\alpha}_{32} + \alpha_{13}\dot{\alpha}_{33} = -(\alpha_{31}\dot{\alpha}_{11} + \alpha_{32}\dot{\alpha}_{12} + \alpha_{33}\dot{\alpha}_{13}), \\ C &= \alpha_{31}\dot{\alpha}_{21} + \alpha_{32}\dot{\alpha}_{22} + \alpha_{33}\dot{\alpha}_{23} = -(\alpha_{21}\dot{\alpha}_{31} + \alpha_{22}\dot{\alpha}_{32} + \alpha_{23}\dot{\alpha}_{33}). \end{aligned}$$

We have, also, as a consequence of (9.2.9) and (9.2.10),

$$\alpha_{11}\dot{\alpha}_{11} + \alpha_{12}\dot{\alpha}_{12} + \alpha_{13}\dot{\alpha}_{13} = 0. \tag{9.3.8}$$

Then, substituting (9.2.14) in (9.3.6), we find

$$AX_2 + BX_3 = 0; \qquad AX_1 + CX_3 = 0; \qquad BX_1 - CX_2 = 0.$$

But $X_3 = 0$, hence $A = 0$, which is a further relation between the α_{ij} and the $\dot{\alpha}_{ij}$.

Differentiating (9.3.4) once more, we obtain, in terms of components,

$$\begin{aligned} \ddot{x}_1 &= \alpha_{11}\ddot{X}_1 + \alpha_{21}\ddot{X}_2 + \dot{\alpha}_{11}\dot{X}_1 + \dot{\alpha}_{21}\dot{X}_2, \\ \ddot{x}_2 &= \alpha_{12}\ddot{X}_1 + \alpha_{22}\ddot{X}_2 + \dot{\alpha}_{12}\dot{X}_1 + \dot{\alpha}_{22}\dot{X}_2, \\ \ddot{x}_3 &= \alpha_{13}\ddot{X}_1 + \alpha_{23}\ddot{X}_2 + \dot{\alpha}_{13}\dot{X}_1 + \dot{\alpha}_{23}\dot{X}_2. \end{aligned}$$

Multiplying the first of these by α_{11}, the second by α_{12}, the third by α_{13}, and adding, we find

$$\ddot{X}_1 = \alpha_{11}\ddot{x}_1 + \alpha_{12}\ddot{x}_2 + \alpha_{13}\ddot{x}_3, \tag{9.3.9}$$

where we have used some orthonormal relations derived from (9.2.9) and (9.2.10) and the fact that $A = 0$. (This is another extension of (9.2.13), beyond (9.3.5), to the acceleration vectors, as a further consequence of the kinematic condition (9.2.3).) Similarly,

$$\ddot{X}_2 = \alpha_{21}\ddot{x}_1 + \alpha_{22}\ddot{x}_2 + \alpha_{23}\ddot{x}_3 \tag{9.3.10}$$

and

$$\begin{aligned} &(\alpha_{31}\dot{\alpha}_{11} + \alpha_{32}\dot{\alpha}_{12} + \alpha_{33}\dot{\alpha}_{13})\dot{X}_1 \\ &\quad + (\alpha_{31}\dot{\alpha}_{21} + \alpha_{32}\dot{\alpha}_{22} + \alpha_{33}\dot{\alpha}_{23})\dot{X}_2 = B\dot{X}_1 - C\dot{X}_2 \\ &\quad = \alpha_{31}\ddot{x}_1 + \alpha_{32}\ddot{x}_2 + \alpha_{33}\ddot{x}_3 = \dot{C}X_2 - \dot{B}X_1. \end{aligned} \tag{9.3.11}$$

If we substitute (9.2.1) into (9.3.9) and (9.3.10) and interpret α_{ij} with the help of (9.2.7) and (9.2.12) as $\alpha_{ij} = \partial X_i/\partial x_j = \partial x_j/\partial X_i$, we find

$$\ddot{X}_1 + (\mu/r^3)X_1 = \mu\,\partial\tilde{R}/\partial X_1, \qquad \ddot{X}_2 + (\mu/r^3)X_2 = \mu\,\partial\tilde{R}/\partial X_2. \qquad (9.3.12)$$

These are the equations of motion in the osculating plane. The direct correspondence of this system to that for inertial coordinates (9.2.1) is noteworthy.

4. MOTION OF OSCULATING PLANE (DIRECTION COSINES)

Taking the right-hand side of the expression for A, Eq. (9.3.7), which we have shown to be equal to zero, and Eq. (9.3.8), we can eliminate $\dot{\alpha}_{12}$ and find

$$\dot{\alpha}_{11} = \frac{\alpha_{12}\alpha_{23} - \alpha_{13}\alpha_{22}}{\alpha_{11}\alpha_{22} - \alpha_{12}\alpha_{21}}\,\dot{\alpha}_{13}.$$

From an explicit development of $\boldsymbol{A}_1 \times \boldsymbol{A}_2 = \boldsymbol{A}_3$ with the help of (9.2.9) we simplify the fraction in the above expression to obtain

$$\dot{\alpha}_{11} = (\alpha_{31}/\alpha_{33})\dot{\alpha}_{13}. \qquad (9.4.1)$$

Similarly,

$$\dot{\alpha}_{12} = (\alpha_{32}/\alpha_{33})\dot{\alpha}_{13}, \qquad (9.4.2a)$$

$$\dot{\alpha}_{21} = (\alpha_{31}/\alpha_{33})\dot{\alpha}_{23}, \qquad (9.4.2b)$$

$$\dot{\alpha}_{22} = (\alpha_{32}/\alpha_{33})\dot{\alpha}_{23}. \qquad (9.4.2c)$$

If these are substituted in (9.3.11), remembering that $X_3 = 0$, we obtain

$$\dot{\alpha}_{13}\dot{X}_1 + \dot{\alpha}_{23}\dot{X}_2 = \alpha_{33}\,\mu\,\partial\tilde{R}/\partial X_3. \qquad (9.4.3)$$

From the third component of (9.2.3),

$$\dot{\alpha}_{13}X_1 + \dot{\alpha}_{23}X_2 = 0,$$

and combining this with (9.4.3),

$$\left.\begin{aligned} \dot{\alpha}_{13} &= -h\,\alpha_{33}X_2\frac{\partial\tilde{R}}{\partial X_3}, \\ \dot{\alpha}_{23} &= h\,\alpha_{33}X_1\frac{\partial\tilde{R}}{\partial X_3}, \end{aligned}\right\} \qquad (9.4.4)$$

where we have put

$$h = \mu/(X_1\dot{X}_2 - X_2\dot{X}_1). \qquad (9.4.5)$$

(The reader should note that contrary to some other standard notations, the letter h stands here for the reciprocal of the angular momentum.)

Simultaneous integration of equations (9.3.12), (9.4.4), (9.4.1), and (9.4.2) solves the problem, since together they give all the elements required from (9.2.14), that is,

$$\left.\begin{aligned} x_1 &= \alpha_{11}X_1 + \alpha_{21}X_2, \\ x_2 &= \alpha_{12}X_1 + \alpha_{22}X_2, \\ x_3 &= \alpha_{13}X_1 + \alpha_{23}X_2. \end{aligned}\right\} \tag{9.4.6}$$

Thus, by referring his analysis to a system based on the osculating orbit plane (as expressed in Eqs. (9.2.3), Hansen was able to separate the motion in the osculating orbit plane from the perturbations of that plane itself, a common feature with numerous formulations since his day.

5. POLAR COORDINATES FOR MOTION IN THE OSCULATING PLANE

We now examine the equations of motion in the X_1, X_2 plane in polar coordinates. Using (9.3.2), Eqs. (9.3.12) yield, after some manipulation,

$$\left.\begin{aligned} \ddot{r} - r\dot{\theta}^2 + \frac{\mu}{r^2} &= \mu\frac{\partial\tilde{R}}{\partial r}, \\ r^2\ddot{\theta} + 2r\dot{r}\dot{\theta} &= \mu\frac{\partial\tilde{R}}{\partial\theta}. \end{aligned}\right\} \tag{9.5.1}$$

As in (9.3.12), these equations were derived for the osculating plane, but have the same form as for inertial coordinates. Since we are dealing with the osculating orbit, it follows that $\dot{r}$ and $\dot{\theta}$, in perturbed motion, are expressed by the standard equations

$$\dot{r} = \frac{an}{\sqrt{1-e^2}}\, e \sin f, \tag{9.5.2}$$

$$\dot{\theta} = \frac{a^2 n\sqrt{1-e^2}}{r^2}, \tag{9.5.3}$$

where $n = \sqrt{\mu/a^3}$, and the elements are understood to have their osculating values. We also note for later reference that (9.4.5), in polar coordinates, yields the angular momentum

$$\mu/h = r^2\dot{\theta}, \tag{9.5.4}$$

or, using (9.5.3),

$$h = \sqrt{\frac{\mu}{a(1-e^2)}}. \tag{9.5.5}$$

Though (9.5.1) is a standard description of the motion for many applications, Hansen proceeds to reformulate these equations, presumably for computational convenience.

If there were no perturbations after time $t = t_0$, we would have the usual relations,

$$r^{(0)} = \frac{a_0(1 - e_0^2)}{1 + e_0 \cos f^{(0)}}, \tag{9.5.6}$$

$$f^{(0)} = \theta - \Pi_0, \tag{9.5.7}$$

$$\tan \frac{f^{(0)}}{2} = \sqrt{\frac{1 + e_0}{1 - e_0}} \tan \frac{E^{(0)}}{2}, \tag{9.5.8}$$

$$E^{(0)} - e_0 \sin E^{(0)} = \sqrt{\frac{\mu}{a_0^3}}(t - T_0), \tag{9.5.9}$$

where the subscripted elements are constants. Suppose, with Hansen, that we take the motion in the perturbed case to be described by a corresponding set, which still uses the elements α_0, e_0, Π_0, T_0 given at t_0:

$$\bar{r} = \frac{a_0(1 - e_0^2)}{1 + e_0 \cos \bar{f}}, \tag{9.5.10}$$

$$\bar{f} = \theta - \Pi_0, \tag{9.5.11}$$

$$\tan \frac{\bar{f}}{2} = \sqrt{\frac{1 + e_0}{1 - e_0}} \tan \frac{\bar{E}}{2}, \tag{9.5.12}$$

$$\bar{E} - e_0 \sin \bar{E} = \sqrt{\frac{\mu}{a_0^3}}(z - T_0), \tag{9.5.13}$$

and add to these

$$r = \bar{r}(1 + v). \tag{9.5.14}$$

Here θ represents the argument of latitude based on the instantaneous osculating orbit. By virtue of Eq. (9.5.11), which retains Π_0 in the role of argument of perigee, (though not measured from the node) the angle θ defines a "quasi-true" anomaly $\bar{f}$. This differs from the unperturbed and perturbed true anomalies, $f^{(0)}$ and f, defined in Chapter 6 through Kepler's equation for the osculating orbit at t_0 and the instantaneous osculating orbit. This second set of conic equations defines $\bar{r}$ and $\bar{f}$ through $\bar{E}$ and "localizes" the in-plane perturbations in terms of z and v. Hence, rather than solve (9.5.1) directly for the polar coordinates, Hansen conducts his analysis in terms of the variables $z(t)$ and $v(t)$ or further transformations of these. Once z and v have been determined for a particular value of time, the computational process is clear: z allows us to compute $\bar{E}$ by (9.5.13), and then $\bar{f}$ by (9.5.12). From this we find θ by (9.5.11) and $\bar{r}$ by (9.5.10). Using the value of v, we obtain r by (9.5.14), and then X_1 and X_2 from (9.3.2).

In the remainder of this section we derive differential equations for z and v. The reader interested in the essentials of Hansen's method may want to bypass these in favor of Section 8, where the standard formulation for inplane perturbations in terms of Hansen's W function is taken up.

We obtain a useful differential equation for v as follows. From (9.5.14),

$$\ddot{v} = \frac{\bar{r}\ddot{r} - r\ddot{\bar{r}}}{\bar{r}^2} - 2\frac{\bar{r}\dot{r} - r\dot{\bar{r}}}{\bar{r}^3}\dot{\bar{r}}. \tag{9.5.15}$$

Then we rewrite (9.5.10) as

$$\frac{1}{\bar{r}} = \frac{h_0^2}{\mu} + \frac{h_0^2\, e_0 \cos\bar{f}}{\mu}, \tag{9.5.16}$$

where, from (9.5.5),

$$h_0 = \sqrt{\frac{\mu}{a_0(1 - e_0^2)}}. \tag{9.5.17}$$

Differentiating (9.5.16) with respect to time once, we obtain

$$\dot{\bar{r}}/\bar{r}^2 = (h_0^2\, e_0 \sin\bar{f}/\mu)\dot{\theta}, \tag{9.5.18}$$

since $\dot{\theta} = \dot{\bar{f}}$. Differentiating (9.5.18) leads to

$$\frac{\ddot{\bar{r}}}{\bar{r}^2} - 2\frac{\dot{\bar{r}}^2}{\bar{r}^3} = \frac{h_0^2\, e_0 \sin\bar{f}}{\mu}\ddot{\theta} + \left(\frac{1}{\bar{r}} - \frac{h_0^2}{\mu}\right)\dot{\theta}^2. \tag{9.5.19}$$

If we multiply (9.5.18) by $2\dot{r}$, and (9.5.19) by r, and add, we get

$$r\frac{\ddot{\bar{r}}}{\bar{r}^2} + 2\frac{\bar{r}\dot{r} - r\dot{\bar{r}}}{\bar{r}^3}\dot{\bar{r}} = \frac{h_0^2\, e_0 \sin\bar{f}}{\mu r}\frac{d}{dt}(r^2\dot{\theta}) + \left(\frac{1}{\bar{r}} - \frac{h_0^2}{\mu}\right)r\dot{\theta}^2. \tag{9.5.20}$$

Introducing (9.5.20) in (9.5.15) gives

$$\ddot{v} = \frac{1}{\bar{r}}\left(\mu\frac{\partial\tilde{R}}{\partial r} - \frac{\mu}{r^2}\right) - \frac{h_0^2\, e_0 \sin\bar{f}}{r}\frac{\partial\tilde{R}}{\partial\theta} + \frac{h_0^2}{\mu}r\dot{\theta}^2, \tag{9.5.21}$$

where we have used (9.5.1). Now we can also write the second of (9.5.1) as

$$r^2\dot{\theta} = \frac{\mu}{h_0} + \mu\int\frac{\partial\tilde{R}}{\partial\theta}\,dt, \tag{9.5.22}$$

reflecting the perturbation of angular momentum. From this

$$r\dot{\theta}^2 = \frac{\mu^2}{r^3}\left\{\frac{1}{h_0^2} + \frac{2}{h_0}\int\frac{\partial\tilde{R}}{\partial\theta}\,dt + \left(\int\frac{\partial\tilde{R}}{\partial\theta}\,dt\right)^2\right\}.$$

Denoting

$$S = h_0 \int \frac{\partial \tilde{R}}{\partial \theta}\, dt, \tag{9.5.23}$$

and using (9.5.14), we can write (9.5.21) as

$$\ddot{v} + \frac{\mu}{r^3} v = \frac{\mu}{\bar{r}} \frac{\partial \tilde{R}}{\partial r} - \frac{h_0^2 \dot{e}_0 \sin \bar{f}}{r} \frac{\partial \tilde{R}}{\partial \theta} + 2 \frac{\mu}{r^3} S + \frac{\mu}{r^3} S^2, \tag{9.5.24}$$

which is the desired equation.

To derive a corresponding equation for z, we note from (9.5.11) that

$$\dot{\theta} = (d\bar{f}/dz)\dot{z}. \tag{9.5.25}$$

But (9.5.12) and (9.5.13) lead to

$$d\bar{f}/dz = \mu/h_0 \bar{r}^2,$$

which, when used with (9.5.25), gives

$$\dot{z} = \frac{h_0}{\mu} \bar{r}^2 \dot{\theta} = \frac{h_0}{\mu} \frac{r^2 \dot{\theta}}{(1 + v)^2}.$$

However, (9.5.22) and (9.5.23) give

$$r^2 \dot{\theta} = \frac{\mu}{h_0} + \frac{\mu}{h_0} S,$$

and so,

$$\dot{z} = \frac{1 + S}{(1 + v)^2}, \tag{9.5.26}$$

which is an equation relating z and t.

The right-hand side of (9.5.24) is of the same order as the perturbing force, but it also includes some terms of higher order. Thus $v = 0(\tilde{R})$. Knowing this, we can rewrite (9.5.26) as $\dot{z} \simeq 1 - 2v + S + 0(\tilde{R}^2)$; thus $z - t$ is also of order of the perturbing force.*

*The reader may justly question the merits of the transformed equations (9.5.24) and (9.5.26), whose right-hand sides still contain the original coordinates r, θ, both explicitly and within S. In practice their unperturbed values would serve to yield first-order results for v and z, etc. But then, similar iterations could be used in solving (9.5.1) directly. The vindication of the new formulation comes from its computational merits; this is discussed further in Section 7. As pointed out earlier, the equations for v and z are not used as a prime computing algorithm in Hansen's standard procedure. Rather, another set of manipulations is given which leads to the so-called W function, whose computational advantages will be the subject of a still later discussion.

6. EULER ANGLES FOR MOTION OF THE OSCULATING PLANE

Turning to the orientation of the X_1, X_2 plane, equations (9.2.8) and (9.4.4) lead directly to

$$di/dt = h\,r \cos(\theta - \sigma)\, \partial\tilde{R}/\partial X_3,$$

$$\dot{\sigma} = h\,r \sin(\theta - \sigma) \cot i\, \partial\tilde{R}/\partial X_3. \tag{9.6.1}$$

We have, of course, from (9.2.5), that $\dot{\Omega} = (1/\cos i)\dot{\sigma}$. These can be integrated directly and introduced into

$$\cos\varphi \sin(\lambda - \Omega) = \cos i \sin(\theta - \sigma), \tag{9.6.2a}$$

$$\cos\varphi \cos(\lambda - \Omega) = \cos(\theta - \sigma), \tag{9.6.2b}$$

$$\sin\varphi = \sin i \sin(\theta - \sigma), \tag{9.6.2c}$$

which can be derived from elementary spherical trigonometry. Thus, φ and λ can be found, and using r obtained from (9.5.14), we can solve for x_1, x_2, x_3 by (9.2.2).

Again, Hansen chooses another approach. Since x_3 differs from its unperturbed counterpart by a quantity of at least first order we may write for (9.6.2c)

$$\sin\varphi = \sin i_0 \sin(\theta - \Omega_0) + s, \tag{9.6.3c}$$

where s is that first-order quantity, and we have used the initial condition $\sigma_0 = \Omega_0$. Now it may seem natural to introduce the corresponding structure into (9.6.2 a & b), but Hansen chooses to write

$$\cos\varphi \sin(\lambda - \Omega_0 - \Gamma) = \cos i_0 \sin(\theta - \Omega_0) - s\left(\tan i_0 + \frac{q}{\kappa \cos i_0}\right), \tag{9.6.3a}$$

$$\cos\varphi \cos(\lambda - \Omega_0 - \Gamma) = \cos(\theta - \Omega_0) + s\,p/\kappa. \tag{9.6.3b}$$

By introducing the perturbed variables s, p, q, Γ, κ, Hansen has given himself more freedom than is necessary. Characteristically, this makes the formal manipulations more involved but ultimately results in certain advantages.

The exact relations between these variables and the osculating elements, which serve as defining equations, can be obtained by somewhat tedious manipulations. They are:

$$\left.\begin{aligned} p &= \sin i \sin(\sigma - \Omega_0), \\ q &= \sin i \cos(\sigma - \Omega_0) - \sin i_0, \end{aligned}\right\} \tag{9.6.4}$$

$$s = \sin i \sin(\theta - \sigma) - \sin i_0 \sin(\theta - \Omega_0), \tag{9.6.5}$$

$$\left.\begin{aligned} \sin(\Omega - \Omega_0 - \Gamma) &= \frac{\sin(\sigma - \Omega_0)(\cos i + \cos i_0)}{\kappa}, \\ \cos(\Omega - \Omega_0 - \Gamma) &= \frac{\cos(\sigma - \Omega_0)(1 + \cos i \cos i_0) - \sin i \sin i_0}{\kappa}, \end{aligned}\right\} \tag{9.6.6}$$

$$\kappa = 1 + \cos i \cos i_0 - \sin i \sin i_0 \cos(\sigma - \Omega_0). \tag{9.6.7}$$

These equations can be verified by substitution into (9.6.3) to obtain (9.6.2), a straightforward exercise which we omit.

If we take the time derivative of p and q and use (9.6.1), we find

$$\left.\begin{aligned}\dot{p} &= hr\sin(\theta - \Omega_0)\cos i\,\frac{\partial\tilde{R}}{\partial X_3},\\ \dot{q} &= hr\cos(\theta - \Omega_0)\cos i\,\frac{\partial\tilde{R}}{\partial X_3}.\end{aligned}\right\} \tag{9.6.8}$$

Thus p and q are of the order of the perturbing force. We note that (9.6.5) can also be written as

$$s = q\sin(\theta - \Omega_0) - p\cos(\theta - \Omega_0); \tag{9.6.9}$$

hence, s is also of the first order. Further,

$$\kappa = \cos i_0(\cos i_0 + \cos i) - q\sin i_0, \tag{9.6.10}$$

so that κ is a quantity of $0(1)$. Now differentiating one of the equations (9.6.6) and employing the other leads to

$$\dot{\Gamma} = (hr/\kappa)s\,\partial\tilde{R}/\partial X_3; \tag{9.6.11}$$

thus Γ is of second order. We can write

$$h = h_0 + 0(\tilde{R}); \qquad \kappa = 2\cos^2 i_0 + 0(\tilde{R}),$$

and so we can represent Γ with sufficient accuracy by

$$\Gamma = \frac{h_0}{2\cos^2 i_0}\int rs\frac{\partial\tilde{R}}{\partial X_3}\,dt. \tag{9.6.12}$$

Even if we take $r = r^{(0)}$, this consists of second-order and higher terms.

In a similar vein, we can also find expressions for p and q in terms of s and its derivative. If we differentiate (9.6.9) with respect to time and utilize (9.6.8), we find $\dot{s}/\dot{\theta} = q\cos(\theta - \Omega_0) + p\sin(\theta - \Omega_0)$. Combining this with (9.6.9) leads to

$$\left.\begin{aligned}p &= -s\cos(\theta - \Omega_0) + \frac{\dot{s}}{\dot{\theta}}\sin(\theta - \Omega_0),\\ q &= s\sin(\theta - \Omega_0) + \frac{\dot{s}}{\dot{\theta}}\cos(\theta - \Omega_0),\end{aligned}\right\} \tag{9.6.13}$$

where $\dot{\theta}$ is obtainable from (9.5.3) as

$$\dot{\theta} = \frac{\sqrt{\mu a_0(1 - e_0^2)}}{r^{(0)2}} + 0(\tilde{R}).$$

Thus, if s and $\dot{s}$ can be found, we can derive very reasonable approximations to Γ, sp, and sq, all second-order terms.

In the historical development of reference 10 Hansen proceeds at this point to derive a differential equation for the quantity

$$u = rs. \tag{9.6.14}$$

We include that here for completeness though it is not essential to his standard method for out-of-plane perturbations, which is resumed in Section 11 with the introduction of a U-function.

One defines

$$\xi_1 = r\cos(\theta - \Omega_0), \qquad \xi_2 = r\sin(\theta - \Omega_0). \tag{9.6.15}$$

Then using (9.6.9), we find

$$u = q\xi_2 - p\xi_1, \tag{9.6.16}$$

and from this,

$$\dot{u} = q\dot{\xi}_2 - p\dot{\xi}_1, \tag{9.6.17}$$

since $\dot{q}\xi_2 - \dot{p}\xi_1$ vanishes.* Further differentiation leads to

$$\ddot{u} = q\ddot{\xi}_2 - p\ddot{\xi}_1 + \dot{q}\dot{\xi}_2 - \dot{p}\dot{\xi}_1. \tag{9.6.18}$$

Now if we solve (9.6.15) for r and θ, differentiate these twice with respect to time, and use (9.5.1) we obtain

$$\ddot{\xi}_1 = -\mu\frac{\xi_1}{r^3} + \mu\frac{\partial\tilde{R}}{\partial\xi_1}; \qquad \ddot{\xi}_2 = -\mu\frac{\xi_2}{r^3} + \mu\frac{\partial\tilde{R}}{\partial\xi_2}, \tag{9.6.19}$$

which is just a restatement of (9.3.12) for $\sigma = \Omega_0$. Similarly, we find, employing (9.4.5), that

$$\xi_1\dot{\xi}_2 - \xi_2\dot{\xi}_1 = \mu/h. \tag{9.6.20}$$

Substituting (9.6.19), (9.6.20), and (9.6.8) in (9.6.18), we obtain

$$\ddot{u} = -\frac{\mu}{r^3}u + \mu\cos i\,\frac{\partial\tilde{R}}{\partial X_3} + \mu\left(q\frac{\partial\tilde{R}}{\partial\xi_2} - p\frac{\partial\tilde{R}}{\partial\xi_1}\right), \tag{9.6.21}$$

from which p and q must be eliminated.

Combining (9.6.16) and (9.6.17), we find, with the aid of (9.6.20),

$$\mu p = h(\xi_2\dot{u} - \dot{\xi}_2 u), \qquad \mu q = h(\xi_1\dot{u} - \dot{\xi}_1 u).$$

From these,

$$\mu\left(q\frac{\partial\tilde{R}}{\partial\xi_2} - p\frac{\partial\tilde{R}}{\partial\xi_1}\right) = h\left(\frac{\partial\tilde{R}}{\partial\xi_1}\dot{\xi}_2 - \frac{\partial\tilde{R}}{\partial\xi_2}\dot{\xi}_1\right)u + h\left(\frac{\partial\tilde{R}}{\partial\xi_2}\xi_1 - \frac{\partial\tilde{R}}{\partial\xi_1}\xi_2\right)\dot{u}. \tag{9.6.22}$$

*This fact was also encountered in the derivation of $\dot{s}/\dot{\theta}$ above.

Now

$$\frac{\partial \tilde{R}}{\partial \xi_1} = -\frac{\partial \tilde{R}}{\partial \theta}\frac{\xi_2}{r^2} + \frac{\partial \tilde{R}}{\partial r}\frac{\xi_1}{r},$$

and

$$\frac{\partial \tilde{R}}{\partial \xi_2} = \frac{\partial \tilde{R}}{\partial \theta}\frac{\xi_1}{r^2} + \frac{\partial \tilde{R}}{\partial r}\frac{\xi_2}{r}.$$

Also

$$\frac{1}{2}\frac{d}{dt}(r^2) = \xi_1\dot{\xi}_1 + \xi_2\dot{\xi}_2,$$

so that (9.6.22) becomes

$$\mu\left(q\frac{\partial \tilde{R}}{\partial \xi_2} - p\frac{\partial \tilde{R}}{\partial \xi_1}\right) = \left[\frac{\mu}{r}\frac{\partial \tilde{R}}{\partial r} - \frac{h}{2r^2}\frac{\partial \tilde{R}}{\partial \theta}\frac{d(r^2)}{dt}\right]u + h\frac{\partial \tilde{R}}{\partial \theta}\dot{u}. \qquad (9.6.23)$$

Using (9.5.14)

$$\frac{d}{dt}(r^2) = (1+\nu)^2\frac{d}{dt}(\bar{r}^2) + 2(1+\nu)\bar{r}^2\dot{\nu}. \qquad (9.6.24)$$

But $d(\bar{r}^2)/dt = \dot{\theta}d(\bar{r}^2)/d\theta$ and

$$\bar{r} = \frac{a_0(1-e_0^2)}{1+e_0\cos(\theta-\Pi_0)}.$$

Further, as we have seen,

$$\dot{\theta} = \frac{\sqrt{\mu a(1-e^2)}}{r^2} = \frac{\mu}{hr^2},$$

where h is defined by (9.5.5). With the aid of these expressions, (9.6.24) becomes

$$d(r^2)/dt = 2\bar{r}(h_0^2/h)e_0\sin\bar{f} + 2\bar{r}^2(1+\nu)\dot{\nu}, \qquad (9.6.25)$$

and then (9.6.21), by use of (9.6.23) and (9.6.25), reads

$$\ddot{u} = -\frac{\mu}{r^3}u + \mu\cos i\frac{\partial \tilde{R}}{\partial X_3} + \left[\frac{\mu}{r}\frac{\partial \tilde{R}}{\partial r} - \frac{\partial \tilde{R}}{\partial \theta}\frac{\bar{r}}{r^2}h_0^2 e_0\sin\bar{f}\right]u$$

$$- h\frac{\partial \tilde{R}}{\partial \theta}\frac{\bar{r}^2}{r^2}(1+\nu)\dot{\nu}u + h\frac{\partial R}{\partial \theta}\dot{u}. \qquad (9.6.26)$$

We can cast this into the form

$$\ddot{u} + \frac{\mu}{r^3}u = \left[\frac{\mu}{\bar{r}}\frac{\partial \tilde{R}}{\partial r} - \frac{h_0^2\, e_0 \sin \bar{f}}{r}\frac{\partial \tilde{R}}{\partial \theta}\right]\frac{u}{1+v}$$
$$+ \mu \cos i \frac{\partial \tilde{R}}{\partial X_3} + h\frac{\partial \tilde{R}}{\partial \theta}\left[\dot{u} - \frac{u\dot{v}}{1+v}\right], \tag{9.6.27}$$

which bears some resemblance to (9.5.24). As in the case of (9.5.24) and (9.5.26), we note that the right-hand side of (9.6.27) contains r and θ.

7. USE OF DIFFERENTIAL EQUATIONS FOR *v*, *z*, AND *u*

Although Hansen ultimately settles on an approach that lies beyond the differential equations for v, z, and u, it is worthwhile to halt at this point and evaluate the situation. Indeed, Perigaud [8] goes no further, pointing out that the application of Hansen's method as developed up to now already has certain advantages over the usual (Cowell) method of integrating three second-order differential equations simultaneously. The technique is as follows. Since v is a quantity of first order, we can ignore the last term on the right-hand side of (9.5.24), and also replace, in the resulting equation, all the perturbed quantities by the values derived from the osculating orbit at the epoch $t = t_0$. This serves to prescribe the partial derivatives of the disturbing function as well. Equation (9.5.23) then determines S, and (9.5.24) yields v, where we choose $v_0 = \dot{v}_0 = 0$ at $t = t_0$. Integration of (9.5.26) gives us z, where $z_0 = t_0$. At this point, we can find r by (9.5.14) and θ by (9.5.13), (9.5.12), and (9.5.11). Then, if desired, the actual values of r and θ can be used in (9.5.23), (9.5.24), and (9.5.26) to give improved values of v and z; however, in many cases the increased accuracy is not worth the effort.

In equation (9.6.27), the first and third terms on the right-hand side are of second order and usually may be ignored; again, we replace the perturbed quantities by their osculating values at epoch. Solution of (9.6.27) thus yields u (and, of course, $\dot{u}$), where $u_0 = \dot{u}_0 = 0$. The quantities s and $\dot{s}$ can be found from (9.6.14) and its derivative. Then p and q are obtained from (9.6.13) and Γ from (9.6.12). In many cases, sp, sq, and Γ are too small to be of importance. Equations (9.6.3) give φ and λ, which with r, yield the rectangular coordinates by application of (9.2.2).

We should note how cumbersome are the forms of (9.6.3a) and (9.6.3b) when we try to obtain $\cos \varphi \sin \lambda$ and $\cos \varphi \cos \lambda$ explicitly; in addition, there is the awkwardness of passing from z to f and $\bar{r}$ analytically.

8. THE *W* FUNCTION

We have seen how Hansen represents perturbed motion in the osculating plane by the quantities $\bar{r}$, $\bar{E}$, v, and z in Eqs. (9.5.10) through (9.5.14). We now show the additional manipulations leading to the so-called W function, which is related to v

and z, and whose series expansion provides the algorithm that has gained a reputation of numerical efficiency.

We begin by writing the counterparts of (9.5.10) to (9.5.14) in terms of the osculating elements:

$$r = \frac{a(1 - e^2)}{1 + e\cos f}, \tag{9.8.1}$$

$$f = \theta - \chi, \tag{9.8.2}$$

$$\tan\frac{f}{2} = \sqrt{\frac{1 + e}{1 - e}}\tan\frac{E}{2}, \tag{9.8.3}$$

$$E - e\sin E = \sqrt{\frac{\mu}{a^3}}\,t + c. \tag{9.8.4}$$

As already demonstrated in Eq. (9.5.3)

$$\dot{\theta} = \frac{\sqrt{\mu a(1 - e^2)}}{r^2}. \tag{9.8.5}$$

But (9.5.11) leads to

$$\dot{\theta} = (d\bar{f}/dz)\dot{z}, \tag{9.8.6}$$

and, by using (9.5.12), (9.5.13), and (9.5.10), we obtain

$$\frac{d\bar{f}}{dz} = \frac{\sqrt{\mu a_0(1 - e_0^2)}}{\bar{r}^2}. \tag{9.8.7}$$

Eliminating $\dot{\theta}$ from (9.8.5) and (9.8.6), and employing (9.8.7) yields

$$\dot{z} = \frac{\bar{r}^2\sqrt{a(1 - e^2)}}{r^2\sqrt{a_0(1 - e_0^2)}}. \tag{9.8.8}$$

Now (9.8.2) and (9.5.11) lead to

$$f = \bar{f} - \chi + \Pi_0,$$

and this in (9.8.1) gives

$$\frac{a}{r} = \frac{1 + \cos\bar{f}\cdot e\cos(\chi - \Pi_0) + \sin\bar{f}\cdot e\sin(\chi - \Pi_0)}{1 - e^2},$$

whence

$$\frac{\bar{r}a}{ra_0} = \frac{\bar{r} + \bar{r}\cos\bar{f}\cdot e\cos(\chi - \Pi_0) + \bar{r}\sin\bar{f}\cdot e\sin(\chi - \Pi_0)}{a_0(1 - e^2)}. \tag{9.8.9}$$

Let us define

$$\left.\begin{aligned}\xi &= \frac{e\cos(\chi - \Pi_0) - e_0}{1 - e_0^2},\\[2ex] \eta &= \frac{e\sin(\chi - \Pi_0)}{1 - e_0^2}.\end{aligned}\right\}\qquad (9.8.10)$$

It is obvious, since χ differs from Π_0, and e from e_0, by quantities of order of the perturbing force, that ξ and η are also quantities of $0(\tilde{R})$. From (9.8.10) we obtain

$$1 - e^2 = (1 - e_0^2)[1 - 2e_0\xi - (1 - e_0^2)\xi^2 - (1 - e_0^2)\eta^2]. \qquad (9.8.11)$$

Utilizing (9.8.10) and (9.8.11), (9.8.9) becomes

$$\frac{\bar{r}a}{ra_0} = \frac{\bar{r} + \bar{r}\cos\bar{f}[\xi(1 - e_0^2) + e_0] + \bar{r}\sin\bar{f}[\eta(1 - e_0^2)]}{a_0(1 - e_0^2)[1 - 2e_0\xi - (1 - e_0^2)\xi^2 - (1 - e_0^2)\eta^2]}.$$

Equation (9.5.10) can be written as

$$\bar{r} = a_0(1 - e_0^2) - e_0\bar{r}\cos\bar{f},$$

so that

$$\frac{\bar{r}a}{ra_0} = \frac{1 + \xi\dfrac{\bar{r}}{a_0}\cos\bar{f} + \eta\dfrac{\bar{r}}{a_0}\sin\bar{f}}{1 - 2e_0\xi - (1 - e_0^2)\xi^2 - (1 - e_0^2)\eta^2}. \qquad (9.8.12)$$

Let us introduce the abbreviations

$$\left.\begin{aligned}A &= 1 + (\xi\bar{r}/a_0)\cos\bar{f} + (\eta\bar{r}/a_0)\sin\bar{f}\\[2ex] B &= 1 - 2e_0\xi - (1 - e_0^2)\xi^2 - (1 - e_0^2)\eta^2;\end{aligned}\right\}\qquad (9.8.13)$$

then (9.8.12) becomes $\bar{r}/r = (a_0/a)A/B$. Using this and (9.8.11) in (9.8.8),

$$\dot{z} = \sqrt{\frac{a_0^3}{a^3}}\,\frac{A^2}{B^{3/2}}. \qquad (9.8.14)$$

Some other relationships of this type can also be found. Equation (9.5.14) gives $1 + \nu = r/\bar{r}$, from which

$$1 + \nu = (a/a_0)B/A. \qquad (9.8.15)$$

Also

$$\frac{h}{h_0} = \sqrt{\frac{a_0(1 - e_0^2)}{a(1 - e^2)}},$$

or

$$\frac{h}{h_0} = \sqrt{\frac{a_0}{a}}\,\frac{1}{B^{1/2}}. \tag{9.8.16}$$

Squaring (9.8.15) and employing (9.8.14) and (9.8.16) yields

$$\dot{z} = \frac{h_0}{h}\,\frac{1}{(1 + \nu)^2}. \tag{9.8.17}$$

Also from (9.8.15), we obtain

$$\left(\frac{\nu}{1 + \nu}\right)^2 = 1 - 2\frac{a_0}{a}\,\frac{A}{B} + \left(\frac{a_0}{a}\right)^2 \frac{A^2}{B^2}.$$

Multiplying both sides of this by h_0/h, using (9.8.14) and (9.8.16),

$$\frac{h_0}{h}\left(\frac{\nu}{1 + \nu}\right)^2 = \frac{h_0}{h} - 2\frac{h}{h_0}A + \dot{z},$$

or

$$\dot{z} = 1 + W + \frac{h_0}{h}\left(\frac{\nu}{1 + \nu}\right)^2, \tag{9.8.18}$$

where

$$\overline{W} = 2\frac{h}{h_0} - \frac{h_0}{h} - 1 + 2\frac{h}{h_0}\xi\frac{\bar{r}}{a_0}\cos\bar{f} + 2\frac{h}{h_0}\eta\frac{\bar{r}}{a_0}\sin\bar{f}. \tag{9.8.19}$$

This is the $\overline{W}$ function which plays a central role in Hansen's method. Before proceeding, we will develop other forms for (9.8.18) and (9.8.19). As Hill* points out, (9.8.17) allows us to rewrite (9.8.18) as $\dot{z} = (1 + \overline{W})/(1 - \nu^2)$ or

$$\dot{z} = 1 + (\overline{W} + \nu^2)/(1 - \nu^2). \tag{9.8.20}$$

In addition, we can eliminate $\dot{z}$ from (9.8.17) and (9.8.18), and find

$$\overline{W} = \frac{h_0}{h}\,\frac{1 - \nu}{1 + \nu} - 1$$

or

$$\overline{W} = 2\frac{h_0}{h}\,\frac{1}{1 + \nu} - \frac{h_0}{h} - 1. \tag{9.8.21}$$

This last allows us to find $\overline{W}$, h_0/h, or ν if the other two are known.

---

*G. W. Hill, *Amer. J. of Math*, **4,** 256, 1881, or *Coll. Math Works,* **1,** p. 348.

9. EXPANSION OF THE W FUNCTION

Now let us consider the $\overline{W}$ function as given by (9.8.19). The factors h, ξ, and η are direct functions of t; however, $\bar{r}$ and $\bar{f}$ are functions of time only through the Hansen variable z. As we have seen in the development immediately following (9.5.26), we can write $z = t + \delta z$, where δz includes all the results of the perturbations and is of $0(\tilde{R})$. We may write

$$\overline{W}[h(t), \xi(t), \eta(t), \bar{r}(z), \bar{f}(z)] = \overline{W}[h(t), \xi(t), \eta(t), \bar{r}(t + \delta z), \bar{f}(t + \delta z)].$$

In regard to $\overline{W}$, Hansen distinguishes those variables which are functions of time only through z by new symbols. He writes $\bar{\rho}$ for $\bar{r}$, $\bar{\omega}$ for $\bar{f}$; he uses ζ for z and τ for t, so that now $z = t + \delta z$ becomes $\zeta = \tau + \delta\zeta$. For emphasis, he also removes the bar over W when he uses these replacements. Then (9.8.19) becomes

$$W = 2\frac{h}{h_0} - \frac{h_0}{h} - 1 + 2\frac{h}{h_0}\xi\frac{\bar{\rho}}{a_0}\cos\bar{\omega} + 2\frac{h}{h_0}\eta\frac{\bar{\rho}}{a_0}\sin\bar{\omega}, \tag{9.9.1}$$

The Taylor expansion of W with respect to ζ, then, is

$$W(t, z) = W(t, \tau) + \frac{\partial W(t, \tau)}{\partial \tau}\delta\zeta + \frac{1}{2}\frac{\partial^2 W(t, \tau)}{\partial \tau^2}(\delta\zeta)^2 + \cdots, \tag{9.9.2}$$

where $W(t, \tau)$ indicates that $\bar{\rho}$ and $\bar{\omega}$ are to be considered as functions of τ only. Thus τ enters the motion only through the Kepler-type equation (9.5.13), involving $z(= \zeta)$, while the direct time dependence of the osculating parameters h, ξ, η is expressed with t. This distinction is known as *Hansen's device* and its computational advantages will appear in the next section.

We write the expressions $\bar{\rho}$ and $\bar{\omega}$, which are the same as (9.5.10) through (9.5.13) with appropriate symbol changes, as:

$$\bar{\rho} = \frac{a_0(1 - e_0^2)}{1 + e_0\cos\bar{\omega}}, \qquad \bar{\omega} = \theta - \Pi_0, \qquad \tan\frac{\bar{\omega}}{2} = \sqrt{\frac{1 + e_0}{1 - e_0}}\tan\frac{\bar{\varepsilon}}{2},$$

$$\bar{\varepsilon} - e_0\sin\bar{\varepsilon} = \sqrt{\frac{\mu}{a_0^3}}(\zeta - T_0),$$

where we have used $\bar{\varepsilon}$ for $\overline{E}$. Now since $\zeta = \tau + \delta\zeta$ where $\delta\zeta$ contains all the terms dependent on the disturbing function, the quantities $\bar{\rho}$ and $\bar{\omega}$ become, when $\delta\zeta$ is suppressed, the same as their unperturbed counterparts, $r^{(0)}$ and $f^{(0)}$. Since we still need the distinction between quantities associated with t and τ, we denote them by ρ and ω, which we take to mean the Keplerian r and f, dependent on the constant elements a_0, e_0, and T_0. $W(t, \tau)$ then becomes

$$W(t, \tau) \equiv W_0 = 2\frac{h}{h_0} - \frac{h_0}{h} - 1 + 2\frac{h}{h_0}\xi\frac{\rho}{a_0}\cos\omega + 2\frac{h}{h_0}\eta\frac{\rho}{a_0}\sin\omega. \tag{9.9.3}$$

The terms in W_0 are at least of the first order since, as has been shown, $h = h_0 + 0(\tilde{R})$, and ξ and η, too, are both of the order of the perturbing force. We have also seen that $\delta\zeta$ (δz) is of the order of $\tilde{R}$. Thus in (9.9.2), the first term on the right-hand side is of first order, the second is of second order, etc. We may then turn our attention to W_0 and first-order terms, with the realization that higher-order terms, if desired, can be introduced by including the derivatives of W_0 as indicated by (9.9.2). Thus, a systematic procedure evolves which hinges on one quantity, namely, the W function.

10. EVALUATION OF W_0

Now the values of h_0 and a_0 are fixed, and those of ρ and ω can be generated at any time from Keplerian motion. The change of W_0 with t, as t influences the osculating elements h, ξ, and η, must thus be investigated. Utilizing (9.8.10) yields

$$W_0 = 2\frac{h}{h_0} - \frac{h_0}{h} - 1 + 2\frac{h}{h_0}\frac{\rho}{a_0(1 - e_0^2)}\{e\cos(\chi - \Pi_0)\cos\omega + e\sin(\chi - \Pi_0)\sin\omega - e_0\cos\omega\}.$$

But we may write $f = \bar{f} - \omega - (\chi - \Pi_0 - \omega)$, and $\rho\, e_0 \cos\omega = a_0(1 - e_0^2) - \rho$, so that, then,

$$W_0 = \frac{2\rho}{h_0 a_0(1 - e_0^2)} he\cos(\chi - \Pi_0 - \omega) + \frac{2\rho}{h_0 a_0(1 - e_0^2)} h - \frac{h_0}{h} - 1. \tag{9.10.1}$$

Use of (9.5.2), (9.5.3), and (9.5.5) leads to

$$r\dot{\theta} - h = he[\cos(\bar{f} - \omega)\cos(\chi - \Pi_0 - \omega) + \sin(\bar{f} - \omega)\sin(\chi - \Pi_0 - \omega)],$$

and

$$\dot{r} = he[\sin(\bar{f} - \omega)\cos(\chi - \Pi_0 - \omega) - \cos(\bar{f} - \omega)\sin(\chi - \Pi_0 - \omega)],$$

whence $he\cos(\chi - \Pi_0 - \omega) = \dot{r}\sin(\bar{f} - \omega) + (r\dot{\theta} - h)\cos(\bar{f} - \omega)$.

Further, (9.5.17) can be written as

$$\frac{1}{h_0 a_0(1 - e_0^2)} = \frac{h_0}{\mu}.$$

These last two expressions in (9.10.1) yield

$$W_0 = \frac{2h_0\rho}{\mu}\cos(\bar{f} - \omega)r\dot{\theta} + \frac{2h_0\rho}{\mu}\sin(\bar{f} - \omega)\dot{r} - \frac{h_0}{h} - 1 + \frac{2\rho h_0 h}{\mu}[1 - \cos(\bar{f} - \omega)]. \tag{9.10.2}$$

Since higher-order effects in the τ-dependence of W have already been allowed for in (9.9.2), we may treat (9.10.2) as if τ were constant; only the t-dependence of W_0 must be studied, and the latest manipulations have simply changed from the osculating parameters h, ξ, η to $r, \theta, h, \bar{f}$ (both groups being equivalent to $a, e, \chi - \Pi_0$). The calculation of $W_0(t)$ now proceeds most conveniently by forming its derivative with respect to t (ignoring τ!). This will be the basis for iterative quadratures, where nth order approximations for r, θ, $h, \bar{f}$ in the integrand yield the $(n+1)$th approximation for W_0 in the familiar manner. Thus, from (9.10.2)

$$\frac{\partial W_0}{\partial t} = \frac{2h_0\rho}{\mu}\left\{\cos(\bar{f}-\omega)(r\ddot{\theta} + \dot{r}\dot{\theta}) - \sin(\bar{f}-\omega)r\dot{\theta}\frac{d\bar{f}}{dz}\dot{z}\right.$$

$$+ \sin(f-\omega)\ddot{r} + \cos(\bar{f}-\omega)\dot{r}\frac{d\bar{f}}{dz}\dot{z} - [\cos(\bar{f}-\omega) - 1]\dot{h}$$

$$\left. + \sin(\bar{f}-\omega)h\frac{d\bar{f}}{dz}\dot{z}\right\} + \frac{h_0}{h^2}\dot{h}. \tag{9.10.3}$$

From (9.5.4)

$$\dot{h} = -\frac{\mu}{(r^2\dot{\theta})^2}(r^2\ddot{\theta} + 2r\dot{r}\dot{\theta}),$$

and utilizing the second of (9.5.1),

$$\dot{h} = -h^2\,\partial\tilde{R}/\partial\theta. \tag{9.10.4}$$

If we substitute this, along with both of (9.5.1), (9.5.2), (9.5.3), and (9.8.7) and (9.8.8), in (9.10.3), we obtain, after some simplification,

$$\frac{\partial W_0}{\partial t} = h_0\left\{2\frac{\rho}{r}\cos(\bar{f}-\omega) - 1 + 2\frac{h^2\rho}{\mu}\left[\cos(\bar{f}-\omega) - 1\right]\right\}\frac{\partial\tilde{R}}{\partial\theta} + 2h_0\rho\sin(\bar{f}-\omega)\frac{\partial\tilde{R}}{\partial r}. \tag{9.10.5}$$

For some applications a simplification in this expression results if one treats the term $-h_0\,\partial\tilde{R}/\partial\theta$ separately. Anticipating (9.10.6), one recognizes this factor as $-(d/dt)(h_0/h)$.

The appearance of $\partial\tilde{R}/\partial r$ and $\partial\tilde{R}/\partial\theta$ in the right-hand side of (9.10.5) opens the way for the usual order-of-magnitude arguments. Since we are interested in W_0 only to first order, and the components of the disturbing force are already multiplicative factors, we can replace r by $r^{(0)}$, $\bar{f}$ by $f^{(0)}$, and h by h_0, and, further, evaluate the partial derivatives of $\tilde{R}$ in terms of these. Since $\bar{f} - \omega$ is $O(\tilde{R})$ we see that $\partial W_0/\partial t$ contains some terms of $O(\tilde{R}^2)$.

The complete procedure now becomes clear. We integrate $\partial W_0/\partial t$ with respect to t, $\overline{W}_0(t = t_0) = 0$ being the initial condition for departure from the osculating orbit at t_0. We then evaluate ρ and ω at $\tau = t$, to obtain $\overline{W}_0$. Now we can cast (9.10.4) into the form

$$\frac{d}{dt}\left(\frac{h_0}{h}\right) = h_0 \frac{\partial \tilde{R}}{\partial \theta}. \tag{9.10.6}$$

Thus, we can also find h_0/h, which, with W_0, gives us v to first order by using (9.8.21). Higher-order terms follow from the derivative of W_0 with respect to τ, as given in (9.9.2), where $\delta\zeta$ (δz) is found by integrating the second term on the right-hand side of (9.8.20). We recognize that in the formalism of Hansen, the bar appears again over W as soon as τ is changed to t. We also note that z, as given by the integral of (9.8.20), involves terms of second order; so did W_0 according to (9.10.5). As a consequence, the accuracy of Hansen's "first-order" perturbations is higher than that normally obtained.

11. THE U FUNCTION

To complete Hansen's method, we can also introduce a function U into the perturbations of the osculating plane, which plays a role analogous to W. Repeating (9.6.9), we have $s = q \sin(\theta - \Omega_0) - p \cos(\theta - \Omega_0)$. To establish an analogy with the in-plane case, we write

$$\bar{U}(t, z) = s. \tag{9.11.1}$$

As with $\overline{W}$, we expand $\bar{U}$ in a Taylor series,

$$U(t, z) = U(t, \tau) + \frac{\partial U(t, \tau)}{\partial \tau}\delta\zeta + \cdots \tag{9.11.2}$$

where

$$U(t, \tau) \equiv U_0 = q \sin(\bar{\omega} + \Pi_0 - \Omega_0) - p \cos(\bar{\omega} + \Pi_0 - \Omega_0), \tag{9.11.3}$$

and we have used $\theta = \bar{f} + \Pi_0$ with $\bar{f}$ being rewritten as $\bar{\omega}$. Thus,

$$\partial U_0/\partial t = \dot{q} \sin(\bar{\omega} + \Pi_0 - \Omega_0) - \dot{p} \cos(\bar{\omega} + \Pi_0 - \Omega_0).$$

But with the aid of (9.6.8), where $\theta = \bar{f} - \Pi_0$, this becomes

$$\partial U_0/\partial t = hr \cos i \sin(\bar{\omega} - \bar{f})\, \partial\tilde{R}/\partial X_3. \tag{9.11.4}$$

Since $\bar{\omega} - \bar{f}$ is $0(\tilde{R})$, $\partial U_0/\partial t = 0(\tilde{R}^2)$ and we may replace h by h_0, r by $r^{(0)}$, i by i_0, etc., also in $\partial\tilde{R}/\partial X_3$. Iterative quadratures of (9.11.4) with respect to t may be executed as we did for $\partial W_0/\partial t$. Since $\bar{\omega}$ is a function of τ it is treated like a constant in these manipulations.*

*Referring to our discussion of (9.6.1) and (9.6.2), we see that direct integration of the time derivatives of i, σ, Ω, as practised by some authors for the out-of-plane motion, fails to introduce higher-order terms to the first approximation, as Hansen does by his series development for U.

Having obtained s, we still need $\dot{s}$ to compute p and q by (9.6.13). This follows to the same order of approximation from the obvious relation $\dot{s} = d\,\overline{U}_0/dt$, calling for the total time derivative of $\overline{U}_0$ (with all time dependencies taken into account). One way of accomplishing this is by writing

$$\frac{d\,\overline{U}_0(t, z)}{dt} = \frac{\partial U_0(t, \tau)}{\partial t} + \overline{\frac{\partial}{\partial \tau} \int \left(\frac{\partial U_0}{\partial t}\right) dt}. \tag{9.11.5}$$

Here the first term on the right denotes (9.11.4), with τ replaced by t, and the second represents the result of integrating (9.11.4), then differentiating with respect to τ, where $\bar{\omega} = \bar{\omega}(\tau)$ and $\bar{\rho} = \bar{\rho}(\tau)$, and replacing τ by t. Thus s and $\dot{s}$ have been calculated to the first level of approximation. Further refinements may be obtained, once $\delta\zeta$ is known from the in-plane solution, by going to the next term in the expansion (9.11.2) for $U(t, z)$.

The remaining procedure is evident: p and q, of $0(\tilde{R})$, follow from (9.6.13), $\kappa = 2\cos^2 i_0$ from (9.6.10) as 0(1), then Γ by quadrature of (9.6.11) as $0(\tilde{R}^2)$. Finally (9.6.3c) yields $\sin\varphi$ and (9.6.3a), (9.6.3b) can, with effort, be rearranged to yield $\cos\varphi\cos\lambda$ and $\cos\varphi\sin\lambda$. This completes the necessary trigonometric terms to compute x_1, x_2, x_3 by (9.2.2) with the help of r from the in-plane solution.

12. A SURVEY AND EVALUATION OF HANSEN'S METHOD

In the preceding sections we have covered the essential development of Hansen's method in considerable detail. We chose to carry the successive manipulations for in-plane and out-of-plane motions in parallel: first in terms of polar and cartesian coordinates, then in terms of z, v, u, and finally in terms of W and U. At the risk of some redundancy, it may be helpful to summarize the governing relations in direct sequence from r, θ to W for the in-plane motion and from Euler angles to U for the out-of-plane motion.

12.1. Relations for the In-Plane Motion

The quasi-conic relations (9.5.10)–(9.5.14) represent relations between r, θ, and a specially defined set of orbit elements. Here a key role is played by the quantities v and z, also known as the *perturbations in the radius and time*. Their relation to W is crucial. Comparing (9.5.11), in terms of the quasi-true anomaly, with the corresponding equation for the osculating orbit (9.8.2) we obtain $f - \bar{f} = \Pi_0 - \chi$, that is, the difference between angular elements rests in the perturbation of the argument of perigee. This quantity pervades equation (9.8.9), the definitions (9.8.10), and (9.8.11) through (9.8.13). We are then led to expressions (9.8.14) for $\dot{z}$, (9.8.15) for $(1 + v)$, and (9.8.16) for the ratio between perturbed and unperturbed angular momenta. A straightforward combination of these results yields (9.8.18) and (9.8.19); in (9.8.18) the first-order effects of $\dot{z}$ are restricted to those due to

$\overline{W}$, and thus the importance of this quantity begins to emerge. It is important to note that in $\overline{W}$, according to (9.8.19), only $\bar{r}$ and $\bar{f}$ are dependent on z, so that

$$\frac{\partial \overline{W}}{\partial z} = \frac{2h}{a_0(1 - e_0^2)}[e_0 \sin \bar{f}(1 + e \cos f) - e \sin f(1 + e_0 \cos \bar{f})]. \tag{9.12.1}$$

A similar expression may be found for $\dot{v}$. Starting with (9.5.14) we have

$$\dot{v} = \frac{1}{\bar{r}}\left[\dot{r} - \frac{d\bar{r}}{dz}\dot{z}(1 + v)\right],$$

where we substitute $\dot{r} = he \sin f$,

$$\frac{d\bar{r}}{dz} = \frac{\mu\, e_0 \sin \bar{f}}{h_0 a_0(1 - e_0^2)}$$

and

$$\dot{z} = \frac{h_0}{h(1 + v)^2}$$

from (9.8.17). Comparison of the resulting equation with (9.12.1) yields

$$\dot{v} = -\tfrac{1}{2}\partial \overline{W}/\partial z. \tag{9.12.2}$$

This relation offers an alternative means for calculating v from $\overline{W}$ instead of proceeding by (9.10.6) and (9.8.21). Equations (9.12.2) and (9.8.18) provide z and v once $\overline{W}$ has been calculated to a given order of approximation. The latter becomes the central operation in Hansen's procedure, especially since it provides a built-in capability for successive refinements. Equation (9.9.2) provides the basic series development for $\overline{W}$ in terms of ζ (an alternate notation for z) the *perturbation of the time*. This enters the Kepler-type equation (9.5.13) for Hansen's coordinates and thus $\bar{\rho}$ and $\bar{\omega}$ (alternate notations for $\bar{r}$ and $\bar{f}$) while the coefficients of (9.9.2) are also functions of time, through the osculating elements. The distinction between these two time-dependences, denoted by τ and t, is the basic device for Hansen's computational approach to W.

The coefficients of (9.9.2) are evaluated by recursive quadratures of their derivatives with respect to t, in terms of the disturbing function $\tilde{R}$, for successive levels of approximation, as in the solution of Lagrange's planetary equations. Thus, the integrand for the first term in (9.9.2) is given by (9.10.5), yielding an approximation to $0(\tilde{R})$ with the inclusion of some higher-order terms. Quadratures of (9.12.2) and (9.8.20) then yield v and z to the same accuracy, where we use $v = z = 0$ at $t = t_0$ if starting from true elements. Using the result for z (as ζ) in (9.9.2), we may include the $\partial W/\partial \tau$ term for a better approximation, etc. Having obtained W, v, and z to the desired accuracy, we obtain $\overline{E}$ from (9.5.13), $\bar{f}$ from (9.5.12), and $\bar{r}$ from (9.5.10). Thereupon θ and r follow from (9.5.11) and (9.5.14) to complete the in-plane solution.

12.2. Relations for the Out-of-Plane Motion

The well-known trigonometric relations (9.6.2), in terms of perturbed angular variables, are the point of departure. Hansen rewrites this right-hand side in terms of the osculating parameters i_0 and Ω_0 at t_0 and the additional variables s, p, q, Γ, κ. The relations (9.6.4)–(9.6.7) between these variables and the perturbed geocentric angles i, σ, θ are manipulated to yield $s = s(p, q, \theta)$ in (9.6.9), $p = p(s, \dot{s}, \theta, \mathring{\theta})$, and $q = q(s, \dot{s}, \theta, \mathring{\theta})$ in (9.6.13); furthermore $\dot{p} = \dot{p}(\partial\tilde{R}/\partial X_3, \theta, h, r, i)$, $\dot{q} = \dot{q}(\partial\tilde{R}/\partial X_3, \theta, h, r, i)$ in (9.6.8) as well as $\dot{\Gamma} = \dot{\Gamma}(\partial\tilde{R}/\partial X_3, s, h, r, i)$ in (9.6.11). Now one denotes $s = U(t, z)$ and distinguishes between the t-dependence of p, q in (9.6.9) and the τ-dependence of θ to obtain a series development for U in (9.11.2) analogous to (9.9.2) for W. Its leading term is obtained by quadrature of $\partial U_0(\partial\tilde{R}/\partial X_3, \bar{\omega})/\partial t$, as given in (9.11.4), with the help of (9.6.8) and renders a first approximation to s. Similarly, $\dot{s}$ follows from $d\,\overline{U}_0/dt$ according to (9.11.5). With the help of s, $\dot{s}$ one calculates p, q from (9.6.13) and Γ from (9.6.11). The quantity κ is obtainable to $0(1)$ from (9.6.7). Thereupon (9.6.3) leads to $\sin\varphi$, $\cos\varphi\sin\lambda$, and $\cos\varphi\cos\lambda$ needed to compute x_1, x_2, x_3 from (9.2.2). Note that the calculations are greatly simplified for a first approximation because p, q, Γ, and κ may be ignored in (9.6.3), since they belong to higher-order terms.

12.3. Application. Oblateness Perturbation

We will follow the sequence of operations outlined above, executing some of the quadratures analytically, to illustrate an approach to a "first approximation" to oblateness perturbations by Hansen's method. We will also indicate where, and why, numerical evaluation should supplement the analytic approach.

The initial conditions will be taken in terms of osculating elements a_0, e_0, i_0, Ω_0, T_0, p_0 at time t_0, where p_0 stands for the argument of perigee, a departure from the usual nomenclature to avoid confusion with other uses of ω in Hansen's notation.

The question of an independent variable must be settled next. If time itself is chosen we have, obviously, no recourse except to expand the disturbing function, etc. in the way discussed in Chapter 8. For reasons that must be clear to the reader by now, we shall not follow that approach. Rather we adopt the true anomaly as the independent variable. We take $\bar{f} \simeq f^{(0)}$, the unperturbed anomaly for the orbit at t_0, in a first-order analysis; for simplicity we will drop the superscript zero. The initial value of f will be denoted by f_0. The independent variable for the integration is changed from time to true anomaly by the usual relation

$$df/dt = h_0^3(1 + e_0\cos f)^2/\mu.$$

We need explicit expressions for $\partial\tilde{R}/\partial\theta$ and $\partial\tilde{R}/\partial r$ in (9.10.5). These follow in a straightforward manner from the first-order oblateness potential

$$\frac{\partial \tilde{R}}{\partial r} = \frac{-3J_2R^2(1 + e_0 \cos f)^4}{2a_0^4(1 - e_0^2)^4}[1 - 3 \sin^2 i_0 \sin^2 (f + p_0)],$$

$$\frac{\partial \tilde{R}}{\partial \theta} = \frac{-3J_2R^2(1 + e_0 \cos f)^3}{2a_0^3(1 - e_0^2)^3} \sin^2 i_0 \sin 2 (f + p_0), \tag{9.12.3}$$

$$\frac{\partial \tilde{R}}{\partial X_3} = \frac{-3J_2R^2 \sin 2i_0(1 + e_0 \cos f)^4}{2a_0^4(1 - e_0^2)^4} \sin (f + p_0).$$

To calculate W_0, we set all the orbit elements in (9.10.5), including those in $\partial\tilde{R}/\partial\theta$ and $\partial\tilde{R}/\partial r$, equal to their values at the epoch, and remember that ρ and ω do not participate in the integration. Now we may write $\partial W_0/\partial t = (\partial W_0/\partial f)(df/dt)$ where the partial derivatives are to be interpreted in the spirit of Hansen's device. Thus,

$$\frac{\partial W_0}{\partial f} = -\frac{3J_2R^2\rho(1+e_0\cos f)}{a_0^3(1-e_0^2)^3}\Big\{[(2+e_0\cos f)\cos(f-\omega)-2]\sin^2 i_0 \sin 2(f+p_0)$$
$$+ [1 - 3\sin^2 i_0 \sin(f+p_0)](1+e_0\cos f)\sin(f-\omega)\Big\}$$
$$-\frac{d}{df}\left(\frac{h_0}{h}\right).$$

Integrating this expression between the limits f_0 and f and, thereafter, setting

$$\omega = f, \rho = \frac{a_0(1 - e_0^2)}{1 + e_0 \cos f},$$

we find

$$\overline{W}_0(f) = \frac{3J_2R^2}{a_0^2(1 - e_0^2)^2(1 + e_0 \cos f)}[A + e_0B + e_0^2C$$
$$+ \sin^2 i_0(A' + e_0B' + e_0^2C')]$$
$$+1 - \frac{h_0}{h}, \tag{9.12.4}$$

where

$$A = 1 - \cos (f - f_0),$$
$$B = (f - f_0) \sin f + \tfrac{1}{2} \cos f - \tfrac{1}{2} \cos (2f_0 - f),$$
$$C = \tfrac{1}{2}[1 - \cos (f - f_0)] + \tfrac{1}{4} \cos (f_0 + f) - \tfrac{1}{6} \cos 2f - \tfrac{1}{12} \cos (3f_0 - f),$$
$$A' = \tfrac{3}{2}[\cos (f - f_0) - 1] + \tfrac{1}{2} \cos 2(f_0 + p_0) + \tfrac{1}{3} \cos (2f + 2p_0)$$
$$-\tfrac{1}{4} \cos (f_0 + f + 2p_0) - \tfrac{7}{12} \cos (3f_0 - f + 2p_0),$$

$$B' = \tfrac{3}{2}(f_0 - f)\sin f + \tfrac{3}{4}[\cos(2f_0 - f) - \cos f]$$
$$+ \tfrac{1}{2}\cos(f_0 + 2p_0) + \tfrac{1}{6}\cos(3f_0 + 2p_0) + \tfrac{1}{4}\cos(f + 2p_0)$$
$$- \tfrac{3}{4}\cos(2f_0 - f + 2p_0) - \tfrac{3}{8}\cos(4f_0 - f + 2p_0) + \tfrac{5}{24}\cos(3f + 2p_0),$$

$$C' = \tfrac{3}{4}[\cos(f - f_0) - 1] - \tfrac{3}{8}\cos(f_0 + f) + \tfrac{1}{4}\cos 2f + \tfrac{1}{8}\cos(3f_0 - f)$$
$$+ \tfrac{3}{8}\cos 2p_0 + \tfrac{1}{12}\cos(2f + 2p_0) + \tfrac{1}{8}\cos(f_0 + f + 2p_0)$$
$$- \tfrac{5}{16}\cos(f_0 - f + 2p_0) - \tfrac{1}{16}\cos(f_0 - f - 2p_0) - \tfrac{5}{24}\cos(3f_0 - f + 2p_0)$$
$$+ \tfrac{1}{48}\cos(3f_0 + f + 2p_0) - \tfrac{1}{16}\cos(5f_0 - f + 2p_0) + \tfrac{1}{24}\cos(4f + 2p_0).$$

In performing these quadratures we have taken into account the initial conditions $\overline{W}_0 = 0$ and $h_0/h = 1$ at $f = f_0$. To find the explicit expression for the last two terms in (9.12.4), we recall from (9.10.6) that

$$1 - \frac{h_0}{h} = -h_0 \int_{t_0}^{t} \frac{\partial \tilde{R}}{\partial \theta}\, dt.$$

Changing to f as independent variable and substituting from (9.12.3) we find

$$1 - \frac{h_0}{h}(f) = \frac{-3J_2R^2 \sin^2 i_0}{4a_0^2(1 - e_0^2)^2}\Big[\cos 2(f + p_0) + \tfrac{1}{3}e_0 \cos(3f + 2p_0)$$
$$+ e_0 \cos(f + 2p_0)\Big]_{f_0}^{f}. \qquad (9.12.5)$$

We next consider the different ways of calculating v and z from $\overline{W}_0$. Indeed, the simplest-looking expression for $\dot{v}$ is (9.12.2). Here the quantity $\partial \overline{W}/\partial z$ represents the derivative of $\overline{W}$ (or, to first order $\overline{W}_0$) with respect to z wherever this variable enters that function through the Kepler-type equation (9.5.13). It is specifically contained in $\bar{r}$ and $\bar{f}$. But these quantities were treated as constants, ρ and ω, during the integration of (9.10.5) by Hansen's device. An intermediate result of that calculation was

$$W_0 = \frac{-3J_2R^2}{a^3(1 - e_0^2)^3}\Big\{(\tfrac{3}{2}\sin^2 i_0 - 1)[fe_0 \sin\omega + (1 + \tfrac{1}{2}e_0^2)\cos(f - \omega)$$
$$- \tfrac{1}{4}e_0^2 \cos(f + \omega) + \tfrac{1}{2}e_0 \cos(2f - \omega)$$
$$+ \tfrac{1}{12}e_0^2 \cos(3f - \omega)]$$
$$+ \sin^2 i_0[\tfrac{1}{2}\cos 2(f + p_0) + \tfrac{1}{6}e_0 \cos(3f + 2p_0) +$$

$$+\tfrac{1}{2}e_0 \cos(f + 2p_0) - \tfrac{1}{4}(1 - \tfrac{1}{2}e_0^2)\cos(f + \omega + 2p_0)$$
$$-\tfrac{5}{16}e_0^2 \cos(f - \omega + 2p_0) - \tfrac{1}{16}e_0^2 \cos(f - \omega - 2p_0)$$
$$-\tfrac{3}{4}e_0 \cos(2f - \omega + 2p_0)$$
$$-\tfrac{1}{12}(7 + \tfrac{5}{2}e_0^2)\cos(3f - \omega + 2p_0)$$
$$+\tfrac{1}{48}e_0^2 \cos(3f + \omega + 2p_0) - \tfrac{3}{8}e_0 \cos(4f - \omega + 2p_0)$$
$$-\tfrac{1}{16}e_0^2 \cos(5f - \omega + 2p_0)]\Big\}_{f_0}^{f}.$$

$$= F(a_0, e_0, i_0, f, f_0, \rho, \omega).$$

Equation (9.12.2) suggests that we form

$$\frac{\partial F}{\partial \zeta} = \left(\frac{\partial F}{\partial \rho}\frac{\partial \rho}{\partial \omega} + \frac{\partial F}{\partial \omega}\right)\frac{\partial \omega}{\partial \zeta} = \frac{\partial W_0}{\partial \zeta},$$

thereafter substitute r for ρ, f for ω, and integrate with respect to t to obtain v. In the established notation this reads

$$v = \frac{1}{2}\int_t^{t_0} \left(\overline{\frac{\partial W_0}{\partial \zeta}}\right) dt. \tag{9.12.6}$$

An alternative approach, which does not require another involvement of W_0 in a quadrature, originates from (9.8.21), which may be written in the form

$$v = \frac{2h_0/h}{(\overline{W}_0 + 1 + h_0/h)} - 1. \tag{9.12.7}$$

After substitution of (9.12.4) and (9.12.5) into this equation it can be evaluated in a straightforward, albeit laborious, manner.

We follow neither of the paths sketched above, but choose to solve for v numerically. The reason is that having v, one must next find z, then use (9.5.12) and (9.5.13) to obtain $\bar{f}$ and ultimately $\bar{r}$, and none of these steps is accomplished analytically with a small effort. (Furthermore, we must face up to contending with (9.6.3) and converting to the trigonometric parts of (9.2.2) before the final answer is in hand.) Thus we intend to exploit the dominant role played by the W-function for in-plane perturbations, but capitalize on numerical evaluation of it where appropriate.

We obtain z from (9.8.20), noting that $v^2 = 0(\tilde{R}^2)$; the required first-order result is simply $dz/dt = 1 + \overline{W}_0$, or in terms of f,

$$z(f) = t + \frac{a_0^{3/2}(1 - e_0^2)^{3/2}}{\mu^{1/2}} \int_{f_0}^{f} \frac{\overline{W}_0 df}{(1 + e_0 \cos f)^2}. \tag{9.12.8}$$

Since the form of (9.12.4) also does not encourage a literal development of this quadrature, the computation of z will be done numerically. Substitution of the results from (9.12.7) and (9.12.8) into (9.5.10)–(9.5.14) provides us with r and θ.

We now proceed to the out-of-plane perturbations and calculate $\overline{U}_0(f)$ in a manner quite analogous to $\overline{W}_0(f)$. Substituting $\partial\tilde{R}/\partial X_3$ from (9.12.3) into (9.11.4), we obtain

$$\frac{\partial U_0}{\partial f} = \frac{3J_2R^2 \cos i_0 \sin 2i_0}{2a_0^2(1 - e_0)^2} \sin(f + p_0) \sin(f - \omega)(1 + e_0 \cos f). \tag{9.12.9}$$

Integration between the limits f_0 and f with subsequent substitution of f for ω yields

$$\begin{aligned}\overline{U}_0(f) = {} & \frac{3J_2R^2 \cos i_0 \sin 2i_0}{8a_0^2(1 - e_0^2)^2(1 + e_0 \cos f)} \\ & \times \Big\{ 2(f - f_0) \cos(f + p_0) - \sin(f + p_0) - \sin(f - 2f_0 - p_0) - 2e_0 \sin p_0 \\ & - 2e_0 \sin f_0 \cos(f + p_0) + 2e_0 \sin f \cos(f - p_0) \\ & + \tfrac{1}{3}e_0 \sin(2f + p_0) - \tfrac{1}{3}e_0 \sin(f - 3f_0 - p_0) \\ & - e_0 \sin(f - f_0 - p_0) \Big\}. \end{aligned} \tag{9.12.10}$$

This represents s according to (9.11.1). With the help of this result we can calculate $\sin\varphi$, $\cos\varphi \sin\lambda$, and $\cos\varphi \cos\lambda$ to first order (numerically) by means of (9.6.3), where we employ the previously computed value for θ. Combining these results with r, as calculated above, in equations (9.2.2), brings us to x_1, x_2, x_3.

For a full evaluation of (9.6.3) we also need p, q, κ, Γ, all of which enter only through higher-order contributions. They require the calculation of $\dot{s}$, which we consider as a matter of general interest. In the expression (9.11.5)

$$\dot{s} = \frac{d\bar{U}_0}{dt} = \frac{\partial \bar{U}_0}{\partial t} + \frac{\partial}{\partial \tau} \overline{\int \frac{\partial \bar{U}_0}{\partial t} dt}$$

we observe that

$$\frac{\partial \bar{U}_0}{\partial t} = \frac{\partial \bar{U}_0}{\partial f} \frac{df}{dt}.$$

A first-order evaluation of this term is to be obtained with the help of (9.12.9), but as we let ω approach f it vanishes. To calculate the second term in (9.11.5) we need the intermediate result $U_0(f)$, which is found in the process of deriving (9.12.10):

$$U_0 = \frac{3J_2R^2 \cos i_0 \sin 2i_0}{8a_0^2(1 - e_0^2)^2}$$

$$\times \Big\{ 2f \cos(\omega + p_0) - \sin(2f + p_0 - \omega) + 2e_0 \sin f \cos(\omega + p_0)$$

$$- \tfrac{1}{3}e_0 \sin(3f + p_0 - \omega) - e_0 \sin(f + p_0 - \omega) \Big\}_{f_0}^{f}.$$

Hence

$$\frac{\partial U_0}{\partial \tau} = \frac{\partial U_0}{\partial \omega}\frac{d\omega}{d\tau} = \frac{h_0^3}{\mu}(1 + e_0 \cos\omega)^2 \frac{\partial U_0}{\partial \omega}$$

$$= \frac{3J_2R^2\mu^{1/2} \cos i_0 \sin 2i_0 (1 + e_0 \cos\omega)^2}{8a_0^{7/2}(1 - e_0^2)^{7/2}}$$

$$\times \Big\{ -2f \sin(\omega + p_0) + \cos(2f + p_0 - \omega) - 2e_0 \sin f \sin(\omega + p_0)$$

$$+ \tfrac{1}{3}e_0 \cos(3f + p_0 - \omega) + e_0 \cos(f + p_0 - \omega) \Big\}_{f_0}^{f},$$

and

$$\dot{s} = \frac{\partial \bar{U}_0}{\partial \tau} = \frac{3J_2R^2\mu^{1/2} \cos i_0 \sin 2i_0(1 + e_0 \cos f)^2}{8a_0^{7/2}(1 - e_0^2)^{7/2}}.$$

$$\times \Big\{ 2(f_0 - f) \sin(f + p_0) + \cos(f + p_0) - \cos(f - 2f_0 - p_0)$$

$$- \tfrac{1}{3}e_0 \cos(f - 3f_0 - p_0) + e_0 \cos(f + p_0 - f_0) - e_0 \cos(f + p_0 + f_0)$$

$$- e_0 \cos(f - p_0 - f_0) + \tfrac{4}{3}e_0 \cos(2f + p_0) \Big\}, \qquad (9.12.11)$$

which checks with a direct differentiation of (9.12.10) according to

$$\frac{d\bar{U}_0}{dt} = \frac{d\bar{U}_0}{df}\frac{df}{dt}.$$

Since actual ephemeris computations require periodic rectification of the orbit, we next consider that operation. Instead of executing a cumbersome numerical differentiation to estimate the velocity vector, and hence orbit elements, the present case offers a more direct way of calculating orbit parameters, based on the conservation of energy and polar angular momentum.

Since the semi-major axis of the osculating orbit represents the total energy for unperturbed Keplerian motion according to $\mu/a = \mu/r - (1/2)v^2$, the law of energy conservation in the presence of the perturbing potential becomes

$$\left[\frac{\mu}{2a} + \frac{J_2 R^2 \mu}{2r^3}(1 - 3\sin^2\varphi)\right]_{t_0}^{t} = 0,$$

where $a = a(t)$ and $r^2 = x_1^2 + x_2^2 + x_3^2$. This yields

$$a = \left\{\frac{1}{a_0} + J_2 R^2[(1 - 3\sin^2\varphi_0)/r_0^3 - (1 - 3\sin^2\varphi)/r^3]\right\}^{-1}.$$

From the definition $h_0^2 = \mu/a_0(1 - e_0^2)$, etc., one also finds

$$e = \left[1 - \frac{a_0}{a}(1 - e_0^2)\left(\frac{h_0}{h}\right)^2\right]^{1/2}.$$

Next, we utilize the elementary conic-section equations $e \sin E = \pm(r\dot{r})/a^{1/2}$ and $e \cos E = rv^2 - 1$, where

$$v^2 = \mu\left(\frac{2}{r} - \frac{1}{a}\right), (r\dot{r})^2 = r^2v^2 - a(1 - e^2) \text{ and } a(1 - e^2) = a_0(1 - e_0^2)(h_0/h)^2.$$

Thus, $E = \tan^{-1}(e \sin E/e \cos E)$, the correct quadrant being identifiable by comparison with the unperturbed case. Then T follows from Kepler's equation.

From the definition of h and conservation of polar angular momentum we have $[(\mu/h)\cos i]_{t_0}^{t} = 0$ and hence $\cos i = (h/h_0)\cos i_0$. Finally, the usual anomaly conversion yields

$$f = 2\tan^{-1}\left[\left(\frac{1 + e}{1 - e}\right)^{1/2}\tan\frac{E}{2}\right],$$

where f now denotes the perturbed true anomaly at the new epoch. Thereupon the well-known trigonometric relations $\sin(p + f) = \sin\varphi/\sin i$ and $\sin(\lambda - \Omega) = \tan\varphi/\tan i$ yield p, the new argument of perigee, and Ω, to complete the set of rectified elements.

The characteristics of this example were investigated by A. G. Lubowe as part of a detailed comparison of several perturbation methods. To mention a few highlights, the standard to which the method was compared was a purely numerical integration programmed in double precision and taking 25 sec of electronic calculator time for a little over nine satellite periods (24 hours of "real time" in this case). The "step size" giving the most accurate values for the Hansen method was about 125 sec; the total computation required 12·2 sec, and gave a root-mean-square error of about 350 ft, with a maximum error of 530 ft. By contrast, a first-order variation of parameters method gave its smallest root-mean-square error (1550 ft) with a step size of 25 sec and total computation time of 46.2 sec; the maximum error was about 2200 ft.

13. COMMENTS ON THE METHOD

Hansen's method has some rather distinctive features. First there are the *ideal coordinates* based on an orbit plane containing the instantaneous radius vector and thus introducing the condition of osculation. A second aspect consists of transforming the z, v, s equations to those for W, U, which reduces the key variables to one for in-plane and one for out-of-plane perturbations. Third, there is Hansen's device distinguishing between time dependence through the anomalistic motion and in the changing orbit geometry. This idea is akin to the recognition of "fast" and "slow" variables in modern averaging methods.

It is significant that Hansen's first approximation can be made to contain quite a few higher-order terms, in contrast with most other techniques, and thus offers greater latitude in choosing between accuracy and step size for numerical work. In addition, the method is arranged to yield cartesian position coordinates quite conveniently. However, the calculation of velocity components as needed for rectification, for example, will require a return to osculating elements (or their equivalent), either by sacrificing the formulation in terms of W, U, or by retroactive computations from z, v, s. Only for perturbations that conserve energy and the polar angular momentum can one calculate the osculating elements in a more convenient way. As an alternative to obtaining these elements, one can resort only to numerical differentiation of the computed position data to evaluate the velocity vector. This approach adds a significant number of manipulations to the basic method and detracts from its efficiency.

Another important characteristic, which the classical applications of Hansen's method share with other traditional astronomical techniques, is the expansion of the disturbing function. We have touched on this subject in Chapters 2, 6, and 8. Such a harmonic analysis is usually conducted in terms of the mean anomaly of the disturbed body or of the time itself. The traditional claims for this procedure are twofold: in the first place, time represents an independent variable which is universally applicable. Once a series expansion has been derived for the disturbing terms acting on a body, it can be used in a variety of applications without *ad hoc* transformations; moreover, solutions of the Keplerian time equations and the calculation of positions at equal time intervals are a straightforward matter. The other reason for classical expansions of the disturbing functions has to do with the literal development of various perturbation theories. Solutions avoiding series expansion may be possible to first order, as illustrated in various examples of this and earlier chapters. However, for higher orders the integrands tend to assume intractable transcendental forms. These difficulties are avoided by introducing the disturbing function as a (trigonometric) series in ascending powers of the perturbation parameter.

In assessing the value of Hansen's method today, we must remember that its acclaim generally predates the age of electronic computers. The ease of incorporating higher-order terms, the number of quadratures, coordinate transformations, and numerical iterations required to establish each point in an ephemeris was then of great importance, the significance of which has been somewhat reduced by the automatic calculator. The advantages of Hansen's method, however, persist in some cases. For example, if one manages to establish a first approximation for a specific case in closed form, some higher-order terms are generally included without extra effort. Whether or not this feature offsets the drawbacks encountered in calculating velocity terms, as required for some perturbations, must be settled in each particular case. This and other considerations have been examined in some of Musen's recent work [12, 13].

REFERENCES

1. D. Brouwer, "Comments on General Theories of Planetary Orbits", in *Proceedings of Symposia in Applied Mathematics,* Vol. IX, p. 161, American Mathematical Society, 1959.
2. G. M. Clemence, "First-order Theory of Mars", *Astron. Papers of the American Ephemeris,* **11,** 1949.
3. P. Herget, *Computation of Orbits,* privately published, 1948, p. 114.
4. P. Herget, "General Theory of Oblateness Perturbations," in *Proceedings of Symposia in Applied Mathematics,* Vol. IX, p. 29, American Mathematical Society, 1959.
5. P. Herget and P. Musen, "A Modified Hansen Lunar Theory for Artificial Satellites," *Astron. J.,* **63,** 430, 1958.
6. P. Musen, "Modified Formulae for Hansen's Special Perturbations," *Astron. J.,* **63,** 426, 1958.
7. P. Musen, "Application of Hansen's Theory to the Motion of an Artificial Satellite in the Gravitational Field of the Earth," *J. Geophysical Res.,* **64,** 2271, 1959.
8. M. Perigaud, "Exposé de la Methode de Hansen pour le Calcul des Perturbations Specials des Petites Planetes," *Annales de l'observatoire de Paris,* **XIV,** C.1-C. 44, 1877.
9. D. Brouwer and G. M. Clemence, *Methods of Celestial Mechanics,* Academic Press, New York, 1961, Chapter XIV.
10. P. A. Hansen, "Auseinandersetzung einer Zweckmässigen Methode zur Berechung der Absoluten Störungen der Kleinen Planeten," *Abhandlungen der Königlichen Sächsischen Gesellschaft der Wissenschaften,* **5, 6, 7,** 1857.
11. R. A. Struble, "A Geometrical Derivation of the Satellite Equations", *Jour. Math. Anal. and Appl.,* **1,** 300, 1960.
12. P. Musen, "Investigations in Hansen's Planetary Theory," *Bulletin Astronomique,* Serie 3, **3,** Fascicule 3, 1968.
13. P. Musen, "On some Possible Simplifications and Changes in Hansen's Lunar Theory," *Jour. of the Astron. Sci.,* **15,** 124, 1968.

ENVOY

Envoy

This to attain: whether heav'n move or earth,
Imports not if thou reckon right.

Paradise Lost: 7, 70-71

The question of comparing the perturbation methods presented in this work must inevitably arise. "Which is best?" can only be answered by "Best in what sense? Most advantageous how? The ultimate for what set of problems?" We can place two objectives into partial opposition: the quest for solutions of the dynamical equations of motion, and the need for production of ephemerides. However, these objectives are not completely orthogonal; insight without accuracy is meaningless, while accuracy alone lacks inspiration.

With this in mind, we may try to summarize the impressions gained from the detailed discussions in various chapters, although an element of subjectivity is unavoidable in such a survey. We note that one type of perturbation method extends over Chapters 5, 7, and 9; its common characteristic being an effort to express the perturbative effects as far as possible in the position coordinates. While the classical Encke method and several modern formulations do this in a straightforward manner, some *ad hoc* combinations of position coordinates and other elements, as well as special manipulatory devices, were introduced in the method of Hansen, as well as those of Brouwer, Strömgren, and Oppolzer (not treated in this text). These modifications were generally designed for special classes of problems and to minimize the computational load in each case. The latter does not represent the vital concern it used to in the past, although circumstances could arise in which it could be of crucial importance, e.g., with certain space-vehicle guidance schemes where onboard calculations are involved. Turning to the other side of the coin, we note that the physical insight obtainable from expressions for perturbations in the position coordinates frequently proves to be considerable, although corresponding results for the velocity perturbations are sometimes difficult to achieve, as in Hansen's method. Perhaps this group of techniques is best characterized as a set of formulations tailored to miscellaneous specific problems, where they can become highly effective.

The other two categories, namely, Lagrange's variation of the elements and canonic perturbation techniques, present a more homogeneous appearance. The wide range of applications given in Chapter 6 for the variation of elements speaks well for the universality of this method. It has proved an effective means for exhibiting changes in orbit geometry, secular trends, and the (semi-analytic) evolution of orbital motion over long periods. As applied to numerous classical studies, as well as various aerospace applications, it probably takes top honors as a reliable working technique satisfying both objectives of the analyst.

Finally we come to the canonic techniques. Here the treatment of intermediary orbits provides room for ingenuity in each case. However, once into the perturbation procedure, most of the analytic work reduces to highly standardized algebraic manipulations. This is largely due to the series expansions introduced for the disturbing function and the generating function. In fact, the monotony of this labor, as exhibited in several lunar theories, has discouraged some potential users from the manual application of this method; on the other hand, this very feature can make it a prime candidate for implementation by automatic symbol manipulators. This approach to orbit computation by canonic methods has recently come into its own.* Obviously, the very length of the expressions involved makes ready interpretation of a specific dynamic situation quite difficult; the approach's present acclaim is based largely on the asymptotic formulations and stability theories, i.e., the study of bounds of the motion it has provided. In addition, the very active field of trajectory optimization relies heavily on Hamiltonian formalism.

So much for a broad-brush comparison of the leading perturbation methods in orbital mechanics. When it comes to details, most specialists in this field probably reflect the preferences of the school that introduced them to the subject. The significant amount of algebraic labor, which is characteristic of all methods in orbital mechanics, restricts the exposure a single individual can attain. Indeed, a parallel execution of several nontrivial examples by the methods presented in this text alone would overtax the endurance of most, though it is probably the only way of making a conclusive comparison. It would require that all approaches be carried at least to second order and be compared with regard to the algebraic labor involved, programming convenience, computing speed, and numerical accuracy

*A. Deprit, "Canonical Transformations Depending on a Small Parameter," *Celestial Mechanics,* (International Journal of Space Dynamics), **1,** 1, 1969.

(with the same application of rectification and multiperiod steps).* It is the authors' hope that over the coming years some readers of this volume may be spurred on in these directions.

*Some impressive efforts along these lines have been made; e.g. J. L. Arsenault, J. D. Enright, and C. Purcell, "General Perturbation Techniques for Satellite Orbit Prediction Study," *ASTIA*, pp. 437–475 and 437–476, 1964; A. H. Cook, "The Contribution of Observations of Satellites to the Determination of the Earth's Gravitational Potential," *Space Science Reviews*, **2**, 355, 1963; N. L. Bonavito, S. Watson, and H. Walden, "An Accuracy and Speed Comparison of the Vinti and Brouwer Orbit Prediction Methods," *NASA TN* D-5203, May 1969. However, more remains to be done.

APPENDICES

Appendix A

INDEPENDENT CALCULATIONS AS VERIFICATION. LAGRANGE'S PLANETARY EQUATIONS AND PERTURBATIONS FROM EXTRATERRESTRIAL GRAVITY (Chapter 6, p. 176)

We consider here the problem of the effect of a stationary gravitating body of mass m_p on an earth satellite. Equation (5.3.8) reduces to

$$\tilde{R} = Gm_p\left(\frac{1}{r_{pm}} - \frac{xx_p + yy_p + zz_p}{r_p^3}\right)$$

for the disturbing function per unit mass of the satellite, where $r_{pm}^2 = (x - x_p)^2 + (y - y_p)^2 + (z - z_p)^2$. Forming $\partial\tilde{R}/\partial x$, $\partial\tilde{R}/\partial y$, $\partial\tilde{R}/\partial z$, and linearizing these in terms of x, y, z, we find

$$\frac{\partial\tilde{R}}{\partial x} = \frac{Gm_p}{r_p^5}\left[x\left(3x_p^2 - r_p^2\right) + 3yy_px_p + 3zz_px_p\right], \text{ etc.}$$

Let us use the following abbreviations:

$$h_1 = l_1x_p + m_1y_p + n_1z_p; \qquad h_2 = l_2x_p + m_2y_p + n_2z_p, \tag{A.1}$$

$$\Sigma = \sin f^{(0)}, \qquad \Psi = \cos f^{(0)}, \qquad \varphi^2 = 1 - e^2 \tag{A.2}$$

A straightforward application of the methods discussed in Chapter 6, Sections 1 and 2, results in the following expressions.

$$a - a_0 = \frac{a^4 m_p}{r_p^5 m_E}\varphi^4\left\{\frac{(3/e^2)(h_2^2 - h_1^2)(1 + 2e\Psi)}{(1 + e\Psi)^2} + \frac{(3h_2^2 - r_p^2) + 6h_1h_2\Sigma\Psi}{(1 + e\Psi)^2}\right\}_{f_0}^{f}, \tag{A.3}$$

$$
\begin{aligned}
e - e_0 = {} & \frac{\varphi^2(a - a_0)}{2ae} \\
& - \frac{3a^3 m_p \varphi}{r_p^5 m_E} \left\{ \frac{\varphi}{6e(1 + e\Psi)^3} \left[\left(h_2^2 - h_1^2\right) \frac{\varphi^6(1 + 3e\Psi)}{e^2} \right. \right. \\
& \qquad - h_1 h_2 \Sigma \left\langle e(8 + 9e^2 - 2e^4) \right. \\
& \qquad\qquad - 3(2 - 9e^2 - 3e^4)\Psi \\
& \qquad\qquad \left.\left. - 3(2 - 9e^2 - 8e^4)\Psi^2 \right\rangle \right] \\
& \left. + \tfrac{5}{2} e h_1 h_2 E \right\}_{f_0}^{f},
\end{aligned}
\tag{A.4}
$$

$$
\begin{aligned}
i - i_0 = {} & \frac{a^3 m_p}{2 r_p^5 m_E} \left\{ \frac{1}{(1 + e\Psi)^3} \left[\frac{\varphi^3(1 + 3e\Psi)}{2e^2} \frac{d}{di} \left(h_2^2 - h_1^2\right) \right. \right. \\
& \qquad \left. - A h_1 \Sigma \frac{dh_2}{di} + B h_2 \varphi^2 \Sigma \frac{dh_1}{di} \right] \\
& \left. + \frac{3}{\varphi} \left[h_1(1 + 4e^2) \frac{dh_2}{di} - h_2 \varphi^2 \frac{dh_1}{di} \right] E \right\}_{f_0}^{f},
\end{aligned}
\tag{A.5}
$$

$$
\begin{aligned}
\Omega - \Omega_0 = {} & \frac{a^3 m_p}{r_p^3 m_E} \frac{1}{2 \sin i} \\
& \cdot \left\{ \frac{\varphi^6(1 + 3e\Psi)}{e^3(1 + e\Psi)^3} \frac{d}{di}(h_1 h_2) - \frac{\Sigma}{2(1 + e\Psi)^3} \left[A \frac{d}{di} h_1^2 + B\varphi^2 \frac{d}{di} h_1^2 \right] \right. \\
& \left. + \frac{3}{2\varphi} \left[(1 + 4e^2) \frac{d}{di} h_1^2 + \varphi^2 \frac{d}{di} h_2^2 \right] E \right\}_{f_0}^{f},
\end{aligned}
\tag{A.6}
$$

$$
\begin{aligned}
& \omega - \omega_0 + \cos i_0(\Omega - \Omega_0) \\
& = \frac{a^3 m_p}{r_p^5 m_E} \left\{ \frac{\varphi^2}{2e(1 + e\Psi)^2} \left[\left(r_p^2 - 3h_1^2\right) \Sigma \left\langle 2 + e^2 + e(1 + 2e^2)\Psi \right\rangle - \frac{3\varphi^4}{e} h_1 h_2 \right] \right. \\
& \qquad + \frac{\varphi^2}{2e(1 + e\Psi)^3} \left[\left(h_2^2 - h_1^2\right) \Sigma \left\langle 2 + e^2 + 3e(1 + e^2)\Psi + (5e^2 - 2)\Psi^2 \right\rangle \right. \\
& \qquad\qquad \left. + h_1 h_2 \frac{2\varphi^4}{e^3} (2 - e^2 + 6e\Psi + 6e^2\Psi^2) \right] \\
& \qquad \left. + \frac{3\varphi}{2} \left(4h_1^2 - h_2^2 - r_p^2\right) E \right\}_{f_0}^{f},
\end{aligned}
\tag{A.7}
$$

$$\chi - \chi_0 + \varphi_0[(\Omega - \Omega_0)\cos i_0 + (\omega - \omega_0)] + (n - n_0)t$$

$$= -\frac{3}{2}\frac{a^3 m_p}{r_p^5 m_E}\varphi^4 n_0(t - t_0)\frac{r_p^2 - 3(h_1\Psi_0 + h_2\Sigma_0)^2}{(1 + e\Psi_0)^2} - \frac{7}{2}\frac{a^3 m_p}{r_p^3 m_E}\varphi \times$$

$$\left\{\frac{\Sigma}{2(1 + e\Psi)^3}\left[\frac{e(18 - 5e^2 + 2e^4) + 3e^2(9 + e^2)\Psi + e^2(11 + 4e^2)\Psi^2}{3}\right.\right.$$

$$\left. - \frac{h_1^2}{r_p^2}A - \frac{\varphi^2 h_2^2}{r_p^2}B\right]$$

$$\left. + \frac{\varphi^6(1 + 3e\Psi)}{e^2(1 + e\Psi)^3}\frac{h_1 h_2}{r_p^2} - \frac{1}{2\varphi}\left[2 + 3e^2 - \frac{3h_1^2}{r_p^2}(1 + 4e^2) - \frac{3h_2^2}{r_p^2}\varphi^2\right]E\right\}_{f_0}^{f}, \quad \text{(A.8)}$$

where

$$A = e(13 + 2e^2) - 3(1 - 9e^2 - 2e^4)\Psi - e(1 - 10e^2 - 6e^4)\Psi^2,$$

$$B = e(5 - 2e^2) + 3(1 + e^2)\Psi + e(1 + 2e^2)\Psi^2, \quad \text{(A.9)}$$

and we have dropped the zero subscript on all elements on the right-hand sides. As before, t and E are the values of time and eccentric anomaly, respectively, that pertain to the appropriate value of f.

Now these equations are sufficiently complex algebraically to demand verification. Accordingly, by repeating the mathematics in terms of E as the independent variable, we obtain a term-by-term check. In addition, the alternative form may offer other advantages. We find, for

$$s = \sin E, \qquad c = \cos E, \quad \text{(A.10)}$$

$$a - a_0 = 2\frac{a^4 m_p}{r_p^3 m_E}\left\{ec + \frac{e^2}{2}s^2 - \frac{3}{r_p^2}\left[h_1^2\left(\frac{s^2}{2} + ec\right)\right.\right.$$

$$\left.\left. + h_1 h_2 \varphi s(e - c) - h_2^2\varphi^2\frac{s^2}{2}\right]\right\}_{E_0}^{E}, \quad \text{(A.11)}$$

$$e - e_0 = \frac{\varphi^2(a - a_0)}{2ae} - \frac{3a^3 m_p \varphi}{r_p^5 m_E e}\left\{\left(h_2^2 - h_1^2\right)\varphi\left[\frac{1 + e^2}{2}s^2 + ec + \frac{e}{3}c^3\right]\right.$$

$$\left. + h_1 h_2\left[\frac{5}{2}e^2 E + \frac{2 + e^2}{2}sc - \left(\frac{7}{3}e + \frac{4}{3}e^3\right)s - \left(\frac{2}{3}e - \frac{e^3}{3}\right)sc^2\right]\right\}_{E_0}^{E}, \quad \text{(A.12)}$$

$$i - i_0 = \cot i \left[\frac{a - a_0}{2a} - \frac{e(e - e_0)}{\varphi^2}\right]$$

$$- \frac{3a^3 m_p}{r_p^5 m_E} \frac{1}{\varphi \sin i} \left\{ h_1 \frac{dh_1}{d\Omega} \left[\frac{1 + 4e^2}{2} E - (3 + e^3)s + \frac{1 + 2e^2}{2} sc + \frac{e}{3} s^3\right]\right.$$

$$+ \frac{d(h_1 h_2)}{d\Omega} \varphi \left[\frac{1 + e^2}{2} s^2 + ec + \frac{e}{3} c^3\right]$$

$$\left. + h_2 \frac{dh_2}{d\Omega} \varphi^2 \left[\frac{E}{2} - \frac{sc}{2} - \frac{e}{3} s^3\right]\right\}_{E_0}^{E}, \tag{A.13}$$

$$\Omega - \Omega_0 = \frac{3a^3 m_p}{r_p^5 m_E} \frac{1}{\varphi \sin i} \left\{ h_1 \frac{dh_1}{di} \left[\frac{1 + 4e^2}{2} E - (3e + e^3)s + \frac{1 + 2e^2}{2} sc + \frac{e}{3} s^3\right]\right.$$

$$+ \frac{d(h_1 h_2)}{di} \varphi \left[\frac{1 + e^2}{2} s^2 + ec + \frac{e}{3} c^3\right]$$

$$\left. + h_2 \frac{dh_2}{di} \varphi^2 \left[\frac{E}{2} - \frac{sc}{2} - \frac{e}{3} s^3\right]\right\}_{E_0}^{E}, \tag{A.14}$$

$$\omega - \omega_0 + \cos i_0(\Omega - \Omega_0)$$

$$= \frac{a^3 m_p}{r_p^3 m_E} \frac{\varphi}{e} \left\{ (1 + e^2)s - \frac{3}{2} eE - \frac{e}{2} sc \right.$$

$$- \frac{3}{r_p^2} \left[h_1^2 \left\langle \frac{s^3}{3} + (1 + e^2)s - 2eE \right\rangle \right.$$

$$+ \frac{h_1 h_2}{\varphi} \left\langle (3e^2 - 2)c - \frac{e + e^3}{2} c^2 + \frac{2 - e^3}{3} c^3 \right\rangle$$

$$\left.\left. + h_2^2 \left\langle \frac{eE}{2} - \frac{esc}{2} - \frac{s^3}{3} \right\rangle \right]\right\}_{E_0}^{E}, \tag{A.15}$$

$$\chi - \chi_0 + \varphi_0[\cos i_0(\Omega - \Omega_0) + (\omega - \omega_0)] + (n - n_0)t$$

$$= \frac{a^3 m_p}{r_p^3 m_E}\Big\{(2 + \tfrac{15}{4}e^2 + 3ec_0 + \tfrac{3}{2}e^2 s_0)E + \tfrac{7}{6}e^3 s^3 - (9e + 2e^3 + \tfrac{3}{2}e^3 s_0^2 + 3e^2 c_0)e$$

$$+ \tfrac{21}{4}e^2 sc - \frac{3}{r_p^2}\Big[h_1^2 \Big\langle(\tfrac{1}{4} + \tfrac{11}{2}e^2 + \tfrac{3}{2}s_0^2 + 3ec_0)E + \frac{7 + 14e^2}{4} sc + \tfrac{7}{6}es^3$$

$$- (9e + 2e^3 + \tfrac{3}{2}es_0^2 + 3e^3 c_0)s\Big\rangle$$

$$+ h_1 h_2 \varphi \Big\langle 3s_0(e - c_0)E + \tfrac{7}{2}(1 + e^2)s^2 + \tfrac{7}{3}ec^3$$

$$+ 3es_0(c_0 - e)s + 7ec\Big\rangle$$

$$+ h_2^2 \varphi^2 \Big\langle \frac{7 - 6s_0^2}{4} E - \frac{7}{4} sc - \frac{7e}{6} s^3 + \frac{3}{2} es_0^2 s\Big\rangle\Big]\Big\}_{E_0}^{E} . \tag{A.16}$$

The reader may verify the identity of (A.3) to (A.8) and (A.11) to (A.16).

A rather interesting feature in these equations is the secular term in eccentricity. Since it is of $0(e)$, it does not manifest itself in (5.3.15) and (5.3.16), which are restricted to nominally-circular orbits. This secular perturbation of eccentric orbits due to luni-solar gravitation has been observed on some of the existing satellites. Turning next to Ω, we see that it approaches a singularity as $i_0 \to 0$, but the same singularity, with opposite sign appears in ω. These two singularities are due to the difficulty in defining the node at $i = 0$. For the simplifying conditions $x_p = z_p = \Omega_0 = 0$, $y_p = r_p, e_0 = 0$, the secular term in Ω becomes $\Delta\Omega_s = -(3m_p a_0^3 \cos i_0/2m_E r_p^3)(f - f_0)$ which agrees with the results of Chapter 5, Section 3.1. Under the same conditions we find the secular term in inclination vanishes, which was also predicted in Chapter 5. In conclusion, we note again that these results apply only for a fixed position x_p, y_p, z_p; the coordinates of the perturbing body must be updated from time to time to allow for its anomalistic motion, and this can be done as part of the rectification procedure discussed in Chapter 6, Section 4.

Appendix B

THE EFFECT OF ATMOSPHERIC DRAG ON AN EARTH SATELLITE (Chapter 6, p. 187)

The components of velocity of a satellite, relative to the air (see Chapter 5), are, in spherical coordinates,

radial: $\dot{r}$
tangential: $r\dot{f} - r\sigma \cos i$
normal: $r\sigma \sin i \cos(\omega + f)$

The components of the drag force per unit mass are thus

$$S = -(C_D A/2m)\rho v_a \dot{r}; \qquad T = -(C_D A/2m)\rho v_a (r\dot{f} - r\sigma \cos i);$$
$$N = -(C_D A/2m)\rho v_a r\sigma \sin i \cos(\omega + f). \tag{B.1}$$

Using (5.3.22), and writing $h = r - R$,

$$\rho = \bar{\rho}_i \exp[-B_i R] \exp[B_i R^2/r],$$

or, employing the true anomaly,

$$\rho = \bar{\rho}_i \exp\left[-B_i R + \frac{B_i R^2}{a(1-e^2)}(1 + e\cos f)\right]. \tag{B.2}$$

Equation (5.16.10) thus leads to

$$\dot{a} = -\frac{C_D A}{m}\rho v_a \frac{a}{1-e^2}\left[1 + e^2 + 2e\cos f - \sqrt{\frac{a^3(1-e^2)^3}{\mu}}\,\sigma\cos i\right], \tag{B.3}$$

where

$$v_a = \left\{\frac{\mu}{a(1-e^2)}(1 + e^2 + 2e\cos f) - 2\sqrt{\mu a(1-e^2)}\,\sigma\cos i + \frac{a^2(1-e^2)^2\sigma^2}{(1+e\cos f)^2}[\cos^2 i + \sin^2 i\cos^2(\omega + f)]\right\}^{1/2}. \tag{B.4}$$

The attempt to solve (B.3), even after transforming to f as the independent variable and resigning ourselves to a first-order solution, is thwarted by its awkward form; further approximations are necessary before progress can be made. These simplifications need not be objectionable if they are kept within bounds and, indeed, such a bound is provided by our inability to express the actual variations of atmospheric density in a precise mathematical way (see Chapter 5). Extreme circumspection would dictate that any approximation which remained accurate to a few per cent could be considered more than adequate. In addition, in the light of the probable short-term variations in C_D, A, and σ, as well as in ρ, elaborate efforts to find the periodic parts of the osculating elements should undoubtedly be avoided.

On the basis of these considerations, one is tempted to expand (B.3) in powers of the eccentricity, thus obtaining quadratures of the type

$$\int \exp(z \cos f) \cos mf \, df,$$

and (for some of the other elements) also

$$\int \exp(z \cos f) \cos mf \sin f \, df,$$

where m is a positive integer, and

$$z = \frac{B_i R^2}{a_0(1 - e_0^2)} e_0. \tag{B.5}$$

The secular changes being given by these integrals evaluated between the limits $f = 0$ and $f = 2\pi$, we then obtain terms involving Bessel functions of imaginary argument,* since

$$\int_0^{2\pi} \exp(z \cos f) \cos mf \, df = 2\pi I_m(z), \qquad \int_0^{2\pi} \exp(z \cos f) \cos mf \sin f \, df = 0. \tag{B.6}$$

However, such an expansion in terms of e invariably results in quite lengthy expressions if the theory is to be extended to orbits with high eccentricities at the required accuracy.†

Now we note that the drag force acts more and more like an impulse as e approaches unity, i.e., the effects near apogee become less and less important as eccentricity increases. This suggests, for large e, that of the integrals encountered, the significant part of each lies near $f = 0$, i.e., when $\cos f$ is close to unity. In this case, one is tempted to expand (B.3) in powers of $1 - \cos f$. The termination of the resulting series would depend on the value of the true anomaly at which $\rho(f)$ falls to a magnitude which is negligible with respect to $\rho(f = 0)$. Here, higher and higher powers of f would have to be included as more nearly circular orbits were examined.

---

*E. Jahnke and F. Emde, *Tables of Functions*, Dover, New York, 1945; H. E. H. Wrinch and D. Wrinch, "Tables of Bessel Functions $I_n(x)$," *Phil. Mag.*, **45,** 846, 1923 and **47,** 62, 1924.

†See I. G. Izsak, "Periodic Drag Perturbations of Artificial Satellites," *Astron. J.*, **65,** 355, 1960, for an application of conventional expansion procedures.

Consider, then, the function

$$x = e(1 - \cos f), \tag{B.7}$$

where we intend to substitute $e - x$ for $e \cos f$ as it occurs in equations of the type (B.3). For small e, higher powers of x rapidly become insignificant; in fact for $e \leq 0.2$, terms in x^3 amount to less than 0.008. We may thus ignore these with respect to unity and never commit errors of more than one per cent. Now for larger values of the eccentricity, the carrying of terms up to only x^2 must provide us with a value of f, say f_{max}, beyond* which we may not proceed without violating our restrictions on accuracy of approximation. We find, for $x^3 = 0.01$,

e	f
0.2	94°
0.4	63°
0.6	50°
0.8	43°
1.0	38°

The quantity z, Eq. (B.5), takes on rather large values for $e \geq 0.2$; so large, that $\exp(z \cos f)$ is a violent function of the true anomaly. For example, taking an orbit with a perigee altitude of 7.5×10^5 m and an eccentricity of 0.2, $\exp(z \cos f)$ has a value of about 8×10^3 at $f = 0$. However, for $f = 64°$, the same parameters yield $\exp(z \cos f) \simeq 80$; i.e., this factor has become one one-hundredth of its perigee value. Thus the entire integrand (B.3), evaluated between $f = 64°$ and 360°–64° cannot contribute more than a few per cent to its total value between zero and 2π. Since the f_{max} for this case is greater than 64°, we conclude that an expansion of (B.3) in terms of x, and truncated beyond x^2, is justified.

We may estimate the range of validity of this approach by finding the magnitude of z such that $\exp(z \cos f_{max})$ is just one one-hundredth of $\exp(z)$. By so doing, we will find the smallest z (and consequently the largest h_q) at which, for a given value of e, the exponential function falls fast enough to keep the proposed approximation within bounds. We find then

e	h_q(max): m
0.2	8.5×10^6
0.4	6.4×10^6
0.6	4.9×10^6
0.8	3.7×10^6
1.0	2.9×10^6

Each of these values of perigee altitude far exceeds those at which we have any knowledge of atmospheric characteristics. As our ignorance of these diminishes, we may be forced to include terms beyond x^2, but at present this is not indicated.

*By symmetry, the proposed expansion is also valid in the range $f = 360° - f_{max}$ to $f = 360°$.

Turning next to (B.4), we note that the maximum difference between v_a and the satellite's inertial velocity, v, occurs at $i = 0$. For equatorial orbits, then

$$v_a = v\left[1 - \frac{2r^2\dot{f}\sigma}{v^2} + \frac{r^2\sigma^2}{v^2}\right]^{1/2}.$$

In this extreme case, v_a is most poorly represented by v at apogee; however, for orbits with $e \geq 0.2$, we need only calculate v at $f_{\max}$. In these circumstances, and for orbits at altitudes where the atmospheric density can be estimated with any accuracy, the second term in the brackets above never exceeds 0.4 and the third term is smaller still. If we now expand this expression, we obtain

$$v_a = v\left[1 - \frac{r^2\dot{f}\sigma}{v^2} + \frac{r^2\sigma^2}{2v^2} - \frac{1}{4}\left(\frac{r^2\dot{f}\sigma}{v^2}\right)^2 + \cdots\right].$$

Here the second term remains less than 0.2, the third and fourth terms together amount to no more than 0.01, and succeeding terms total even less.

As a consequence, we may ignore terms of second and higher powers of σ in the expansion of (B.4) and obtain

$$v_a = \sqrt{\frac{\mu(1+e)}{a(1-e)}}\left[1 - y - \frac{(1+y)x}{(1+e)^2} - \frac{x^2}{2(1+e)^4}\right], \qquad \text{(B.8)}$$

where we have set

$$y = \sqrt{\frac{a^3(1-e^2)^3}{\mu}}\,\frac{\sigma\cos i}{(1+e)^2}, \qquad \text{(B.9)}$$

and have ignored terms of order x^3, y^2, and yx^2.

Transforming to the true anomaly as the independent variable, Eq. (B.3) leads to

$$da/df = -\alpha a^2(1+e)\exp(z\cos f)$$
$$\times\left\{1 - 2y - \frac{1 - 2e + (2 + 4e)y}{(1+e)^2}x - \frac{3 - 6e^2}{2(1+e)^4}x^2\right\}, \qquad \text{(B.10)}$$

where

$$\alpha = \frac{C_D A}{m}\bar{\rho}_i \exp\left[-B_i R + \frac{B_i R^2}{a(1-e^2)}\right]. \qquad \text{(B.11)}$$

Now the restriction $f \leq f_{\max}$ is tantamount to limiting the altitude range through which the satellite can move. Thus, single values of $\bar{\rho}_i$ and B_i can be selected for the specific case under investigation and we may treat α as a constant throughout one revolution. Utilizing (B.7) and taking the orbit elements on the right-hand side of (B.10) as invariant, we obtain, as a first-order solution, integrals of the type (B.6). Hence

$$\frac{\Delta a}{\Delta j} = -\frac{2\pi\alpha a^2}{(1+e)^3}\cdot\{(A_{10} - 2yA_{20})I_0(z) + (A_{11} + 2yA_{21})I_1(z) + A_{12}I_2(z)\}, \quad \text{(B.12)}$$

where j is the revolution number, and

$$\begin{aligned}
A_{10} &= \tfrac{1}{4}(4 + 12e + 15e^2 + 28e^3 + 30e^4),\\
A_{20} &= 1 + 5e + 10e^2 + 9e^3 + 3e^4,\\
A_{11} &= e(1 + 3e - 3e^2 - 8e^3),\\
A_{21} &= e(1 + 4e + 5e^2 + 2e^3),\\
A_{12} &= -\tfrac{3}{4}e^2(1 - 2e^2).
\end{aligned}$$

The equations for changes in e, i, Ω, and ω can be treated similarly. We find

$$\begin{aligned}
\frac{\Delta e}{\Delta j} = -\frac{2\pi\alpha a(1-e)}{(1+e)^4}&\{(E_{10} + yE_{20})I_0(z) + (E_{11} - yE_{21})I_1(z)\\
&-(E_{12} - yE_{22})I_2(z) + (E_{13} + yE_{23})I_3(z)\}, \quad \text{(B.13)}
\end{aligned}$$

where

$$\begin{aligned}
E_{10} &= (e/2)(1 + 5e + 17e/2 + 22e^2 + 15e^3),\\
E_{20} &= (e/4)(5 - 13e - 68e^2 - 77e^3 - 27e^4),\\
E_{11} &= 1 + 5e + 79e^2/8 + 11e^3 - 19e^4/4 - 8e^5,\\
E_{21} &= 2 + 14e + 195e^2/8 + 37e^3/4 - 69e^4/8 - 11e^5/2,\\
E_{12} &= (e/2)(1 + 5e + 25e^2/2 + 4e^3 - 3e^4),\\
E_{22} &= (e/4)(11 + 29e + 20e^2 - 3e^3 - 5e^4),\\
E_{13} &= (e^2/8)(1 + 8e + 6e^2),\\
E_{23} &= (e^2/8)(3 + 10e + 11e^2 + 4e^3).
\end{aligned}$$

$$\begin{aligned}
\frac{\Delta i}{\Delta j} = -\frac{2\pi\alpha a(1-e)}{(1+e)^4}\,y\tan i\\
\times\{&(B_{10} - yB_{20} + \cos 2\omega\cdot B_{30})I_0(z)\\
&-e(1 + \tfrac{1}{2}\cos 2\omega)(B_{11} - yB_{21})I_1(z)\\
&+[\cos 2\omega(B_{12} - yB_{20}) + 2B_{30}]I_2(z)\\
&-\cos 2\omega[\tfrac{1}{2}e(B_{11} - yB_{21})I_3(z) - B_{30}I_4(z)]\}, \quad \text{(B.14)}
\end{aligned}$$

where

$$\begin{aligned}
B_{10} &= \tfrac{1}{4}(1 + 7e + 97e^2/4 + 39e^3 + 20e^4),\\
B_{20} &= \tfrac{1}{4}(1 + 9e + 20e^2 + 17e^3 + 5e^4),\\
B_{30} &= (e^2/32)(11 + 32e + 20e^2),\\
B_{11} &= \tfrac{1}{4}(3 + 21e + 43e^2 + 24e^3),\\
B_{21} &= \tfrac{1}{4}(5 + 14e + 13e^2 + 4e^3),\\
B_{12} &= \tfrac{1}{4}(1 + 7e + 97e^2/4 + 39e^3 - 10e^4).
\end{aligned}$$

$$\begin{aligned}
\frac{\Delta\Omega}{\Delta j} = -\frac{2\pi\alpha a(1-e)}{(1+e)^4}\, y \sin\omega \cos\omega/\cos i \\
\times\{2B_{30}I_0(z) - e(B_{11} - yB_{21})I_1(z) \\
+2(B_{10} - yB_{20})I_2(z) - e(B_{11} - yB_{21})I_3(z) + 2B_{30}I_4(z)\}.
\end{aligned} \tag{B.15}$$

$$\frac{\Delta\omega}{\Delta j} = -\cos i\,\frac{\Delta\Omega}{\Delta j}. \tag{B.16}$$

Note that the factors $y \tan i$ of (B.14) and $y/\cos i$ of (B.15) are well behaved for all values of i.

In the generation of the effect on perigee passage we cannot employ the relation involving the mean anomaly since we have only the secular part of Δa, which does not allow us to evaluate $\int n\, dt$. For this reason, we use (6.6.16). Now, the eccentric anomaly can be written

$$E = f + 2\sum_{n=1}^{\infty} (-1)^n \frac{1}{n}\left[\frac{1 - \sqrt{1 - e^2}}{e}\right]^n \sin nf.$$

However, $\sin nf$ can always be expressed in the form $\sin f \Sigma_l \cos lf$, thus giving rise to integrals similar to the second of (B.6). This leaves us with quadratures involving the true anomaly itself. By symmetry properties of the integrands and recursion relations among Bessel functions it can be shown that

$$\int_0^{2\pi} f \cos mf \exp(z\cos f)df = 2\pi^2 I_m(z). \tag{B.17}$$

We then find, after some simplification,

$$\frac{\Delta\tau}{\Delta j} = -\frac{3\pi}{2}\sqrt{\frac{a}{\mu}}\,\frac{\Delta a}{\Delta j}. \tag{B.18}$$

To estimate the accuracy of the formulas given in the preceding section, we have had the exact equations of motion (in Cowell's form) integrated numerically. From the resulting position and velocity components the osculating elements were obtained, paying careful attention to truncation and roundoff errors. The atmospheric density used was then approximated in the form of (B.2), and the changes in elements computed by the equations given here.

Initial values of the elements for a few of the cases investigated are presented in Table 1. A comparison of results is afforded by Table 2. The agreement can be seen generally to be within a few per cent as hoped.

TABLE 1

INITIAL CONDITIONS

Case No.	a_0(m)	e_0	i_0 (deg)	Ω_0 (deg)	ω_0 (deg)	τ_0 (sec)
I	6.55×10^6	0	30	0	—	—
II	7.28×10^6	0.1	30	0	0	0
III	7.28×10^6	0.1	135	60	60	0
IV	8.20×10^6	0.2	30	0	0	0
V	1.09×10^7	0.4	30	0	0	0
VI	1.64×10^7	0.6	150	210	150	0

TABLE 2

CHANGES IN ELEMENTS ($C_DA/m = 1, \Delta j = 1$)

Case	$-\Delta a$ (km)	$-\Delta e$ $(\times 10^{-5})$	$-\Delta i$ $(10^{-6}$ deg)	$\Delta\Omega$ $(10^{-6}$ deg)	$\Delta\omega$ $(10^{-6}$ deg)	$\Delta\tau$ (sec)
I N*	1.37	15.0	83.5	0	—	—
A*	1.33	0	95.4	0	—	—
II N	0.189	2.27	17.7	0	0	0.123
A	0.183	2.20	17.2	0	0	0.117
III N	0.228	2.74	8.45	−14.8	−1.50	0.151
A	0.220	2.66	8.05	−15.2	−1.15	0.140
IV N	0.193	1.85	19.1	0	0	0.133
A	0.187	1.80	12.4	0	0	0.126
V N	0.305	1.66	6.15	−0.520	0	0.237
A	0.298	1.63	8.10	0	0	0.233
VI N	0.835	2.04	6.32	5.66	5.74	0.751
A	0.798	1.94	4.97	6.89	5.97	0.762

*N = numerical integration, A = analytic approximation.

In closing, we note that, elaborate as this treatment may seem, it assumes a very simple physical model, namely, a rotationally symmetric atmosphere. As stated, high-altitude density data are uncertain and subject to fluctuations not completely understood. Thus, it is difficult to refine the model used here, although attempts have been made to account for some irregularities.*

*See, e.g., H. K. Kalman-Bijl, "Daytime and Night-time Atmospheric Properties Derived from Rockets and Satellite Observations," *J. Geophys. Res.*, **66**, 787, 1961.

Appendix C

COMMENTS ON THE EFFECT OF RADIATION PRESSURE (Chapter 7, p. 221)

The most significant features about Eqs. (7.5.71) and (7.5.72) are the secular terms in both displacements. The effect on the unperturbed circular orbit is best exhibited by observing the amplitude and location of the maximum inward and outward deviation, ξ_{max} and ξ_{min}, noting that these occur when $d\xi/d\theta = 0$. With the help of (7.5.71) this is equivalent to

$$\theta = -(1/6)\cot\theta. \qquad \text{(C.1)}$$

Inspection of this transcendental equation shows that in each interval of 2π, representing one revolution of the satellite in its orbit, there exist two roots, one in the neighborhood of an odd multiple value of π and the other near an even multiple value of π. If the former be designated θ_1, it is seen from (7.5.71) that it marks the instant when "perigee" occurs. The actual anomalistic position of the satellite at such a time is however $\theta_q = \theta_1 + \eta(\theta_1)/r^{(0)}$. The sequence of numerical values for θ_q in radians runs approximately as follows

$$\theta_q = 3.08 + \frac{\eta(3.08)}{r^{(0)}};\ 2\pi + 3.13 + \frac{\eta(2\pi + 3.13)}{r^{(0)}};$$

$$\ldots;\ (2j+1)\pi + \frac{11F_p r^{(0)^3}}{2\mu m} \qquad \text{(for } j \text{ large)},$$

where j identifies the number of the orbital periods elapsed since launch. A corresponding series can be written for successive apogee locations, which approach the limit $\theta_Q = 2\pi j - 11F_p r^{(0)^3}/2\mu m$ for large values of j. These results show that ξ_{max} and ξ_{min} never occur exactly opposite each other. However, for the sake of a simplified discussion, let us assume that they occur at $\theta_q = (2j + 1)\pi$ and $\theta_Q = 2j\pi$. Then the distance between extreme excursions of the perturbed path is

$$2\bar{a} = 2r^{(0)} + \xi(\theta_q) + \xi(\theta_Q) = 2r^{(0)} + 3\pi F_p r^{(0)^3}/2\mu m. \tag{C.2}$$

Since this is a constant, we conclude that, in this sense, the size of the orbit is not changing. However the degree of deformation from circularity can be expressed as

$$\bar{e} = [\xi(\theta_q) - \xi(\theta_Q)]/2r^{(0)} = 3F_p r^{(0)^2}(j - \tfrac{1}{4})\pi/\mu m. \tag{C.3}$$

This indeed contains the index j and shows that the orbit becomes increasingly more eccentric with time. The average rate at which eccentricity accumulates, according to this approximate analysis, is

$$\Delta\bar{e}/2\pi = \bar{e}' = 3F_p r^{(0)^2}/2\mu m, \tag{C.4}$$

where $\Delta\bar{e}$ is the increment of $\bar{e}$ over one period.

A physical interpretation of the way in which the apsides are formed by radiation pressure is as follows. The satellite is being accelerated tangentially by F_p over the interval $(2j + 1/2)\pi < \theta < (2j + 3/2)\pi$ and, to balance the additional centrifugal force resulting from the increased circumferential speed, a decrease in r is required to enhance the gravitational attraction. Thus, $\xi_{\min}$ occurs in the neighborhood of $\theta = (2j + 1)\pi$. The mechanism acts in the opposite way to generate $\xi_{\max}$ near $\theta = 2j\pi$. The fact that $|\xi_{\max}|$ and $|\xi_{\min}|$ continue to increase from one revolution to the next is plausible if we consider, as the analog of the satellite, a linear oscillator in its motion about the neutral position $r^{(0)}$ whose excitation is in resonance with the free oscillations. An unlimited build-up of the response in terms of $\xi_{\max}$ and $\xi_{\min}$ is to be expected for this linearized model. One is led to seek refinements of this model yielding a more realistic picture of the perturbed motion for large values of ξ and η. The first occasion for revisions arises from the linearizations of the gravitational forces, leading to (7.4.15) to (7.4.17). A more complete representation of these forces would be of the type

$$\frac{\partial}{\partial\xi}\left(-\frac{\mu m}{r}\right) = \frac{\mu m}{a_0^2}\left[1 - \frac{2\xi}{a_0} + \frac{3\xi^2}{a_0^2} - \frac{3}{2a_0^2}(\eta^2 + \xi^2) + \frac{27}{2}\frac{\xi^3}{a_0^3} + \frac{6}{a_0^3}(\xi\eta^2 + \xi\zeta^2) + 0\left(\frac{\xi^4}{a_0^4}\right)\right], \tag{C.5}$$

etc., if the nominal orbit is circular. Since $i_0 = x_P = z_P = 0$, $y_P = r_P$ and we assume the radiation field to be perfectly collimated, the perturbing forces are $Q_\xi = -F_p \sin\theta$, $Q_\eta = -F_p \cos\theta$, and $Q_\zeta = 0$. Substituting this together with (C.5) into (7.4.5)–(7.4.7) we arrive at the nonlinear equations of motion

$$\begin{aligned} &\xi'' - 2\eta' - 3\xi + b_1\xi^2 + b_2\eta^2 + b_3\xi^3 + b_4\xi\eta^2 + \gamma\sin\theta = 0, \\ &\eta'' + 2\xi' - b_1\xi\eta + b_4\xi^2\eta + b_2\eta^3 + \gamma\cos\theta = 0, \end{aligned} \tag{C.6}$$

and, of course, $\zeta \equiv 0$. The coefficients $b_1, \ldots$, etc., represent the following abbreviations: $b_1 = 3/a_0$, $b_2 = -3/2a_0$, $b_3 = 27/2a_0^2$, $b_4 = 6/a_0^2$, and $\gamma = -F_p n^6/\mu^4$. Our question now is whether the nonlinear components of the gravitational force (C.5) suffice to eliminate the singular response of the linear model. If we stipulate that such a bounded solution be of the form

$$\bar{\xi}_P = c_1 \sin\theta + c_2 \cos\theta \qquad \text{and} \qquad \bar{\eta}_P = d_1 \sin\theta + d_2 \cos\theta, \tag{C.7}$$

(which cannot, of course, be expected to satisfy (C.6) except in an "average" sense) then our question reduces to finding bounded values for c_1, c_2, d_1, d_2. The values $\bar{\xi}_p$, $\bar{\eta}_p$ of (C.7) can be calculated as an approximate solution of (C.6) by the Ritz-Galerkin method.* The so-called Ritz conditions by which one finds the undetermined coefficients are

$$\int_0^{2\pi} E_1 \sin\theta\, d\theta = 0, \int_0^{2\pi} E_1 \cos\theta\, d\theta = 0, \int_0^{2\pi} E_2 \sin\theta\, d\theta = 0, \int_0^{2\pi} E_2 \cos\theta\, d\theta = 0,$$

where E_1 and E_2 represent the left-hand sides of the first and second equation, respectively, of (C.6). These conditions ultimately reduce to the algebraic equations

$$\begin{aligned}
4c_1 - 2d_2 - \tfrac{3}{4}(b_3c_1^3 + b_4c_1d_1^2) - \tfrac{1}{4}(3b_3c_1c_2^2 + b_4c_1d_2^2 + 2b_4c_2d_1d_2) &= \gamma,\\
4c_2 + 2d_1 - \tfrac{1}{4}(3b_3c_1^2c_2 + 2b_4c_1d_1d_2 + b_4c_2d_1^2) - \tfrac{3}{4}(b_3c_2^3 + b_4c_2d_2^2) &= 0,\\
2c_2 + d_1 - \tfrac{3}{4}(b_4c_1^2d_1 + b_2d_1^3) - \tfrac{1}{4}[b_4(c_2^2d_1 + 2c_1c_2d_2) + 3b_2d_1d_2^2] &= 0,\\
-2c_1 + d_2 - \tfrac{1}{4}[b_4(2c_1c_2d_1 + c_1^2d_2) + 3b_2c_1^2c_2] - \tfrac{3}{4}(b_4c_2^2d_2 + b_2d_2^3) &= \gamma.
\end{aligned} \tag{C.8}$$

As was to be expected, the linear terms of the left-hand sides of (C.8) possess a vanishing determinant, which simply reflects the resonance that we have already discovered for the linearized dynamic model. Unfortunately, substitution of typical values for γ and b_1, b_2, b_3, b_4 into (C.8) shows that the values of the bounded solutions for $c_1, \ldots, d_2$ in the nonlinear system are so large that they are of no practical interest. This indicates that the nonlinearities of the gravitational field are too weak to impose a bound on the singular response indicated by (7.5.71) and (7.5.72). On the other hand, experience tells us that such a simple secular response does not occur in reality. The number of physical effects which could interfere with this secular perturbation is quite large; we discuss some below.

One question that comes to mind immediately is whether the actual nonuniform light intensity distribution around the orbit might not affect the situation in a significant way. However, considering the same linearized model as in Chapter 7, Section 5, but using $\psi \neq 0$ we note that the secular response should persist as long as a constant component in the intensity distribution around the orbit underlies the cyclic one. This will of course always be the case, no matter how elaborate a

*See, for example, F. R. Arnold, *Steady State Oscillations in Non-linear Systems of Two Degrees of Freedom*, Ph.D. Dissertation, Stanford Univ. (Div. of Eng. Mech.), 1954.

trigonometric series we envision for the intensity distribution, since the radiation pressure cannot reverse its sense on any portion of an orbit that does not enclose the sun. Hence its average value around the orbit must differ from zero.

Next, one might argue, since the coordinates x_P, y_P, z_P change with time, that the apparent solar motion might affect the perturbations. But if one substitutes typical numerical values for the constants in (7.5.71) and (7.5.72)—e.g., pertaining to Echo I—one finds that the predicted secular response is so rapid that annual motions can hardly be expected to exert a significant influence on it.

Another physical effect that comes to mind is the possible interference from the earth's oblateness. In the remainder of this appendix we give this matter some attention. Consider again the satellite orbit in the x, y plane, where P is located on the y axis, and also assume that this plane contains the earth's equator. The crucial feature of this model is that the apsidal precession from the equatorial bulge acts to distribute the instantaneous perturbations from radiation pressure around the orbit (in a loose manner of speaking) so that they do not accumulate on top of each other but combine in such a way that their cumulative perturbation is bounded.

For the present discussion, we pursue a heuristic argument which might serve as a first look at this problem. (In a very informal way, the rationale to be developed here corresponds to that of the "averaging" techniques used for certain advanced perturbation studies.) Let us recall what we know about the oblateness and radiation effects individually. We note from (6.3.12) and (6.3.13) that the line of apsides of an eccentric osculating orbit in the equatorial plane precesses at the following rate relative to an inertial reference $\dot{\tilde{\omega}} = \dot{\omega} + \dot{\Omega} = 3J_2R^2n/2a_0^2$. On the other hand, the secular perturbation impressed on the ξ component of the osculating orbit by radiation pressure at any instant can be written in the form $3F_pa_0^3n \times \cos\theta/2\mu$, according to (7.5.71). Now we may apply the superposition theorem for first-order perturbations to this case and state that the ξ components of two osculating orbits at the times t_1 and t_2, which are Δt apart, shall be related by

$$ {}_2\xi(\theta) = {}_1\xi(\theta - \dot{\tilde{\omega}}\Delta t) + (3F_pa_0^3n/2\mu)\cos\theta\,\Delta t, \tag{C.9} $$

where the presubscripts identify ξ at t_1 and t_2. Pursuing this argument backward to the initial instant t_0 and changing the independent variable to $\tilde{\omega}$, we find that

$$ \begin{aligned} \xi(\theta, \tilde{\omega}) &= -c\int_{\tilde{\omega}_0}^{\tilde{\omega}} \cos(\theta - \tilde{\omega})d\tilde{\omega} + \xi(\theta, \tilde{\omega}_0) \\ &= -c[\sin(\theta - \tilde{\omega}_0) - \sin(\theta - \tilde{\omega})] + \xi(\theta, \tilde{\omega}_0) \\ &= -2c\sin\tfrac{1}{2}(\tilde{\omega} - \tilde{\omega}_0)\cos(\theta - \tfrac{1}{2}\tilde{\omega} + \tfrac{1}{2}\tilde{\omega}_0) + \xi(\theta, \tilde{\omega}_0), \end{aligned} \tag{C.10} $$

where

$$ c = 3F_pa_0^3n/2\mu\dot{\tilde{\omega}}, \tag{C.11} $$

and $\tilde{\omega}$ is really a fictitious angle, namely, the location of perigee if oblateness were acting alone. Noting that in our model the first appearance of a perigee is caused by radiation pressure at $\tilde{\omega}_0 = \pi$, (C.10) becomes

$$\xi(\theta, \tilde{\omega}) = -2c \cos \tfrac{1}{2}\tilde{\omega} \sin (\theta - \tfrac{1}{2}\tilde{\omega}) + \xi(\theta, \tilde{\omega}_0). \qquad \text{(C.12)}$$

Remembering further that the initial conditions call for a circular orbit, we set $\xi(\theta, \tilde{\omega}_0) \equiv 0$. The final expression for $\xi(\theta, \tilde{\omega})$ lends itself to a simple geometric interpretation. The perigee of the actual orbit first appears at $\omega = \pi$ and precesses toward $\omega = 3\pi/2$ where it reaches a maximum depression equal to $-2c$. Thereafter it moves to $\omega = 2\pi$ where it returns to zero amplitude only to reappear immediately at $\omega = \pi$. From (C.12) we observe that the rate of this precession is $\dot{\omega} = \dot{\tilde{\omega}}/2$.

In an expression like (C.12), the question arises of the magnitudes which the amplitude $2c$ may reach before the results of this linearized analysis cease to be valid. If the estimates resulting from a nonlinear system such as (C.8) can be trusted at all, these would indicate that $2c$ may be a sizable fraction of a_0 before nonlinear restoring forces come into play. Similarly, an extension of (7.5.71) and (7.5.72) to cases involving nonuniform illumination of the orbit ($\psi \neq 0$) leads us to believe that an allowance for the actual intensity distribution around the orbit would affect the amplitude parameter $2c$ somewhat but would not alter the form of (C.12).

So far we have considered only a model with stationary P but it seems clear that our entire argument regarding the simultaneous perturbations of the osculating orbit due to oblateness and radiation pressure can be reproduced in a slowly moving reference frame which is governed by the angular rate σ_P of the line $\overline{EP}$ in the equatorial plane. We merely replace the apsidal precession rate $\dot{\tilde{\omega}}$, which is valid in an inertial frame, by the precession relative to $\overline{EP}$: $\dot{\omega}_r = \dot{\tilde{\omega}} - \sigma_P$. Thus, the amplitude parameter becomes

$$2c = \frac{3F_p a_0^3}{\mu} \Big/ \left[\frac{3J_2R^2}{2a_0^2} - \frac{\sigma_P}{n}\right], \qquad \text{(C.13)}$$

and the rate of apsidal precession in an inertial frame is now $\dot{\omega} = 1/2(\dot{\tilde{\omega}} + \sigma_P)$. We see that the denominator in (C.13) vanishes if $\dot{\tilde{\omega}} = \sigma_P$, i.e., if the motion of P is in resonance with the apsidal precession (in inertial coordinates) due to oblateness. In that event, the perturbing mechanism (in the rotating coordinate system) is entirely analogous to the model which led to (7.5.71) and (7.5.72) and hence the orbit deteriorates without bound. This condition obtains for a satellite orbit with the critical radius $a_0 \simeq 12200$ km. For an Echo-type orbit with $a_0 = 8000$ km one finds a maximum depression of perigee in the order of 56 km. However this simplified calculation assumes an equatorial satellite orbit with the sun also located in that plane. If an allowance is made for the effects of a 50° inclination on the apsidal precession and the resolution of pressure forces acting on the satellite, the calculation would yield approximately 560 km for the maximum depression of perigee. This can be considered fair agreement with the observed value of 640 km, after taking into account the approximations still contained in this approach.

To summarize, the secular effect from the equatorial bulge modifies the geometry that controls the accumulation of secular effects from the radiation pressure. The most satisfactory approach to this situation would be the inclusion of higher-order coupling terms between the two physical effects, which one could get by extending the formulations of Chapters 6 and 7 beyond the first order. The reader is referred to the work of Shapiro and Jones, and of Levin* for more discussion of solar pressure phenomena.

*See reference 15 of Chapter 6 and reference 18 of Chapter 5.

Appendix D

REVERSIBILITY OF CANONICAL TRANSFORMATIONS (Chapter 8, p. 229)

We prove here that for variables connected by a canonical transformation, one can write the new in terms of the old, that is,

$$\tilde{q}_i = \tilde{q}_i(q_j, p_j); \qquad \tilde{p}_i = \tilde{p}_i(q_j, p_j); \qquad i, j = 1, \ldots, n+1, \tag{D.1}$$

(where we have an n-dimensional problem and deal with an augmented set of variables) as well as the old in terms of the new, namely,

$$q_i = q_i(\tilde{q}_j, \tilde{p}_j), \qquad p_i = p_i(\tilde{q}_j, \tilde{p}_j), \tag{D.2}$$

or mixed representations, i.e., the canonic nature of the transformation makes it fully reversible or to any intermediate degree. We demonstrate this by proving that the Jacobian determinant of the transformation does not vanish.

For this purpose, let us temporarily designate the q_i by x_i ($i = 1, \ldots, n+1$) and the p_i by x_i ($i = n+2, \ldots, 2n+2$). Then Hamilton's equations can be written vectorially as

$$\dot{\mathbf{x}} = C\,\partial\mathscr{H}/\partial\mathbf{x}, \tag{D.3}$$

where $\dot{\mathbf{x}}$ has the components $\dot{x}_i$($i = 1, \ldots, 2n+2$) and $\partial\mathscr{H}/\partial\mathbf{x}$ has the components $\partial\mathscr{H}/\partial q_1, \ldots, \partial\mathscr{H}/\partial p_{n+1}$. The quantity C is a square $2n+2$ by $2n+2$ matrix of the form

$$C = \begin{pmatrix} 0 & \mathrm{I} \\ -\mathrm{I} & 0 \end{pmatrix}, \tag{D.4}$$

where 0 and I are the null and unit matrices, respectively, each of dimension $n+1$ by $n+1$.

Now consider a new set of variables

$$X_i = X_i(x_1, \ldots, x_{2n+2}), \qquad i = 1, \ldots, 2n + 2. \tag{D.5}$$

We have immediately

$$\dot{\boldsymbol{X}} = J\dot{\mathbf{x}}, \tag{D.6}$$

where J is the Jacobian matrix of the transformation with the elements

$$J_{ij} = \frac{\partial X_i}{\partial x_j}. \tag{D.7}$$

Further

$$\frac{\partial \mathscr{H}}{\partial x_j} = \sum_i \frac{\partial \mathscr{H}}{\partial X_i} \frac{\partial X_i}{\partial x_j},$$

or

$$\frac{\partial \mathscr{H}}{\partial \mathbf{x}} = J^T \frac{\partial \mathscr{H}}{\partial \mathbf{X}}, \tag{D.8}$$

where J^T is the transpose of J. From (D.3), (D.6), and (D.8) we have

$$\dot{X} = JCJ^T\, \partial\mathscr{H}/\partial\mathbf{X}.$$

Since the old and new coordinate systems are both augmented, the time does not appear explicitly in either Hamiltonian and, according to Chapter 7, Section 2, both are constants. Moreover, the transformation itself, written in the form (8.2.3), does not contain time explicitly; in addition, an examination of (8.2.22)–(8.2.24) reveals that the old and new Hamiltonians are identical. Hence for the transformation (D.5) to be canonical we must have

$$JCJ^T = C. \tag{D.9}$$

Since the determinant of the product of matrices is equal to the product of the determinants of each, and further, the determinant of the transpose of a matrix is equal to the determinant of the matrix, (D.9) leads to

$$|J| = \pm 1. \tag{D.10}$$

This is enough to prove the reversibility of canonical transformations.

A heuristic argument makes it plausible that only the plus sign of (D.10) applies in this case. Suppose we generate the identity transformation; then $|J| = +1$. But, of course, we can carry out any other transformation by a series of infinitesimal changes in the "new" coordinates. In each of these $|J|$ is constrained to have only the values ± 1. Since a discrete change in $|J|$ seems unreasonable for an infinitesimal departure from the identity transformation, the plus sign must always apply:

$$|J| = +1. \tag{D.11}$$

Appendix E

THE JACOBI THEOREM (Chapter 8, p. 236)

Equations (8.2.37) and (8.2.38) constitute necessary conditions that q_i, p_i, and α_i, and β_i be related by a contact transformation. It remains to establish the sufficiency of these conditions. This is accomplished by the Jacobi theorem (Chapter 8 [1, p. 125] or [6, p. 133]). The theorem states that if $S(q, \alpha, t)$ satisfies the Hamilton-Jacobi equation

$$\partial S/dt + \mathscr{H}(q, \partial S/\partial q, t) = 0 \equiv \mathscr{H}^*, \tag{E.1}$$

and the variables

$$q_i = q_i(\alpha, \beta, t), \tag{E.2}$$
$$p_i = p_i(\alpha, \beta, t), \tag{E.3}$$

are related to the canonic constants α_i and β_i by virtue of

$$\beta_i = \frac{\partial S(q, \alpha, t)}{\partial \alpha_i}, \tag{E.4}$$

$$p_i = \frac{\partial S(q, \alpha, t)}{\partial q_i}, \tag{E.5}$$

then q_i and p_i satisfy the canonic equations with $\mathscr{H}$.

From (E4) and (E5) it follows that

$$\frac{\partial \beta_i}{\partial q_j} = \frac{\partial p_j}{\partial \alpha_i} \quad \text{and} \quad \frac{\partial \beta_i}{\partial t} = \frac{\partial^2 S(q, \alpha, t)}{\partial \alpha_i \, \partial t}.$$

Using this in

$$\frac{\partial \beta_i}{dt} = \sum_j \frac{\partial \beta_i}{\partial q_j} \dot{q}_j + \frac{\partial \beta_i}{\partial t} = 0,$$

we find

$$\frac{\partial^2 S}{\partial \alpha_i \, \partial t} + \sum_j \frac{\partial p_j}{\partial \alpha_i} \dot{q}_j = 0. \tag{E.6}$$

Noting from (E.5) that $p_i = p_i(q, \alpha, t)$, we can differentiate (E.1) with respect to α_i and obtain

$$\frac{\partial^2 S}{\partial t \partial \alpha_i} = \sum_j \frac{\partial \mathscr{H}}{\partial p_j} \frac{\partial p_j}{\partial \alpha_i} = 0. \tag{E.7}$$

Subtracting (E.7) from (E.6) we have

$$\sum_j \left(\dot{q}_j - \frac{\partial \mathscr{H}}{\partial p_j} \right) \frac{\partial p_j}{\partial \alpha_i} = 0 \qquad \text{for} \qquad i = 1, \dots, n. \tag{E.8}$$

Since the functions p_j must be linearly independent of each other to represent independent degrees of freedom for the dynamical system, the determinant

$$\left| \frac{\partial (p_1 \, p_2 \dots p_n)}{\partial (\alpha_1 \dots \alpha_n)} \right|, \tag{E.9}$$

will not vanish and hence

$$\dot{q}_j = \partial \mathscr{H} / \partial p_j \qquad \text{for all } j. \tag{E.10}$$

If we now differentiate (E.5) with respect to time and use (E.10) there results

$$\dot{p}_i = \frac{\partial^2 S}{\partial t \partial q_i} + \sum_j \frac{\partial^2 S}{\partial q_i \partial q_j} \frac{\partial \mathscr{H}}{\partial p_j}. \tag{E.11}$$

Furthermore, differentiating (E.1) with respect to q_i while noting again that $p_i = p_i(q, \alpha, t)$ according to (E.5), we find

$$\frac{\partial^2 S}{\partial t \partial q_i} + \frac{\partial \mathscr{H}}{\partial q_i} + \sum_j \frac{\partial \mathscr{H}}{\partial p_j} \frac{\partial^2 S}{\partial q_j \partial q_i} = 0. \tag{E.12}$$

(E.11) and (E.12) yield

$$\dot{p}_i = -\partial \mathscr{H} / \partial q_i. \tag{E.13}$$

Since α_i and β_i satisfy a canonical system with $\mathscr{H}^* \equiv 0$, we recall from Appendix D that

$$\left| \frac{\partial (q, p)}{\partial (\alpha, \beta)} \right| = 1$$

and hence (E.4) and (E.5) may be interpreted as $q_i = q_i(\alpha, \beta, t)$ and $p_i = p_i(\alpha, \beta, t)$. Since there are $2n$ constants, α_i and β_i, these expressions encompass all the solutions of (E.10) and (E.13). Thus a complete integral of (E.1) amounts to a general solution of the $2n$th order dynamical system.

Appendix F

VARIATION OF CANONIC CONSTANTS (Chapter 8, p. 248)

In Section 4 of Chapter 8 we mentioned that either the usual Keplerian solution or an *intermediary orbit*, such as the one suggested by Vinti, may serve as starting point for a perturbation analysis. This initial approximation is the solution of the Hamilton-Jacobi equation (8.4.3). We must now show that a "variation-of-constants" procedure can be applied to the α_i and β_i from that solution* to satisfy higher-order effects according to (8.4.4).

The solution of (8.4.3) satisfies

$$\dot{q}_i = \partial\mathscr{H}_0/\partial p_i \qquad \text{and} \qquad \dot{p}_i = -\partial\mathscr{H}_0/\partial q_i, \tag{F.1}$$

with $q_i = q_i(\alpha, \beta, t)$ and $p_i = p_i(\alpha, \beta, t)$. If we now let $\alpha_j = \alpha_j(t)$ and $\beta_j = \beta_j(t)$, so as to accommodate the perturbations, (F.1) takes the form

$$\partial q_i/\partial t = \partial\mathscr{H}_0/\partial p_i \qquad \text{and} \qquad \partial p_i/\partial t = -\partial\mathscr{H}_0/\partial q_i. \tag{F.2}$$

Then (F.2) must still be satisfied, while the perturbed system as a whole obeys the equations

$$\frac{dq_i}{dt} = \dot{q}_i = \frac{\partial\mathscr{H}}{\partial p_i} \qquad \text{and} \qquad \frac{dp_i}{dt} = \dot{p}_i = -\frac{\partial\mathscr{H}}{\partial q_i}. \tag{F.3}$$

If we write (F.3) out:

$$\frac{\partial q_i}{\partial t} + \sum_r \left(\frac{\partial q_i}{\partial \alpha_r}\dot{\alpha}_r + \frac{\partial q_i}{\partial \beta_r}\dot{\beta}_r\right) = \frac{\partial\mathscr{H}_0}{\partial p_i} + \frac{\partial\tilde{\mathscr{H}}_1}{\partial p_i}, \tag{F.4}$$

$$\frac{\partial p_i}{\partial t} + \sum_r \left(\frac{\partial p_i}{\partial \alpha_r}\dot{\alpha}_r + \frac{\partial p_i}{\partial \beta_r}\dot{\beta}_r\right) = -\frac{\partial\mathscr{H}_0}{\partial q_i} + \frac{\partial\tilde{\mathscr{H}}_1}{\partial q_i}; \tag{F.5}$$

*Cf. W. M. Smart, *Celestial Mechanics*, Longmans, Green and Co., New York, 1953, pp. 136, 158.

the first terms on each side may be equated to each other by virtue of (F.2). Multiplying (F.4) by $\partial p_i/\partial \alpha_j$ and (F.5) by $-\partial q_i/\partial \alpha_j$, adding them and summing over i, we find

$$\frac{\partial \tilde{\mathscr{H}}_1}{\partial \alpha_j} = \sum_r \dot{\alpha}_r[\alpha_r, \alpha_j] + \sum_r \dot{\beta}_r[\beta_r, \alpha_j]. \tag{F.6}$$

Similarly

$$\frac{\partial \tilde{\mathscr{H}}_1}{\partial \beta_j} = \sum_r \dot{\alpha}_r[\alpha_r, \beta_j] + \sum_r \dot{\beta}_r[\beta_r, \beta_j]. \tag{F.7}$$

Now it so happens among two sets of canonic variables, such as p_i, q_i and α_j, β_j, that all their Lagrange brackets vanish, except for*

$$[\beta_j, \alpha_j] = -[\alpha_j, \beta_j] = 1.$$

Therefore (F.6) and (F.7) reduce to

$$\dot{\beta}_i = \frac{\partial \tilde{\mathscr{H}}_1}{\partial \alpha_i} \qquad \text{and} \qquad \dot{\alpha}_i = -\frac{\partial \tilde{\mathscr{H}}_1}{\partial \beta_i}, \tag{F.8}$$

which is the Hamiltonian system governing the variation of canonic constants and corresponding to (8.4.4). In comparing this approach with Lagrange's variation of parameters, one notes that, in the latter case, Keplerian motion was characterized by parameters α_i, β_i that generally differed from (8.4.5). Thus, when converted to time-dependent osculating elements for the perturbed motion, they are not necessarily a canonic set and the planetary equations, which take the place of (F.8), have a non-Hamiltonian form. Hence, canonic transformations are not used in their solution but rather recursive quadratures, leading to Picard iterants.

Ibid.

SOME USEFUL CONSTANTS*

$G = (6.668 \pm .005) \times 10^{-11}$ Newtons m/kg^2
$M_E = (5.977 \pm .004) \times 10^{24}$ kg
$\mu = GM_E = (3.986\ 032 \pm .000\ 030) \times 10^{14}$ m^3/sec^2
$\sigma = 7.292\ 115\ 08 \times 10^{-5}$ rad/sec
$R = 6\ 378\ 165 \pm 25$ m
$M_S/M_E = 332\ 700$
A.U. = 149 598 845 $\pm$ 250 km

Body	a (A.U.)	e	M/M_E	R (km)
Mercury	0.387099	0.206	0.054	2420
Venus	0.723332	0.00682	0.815	6100
Earth	1.00	0.0168	1.00	6.378
Mars	1.52369	0.0933	0.108	3380
Jupiter	5.2028	0.0483	317.8	71350
Saturn	9.540	0.0559	95.2	60400
Uranus	19.18	0.0471	14.5	23800
Neptune	30.07	0.0085	17.2	22000
Pluto	39.44	0.2494	0.8 (?)	3000
Moon	384,404†	0.0549	1/81.33	1738

*Mostly from C. W. Allen, *Astrophysical Quantities*, University of London Press, 2nd ed., 1963.
†In kilometers.

SOME USEFUL CONSTANTS

INDEX

INDEX

ABCDE7987654321